Macmillan Texts for Industrial, Vocational and Technical Educat

SEP 2002

Motor Vehicle Technology for Mechanics

P P J Read
V C Reid

STRATTON UPPER SCHOOL LIBRARY

Macmillan Education
Between Towns Road, Oxford OX4 3PP
A division of Macmillan Publishers Limited
Companies and representatives throughout the world

ISBN 0333 60159 9

Copyright text © P. P. J. Read and V. C. Reid 2000
Design and illustration © Macmillan Publishers Ltd 2000

First published 2000

All rights reserved; no part of this publication may be reproduced, stored in a retrieval system, transmitted in any form or by any means, electronic, mechanical, photocopying, recording, or otherwise, without the prior written permission of the Publishers.

www.macmillan-africa.com

Illustrations by TechType, Abingdon

Cover illustration by Science Photo Library

Printed and bound in Malaysia

2007 2006 2005
11 10 9 8 7 6 5

Acknowledgements

The authors would like to thank the following companies and organisations, who have kindly provided not only technical advice regarding their products and services, but also permission to reproduce some of their technical illustrations: Automobile Association; Britool Ltd; British Leyland; British Telecom plc; City & Guilds Institute of London; *Commercial Motor*; Dunlop Tyre Company Ltd; Ford Motor Company Ltd; Haynes Publishing; Health & Safety Executive; Joseph Lucas Ltd; Michelin Tyre Company; Nissan Motor Corporation; Post Office; RTITB Services Ltd; SAAB Ltd; Toyota Motor Corporation.

Special thanks go to: Dr Wilkinson-Mensah, Head of Motor Vehicle Department, ATTC, Accra; Frank Andrews; Roy Brooks; Richard Charlesworth; Tom Corless; Jack Hirst; our respective employers, Tameside College and Bolton Institute; and finally our long-suffering families.

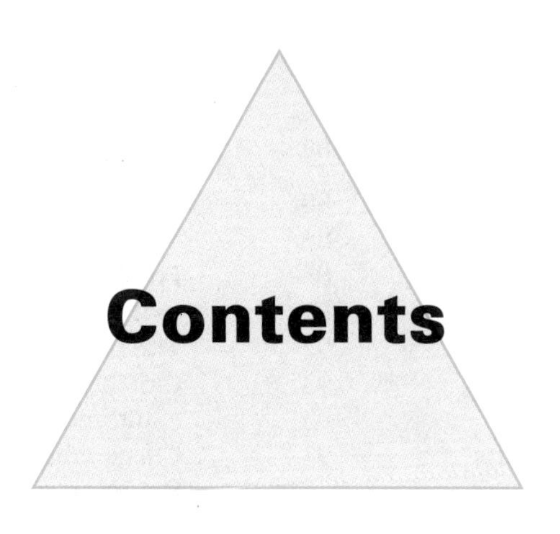

Contents

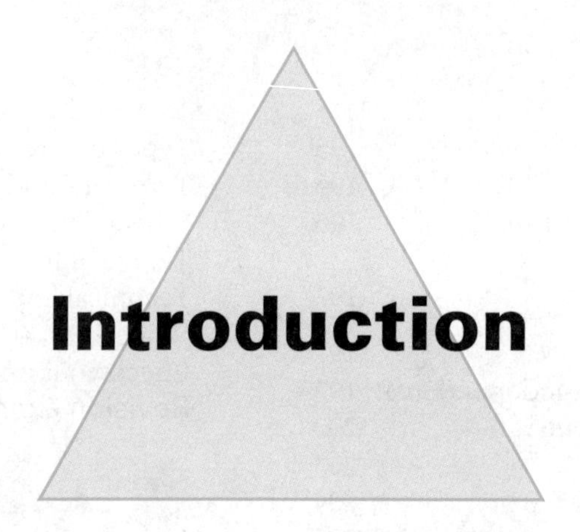

Introduction

This book is an introductory text for students undertaking a wide range of studies in motor vehicle technology at technical colleges and institutes of education and training. Our aim is to provide a broad understanding of the many systems and component parts that constitute the basis of a modern motor vehicle. The book should also be a valuable source of information and reference.

We have omitted unnecessary detail and theory. The book provides clear explanations of motor vehicle technology, which should be of value both to the novice motor mechanic and to the more experienced motor vehicle technician. Each chapter takes the reader systematically through the details of each component system. Key topics are emphasised, and are reinforced by numerous illustrations. At the end of each chapter there is a 'Check your understanding' section followed by self-test and proven exercise questions. These should help to reinforce the reader's knowledge and understanding, and allow for self-checking. The book also features numerous charts and checklists for fault finding and maintenance, and includes a number of practical projects.

Motor vehicle studies is very much a hands-on practical trade, but we believe it is important that all motor vehicle students should have an appropriate level of background knowledge, because the successful motor vehicle technicians of today and tomorrow are the ones who can relate the theory to the practice. We hope that you enjoy reading this book, and that you find its contents informative and useful.

1 The motor car and you

Introduction

No one can state with certainty when the first mechanically propelled vehicle was driven on the road. It is usually thought to have been a large, clumsy steam-driven artillery tractor made by Frenchman Joseph Cugnot in 1769. Unfortunately, it was not a success: it was very heavy, it was difficult to drive, and it had little power. Figure 1.1 gives an idea of its appearance.

From around the same time many people in Europe and the USA were experimenting with powered transport. One of the best known was an Englishman, Richard Trevithick, who made a working 'road locomotive' powered by steam in 1801. During the 1820s and 1830s several steam-powered, passenger-carrying 'road coaches' were in use in England and France. They fell into disuse because of the growth of the railway networks. In England there were also severe restrictions on their use. An Act of Parliament of 1865 limited their speed to 4 mph (6.4 km/h), and a man had to walk in front carrying a red flag!

The first vehicles that we would recognise as motor cars appeared, in very small numbers, on the roads towards the end of the nineteenth century. They were mostly powered by internal combustion engines working on the Otto cycle, patented in Germany by Dr Nikolaus Otto and subsequently developed by Gottlieb Daimler. Even so, some inventors continued to use steam or even electricity as their power source.

Karl Benz, another German, is credited as the world's first motor manufacturer. He was granted a patent for his 'motor wagon' in January 1886. His car, a three wheeler, was running on the streets of Mannheim in June of that year. This was followed a few months later by Daimler's

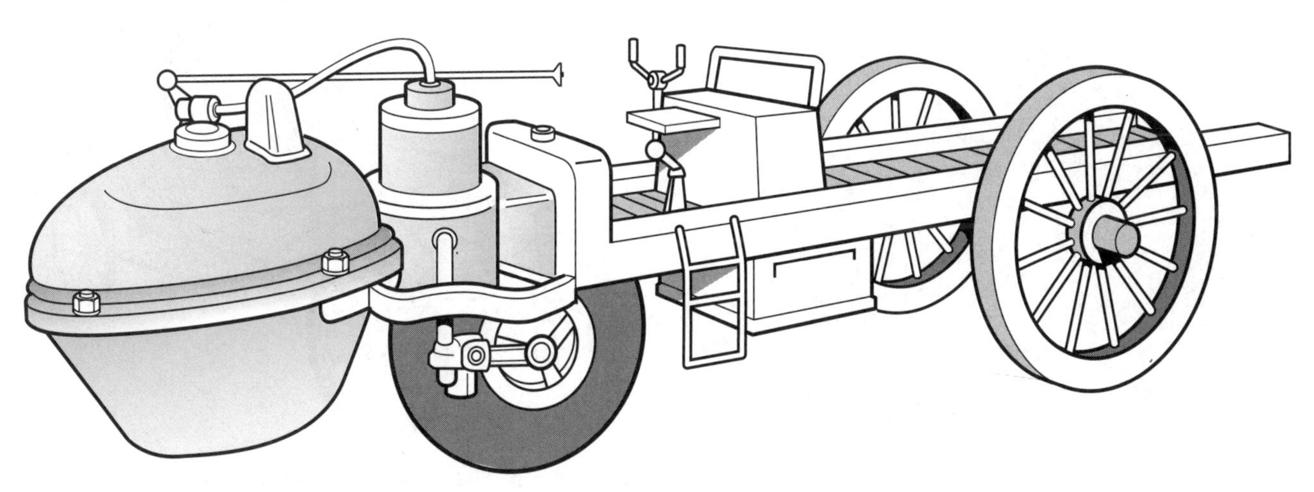

Figure 1.1 Joseph Cugnot's steam tractor.

installation of an engine into what had been a horse-drawn carriage, so making a successful 'horseless carriage'. Eventually the firms of Daimler and Benz joined together. They continue today, but are better known as Mercedes-Benz. An early Benz four-wheel car of about 1891 is shown in Figure 1.2. In those early days only the rich could afford to purchase these hand-built vehicles.

The man who is said to have brought motoring to ordinary people was Henry Ford of the USA. He pioneered the use of mass production, which made cars quickly and relatively cheaply, so that working people could afford to buy them. The famous Ford Model T (Figure 1.3) was in production from 1908 to 1927, during which time over 15 million were made. It may look crude by today's standards, but it was a very well made and reliable machine.

It was not until the second half of this century that greater numbers of one model of car were made, and that was the Volkswagen Type 1, better known as the Beetle.

As time passed, so motor cars became more reliable. Many of the hundreds of small firms making cars have ceased to exist, or have combined to form a relatively small number of large organisations making and exporting vehicles all over the world.

Modern motor cars have a very different appearance from those made a century ago. But essentially they do the same job, using the energy contained in fuel to transport us and our goods with little effort on our part. The Model T Ford had an internal combustion engine, and a transmission system of clutch, gearbox and rear axle driving wheels shod with air-filled tyres. A steering wheel, brakes and suspension made it safe and comfortable, just like the cars of today.

Study this book with great care. If you do not understand the basic principles of the motor vehicle, you will never be able to understand properly its more advanced technology, or succeed in your work.

Look after yourself

No matter how well designed or built modern vehicles are, during use they will need to be regularly inspected and serviced to ensure that they remain in a safe, serviceable and reliable condition. This book provides an insight into their various systems and components. Cars and commercial vehicles are large, heavy and mobile, and they can be dangerous, particularly to those who work on them without care. It is essential that you look after yourself, and those around you.

Figure 1.2 An early motor car by Karl Benz, circa 1891.

Figure 1.3 The Model T Ford by Henry Ford, circa 1908.

Workshop safety

> Although there are numerous safety hazards associated with any workshop, the selection of the correct tools and equipment will do much to minimise any potential danger. If you and your colleagues work safely, taking care not to make hazards as you do so, no harm should come to you.

A busy vehicle workshop can become full of danger if those who work there are careless and untidy. For example, there are many accidents waiting to happen in the workshop in Figure 1.4, and some of them could easily be fatal. Can you spot them? Look for hazards in your daily work, and learn to develop a positive attitude towards workshop safety: help to prevent accidents.

Here are some rules that will help you to stay healthy:

1. Always obey any safety signs in your workplace, such as those in Figure 1.5.

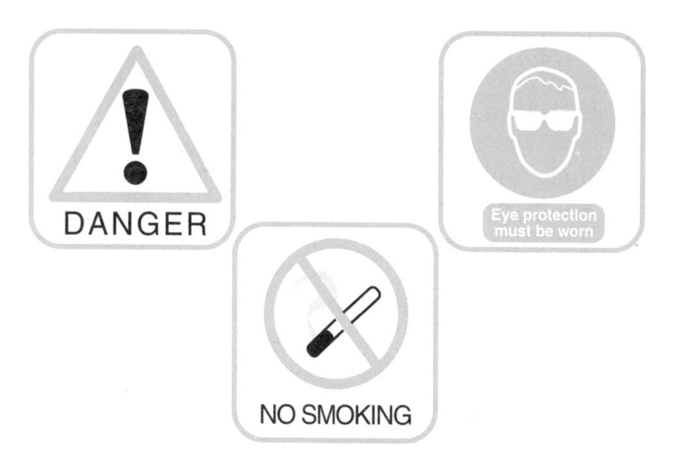

Figure 1.5 Typical safety signs.

Figure 1.4 Look for the safety hazards in this workshop.

2. When you need to work under a vehicle make sure that it is properly supported (Figure 1.6). It must be on axle stands or solid supports or, if it is on a hoist, make sure that swinging arms cannot move out or that the vehicle cannot roll off a platform. Allow for the loss of balancing weight if you remove heavy components.
3. Use lifting tackle, a crane or a transmission jack to lift heavy units. Lifting hooks and slings must be strong enough for the weight.
4. When lifting heavy weights yourself, make sure that you lift no more than you can comfortably manage, probably about 20 kg. Keep your back straight, and use the strong muscles in your legs for lifting (Figure 1.7).
5. The fine dust from brake and clutch linings is dangerous, and must not be breathed into your lungs. Always wear a mask for this work, and never blow dust away with an airline (Figure 1.8).
6. Drain petrol tanks in the open air, away from cigarettes and exposed flames. Remember that the fumes are more dangerous than the

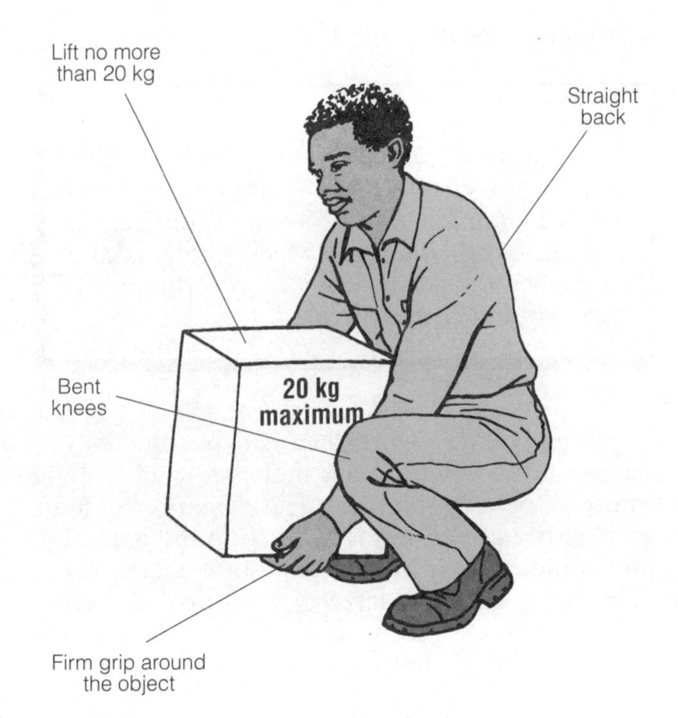

Figure 1.7 Adopt the correct lifting stance.

Figure 1.6 Safety first: always use axle stands.

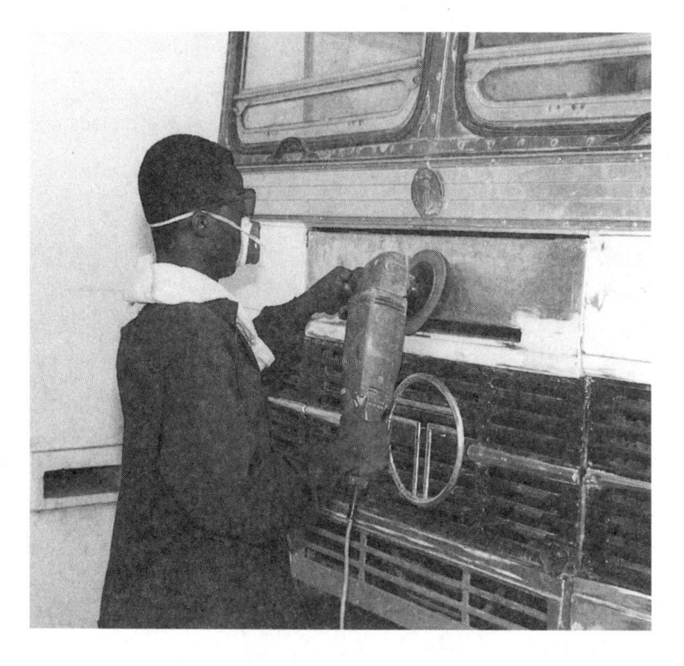

Figure 1.8 Dust is a killer: always wear a mask.

liquid. Never weld a fuel tank of any sort unless it has been completely cleansed of fumes.

7. Do not touch any part of an electronic ignition system while the ignition is switched on. Although the current itself may not injure you, the shock may cause you to jump and collide with hard objects. Condenser discharge ignition systems can cause a shock up to 24 hours after being switched off.
8. Never cut open or throw away airbag modules or explosive seat-belt tensioners that have not been activated, as the chemicals in this state are very dangerous.
9. Always inflate heavy vehicle tyres on split rims, or on wheels with separate rims, inside a protective cage (Figure 1.9). If the wheel blows apart it may cause severe or even fatal injuries.
10. Remember that a clean and tidy workplace is a safe workplace.

Figure 1.9 Always use a tyre cage when inflating tyres.

Personal protective equipment

Personal protective equipment (PPE) comprises all the items that you may need to wear to protect yourself.

From your head down these include:

1. ear defenders against excessive noise (Figure 1.10);
2. goggles or a visor to protect your eyes from particles or liquids (Figure 1.10);
3. masks to filter out dust or gases;
4. overalls of the correct type to shield your skin;
5. gloves to protect your hands, particularly from diesel oil and acids;
6. industrial shoes or boots to protect your feet.

Apart from PPE, something else to think about is your personal condition. Look at Figures 1.11a and 1.11b and decide who is less likely to suffer an accident.

Figure 1.10 Wear the right personal safety equipment.

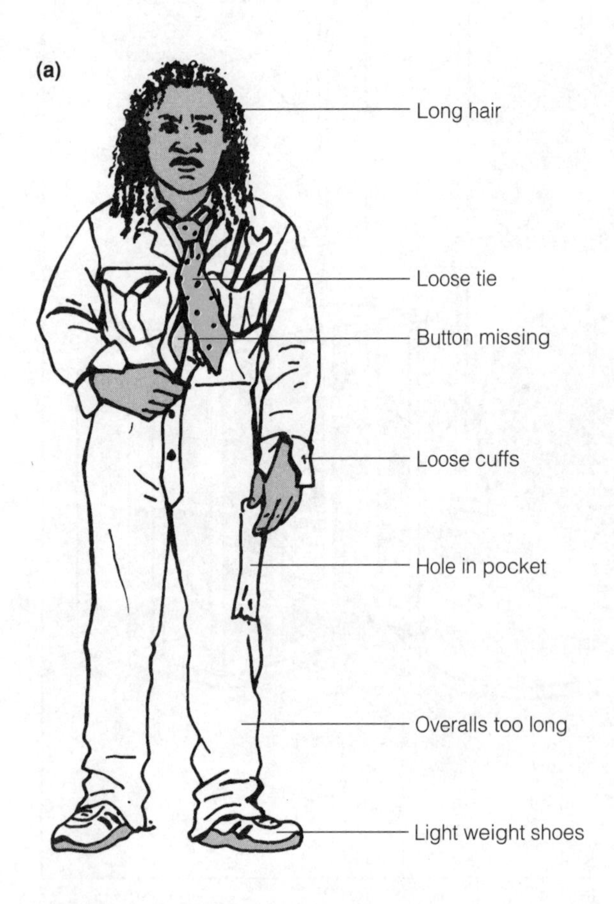

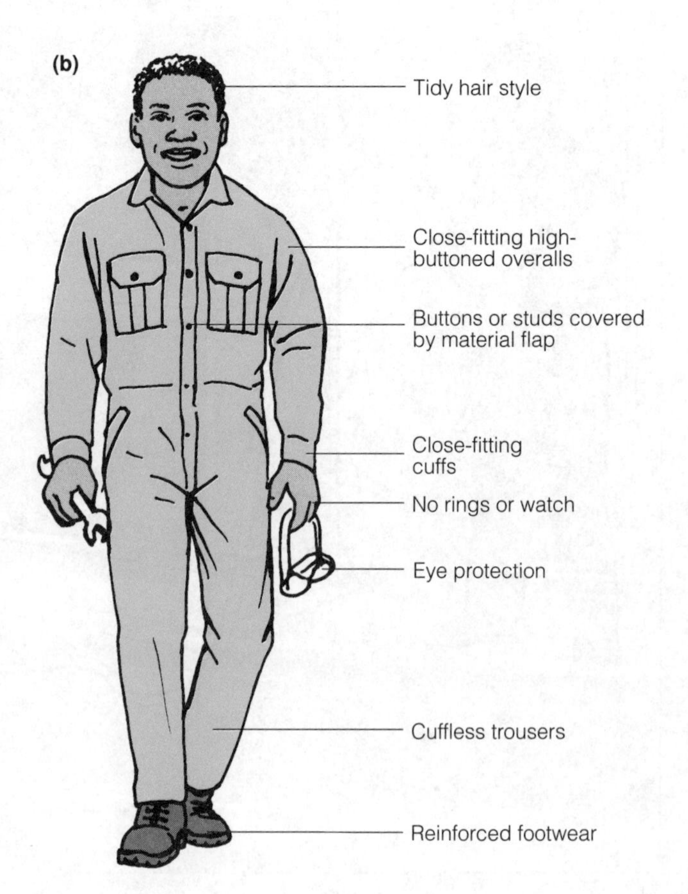

Figure 1.11 Which one are you?

Fire prevention

Inflammable liquids and gases are often associated with vehicle servicing and repair, and so there is always the possibility of a fire. Always take special care when working with such substances.

> Three components are needed to produce fire:
>
> - a supply of oxygen;
> - some combustible material;
> - a source of ignition.

Remove any one of these elements and you eliminate the risk of fire.

Because of the type of work that a mechanic is required to do, it is essential to take a positive approach towards fire prevention. Your personal safety may depend upon it. Working on a petrol fuel system with the ignition switched on, with an open flame nearby, or with a lighted cigarette in your mouth, can be a recipe for disaster. If possible, disconnect the battery before you start any major work.

Being clean and tidy is also good fire prevention (Figure 1.12). See the fire safety checklist in Table 1.1.

Table 1.1 Fire safety checklist

Rubbish	No unnecessary accumulation
Flammables	Safely stored, contained; no breakages or spills
Housekeeping	Work area neat and tidy
Wiring	Good connections, earthed
Machinery	Clean, working properly
Combustibles	Away from heat
Smoking	Safe area, safe disposal
Ventilation	Of waste, high fume areas
Extinguishers	Correct ones, well marked, regularly checked
Exits, passageways	Clear, unobstructed
Evacuation alarm	Recognised by all
Evacuation procedures	Practised, known by all

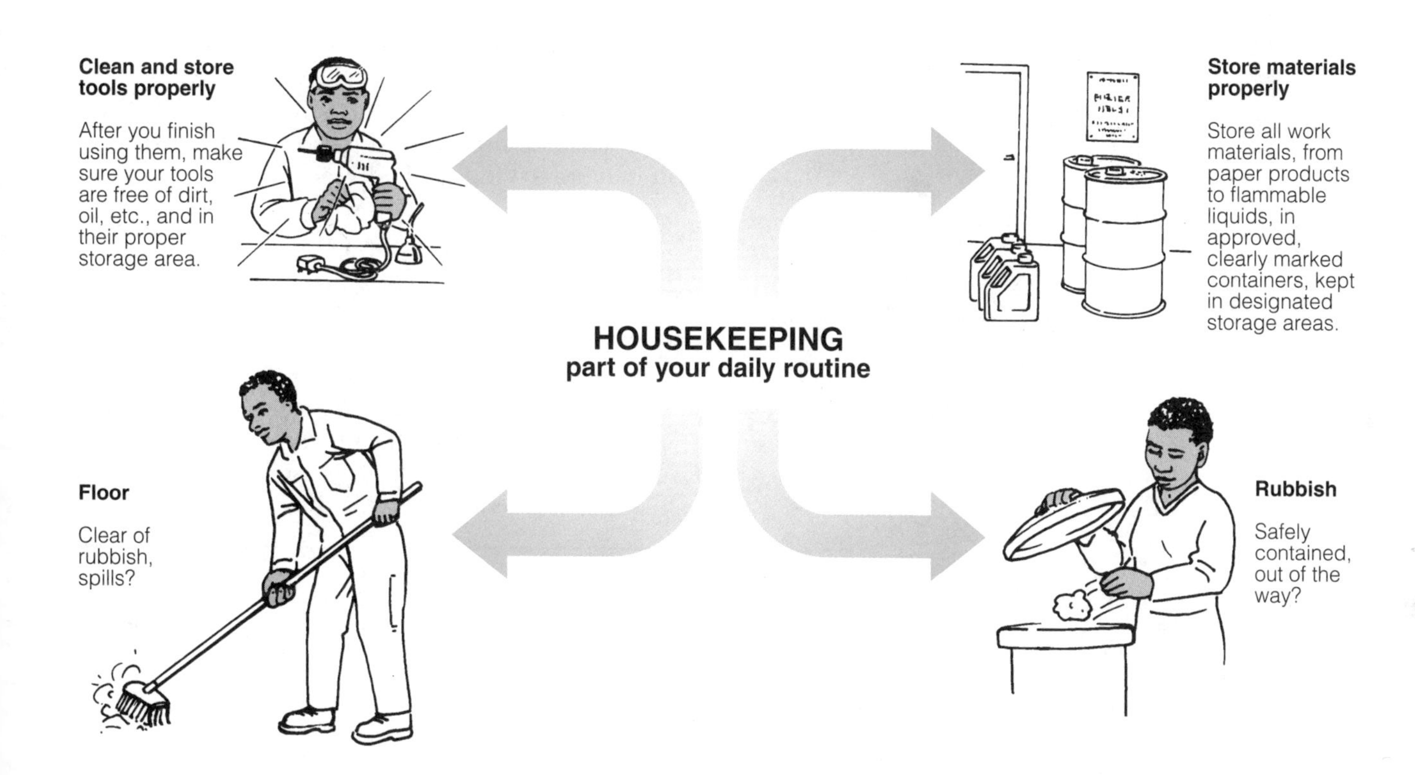

Figure 1.12 Keeping the workshop clean and tidy is an important part of fire prevention.

Fire-fighting equipment

All workshops should have a range of equipment to deal with fires before they get out of hand. The requirements will probably be listed in local regulations, and will be required before a fire certificate is issued. Fire-fighting equipment must be kept in good working order.

Fires can be broadly classified as those involving combustible material, electricity, or liquids. The difficulty when dealing with vehicle or vehicle workshop fires is that all three may be involved at the same time. Here are some guidelines for dealing with them.

Combustible material

This includes such things as cleanimg rags or wipes, upholstery, paper and wood. This sort of fire can be drenched with water, smothered with a blanket or sand, or beaten out with a shovel or beater (Figure 1.13).

Figure 1.13 Ways to fight a fire involving ordinary combustibles – not petrol, oil or electrical fires.

Electricity

Disconnect the supply and smother the fire. If the fire involves mains electricity the smothering material must not be an electrical conductor.

Liquids

The golden rule is never to throw water onto such a fire; it may violently splatter burning material over you. A smothering agent is needed, such as foam. Small liquid fires can be smothered with a fire-resistant blanket.

> Each part of a workshop should have a **fire point**, where the items that may be needed to fight a fire are gathered together. Make sure that you know where these are in your place of work.

Fire evacuation

If there is a fire, the first requirement is warn everyone so that they can evacuate the building to prevent possible loss of life. All workshops should be fitted with some form of **fire alarm**. There should also be clearly marked escape routes to **fire exits** that can be opened immediately.

These passageways and exit doors must be kept absolutely clean and clear at all times. You may be asked to go through a **fire drill** – a practice in case of fire. Treat this seriously; next time you may be saving your life!

First aid

> If an accident occurs, the injured person must receive immediate medical attention. Raise the alarm, and obtain the assistance of a person qualified in first aid procedures.

Minor injuries can be treated from the workshop's **first aid box**, which should contain assorted bandages and sterile dressings with which to dress the wound.

If the accident is more serious, and especially if limbs seem to have been broken, the casualty must not be moved until they have been attended by qualified medical personnel.

In cases of electrical shock, and where the casualty is still connected to the circuit, the current supply must first be turned off before administering first aid. If this is not possible an insulator such as wood may be used to separate them from the power supply.

CHECK YOUR UNDERSTANDING

- The basic components and layout of many vehicles are very similar to those of the Model T Ford of 1908.
- For safety and good health it is essential to look after yourself, and those around you.
- The motor vehicle workshop, and motor vehicles themselves, can be hazardous to the careless mechanic.
- Good housekeeping is the basis of health and safety.
- Lift weights using your leg muscles; use a lifting device whenever you can.
- Look for hazards, and prevent accidents.
- Wear the correct protective clothing and equipment.
- Prevent fires rather than put them out.
- Warn others first, and use the correct fire-fighting equipment only if it is safe to do so.
- For injuries other than very minor ones call for qualified medical aid.

REVISION EXERCISES AND QUESTIONS

1. Who first commercially manufactured motor vehicles?
2. Which car set the pattern for many of those in use today?
3. State in one short sentence how you can prevent damage to the health of yourself and others in a motor vehicle workshop.
4. What activity forms the basis of an effective health and safety routine in the vehicle workshop?
5. How can you protect yourself from dust and hazardous liquids?
6. What should be the first step when you discover a fire?
7. Where will you find the equipment to deal with a fire?
8. What condition must fire exits and the passageways leading to them be kept in?
9. What is the first step in helping someone who has suffered electric shock?

2 Chassis and body construction

Introduction

> Manufacturers of light vehicles commonly employ one of three layouts for the drive components: front engine and rear-wheel drive, front engine and front-wheel drive, and four-wheel drive.

Front engine and rear-wheel drive is sometimes called the **conventional layout** because it largely follows the designs of vehicles manufactured during the first half of the twentieth century (Figure 2.1). The engine is located longitudinally (that is, lengthways), and drives the rear wheels through a transmission line of clutch, gearbox, propeller shaft and final drive.

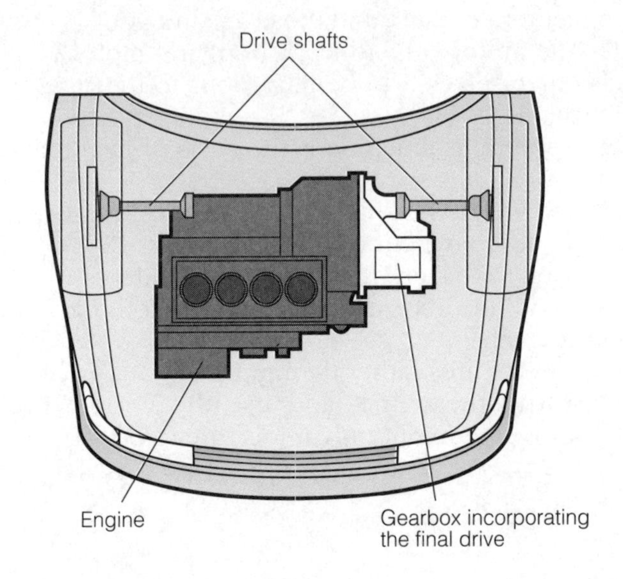

Figure 2.2 A front-wheel-drive transverse layout.

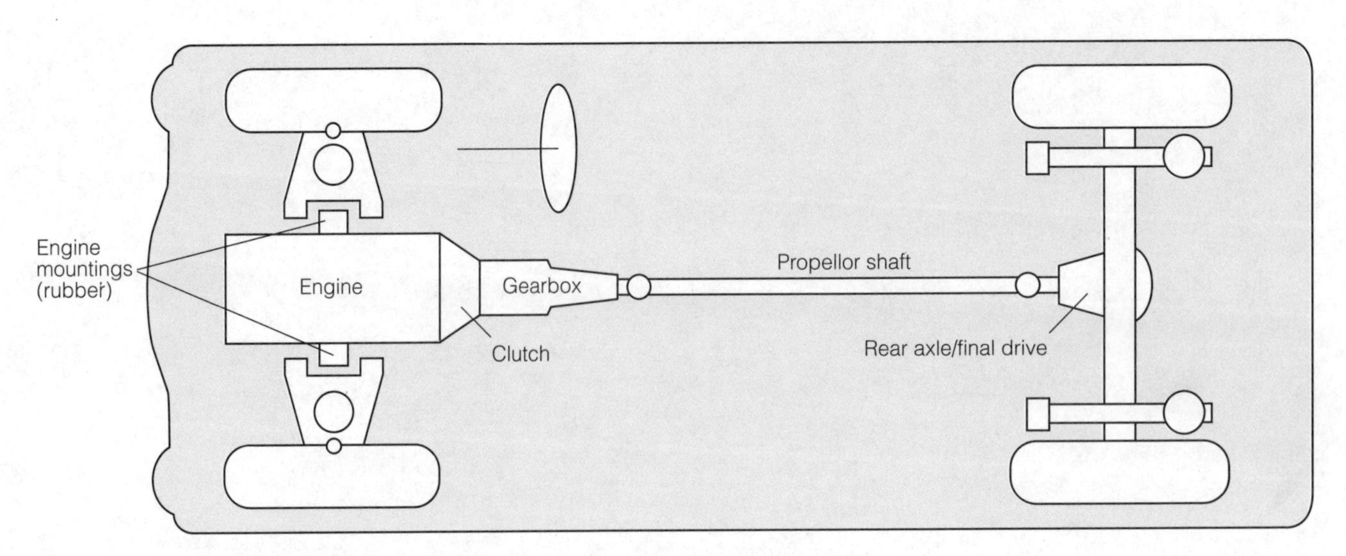

Figure 2.1 Conventional layout: front engine, rear-wheel drive.

Many vehicle manufacturers have now changed from the conventional layout to front engine and front-wheel drive (Figure 2.2). The engine and the compact, one-piece transmission unit are located across the engine compartment in what is known as **transverse layout**. This allows a greater amount of the vehicle's space to be used for the passenger compartment.

Four-wheel drive was once solely intended for off-road vehicles. However, this type of drive can also improve the handling of vehicles driven primarily on the road, and is becoming increasingly used on high-performance machines. An example of an advanced modern design is shown in schematic form in Figure 2.3. This is for the Ford Galaxy 4 × 4. It uses a six-cylinder transverse engine, automatic transmission and independent suspension.

Medium and heavy commercial vehicles follow the conventional layout in that the engine is at the front, with a transmission system driving the rear wheels (Figure 2.4). Although rarely used for cars now, the ladder-type **chassis frame** is the normal construction for commercial vehicles.

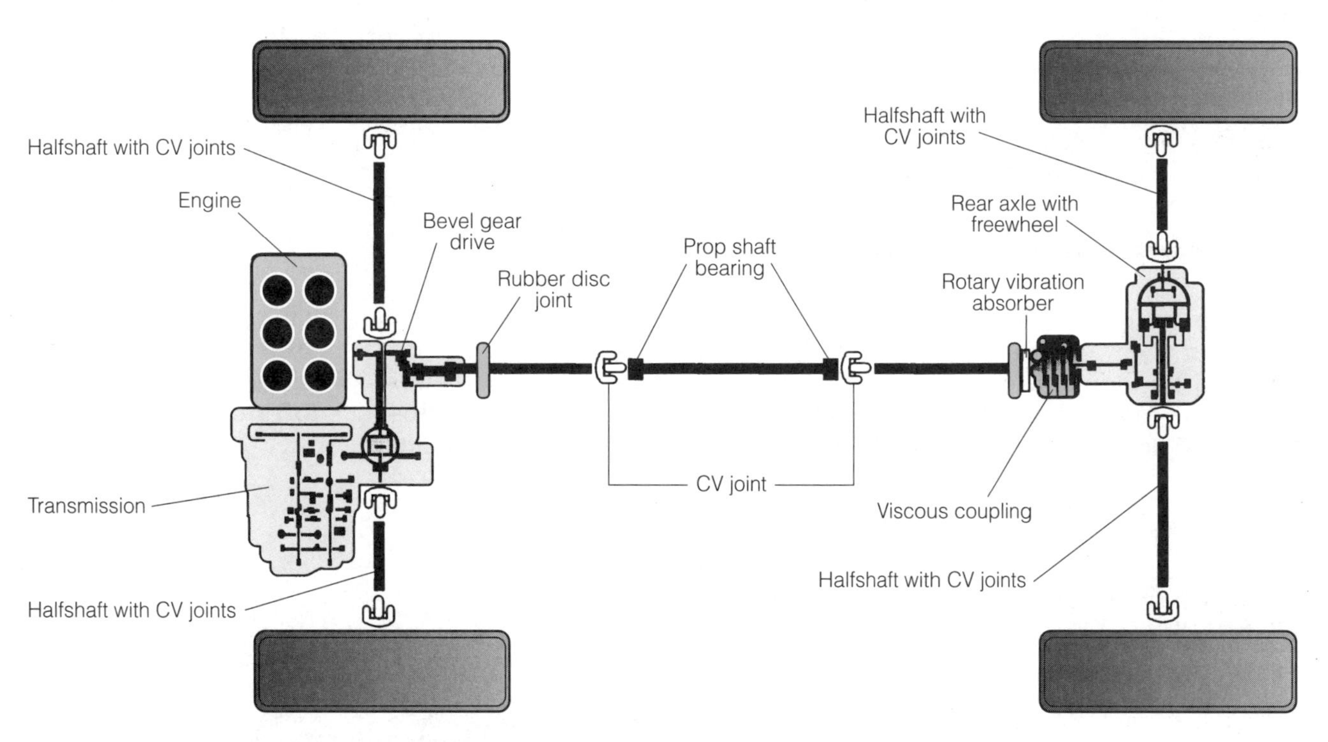

Figure 2.3 Four-wheel drive: the Ford Galaxy 4 × 4.

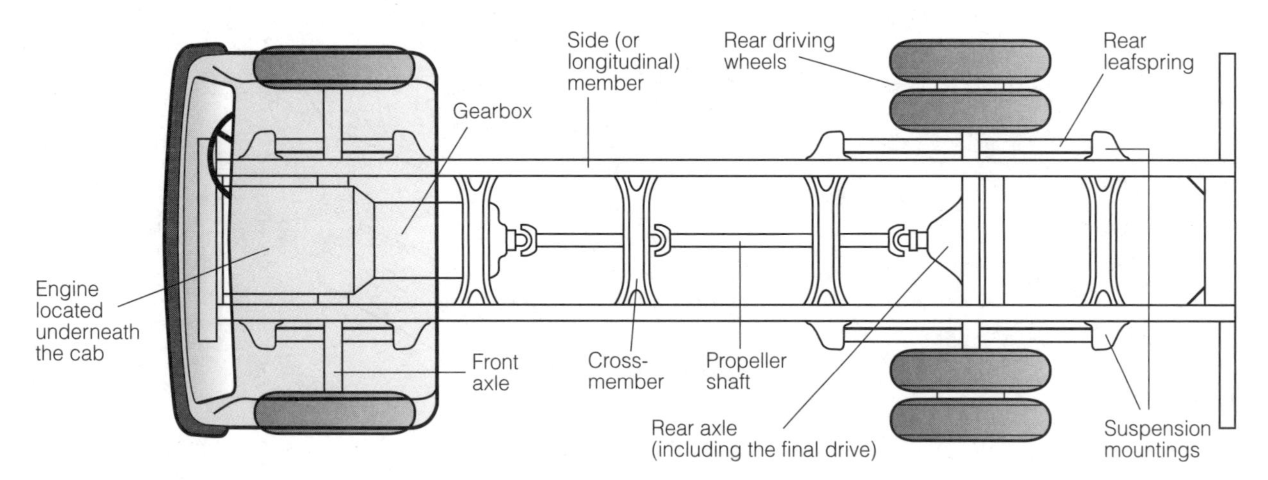

Figure 2.4 Conventional heavy vehicle layout: ladder chassis.

Light vehicle body construction

Early motor vehicles had separate, strong chassis frames, mostly similar to that shown in Figure 2.4. This made it quite easy to attach units such as the engine, gearbox and road springs, and provided convenient mounting places for the body. If a different body was needed, it could be changed with little or no alteration to the chassis. Even now, most heavy commercial and many four-wheel drive vehicles continue to use a separate chassis.

> Today, almost all motor cars, most vans and even some buses are of **integral construction**, also known as **unitary** or **monocoque** construction.

In this design the whole basic body structure shares in the work of supporting all the loads imposed on the vehicle. Panels or members that share the load are called **stressed panels**. Very often their creases and bends are there to increase strength rather than change the vehicle's appearance. **Unstressed panels** are those that do not contribute significantly to the strength of the structure. In integral construction the **floorpan** and all the body panels are bonded together to form a complete structure (Figure 2.5). Although the metal used is much thinner than that in a chassis, the shaped and joined panels provide a very strong but relatively lightweight bodyshell.

Design and production costs are very high, which means that integral construction is used only for mass-produced vehicles. A further disadvantage of this type of construction is that the resulting box-like shape tends to amplify road and engine noise for the occupants. Special sound-deadening materials are used to minimise the transmission of noise (Figure 2.6).

The subframe

The relatively thin metal of an integrally constructed vehicle means that concentrated loads from the engine and suspension units could cause excessive local stress and noise. These problems are overcome by using **subframes** to spread the load and reduce noise transfer (Figure 2.7).

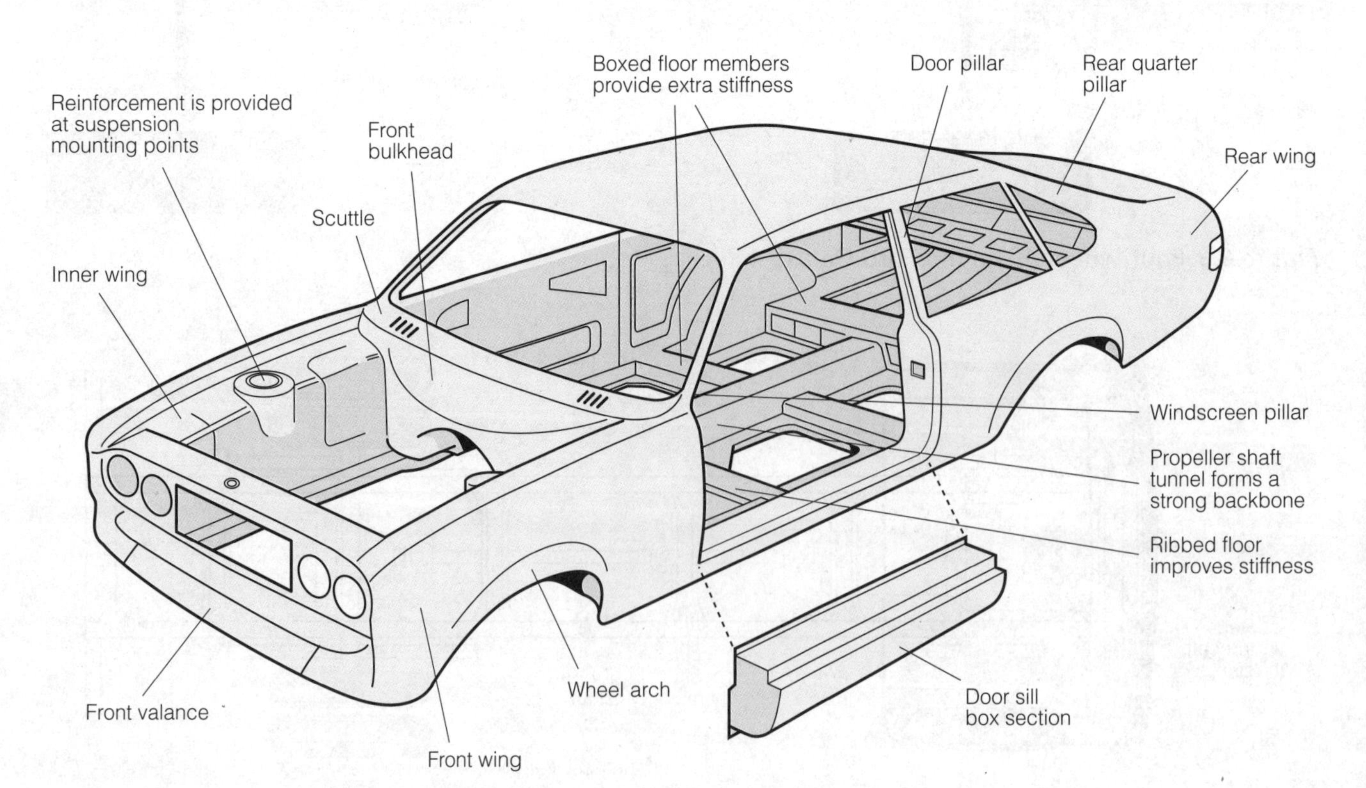

Figure 2.5 Integral construction.

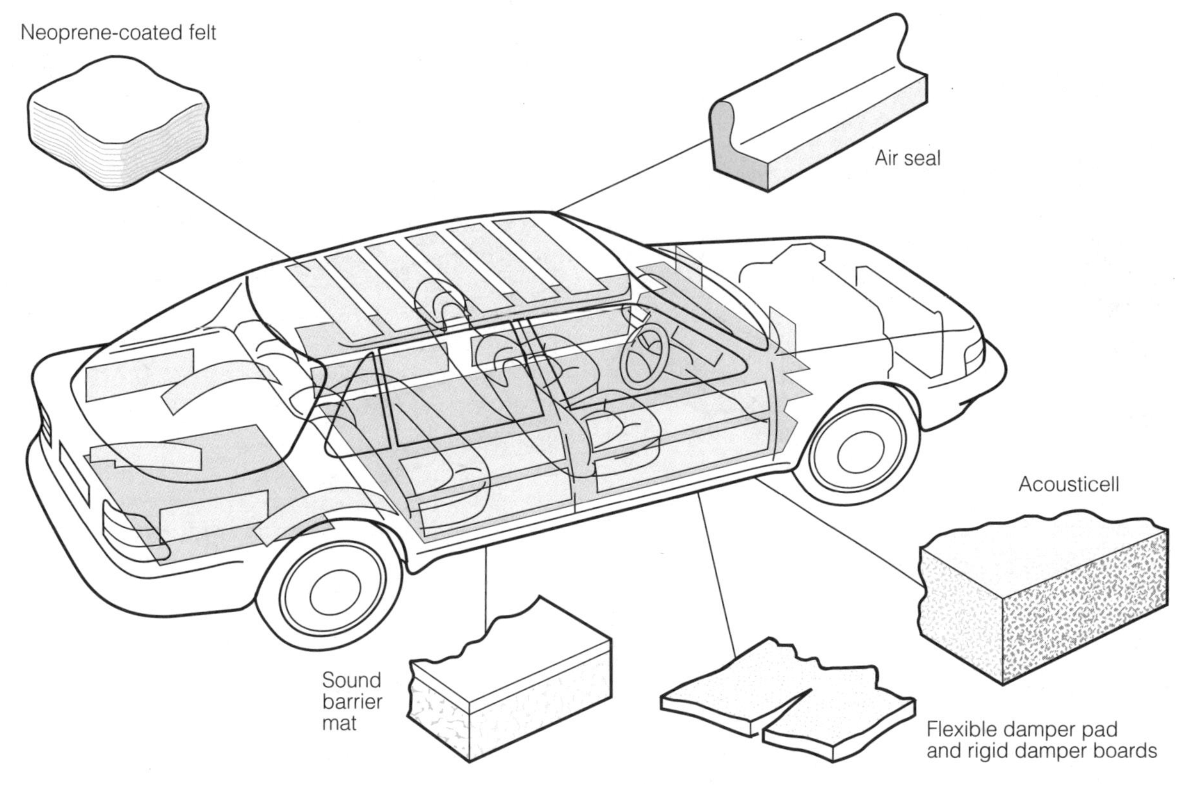

Figure 2.6 Sound-deadening materials.

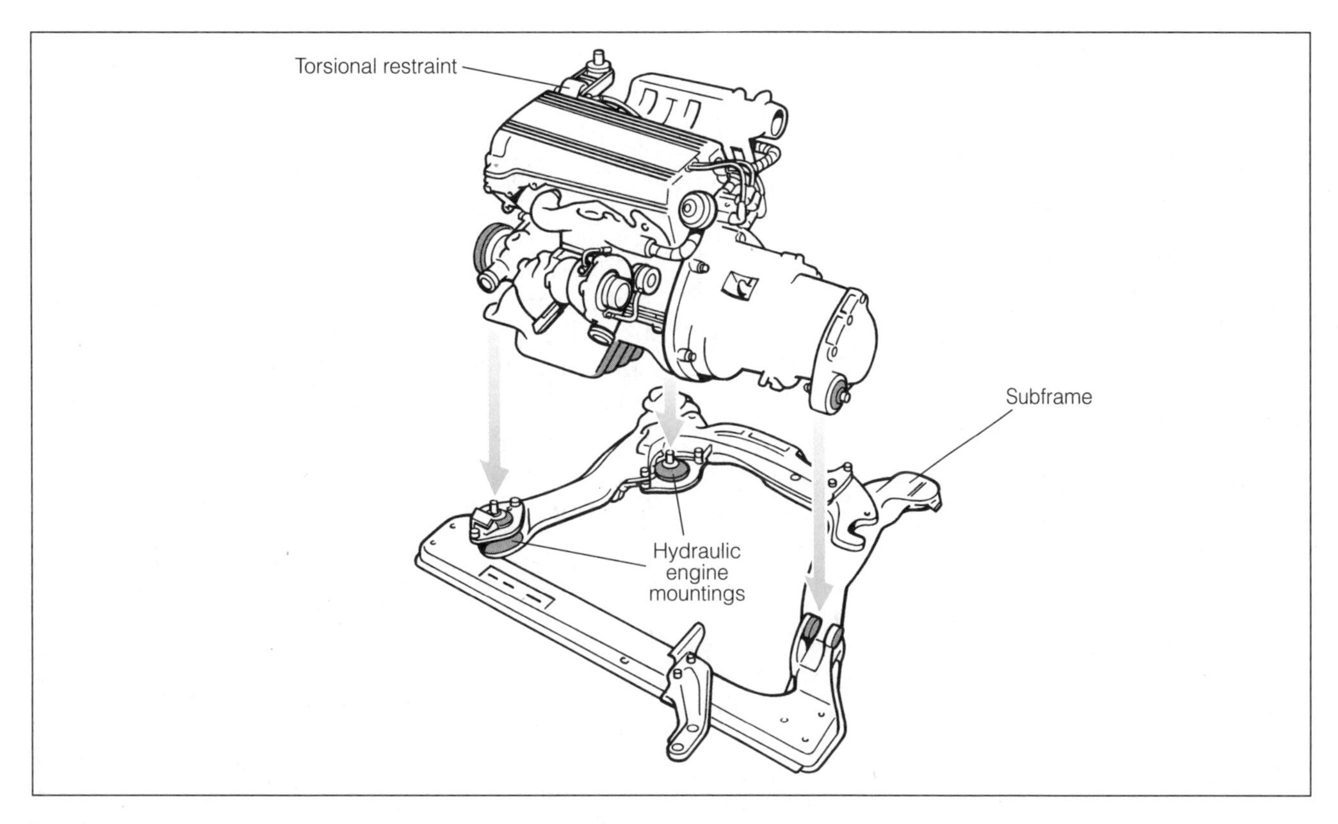

Figure 2.7 Engine mounting/subframe.

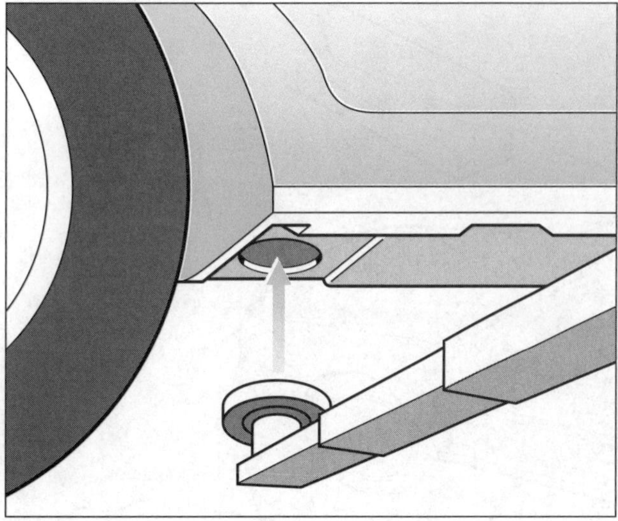

Figure 2.8 Jacking points.

Jacking points

In order to avoid concentrated stress and prevent damage, it is essential to use only the proper jacking points, or the manufacturer's designated lifting pads, when lifting integrally constructed vehicles (Figure 2.8). It is also important, particularly if a vehicle is to remain suspended on a hoist for any period of time, that the doors are closed.

Using two-post hoists
Adjust the arms to balance the vehicle before lifting, especially if a heavy component such as a subframe is to be removed. Make sure that the arms cannot move outwards when the vehicle has been lifted.

Body protection

To protect the bodyshell from corrosion, protective coatings are applied to all its surfaces. Many vehicles now use galvanised steel for some components or even for the whole bodyshell.

Many makers use **electrostatic coatings** for the initial phosphate and primer coatings, usually by immersion into tanks of paint. Robots apply other primer coats and the final colour and lacquer coatings.

At appropriate times in this process special anti-corrosion treatments are applied. These include anti-stone chip material around the sills and apron, underbody coatings, sealers for all seams, and, for some makes, hot wax injected into the cavities. Plastic wheel-arch liners are now commonplace. All these measures are aimed at preventing corrosion of the internal and external surfaces. Body and finish damage must be repaired by methods approved by the manufacturer if corrosion is to be avoided.

Safety design features

An important design feature of any modern vehicle is its ability to protect the occupants from serious physical harm resulting from a collision. In recent years the regulations governing vehicle construction have been updated, making safety a primary consideration. All vehicles are now required to pass certain technical safety standards.

Crumple zones

The purpose of a **crumple zone**, or deformation element, is to ensure that in the event of a severe front or rear impact the vehicle's structure absorbs as much energy as possible. This reduces the rate of deceleration felt by the occupants, and reduces the risk of injury.

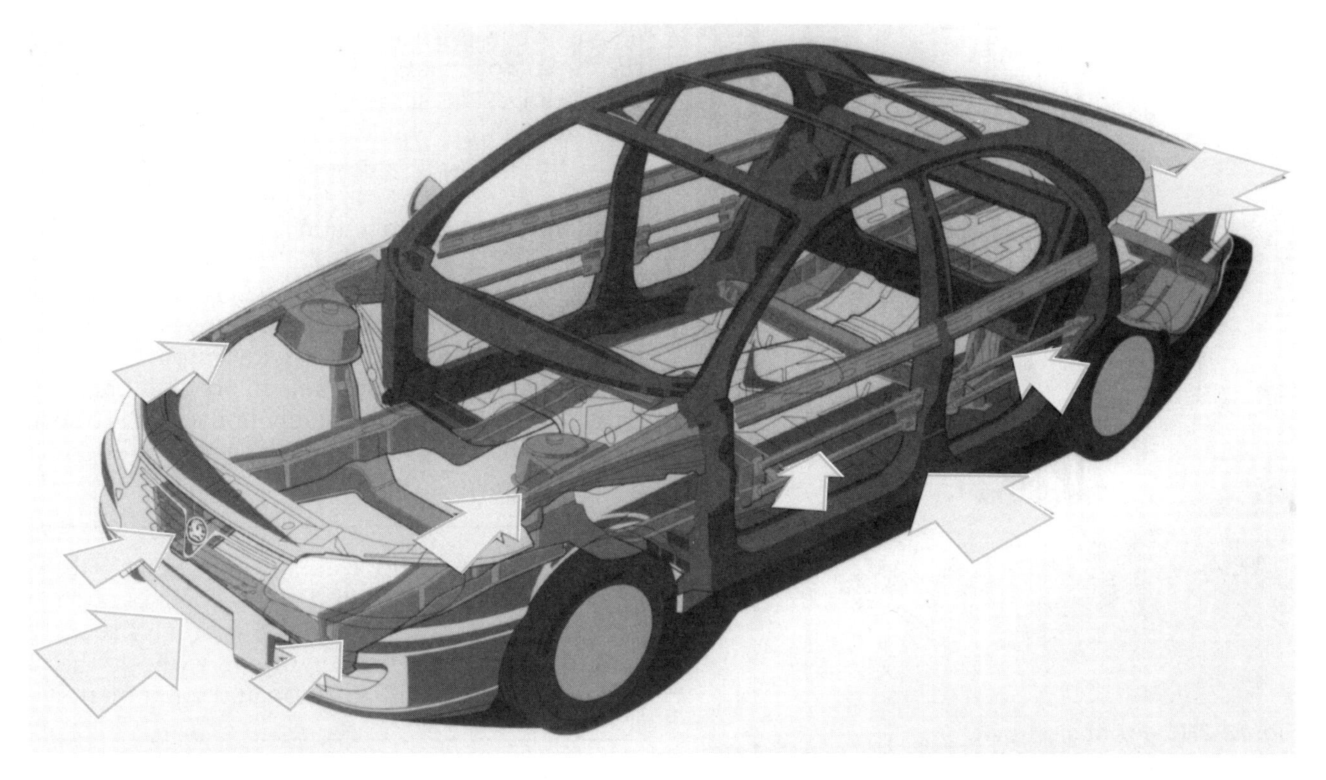

Figure 2.9 Internal structure of an integral body. The arrows show how the shock of a collision or a side impact is spread and absorbed.

Figure 2.9 shows the internal structure of an integral body. The front arrows show how the shock of a frontal collision is transferred along the front body members, which are designed to collapse progressively, absorbing energy as they do so and protecting the passenger compartment. The intention is to create a **passenger safety cell** in which the occupants are protected from physical impact and excessive body stresses.

The rear of the vehicle acts in exactly the same way. Note that if the spare wheel lies flat in the boot floor, it may be part of the rear crumple zone, and if so it must be kept inflated.

Side impact protection

To prevent intrusion into the passenger area as a result of side impact, an increasing number of vehicles are now designed with side impact protection features.

One of the most common types comprises strengthening beams fitted into the frame of each door. The side arrows in Figure 2.9 show how these beams help to spread the load of a side impact.

Seat-belts

The purpose of a seat-belt is to prevent the wearer from being thrown forwards and possibly being injured during a frontal impact (Figure 2.10). It is essential to have an automatic device to restrain the body, because in a collision the time to act is too short – one tenth of a second – and the forces are too great to resist. In a really severe crash a human baby effectively weighs the same as a baby elephant.

A seat-belt is made of a woven fabric usually mounted on a spring-loaded inertia mechanism (Figure 2.11). Under normal driving conditions the seat-belt can be easily pulled off the spool against spring tension. When the vehicle decelerates rapidly as a result of hard braking or impact,

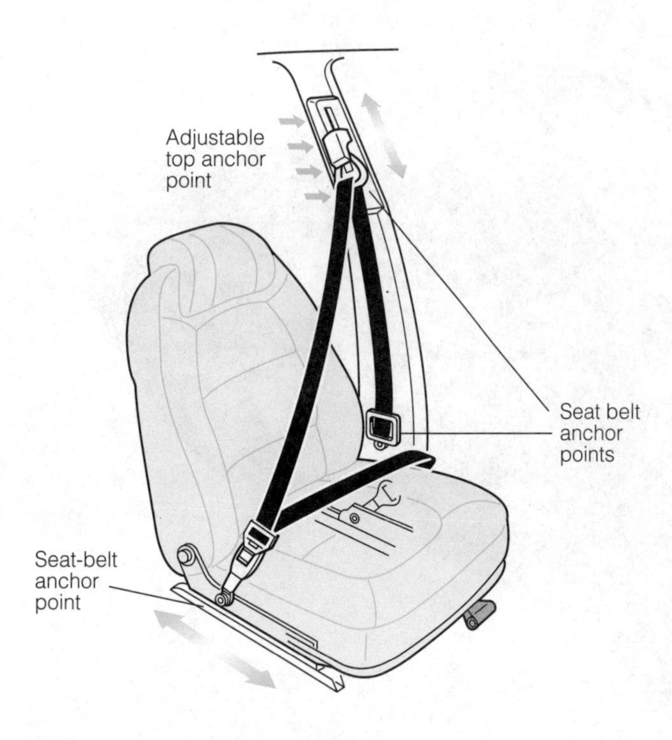

Figure 2.10 Front seat-belt.

a sensor ball is thrown forwards and by means of the actuator plate prevents the spool from unwinding. The seat-belt is now locked in position. When the vehicle comes to rest the ball falls back and the seat-belt is released. It is important that the seat-belts and anchorages are checked frequently and are maintained in good condition.

To make seat-belts more effective by taking out the free play and stretch of the fabric, most are now fitted with an **automatic tensioner** or pretensioner (Figure 2.12). In an impact, special sensors activate a mechanism to pull the belt tight. This mechanism, usually housed in the seat-belt reel housing, is commonly operated by a small explosive charge.

> These devices are perfectly safe unless tampered with or serviced without knowledge of the correct procedure. Do not work on them without the maker's service information and equipment.

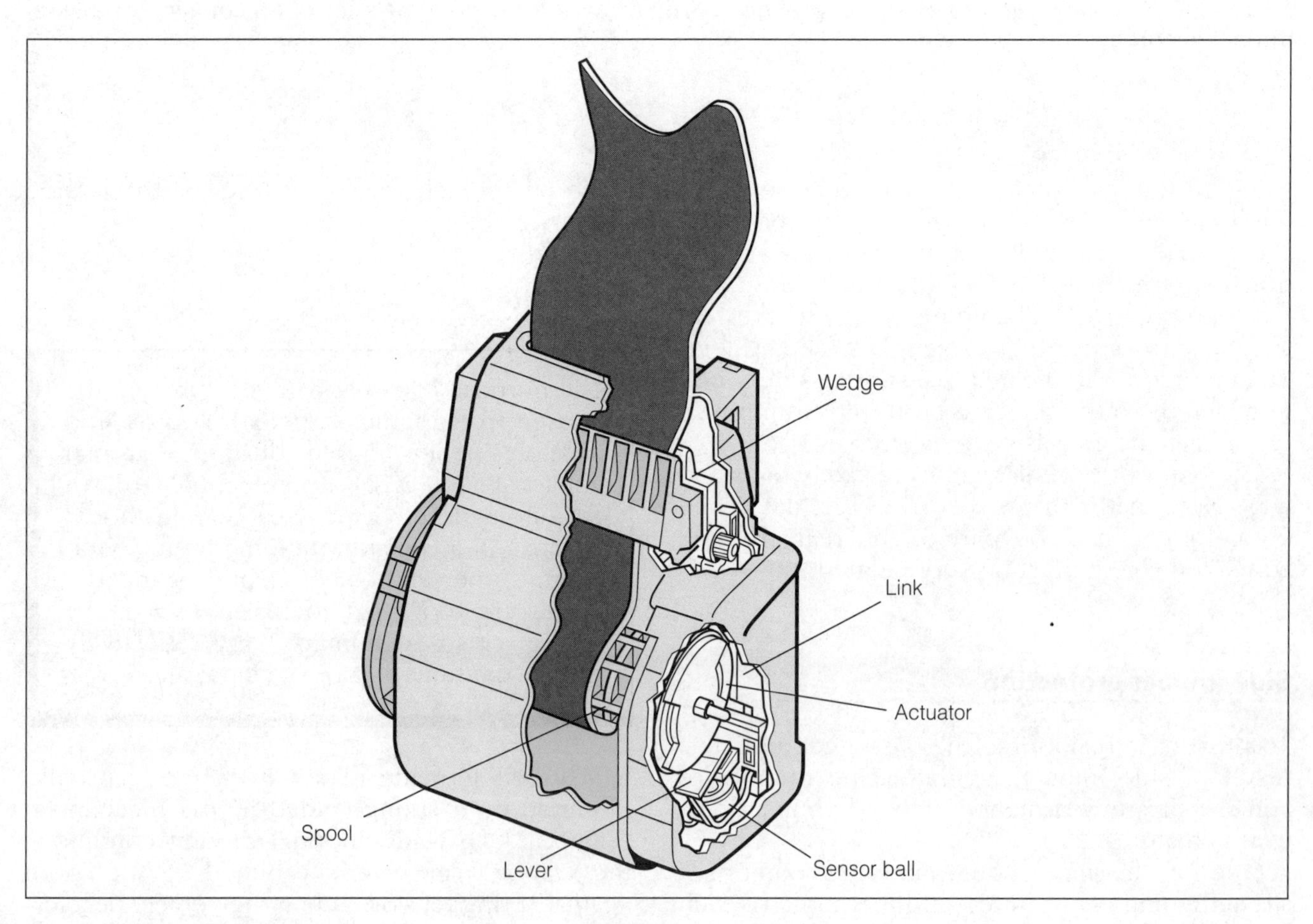

Figure 2.11 Inertia seat-belt.

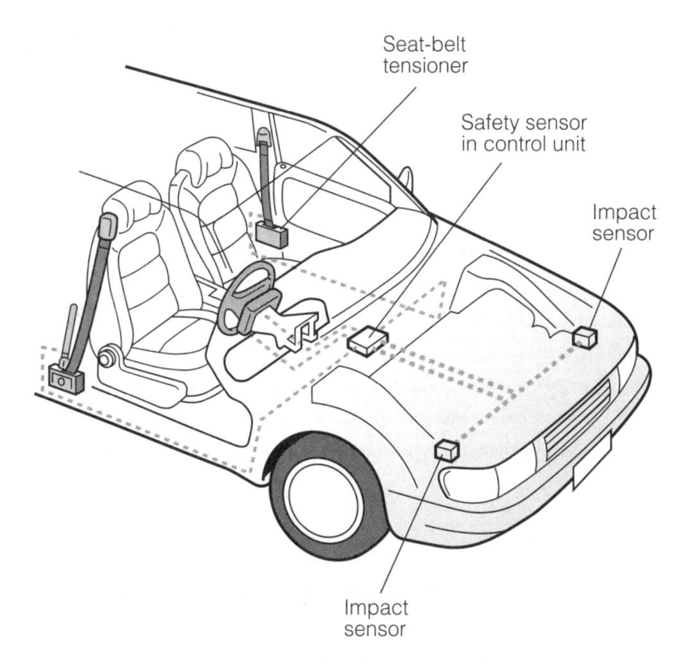

Figure 2.12 Automatic seat-belt tensioners.

Airbags

One of the major safety developments has been the fitting of airbags as part of the equipment of new vehicles. Inflated airbags protect the driver and front seat passenger from striking, respectively, the steering wheel or dashboard (Figure 2.13).

American vehicles often use airbags as the sole means of preventing injury. European-designed vehicles use the airbag as an additional aid in conjunction with the seat-belt.

Figure 2.13 Airbag safety protection: 40 milliseconds after impact, the airbag is almost totally inflated.

Under no circumstances should a European-designed vehicle with airbags be driven without using the seat-belts if full protection is to be retained.

Side airbags, where fitted, give extra protection against side impact.

In a frontal impact the airbag inflates, and then empties, in one tenth of a second (Figure 2.13). In that time the occupant moves forwards into the inflated bag under the influence of inertia, and then, as the vehicle comes to rest, relaxes back into the seat again.

Airbag operation

In an impact above 25 km/h, inertia sensors send a signal to the **electronic control unit (ECU)**, which triggers the igniter unit. Pellets that create a gas when burnt are then ignited, and the airbag inflates. As the body of the occupant sinks into the airbag, the gas is forced out of vent holes.

There are a number of important points of which you must be aware:

1. In normal operation, and when stored correctly, there is no danger from the airbag module.
2. When removed from a vehicle or awaiting fitting, the airbag module must be stored in a container away from any source of ignition, and must not be dropped or damaged. In some countries an explosives licence may be needed to work on the airbag module.
3. The nitrogen gas that inflates the airbag is part of the air that we breathe, and is quite harmless.
4. The white dust that is seen after inflation is also harmless; it is used to lubricate the bag.
5. The contents of an unused module are, however, **extremely dangerous**. The propellant contains sodium azide, which is very toxic in its unburnt state. It will self-ignite at 200 °C, can ignite just by friction or pressure, and produces a lethal gas when mixed with acid.

> Never cut an unused airbag module, or damage it in any way – it could be lethal.

Here are some guidelines for handling vehicles with airbags:

1. Always disconnect the battery before removing an airbag module.
2. Note that some American vehicles have up to half an hour's delayed activation built in to the airbag controller *after* the battery has been disconnected.
3. When disposing of an 'untriggered' but unwanted airbag module detonate it in accordance with the manufacturer's instructions.

CHECK YOUR UNDERSTANDING

- There are three types of vehicle layout that manufacturers commonly employ: conventional front engine and rear-wheel drive, front engine and front-wheel drive, and four-wheel drive.
- The two main types of vehicle construction are the composite design or ladder type, and the integral (also known as unitary or monocoque), sometimes with a subframe.
- A vehicle of unitary construction needs a subframe to support the weight of components such as the engine and suspension units.
- Vehicle body panels are often referred to as either stressed or unstressed. Creasing, coachlines or other shaping give a panel additional strength, and make the bodyshell stronger.
- To meet current safety requirements, modern vehicles are designed with the following features: crumple zones, also known as deformation elements; passenger safety cell; side impact protection, such as strengthening bars, pads and airbags; seat-belts, seat-belt tensioners and front airbags.
- To prevent corrosion, special treatments are applied. Galvanised steel may be used for bodywork and plastic for components.

REVISION EXERCISES AND QUESTIONS

1. Briefly explain the difference between chassis-based and integral body construction.
2. Give another name for integral construction.
3. Why are subframes used with integral bodies?
4. What is a stressed panel?
5. What is the purpose of a crumple zone?
6. Which two main items of equipment may be found on European-designed vehicles that protect occupants in frontal impacts?
7. When do you need to take special precautions with a vehicle equipped with airbags, and what are they?

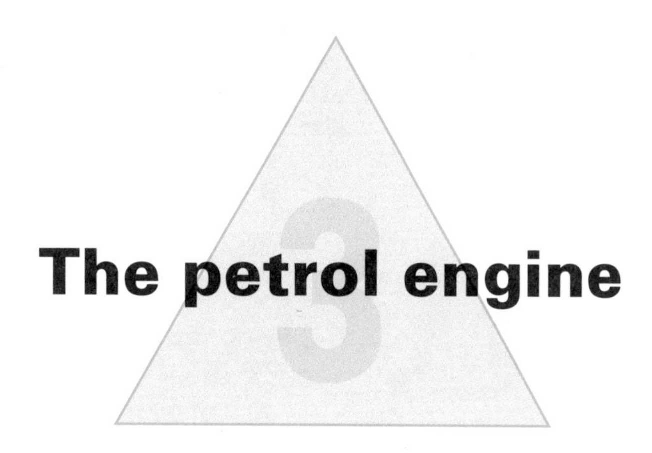

The petrol engine

Introduction

During the first 100 years of the motor vehicle, several forms of power have been tried, sometimes with limited success. Electric power has been used for specialist vehicles for many years, and is again becoming a usable alternative for the car, light van and bus. But the engine that is found in most vehicles is the heat engine, normally called the **internal combustion engine**.

Combustion is a word that describes the act of burning. Internal combustion means that the fuel is burnt inside the engine. With external combustion the burning takes place outside the engine, as in the steam engine for example.

The engine provides the power to turn the vehicle's wheels, and although it appears to be very complicated, the principle on which it works is relatively simple. The engine converts energy, just as you and I convert energy. We take in food (fuel) as energy, and our body converts this to heat (this keeps our blood warm) and motion (walking and running), as well as using it to fuel the internal functions of the body (operating the lungs and heart). To enable the body to 'burn' the food taken in, it also needs oxygen, which we obtain by breathing.

The internal combustion engine works in a similar way. Energy is taken in in the form of fuel, mixed with oxygen, and burnt. The burning creates heat, which is then converted into movement and used to drive the vehicle. The engine, and indeed the vehicle as a whole, is therefore a machine that converts energy. Energy can only be converted; it can never be created, and can never be destroyed. Let us now look more closely at how the engine achieves this conversion.

Energy conversion process

Fuel and oxygen are converted to heat energy by combustion. The heat created during the combustion process causes the gases trapped inside the cylinder to expand. This expansion causes a pressure build-up, which is then converted to mechanical energy as the expanding gases force a piston down the cylinder.

The up-and-down movement of the piston is converted to rotary motion (to turn the vehicle's wheels) by a connecting rod and crank. This is like the rider's legs and the chain wheel of a bicycle.

The energy of motion and of vehicle movement is called **kinetic energy**. To stop a vehicle this energy must be converted to another form. The brakes do this by converting kinetic energy into heat. When all the kinetic energy has been converted the vehicle is stationary (Figure 3.1).

The internal combustion engine is not a very efficient energy converter, as it cannot turn all the fuel into mechanical energy. Surprisingly, much of the fuel is wasted in the form of heat, either down the exhaust pipe with the waste gases, or absorbed by the cooling system and radiated to the atmosphere. Only some 25 per cent of the chemical energy fed into the engine is used to drive the vehicle.

As the piston moves up and down the cylinder it must stop (although very briefly) at the top and bottom every time it changes direction. These points are known as **top dead-centre (t.d.c.)** and **bottom dead-centre (b.d.c.)** (Figure 3.2). The distance travelled by the piston between t.d.c. and b.d.c. is called the **stroke**. The diameter of the cylinder is called the **bore**.

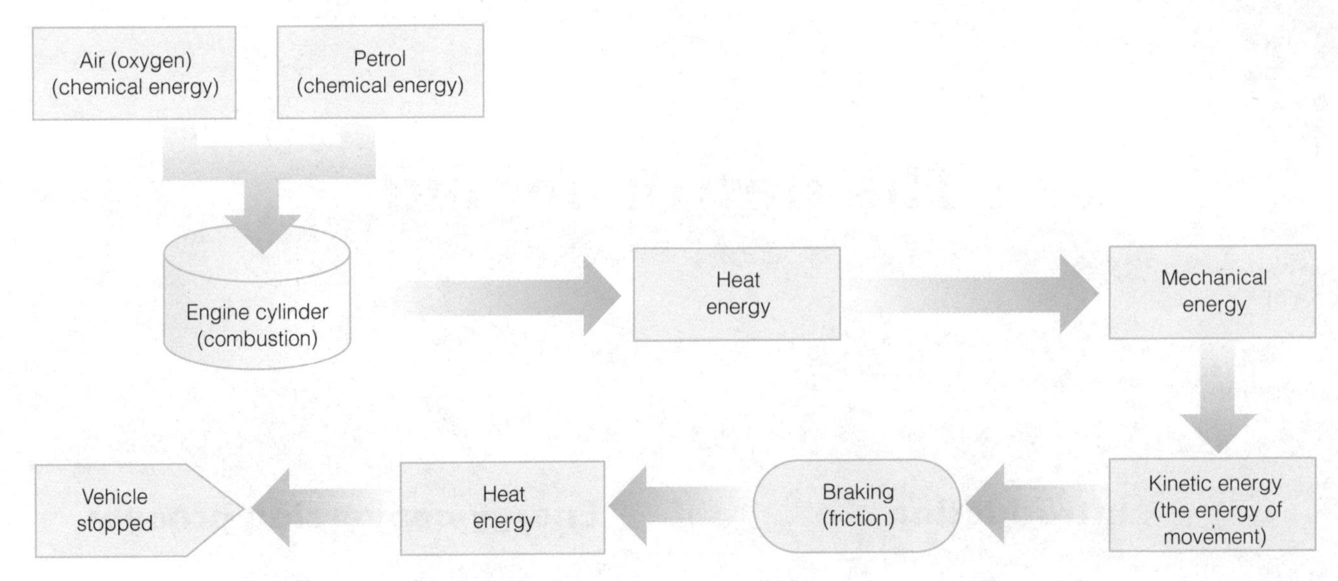

Figure 3.1 Energy conversion in a vehicle.

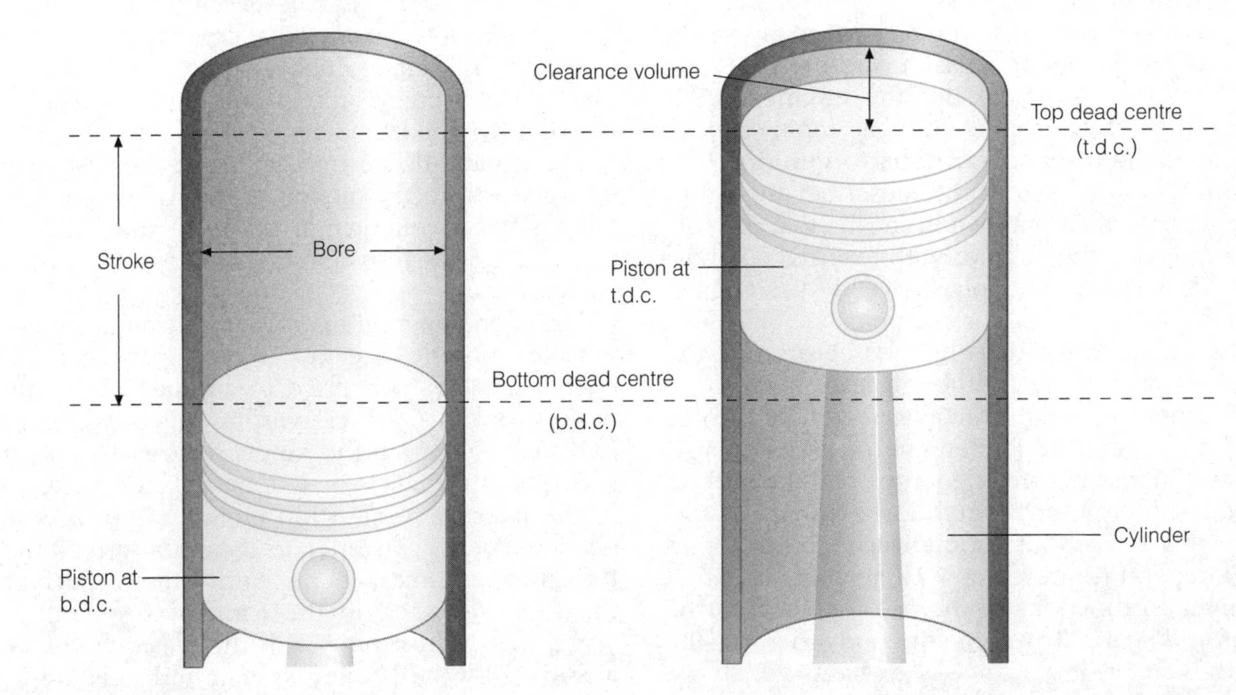

Figure 3.2 Piston and cylinder.

Calculations

The engine capacity of a vehicle is often displayed on the body by a badge such as 1.3, 2000 or 2 litre. This represents the **engine capacity** or the **total swept volume**, which is calculated as follows.

> The swept volume of one cylinder is found by multiplying the cross-sectional area by the stroke. Multiply this by the number of cylinders for the swept volume or capacity of the engine.

First calculate the cross-sectional area of the cylinder using this formula:

cross-sectional area = πr^2

where π = 3.142 (or 22/7) and r = radius of the cylinder bore (diameter divided by 2).

When the area has been calculated it is multiplied by the length of the stroke, l, to give the swept volume:

volume of one cylinder = $\pi r^2 l$

Therefore

engine capacity = $\pi r^2 l \times n$

where n = the number of cylinders.

The dimensions of cylinders are invariably given in millimetres, but capacity is in cubic centimetres. It is necessary at some point then to convert the figures.

In the following example we calculate the capacity or swept volume of a four-cylinder engine with a bore of 80 mm and a stroke of 70 mm. The bore and stroke dimensions are divided by 10 to bring them to centimetres.

cylinder swept volume = $\pi \times r^2 \times l$
= $\pi \times 8.0/2 \times 8.0/2 \times 7.0$ cm^3
= 352 cm^3
total swept volume
= cylinder swept volume × no. of cylinders
= 352 cm^3 × 4
= 1408 cm^3 or 1.408 litres

This would be said to be a 1.4 litre engine.

Main engine components and their function

This section provides a brief introduction. More detailed explanations appear later in the chapter.

The **cylinder block** contains one or more cylinders in which each piston is located and which guides the piston movement (Figure 3.3). It also provides mounting points for the crankshaft and, on some engines, for the camshaft too. On water-cooled engines it also incorporates a jacket for cooling water to flow round.

The **piston** and its seals, the piston **rings**, transmit the force of the expanding gas to the connecting rod (Figure 3.3).

The **connecting rod** connects the piston to the crankshaft, and has two bearings. It is attached to

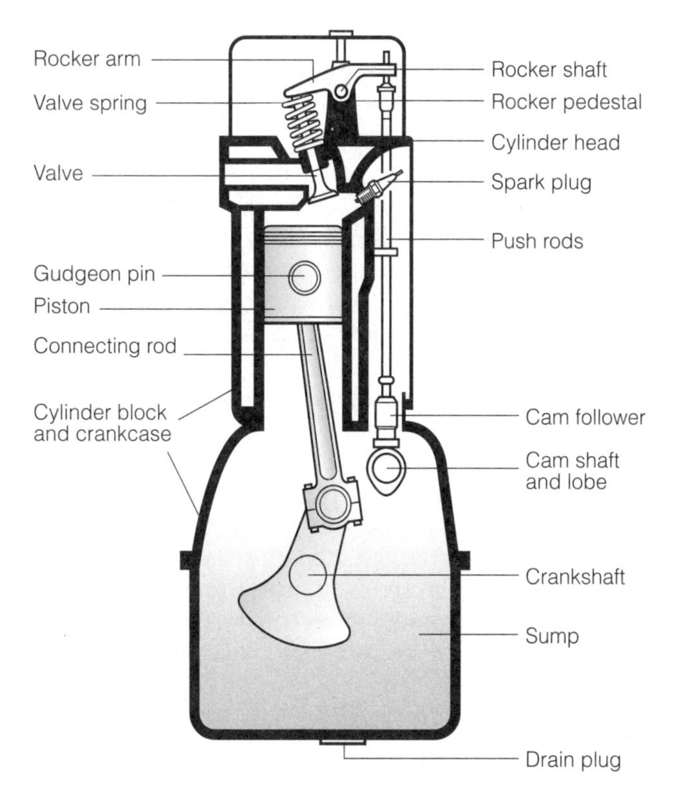

Figure 3.3 Main engine components.

the piston by the **gudgeon pin**, which runs in a bearing called the **little end**. The other, larger end of the connecting rod is connected to the crankshaft by means of the **big end** bearing.

The **crankshaft** is mounted in bearings in the crankcase, and is free to rotate. The crankshaft and connecting rod convert the linear or up-and-down motion of the piston to rotary motion. One end of the crankshaft has an attachment that drives the camshaft.

The **flywheel** is fastened to one end of the crankshaft. It is relatively heavy, in order to provide the momentum that keeps the engine turning between power strokes.

Valves open and close the inlet and exhaust ports at predetermined times to control the entry of the fresh charge of fuel and the exit of burnt exhaust gases. They are often called **poppet valves**.

The **camshaft** is mounted in bearings, and is driven by the crankshaft. It has a number of lobes called **cams** protruding along its length but spaced at intervals around the circumference. The cams open each valve in sequence for a set angle of crankshaft rotation. On a four-stroke engine the camshaft rotates at half the speed of the crankshaft.

Engine operating cycles

Many internal combustion engines rely on a fact of physics to operate. The air around us is at a pressure of 1 bar (10 N/cm^2). If a space at lower pressure is opened to the atmosphere, air will rush in until the pressure is equalised. A puncture in a tyre proves that the reverse is also true: high pressure that can escape will do so until the pressures are equal.

In the internal combustion engine, air or an air/fuel mixture flows into a cylinder and is compressed in the combustion chamber by the upward movement of a piston. After combustion and the power stroke the spent gases flow out through the exhaust. All internal combustion engines breathe in fresh air, and breathe out spent gases. The two main types of piston or reciprocating engine are known as two-stroke and four-stroke engines.

The Otto (four-stroke) cycle

Most motor vehicle petrol engines operate on the **four-stroke cycle** or **Otto cycle**, named after Nikolaus Otto, who invented it. There are four strokes in each cycle: **induction**, **compression**, **power**, and **exhaust**.

Induction

The piston moves down the cylinder, and as it does so the space above the piston increases (Figure 3.4a). At the same time the inlet valve opens, and because piston movement is creating more space, air rushes in because of the pressure of the atmosphere. You and I do something similar every time we breathe: our chests expand and air flows into our lungs.

In the petrol-powered Otto cycle engine, fuel is mixed with the air before it enters the cylinder. When the piston reaches the bottom of its stroke the inlet valve closes.

Compression

The inlet and exhaust valves are closed; the cylinder is sealed (Figure 3.4b). The piston moves upwards, compressing the air/fuel mixture into a small space (the combustion chamber). The temperature also rises, as you may have discovered when pumping up a bicycle tyre. The increase in temperature helps the air/fuel mixture to burn.

Power

As the piston reaches the top of the cylinder during compression, an electric spark ignites the mixture, which burns very rapidly (Figure 3.4c). The temperature rises very quickly and so does the pressure, which forces the piston down the cylinder on the power stroke.

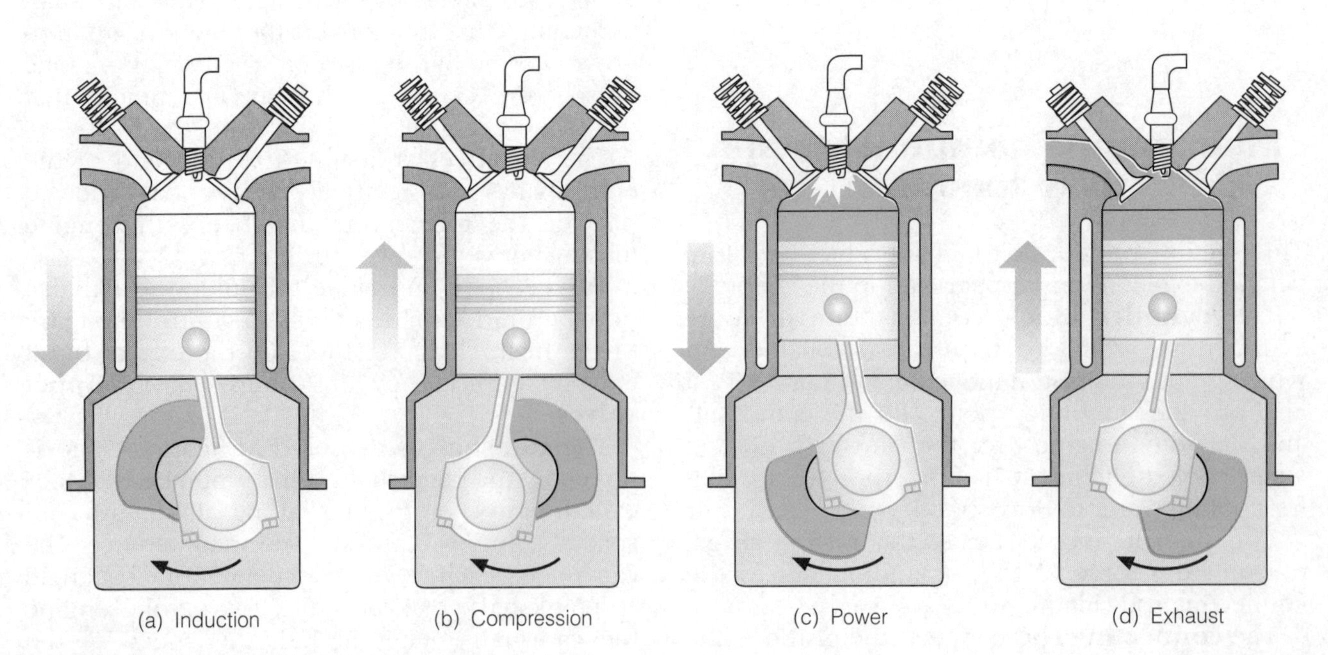

Figure 3.4 The Otto four-stroke cycle.

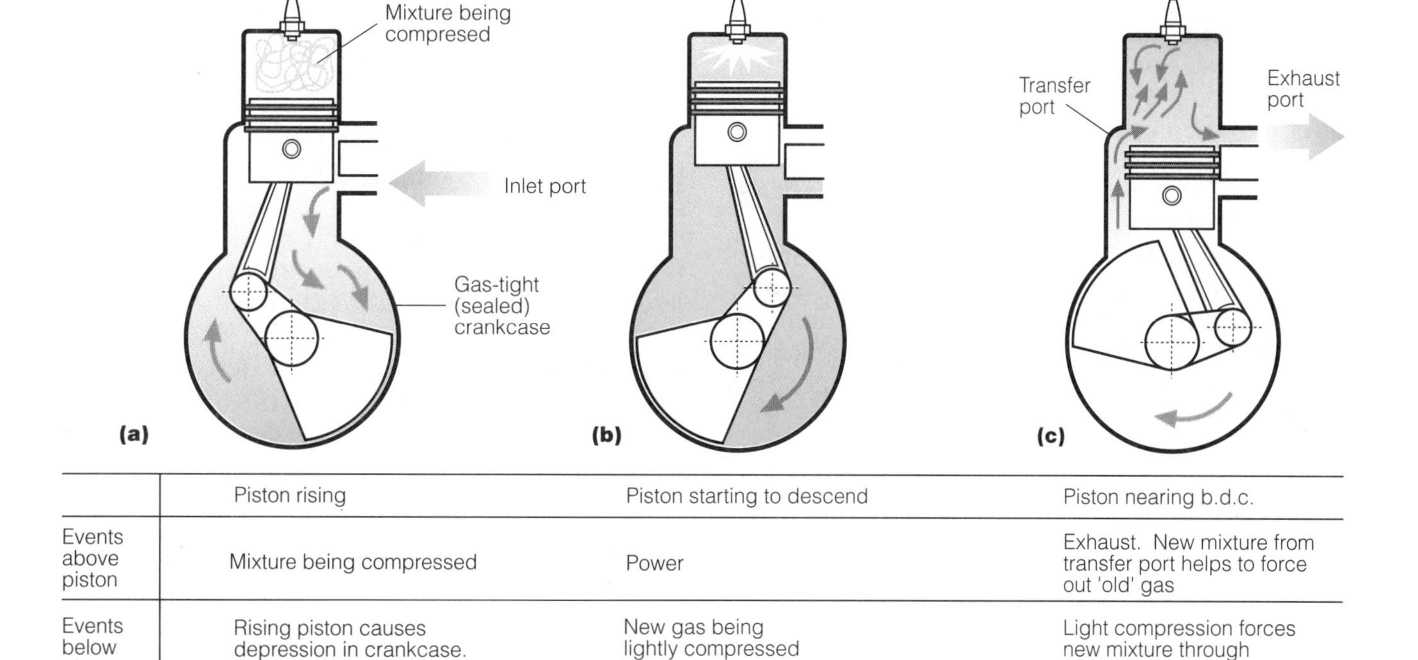

	Piston rising	Piston starting to descend	Piston nearing b.d.c.
Events above piston	Mixture being compressed	Power	Exhaust. New mixture from transfer port helps to force out 'old' gas
Events below piston	Rising piston causes depression in crankcase. New mixture rushes in to fill it	New gas being lightly compressed	Light compression forces new mixture through transfer port

Figure 3.5 The two-stroke cycle.

Exhaust

At the bottom of the power stroke the exhaust valve opens and the burnt gases begin to flow out (Figure 3.4d). The piston returns to the top of the cylinder, pushing out the exhaust gases as it does so. At the top the exhaust valve closes and the inlet valve opens, ready to repeat the cycle.

Engine rotation

The piston and crankshaft are linked together by the **connecting rod** or **conrod**. During the four strokes of the Otto cycle the crankshaft will revolve twice. At the same time the camshaft, with the inlet and exhaust cams for the cylinder, will revolve just once.

The two-stroke cycle

As the name suggests, this cycle is completed in only two strokes of the piston and one crankshaft revolution. This is achieved by exhausting the spent gases and filling the cylinder with a fresh charge at the same time.

This can be achieved in two ways. The new charge can be compressed and supplied under pressure by a separate charging cylinder or a blower, or by using the downward motion of the piston and the engine crankcase. A version of the former will be found in the chapter on compression ignition engines, but now the crankcase compression version is explained (Figure 3.5).

Instead of valves in the top of the cylinder the two-stroke engine has openings called **ports** in the cylinder wall. The piston acts as a valve to open or close them. The crankcase also has gas-tight seals to prevent pressure loss.

As can be seen from the diagram (Figure 3.5a), events are occurring above and below the piston at the same time, so we must consider two actions at a time. Below the piston, fresh mixture is rushing into the crankcase depression because the inlet port has been uncovered. At the top of the cylinder, the mixture is being compressed. As the piston reaches t.d.c. the mixture is ignited, and the piston is pushed down on the power stroke. This closes the inlet port, and the piston then starts to compress the fresh mixture in the crankcase, a process called **crankcase compression** (Figure 3.5b).

Towards the bottom of the stroke two things happen again. The exhaust gases escape through the exhaust port, and the pressurised mixture in the crankcase now flows through the **transfer port** into the cylinder (Figure 3.5c). It is directed upwards in such a way that it helps to push the last of the burnt gases out of the exhaust port.

As the engine continues turning, the piston rises to seal off the transfer port and start the compression stroke. The upward movement of the piston creates a depression in the crankcase. As the piston moves up the cylinder the inlet port is uncovered, so more fresh mixture enters. The cycle then continues.

In one rotation of the crankshaft there are two strokes, each stroke providing two functions. They are **power/exhaust** and **compression/ induction**.

Comparison of two-stroke and four-stroke engines

The principle disadvantage of the two-stroke engine compared with the four-stroke engine is its poor **volumetric efficiency**. This is the ratio of mixture drawn into the cylinder compared with the amount that would theoretically fill it at atmospheric pressure. Poor volumetric efficiency is due to inefficient **scavenging**: that is, the removal of exhaust gases and their replacement by fresh mixture. The fresh mixture does not adequately remove all the spent gases, and some of it also mixes with the exhaust and is lost into the exhaust system.

But the two-stroke engine does have the benefit of a power stroke every revolution, and it develops a smoother turning effort or **torque**. It also has fewer moving parts, and is simpler and cheaper to make than a four-stroke engine.

The main disadvantage of the four-stroke engine is that with a power stroke only every two revolutions of the crankshaft it has an unbalanced cycle, as the power stroke must turn the crankshaft and move the piston through three other strokes. It is also more complex in construction.

However, the four-stroke engine is quieter, and gives better fuel economy.

Engine layouts

Multi-cylinder arrangements

Although there are many single-cylinder engines they are generally small and limited in their application. They are frequently used for motor cycles, water pumps, generators and boats. To increase the power of an engine the cylinder can be made larger, or there can be more of them.

It would seem logical to develop a large single-cylinder engine, as there would be fewer parts. But the disadvantage of one power stroke in every four means that there are considerable out-of-balance forces because of the heavy **reciprocating** parts (these are the components, such as the piston, that move up and down rather than rotate). The resulting roughness and vibration must be smoothed away with a large flywheel, as is often the case with stationary and marine engines.

The car needs instant response as well as smooth running. A large flywheel gives reasonably smooth running, but it absorbs a great deal of energy and takes a long time to build up speed. The reverse is also true: the kinetic energy takes a long time to dissipate. Other components must also must be heavier in construction to take the load on them. This would result in a very poor power-to-weight ratio (this is the ratio that compares the power produced by an engine and its weight).

> Economy and good performance require engines to be light in weight but produce a lot of power. This is best achieved by increasing the number of cylinders: the engine will run more smoothly, will have a better power-to-weight ratio, and will be more responsive to required changes in speed and torque.

For example, the firing intervals of a four-cylinder engine can be arranged to give a power stroke every 180° of crankshaft rotation, giving four power strokes for every two crankshaft revolutions.

The disadvantage is that multi-cylinder engines are more complicated and costly, because of the number of parts.

Cylinder layouts

Four cylinders are considered the usual minimum, arranged in one line. To obtain smoother performance six and eight cylinders may be employed (Figure 3.6). Other layouts in use include two, three, five and even twelve cylinders.

Space considerations often demand that multiple cylinders are mounted into two banks arranged as a 'vee', but operating a common crankshaft (Figure 3.7).

There have been successful designs in the past of the type known as a **horizontally opposed engine** (Figure 3.8). Such engines can be housed below the floor line to increase the space available for people or luggage.

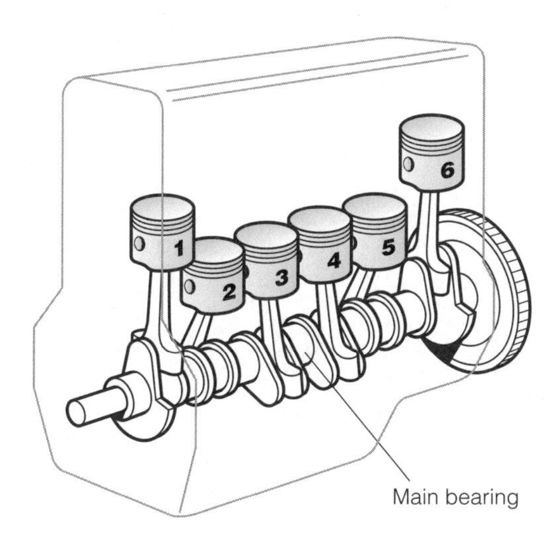

Figure 3.6 Six-cylinder in-line engine.

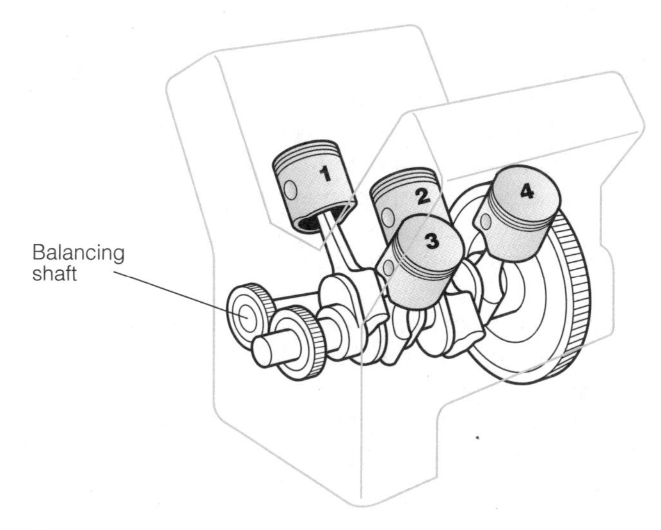

Figure 3.7 Vee engine layout.

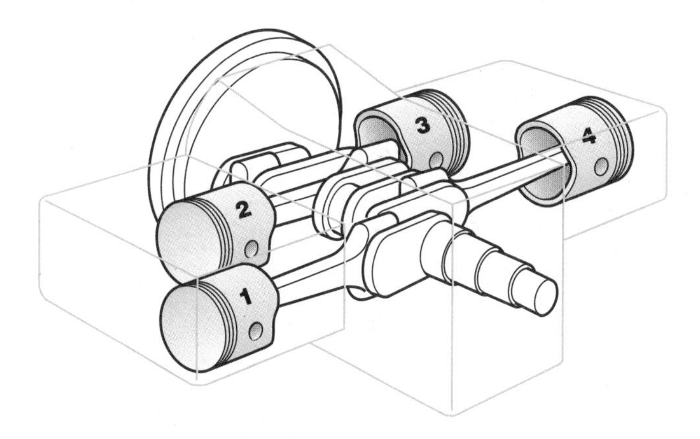

Figure 3.8 Horizontally opposed engine.

The firing order

To obtain the maximum benefit of smooth running the reciprocating masses and the firing order must be carefully arranged. To obtain this a four-cylinder in-line engine has a crankshaft arrangement in which the pistons at each end are at t.d.c. (top dead-centre) and the centre two are at b.d.c. (bottom dead-centre). The firing order for this engine would be cylinders 1–3–4–2 or 1–2–4–3, thus giving a power stroke every 180° of crankshaft rotation. Determining the firing order by cam arrangement is explained later in the chapter.

To obtain a well-balanced six-cylinder engine the pistons would be moving as three pairs, arriving at t.d.c. at 120° intervals (Figure 3.6). They would be arranged to fire in the sequence 1–5–3–6–2–4, or 1–4–2–6–3–5. Such an engine has a power stroke every 120° of crankshaft rotation.

Engine components

The cylinder block and crankcase

The purpose of the cylinder block is to hold the cylinders rigidly in position. On most light vehicles the cylinder block extends to form part of the crankcase, and therefore it also supports the crankshaft bearings. The name given to this type of construction is **monoblock**.

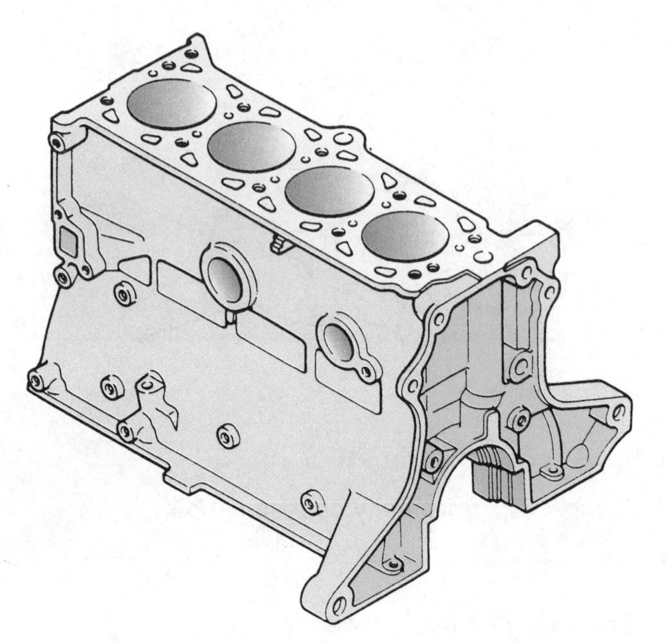

Figure 3.9 Cylinder block and crankcase for overhead camshaft engine.

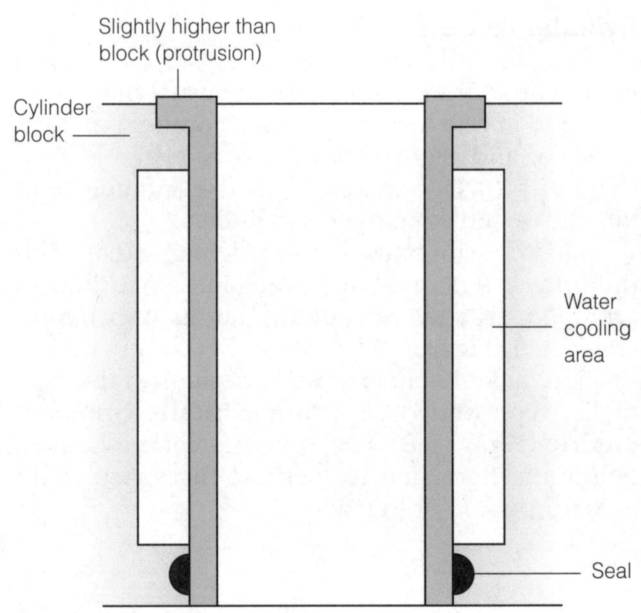

Figure 3.10 Wet liner.

Because a monoblock is complicated in shape it is normally cast in close-grain cast iron. This is cheap, hard wearing, strong, rigid, light and easy to cast. To give the casting strength and rigidity it is internally webbed to carry and transmit the loads on the main and camshaft bearings (Figure 3.9).

An alternative material to cast iron is aluminium alloy, which has the advantage of being very light. The major disadvantage is that the alloy is not very hard wearing. It is therefore necessary to have some form of cast iron insert or liner that forms the hard-wearing cylinder. Aluminium blocks are cast without cylinders, but the top and bottom of the cylinder openings are machined to take the separate **cylinder liners**. Individual liners must be kept rigidly in place when the engine is assembled to prevent coolant or gases from leaking past them.

Liners in direct contact with the coolant are called **wet liners** (Figure 3.10), and those pressed into a complete block are called **dry liners**. These components are dealt with in more detail in Chapter 8 on compression ignition (diesel) engines.

The outer casing of the cylinder block contains the water jacket. Water passages must direct the coolant to the hottest areas of the cylinder and enable the heat to be taken away quickly. On air-cooled engines the outer surface of the casting will have fins cast onto the block to create a large surface area over which air can flow to cool the cylinders.

The top of the cylinder block is machined to take the cylinder head. The water passages that cool the block are carried through into the head, together with an oil flow to lubricate the valve gear. Bolts or studs and nuts retain the cylinder head to the block.

Head gasket

The purpose of the cylinder head gasket is to form a gas-tight, water-tight and oil-tight seal between the cylinder head and the block. It is made from solid, annealed copper, or a thin sandwich of asbestos between copper, or it may be a thin sheet of stainless steel (Figure 3.11). Water passages, oil feeds and returns, and stud or bolt holes are cut through the gasket. Modern metal gaskets have corrugations around areas that have to be sealed, and they may also be coated with substances that help to form a seal.

The sequence for releasing and tightening cylinder head retaining bolts or nuts is vitally important, as also is the tightening torque. The numbers in Figure 3.11 show a typical tightening sequence.

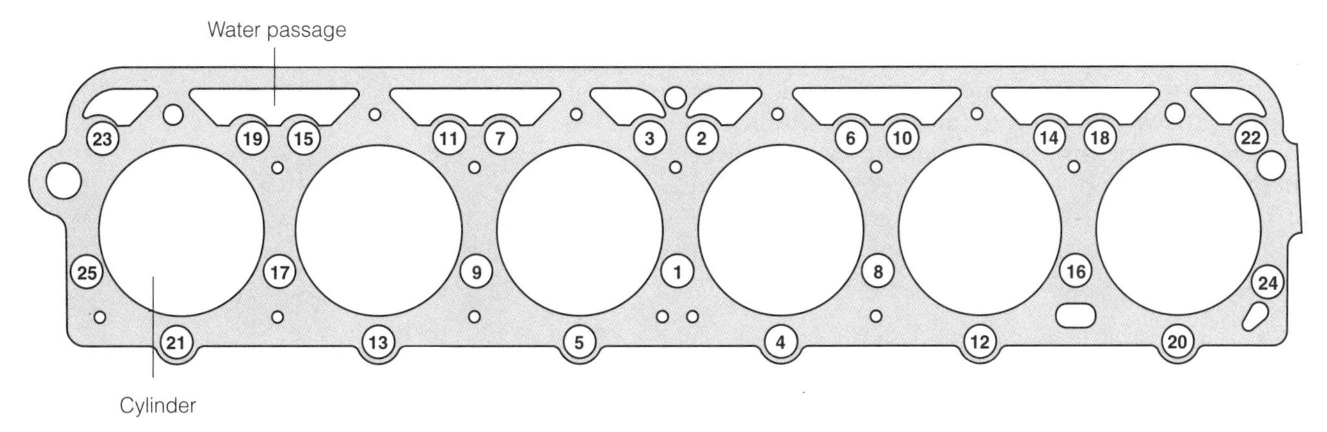

Figure 3.11 Head gasket. The numbers refer to the typical order in which the cylinder head bolts (or nuts) should be tightened. The gasket itself may be very thin indeed.

On many modern vehicles cylinder head temperature is a very important requirement when removing or retightening the retaining bolts or nuts. The head may be warped beyond repair if it is not at the correct temperature when this work is done.

The cylinder head

The cylinder head seals the working end of the cylinder (Figure 3.12). On some engines the top of the piston is recessed to form the combustion chamber, but on others a recess is made in the face of the head. The inlet and exhaust ports, together with the inlet and exhaust valves, are located in the head.

Above the head is situated the valve gear and, with many modern engines, also the camshaft. Space is also made for the spark plugs, or for the injectors and heater plugs on compression ignition engines. A water jacket is provided around the combustion chamber to take away excess heat. On air-cooled engines large fins form part of the cylinder head so that the excess heat can be quickly taken away.

The head is sometimes made of a similar material to that of the cylinder block. This is to overcome the problems associated with differing expansion rates. However, increasing use is being made of aluminium alloy cylinder heads to lower engine weight and improve heat dissipation.

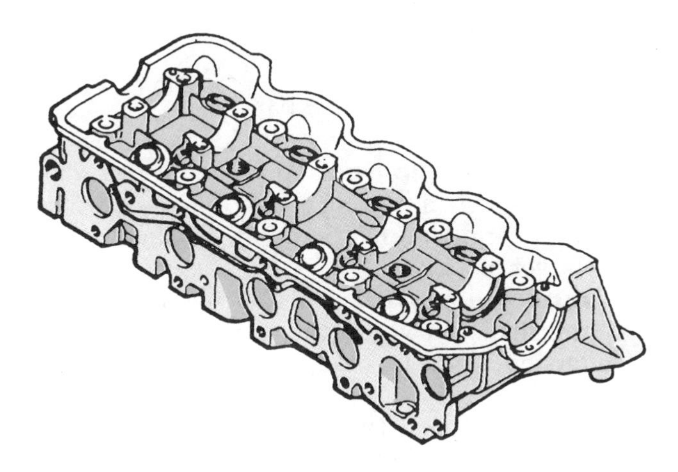

Figure 3.12 Overhead camshaft cylinder head.

Crankshaft

The crankshaft of an engine is similar to the cranks on a bicycle (Figure 3.13). The rider's feet push on the pedals, which turn the cranks mounted on the centre spindle, converting the up-and-down movement of the legs into rotary

Figure 3.13 The crankshaft of an engine is similar to the cranks on a bicycle.

motion. In that way a pushing effort is converted into a turning force called **torque**.

The piston in an engine is connected to the crankshaft by the connecting rod. In much the same way as the bicycle, the up-and-down movement of the piston is converted into rotary torque at the crankshaft. Because far greater forces are being converted, all the components are much stronger, and the crankshaft is supported in more bearings.

The crankshaft is normally a robust, one-piece alloy steel forging machined to very fine tolerances. Some manufacturers use steel alloys or cast iron containing copper, chromium and nickel. Cast iron crankshafts have proved to be very durable; they have good wearing properties and are less prone to fatigue than forged steel shafts. The journals may be hardened by processes such as nitriding or induction hardening.

As can be seen from Figure 3.14, the crankshaft has a number of identifiable parts:

1. **Main bearing journal**. Any part of the shaft that rotates in a bearing is called a journal. The main bearing journals support the shaft in the cylinder block.
2. **Crank pin journal**. This is the part of the crankshaft to which the connecting rod is attached, and is often called the **big-end** journal.
3. **Crank radius**. This is the term used to describe the offset from the main journals to the crank pin; it is like the length of the pedal crank on a cycle. In the same way as the cycle rider's foot moves two crank lengths from highest to lowest position, so the piston moves an amount that is twice the crank offset. This is the **stroke** of an engine.
4. **The webs**. The big-end journals and the main bearing journals are held together by the webs, which may also incorporate counterbalance weights.
5. **Fillet radius**. A sharp corner in this position would create a weak spot, so a radius is provided to avoid any problems.
6. **Crank throw**. A single-cylinder engine has a single-throw crankshaft, while a four-cylinder engine would have a four-throw crankshaft. However, engines of 'vee' configuration often share big-end journals between two opposing cylinders.
7. **Crankshaft throw**. This describes how far the centre of the big-end journal is offset from the centre of the crankshaft main journal (Figure 3.15): the larger this measurement, the greater the turning force applied to the crankshaft while increasing the piston's effective stroke.

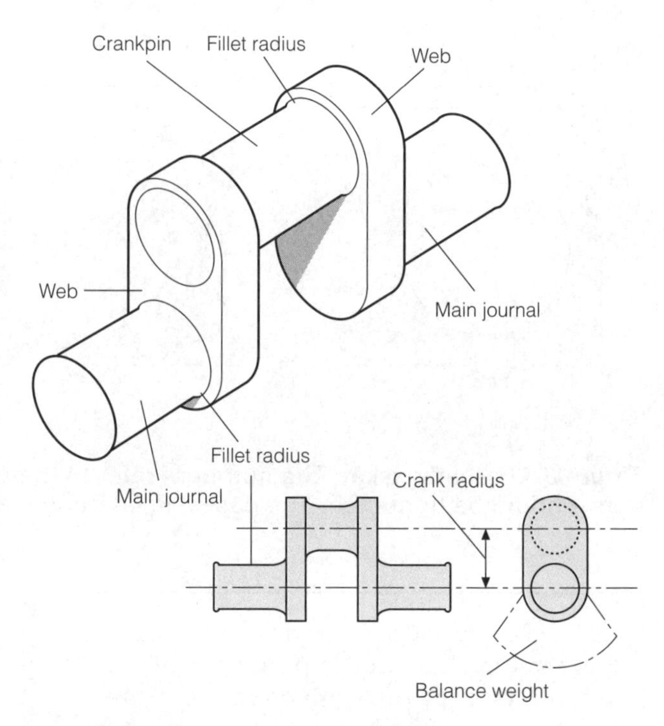

Figure 3.14 Single-throw crankshaft.

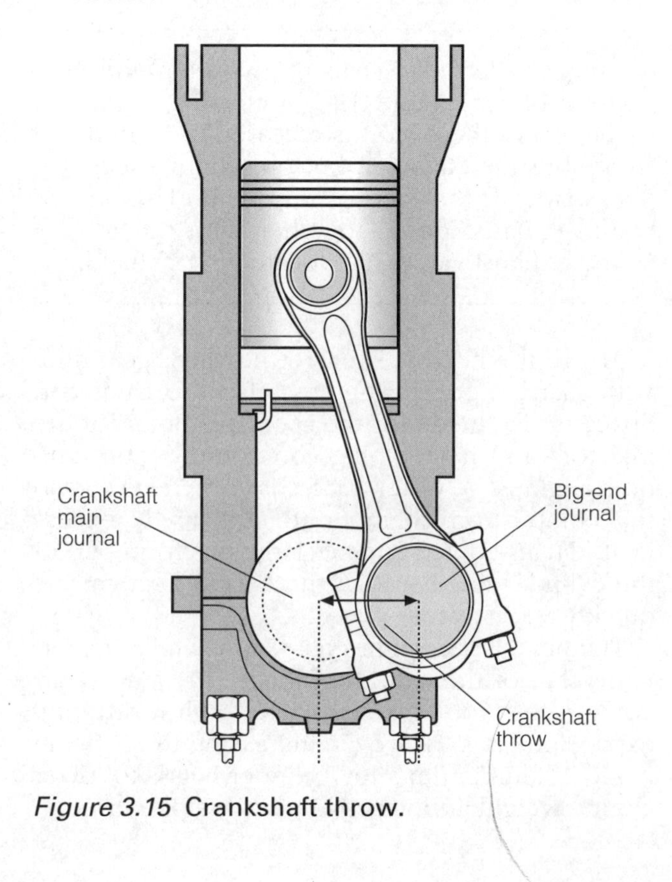

Figure 3.15 Crankshaft throw.

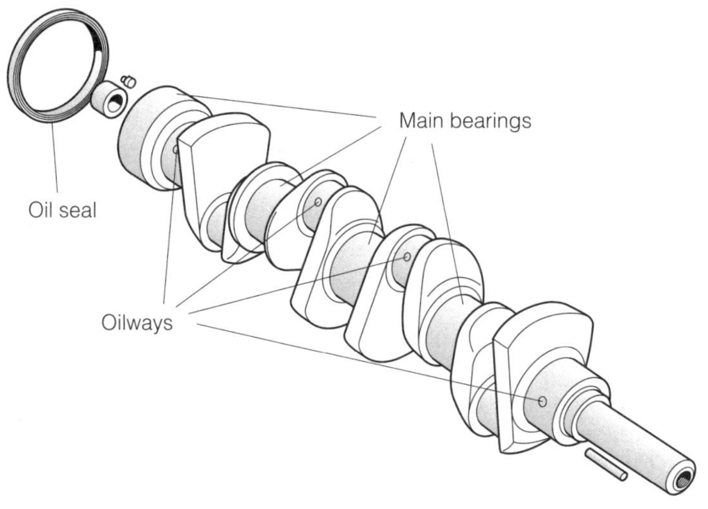

Figure 3.16 Five-bearing crankshaft.

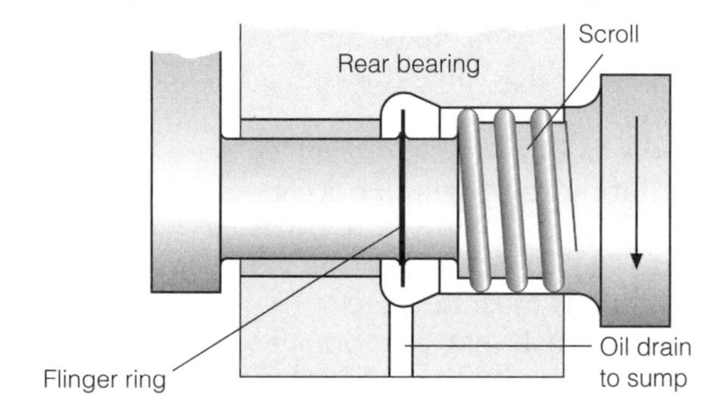

Figure 3.17 'Scroll'-type oil retainer.

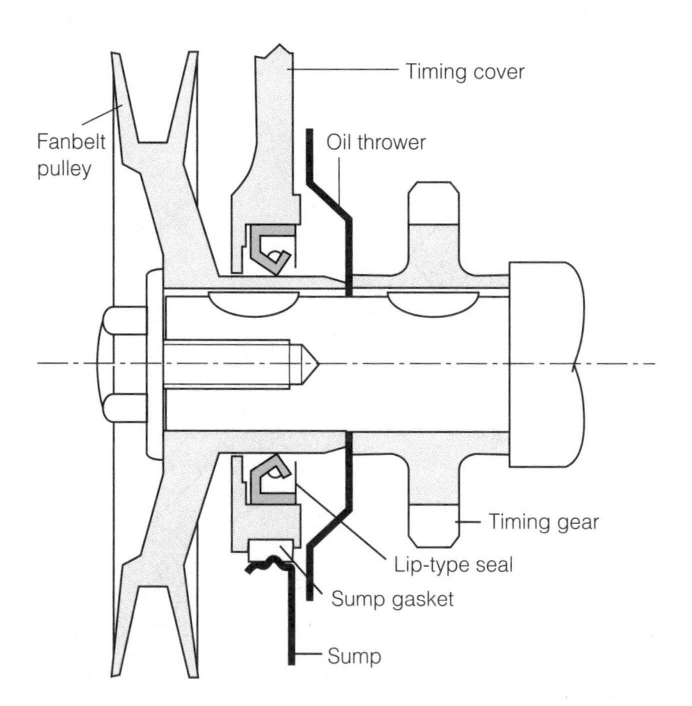

Figure 3.18 Oil thrower and lip seal.

8. **Internal oilways**. To supply oil to the big-end journals the crankshaft has internal oilways drilled from the adjacent main bearing journal (Figure 3.16). Oil flows into the main bearings from the oil gallery, and from there it is fed along the crankshaft oilways to each of the big-end bearings.
9. **Other requirements**. One end of the crankshaft forms a boss to which the flywheel is attached. The other end usually has some form of keyway machined into it to provide a positive drive for the timing gears, sprockets or pulleys. Pulleys for auxiliary drives may also need to be mounted there.

At both ends of the shaft some form of oil sealing must be used to prevent leakage from the revolving journals. At the flywheel end an oil seal as shown in Figure 3.16 is commonly found, but an oil scroll and flinger ring may be used instead (Figure 3.17). The scroll or quick thread 'screws' the oil back towards the inside of the engine. At the same time, the centrifugal force of the spinning crankshaft forces oil to climb the thrower. When it reaches the edge it is thrown off into a channel and returns to the sump.

The cover at the timing gear end usually has a lipped seal, made from synthetic rubber stiffened by a metal shell (Figure 3.18). It has an inner lip that rubs on the crankshaft to stop oil leakage. Light contact is maintained by the use of a steel garter spring.

The flywheel

This is usually a cast iron disc attached to the rear end of the crankshaft. Its main purpose is to keep the engine turning smoothly at idling speed. It also provides the face on which the clutch is mounted, and has the starter motor ring gear attached to its outer edge.

It is important that the flywheel is balanced and mounted concentrically; an off-centre or out-of-balance flywheel would cause severe vibration. To prevent incorrect mounting the flywheel is attached to an accurately machined flange with unequally spaced bolts or dowels.

Recent developments include lighter, two-part flywheels with shock-absorbing springs.

Main bearings

The crankshaft revolves in shell-type main bearings (Figure 3.19). Earlier designs had a main bearing between every two cylinders, but most engines now have a main bearing between each cylinder to provide the best support. Each bearing is split to allow the crankshaft to be fitted. The lower half is called the **cap**; it is located by dowels or grooves, and is bolted securely to its mating surface on the crankcase. These caps are secured and line-bored together in manufacture, and they must never be changed around.

The bearing surface is formed from thin-wall **shell bearings**, which, like the case and caps, are in two halves. One part fits snugly in the crankcase, the other in the cap. They are of steel strip lined with a thin film of bearing material, accurately made to very fine tolerances. The bearing metal consists of 80 per cent tin with some antimony and copper. On heavy-duty engines, tin, lead and copper may be used. Once again, if these bearings are to be reused they must never be changed around.

A similar composition is used for the half-moon-shaped thrust bearings or washers that are fitted to both sides of one of the main bearings. They hold the crankshaft in its correct position lengthways, and take the end thrust of clutch operation.

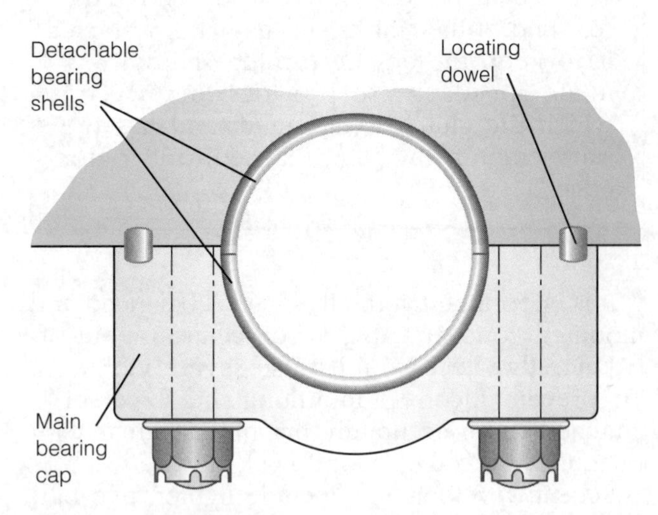

Figure 3.19 Main bearing.

The camshaft

To enable the engine to function, the crankshaft must drive other parts, such as the camshaft (Figure 3.20). The camshaft operates the valve mechanism that opens and closes the inlet and exhaust valves.

Older engines had the camshaft in the cylinder block, operating the valves by cam-follower pushrods and rocker arms. This type of engine is referred to as a push-rod **overhead valve engine** (OHV) (Figure 3.21), relative to an even earlier design with valves in the cylinder block, called a **side valve engine** (Figure 3.22). Many engines now have the camshaft in the cylinder head, and are described as **overhead camshaft engines** (OHC). The cams may act on rocker arms or directly over the valve through a bucket-type cam follower.

As the inlet and exhaust valves need open only once during each cylinder cycle of two crankshaft revolutions, the camshaft turns at half engine speed. The valve timing (the point at which the valves open) must be exact.

The camshaft may also operate such other components as the fuel pump, the ignition distributor and the oil pump.

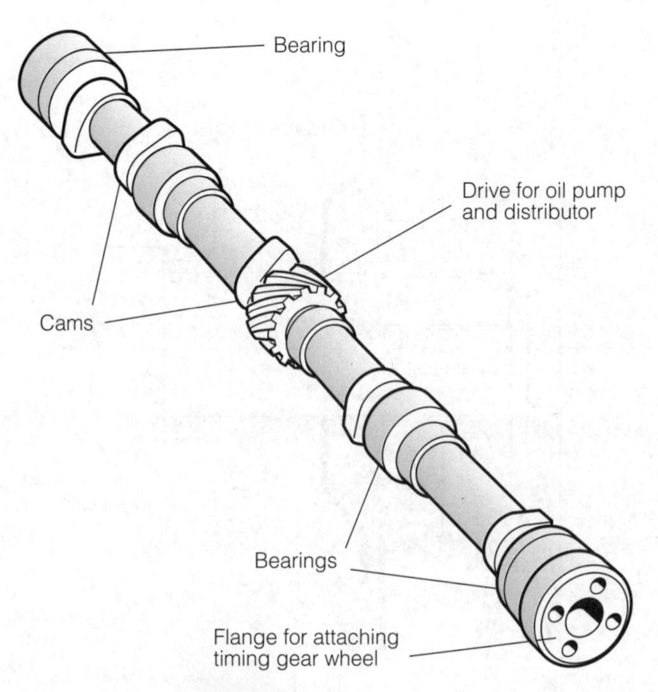

Figure 3.20 Camshaft.

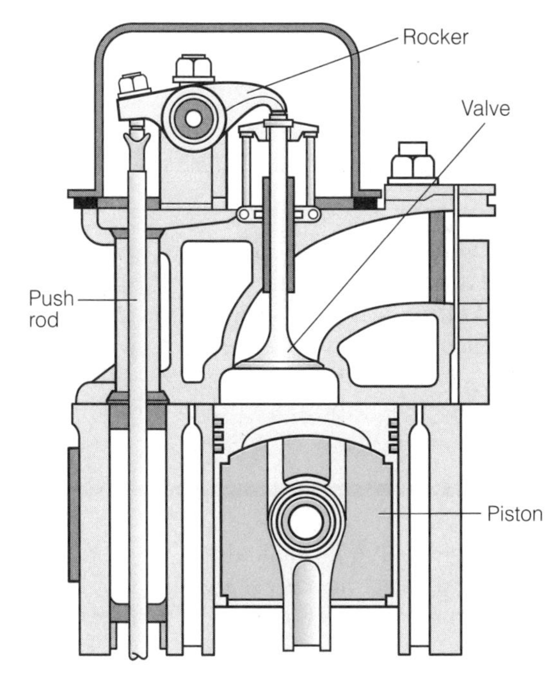

Figure 3.21 Push-rod overhead valve (OHV) engine.

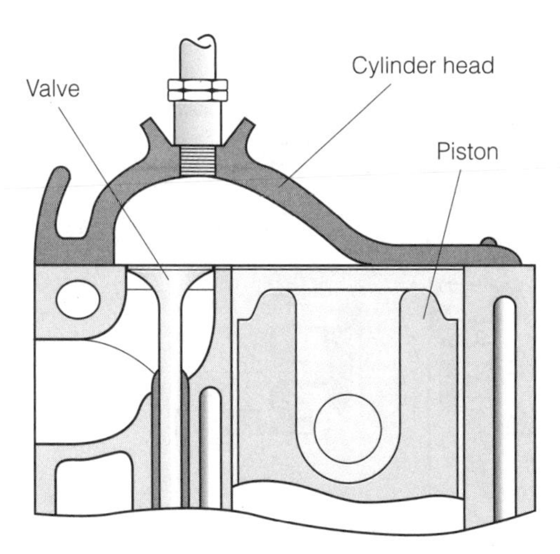

Figure 3.22 Typical side-valve design.

Camshaft drive

Camshafts may be driven by one of three methods: gears, sprockets and chain, or toothed belt.

Gears

This is the most expensive method of driving the camshaft, because it requires absolute precision in the positioning of the shafts and idler gears during manufacture (Figure 3.23). It is very reliable and, if fibre or nylon idler gears are used, can be very quiet.

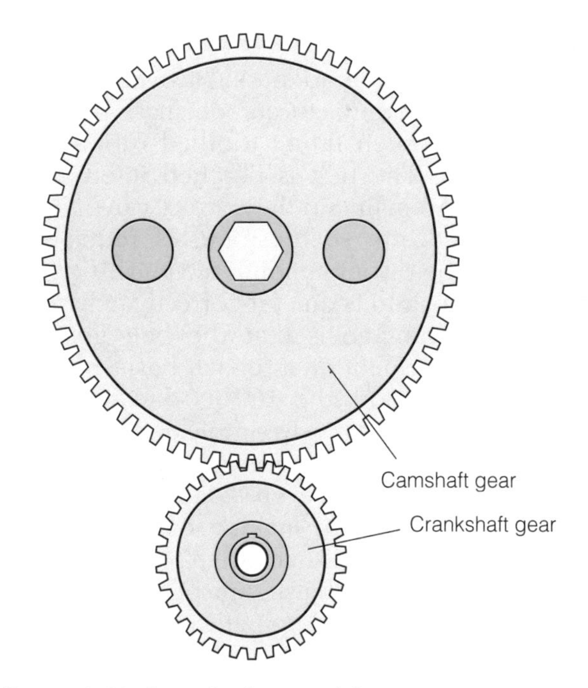

Figure 3.23 Camshaft gear drive.

Sprockets and chain

A lower-cost drive is obtained with an endless chain running over sprockets (Figure 3.24). A tensioner must be used to prevent a slack chain from jumping over teeth and losing the timing. This drive is quiet and reliable. Most engines with camshafts in the cylinder block are chain driven.

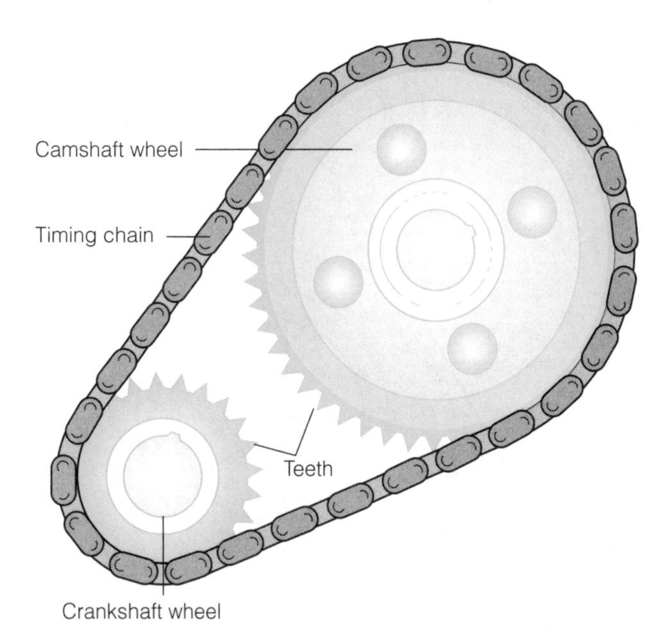

Figure 3.24 Camshaft sprocket and chain drive.

Toothed belt

With the widespread adoption of overhead camshafts, many manufacturers of mass-produced vehicles have been fitting toothed rubber belts (Figure 3.25). The belt is notched internally to form teeth and maintain the correct valve timing. Again, some form of tensioner is required to prevent the belt from jumping teeth. This type of drive is cheap, and is quiet if correctly tensioned.

One disadvantage is that the belt generally requires replacement on a regular basis, normally between 60 000 km and 100 000 km. On some vehicles this is a relatively simple and cheap job, while on others it is more complicated. Many engines will suffer severe damage from an upward-moving piston making contact with an open valve if the camshaft drive loses timing or breaks. The correct adjustment of tensioners, or the maintenance of automatic units, and the replacement of toothed belts are essential to avoid problems.

Poppet valves

> The valve normally used in the four-stroke internal combustion engine is the **poppet valve** (Figure 3.26). Its purpose is to let the gases in and out of the cylinder. When the valve is closed it must form a gas-tight seal, and when it is open it must offer limited resistance to the flow of gases.

The poppet valve is basically a disc on a stem. The inlet port and its valve are usually larger in diameter than the exhaust port and valve, to

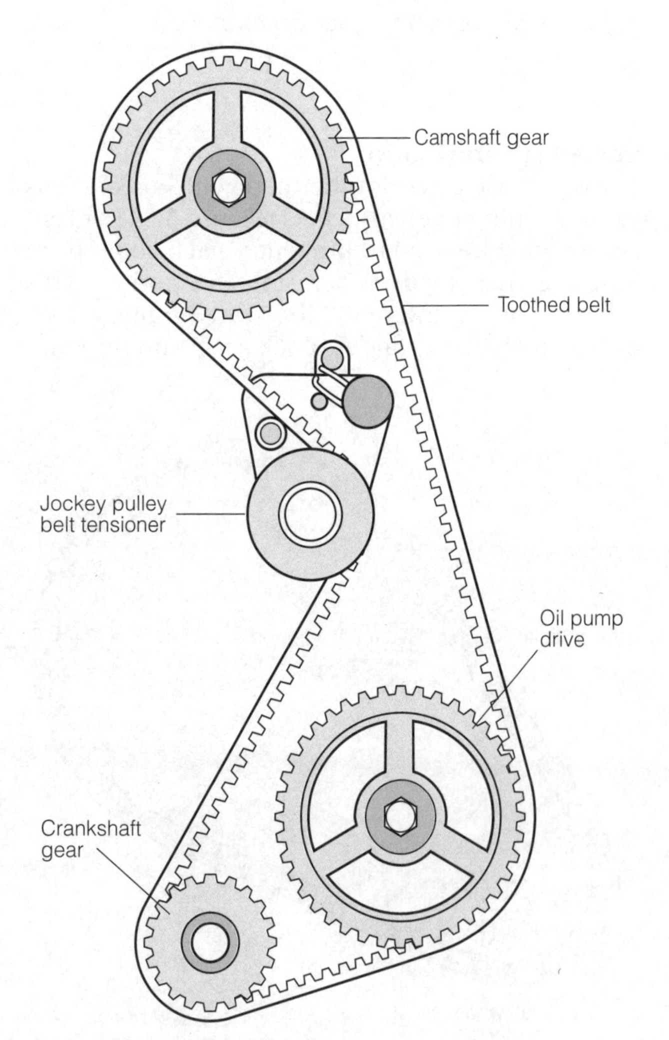

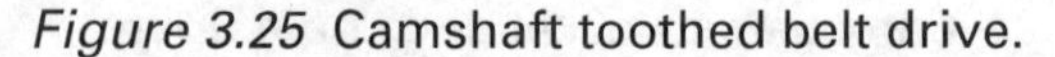

Figure 3.25 Camshaft toothed belt drive.

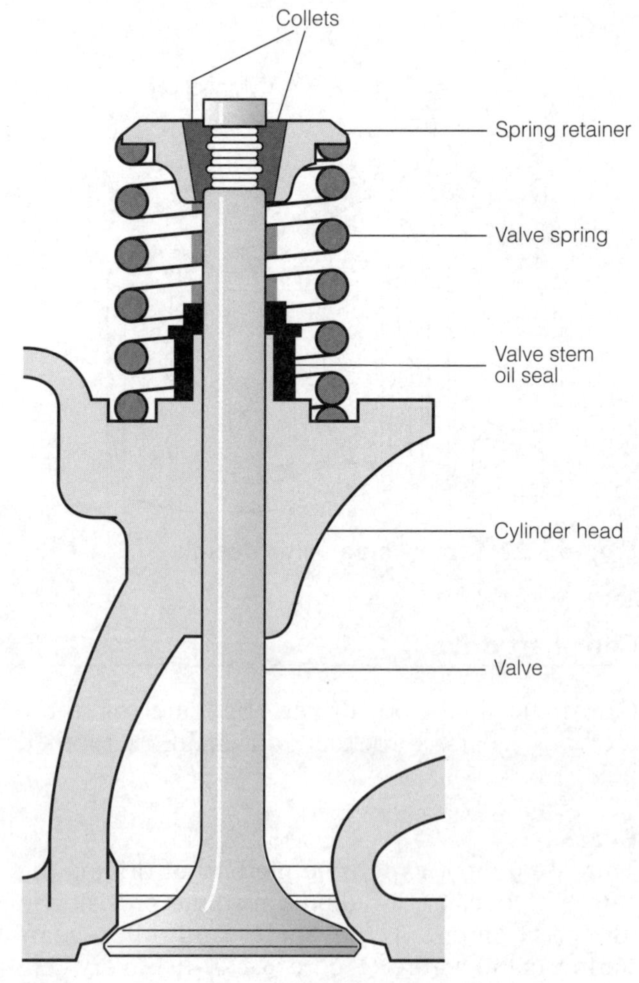

Figure 3.26 Poppet valve assembled in cylinder head.

provide easier gas flow into the combustion chamber. The valve is held closed by a strong spring (or springs). The spring must also keep the valve stem in contact with the operating mechanism at all times during the opening and closing period. One problem with poppet valves is **valve bounce**, a condition in which at high speeds the valve bounces back open when it should be closed. If this problem occurs at a high but permitted engine speed, the valve springs are weak and must be renewed.

The collets fit around the valve stem and lock into a groove, forming a cone, where they are held in place by the spring retainer and the spring tension.

The valves operate under extreme conditions, as gas temperatures may exceed 2000 °C; the exhaust valve head is the hottest part of the combustion chamber. Valves are forged from an alloy steel usually containing nickel, chromium and silicon or cobalt. The valve head and its seat are normally machined to an angle of 45°.

The valve seating is often an insert that is either an interference press fit or is screwed into the cylinder head. Valve seats are made from very hard special alloy steels such as Stellite, composed of tungsten, cobalt, chromium and carbon, to withstand the continuous pounding of the valves and the high temperatures.

The valve is guided in its operation by the **valve guide**, which is generally inserted into the cylinder head but can be pressed out and renewed when worn. The guide is usually made from fine-grain cast iron or sometimes bronze. After inserting a guide the valve seat must be remachined to ensure that valve and guide are in perfect alignment. Worn inlet valve guides allow oil to be drawn down the valve stems and into the combustion chamber, as well as causing uneven valve seating wear.

Some valve seats and guides are made integral with the cylinder head.

Valve location

Side-valve engines were once common, but this layout is now largely confined to small industrial engines. When the valves are mounted in the cylinder head, their location is determined by the shape of the combustion chamber. Engines with hemispherical combustion chambers, particularly those with more than two valves, often have their valves inclined (Figure 3.27). Three, four and even five valves per cylinder are often used for high-performance engines (Figure 3.28).

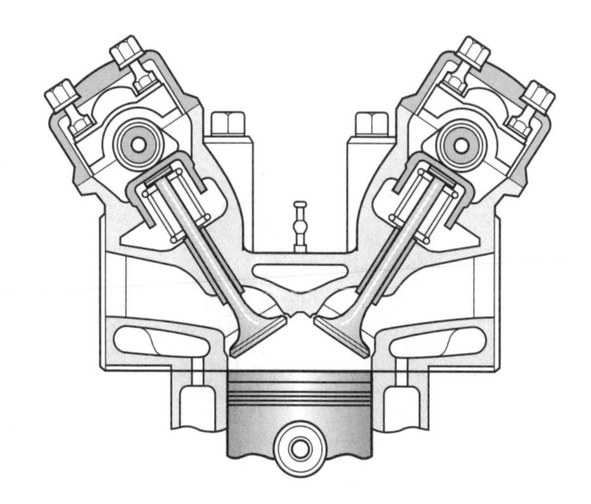

Figure 3.27 Inclined layout using twin overhead camshaft.

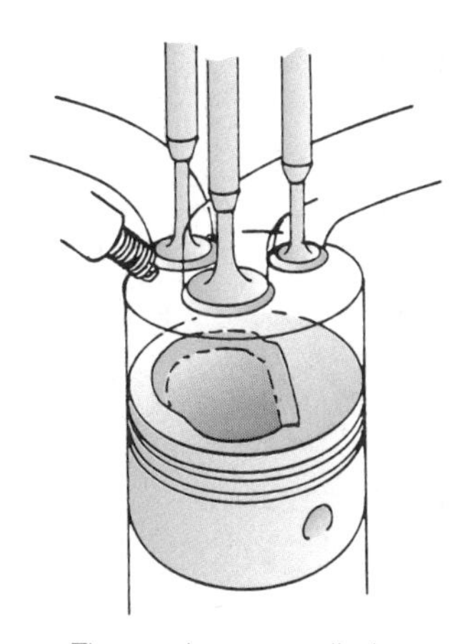

Three valves per cylinder

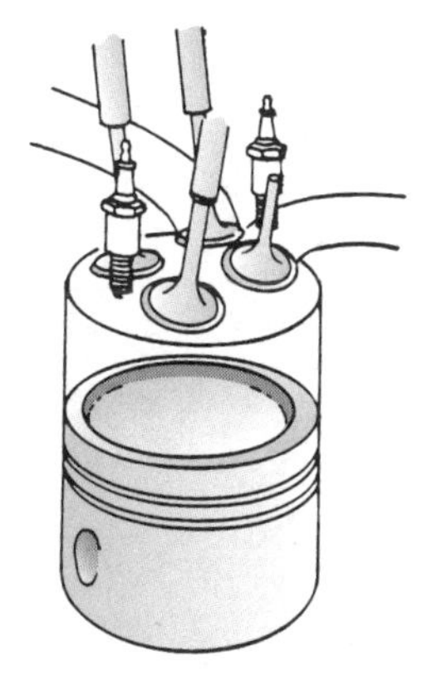

Four valves, two spark plugs

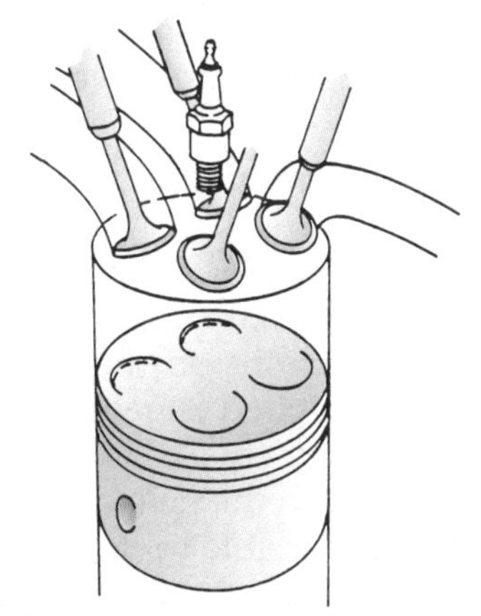

Four valves, centre spark plug (the most common arrangement)

Figure 3.28 Multiple valve arrangements.

Operating mechanisms

Early designs have their camshafts located in the crankcase. Each cam operates a push rod and a rocker arm that forces the valve open. Between the cam and the pushrod is a hardened **cam follower** or **tappet**, which takes the rubbing wear of the camshaft and is held in a guide machined into the crankcase.

> Modern engines usually have overhead camshafts (Figure 3.29). In this arrangement the camshaft is located on top of the engine, and acts either directly onto a cap or bucket tappet covering the valve spring, or through a rocker arm.

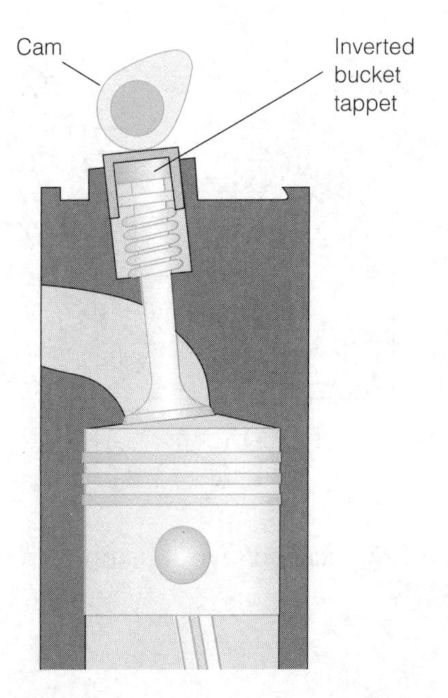

Figure 3.29 Single overhead camshaft (OHC).

Valve timing

One of the problems facing engine designers is how to make sure that the cylinder is filled with fresh mixture on the induction stroke. On naturally aspirated engines (those without any form of charging), this is limited to how much can be forced into the cylinders by atmospheric pressure. It is impossible to design an engine that can completely fill its cylinders with new mixture at all engine speeds: therefore the manufacturer designs the engine to operate most efficiently at what is considered to be its most usual running speed.

> **Volumetric efficiency** (the amount of fresh mixture drawn into the cylinder) should ideally be 100 per cent, but this is rarely achieved, and the efficiency falls as engine speed increases. The lower the volumetric efficiency of any particular engine, the less power it produces.

To improve cylinder filling the inlet valve is opened before top dead-centre (t.d.c.) and closes after bottom dead-centre (b.d.c.). The exhaust valve is opened before b.d.c. and closed after t.d.c. (Figure 3.30). There is a period at the top of the piston's stroke when both valves are open together. This is called **valve overlap**. The effect of this is to allow the depression created by the escaping exhaust gas to help bring the incoming mixture into the cylinder. Similarly, delaying the closing of the inlet valve allows the movement of the fresh gases to squeeze a little more into the cylinder.

Early opening of the exhaust valve is possible because there is little pressure left in the burnt gases at this point, but enough for them to rush out as the exhaust valve opens. This helps scavenging of the cylinder, and increases the depression already referred to.

Conventional camshafts have fixed cams, and the timing is likewise fixed where it is set on assembly. There are some engines, however, in

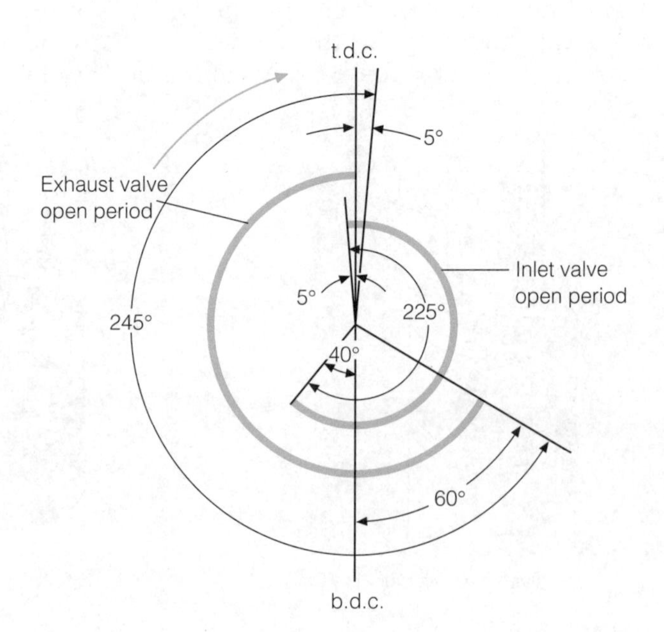

Figure 3.30 Valve timing diagram.

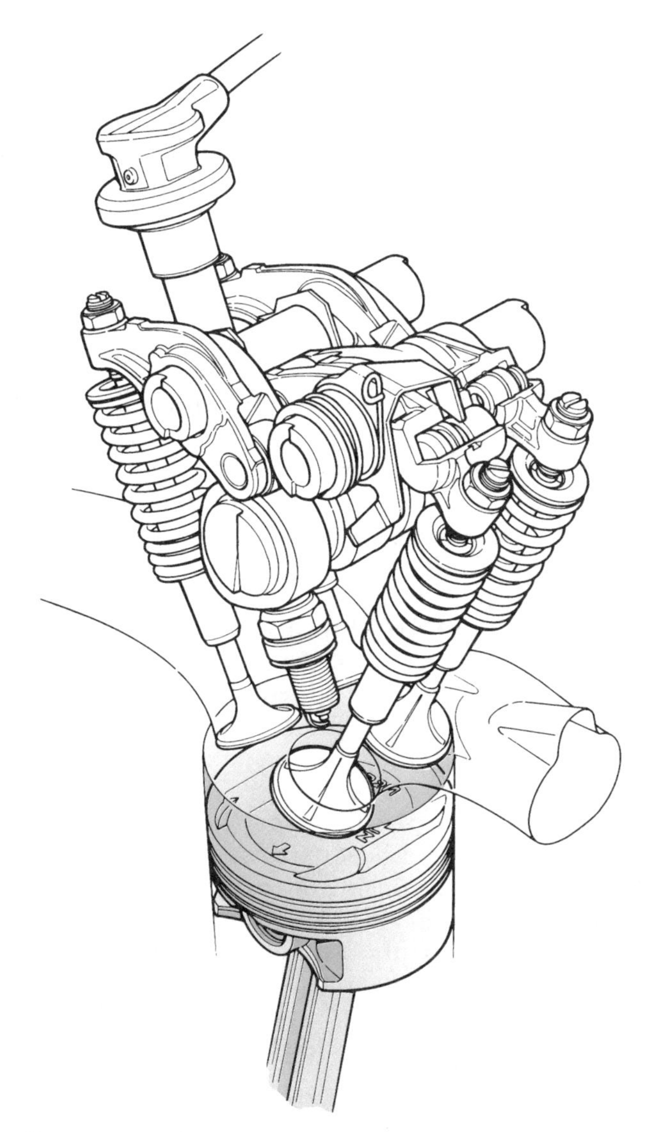

Figure 3.31 Variable valve timing mechanism.

which valve timing is altered during engine operation (Figure 3.31).

Valve clearances

When the valves become hot the stems expand, which calls for some working clearance to allow the valves to close properly (Figure 3.32). This clearance is specified by the manufacturer, as is the method of adjustment.

Failure in ensuring the correct working clearance will result in either of the following conditions.

Clearance too wide

The valve will open late and shut early, causing a small drop in volumetric efficiency and power. There is also likely to be mechanical noise.

Clearance too small

Heat expansion may prevent the valve from closing onto its seat. This permits gas seepage to occur, resulting in poor compression and loss of power. If the engine is run for any length of time in this condition the valves and seats could be burnt away.

Hydraulic tappets

Self-adjusting hydraulic tappets are commonly used on many modern engines (Figure 3.33). This type of tappet will maintain the correct valve

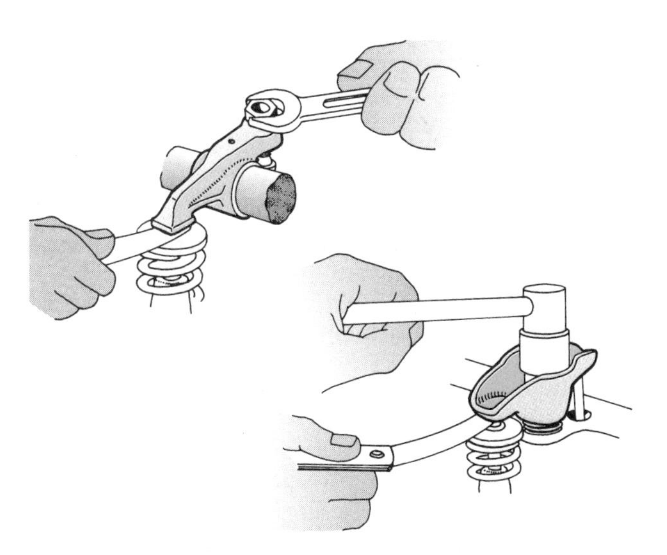

Figure 3.32 Adjusting valve clearance.

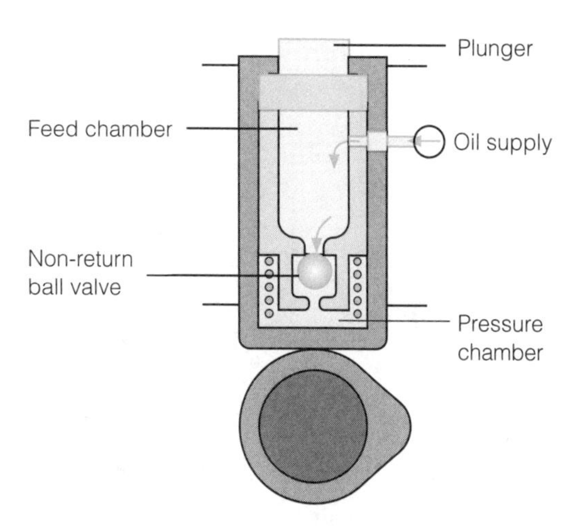

Figure 3.33 Hydraulic self-adjusting tappet.

clearances irrespective of wear to the moving parts and changes in temperature as the engine warms up. No periodic maintenance is necessary, valve timing does not alter, and valve noise is eliminated.

Oil pressure from the engine's main oil gallery enters the feed chamber of the tappet, passes the non-return ball valve, and fills the pressure chamber. This forces the plunger to take up any clearance. When the camshaft rotates, the upward movement of the cam causes the ball to close and seal the pressure chamber. The outer and inner parts of the tappet then hydraulically lock up to make it solid. Because of a slight leakage up the side of the plunger, compensated by constant oil pressure supply, zero valve clearance combined with correct valve seating is always maintained.

The piston

> The purpose of the piston is to transmit the pressure created by the combustion process to the connecting rod (Figure 3.34).

The piston must meet a number of requirements to do this effectively:

1. It must carry piston rings to form a gas-tight and oil-tight seal in the cylinder.
2. It must move freely, with minimum friction.
3. It must be as light as possible.
4. It must be strong enough to cope with the heat and pressure created during combustion.

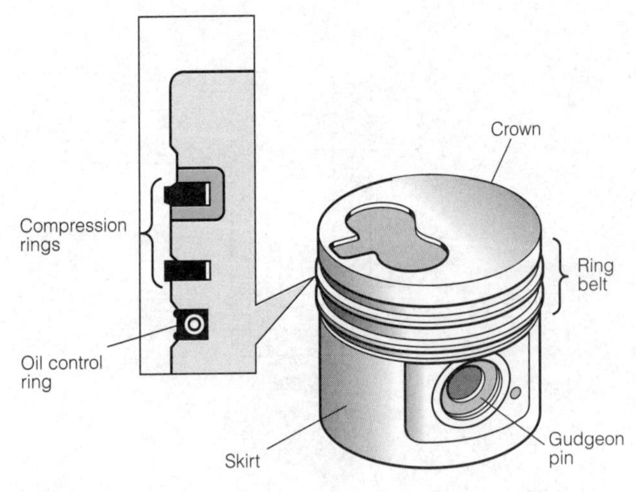

Figure 3.34 Compression ignition (CI) engine piston.

Pistons are made from aluminium alloy, and have the following features:

1. The top of the piston, the **crown**, must be strong to cope with the heat and pressure.
2. The crown may be flat, domed or recessed, depending upon the design of the combustion chamber.
3. There may be recesses in the crown to accommodate the valve heads.
4. There will be at least two **compression rings** to seal against gas pressure leaking into the crankcase, and at least one **oil control ring** to prevent oil from rising up the piston into the combustion chamber.
5. The rings will be held in grooves machined around the top of the piston in an area called the **ring belt**. On some engines these ring grooves may be cast in using a harder material. This part of the piston has quite a large clearance between itself and the cylinder wall.
6. The lowest part of the piston is called the **skirt**. It is a good fit inside the cylinder to steady the piston and yet allow it to move freely. Excessive clearance here results in noise, called **piston slap**. The skirt may be split to allow for heat expansion and to control piston free play inside the cylinder.
7. Built into the skirt are the bosses for the **gudgeon pin**, the swivel connection at the **little end** of the conrod. Both the bosses and the gudgeon pin itself are strongly made, and are finely machined to be a very good fit when hot.
8. The gudgeon pin is normally fully floating and retained by a **circlip** in each boss (Figure 3.35). This prevents the pin from gouging out the cylinder wall. Some gudgeon pins are of the semi-floating type: that is, they are a press fit in the small end of the connecting rod.

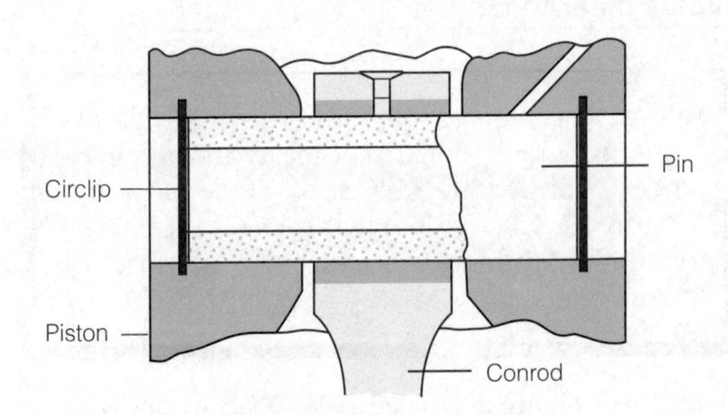

Figure 3.35 Gudgeon pin location.

9. An additional oil control ring may be fitted at the base of the skirt.

Piston rings

Because a clearance is necessary between the piston and the cylinder walls a gas-tight seal is not possible. The purpose of the piston rings is to:

- act as a gas seal;
- provide a path to help conduct the heat of combustion from the piston into the cylinder walls and so into the coolant;
- control the amount of oil on the cylinder walls to prevent any excess from entering the combustion chamber.

Piston rings are generally made from fine-grain cast iron, and have excellent wear qualities. A gap is necessary for assembly and removal; it also allows the ring to give a uniform radial pressure of around 150 kPa when compressed into the bore. Although the standard design of the compression rings is of a rectangular section, there are many variations (Figure 3.36).

The oil control ring or rings are mounted below the compression rings. They apply a pressure of around 300 kPa and, again, may vary in design (Figure 3.37).

Piston ring gaps are checked by putting each ring into the cylinder as it would be on the piston, and checking the gap with feeler blades. The position is very important; the lowest part of the cylinder where the rings do not rub will be virtually unworn, while the centre section where they do may be very different. The gap should be

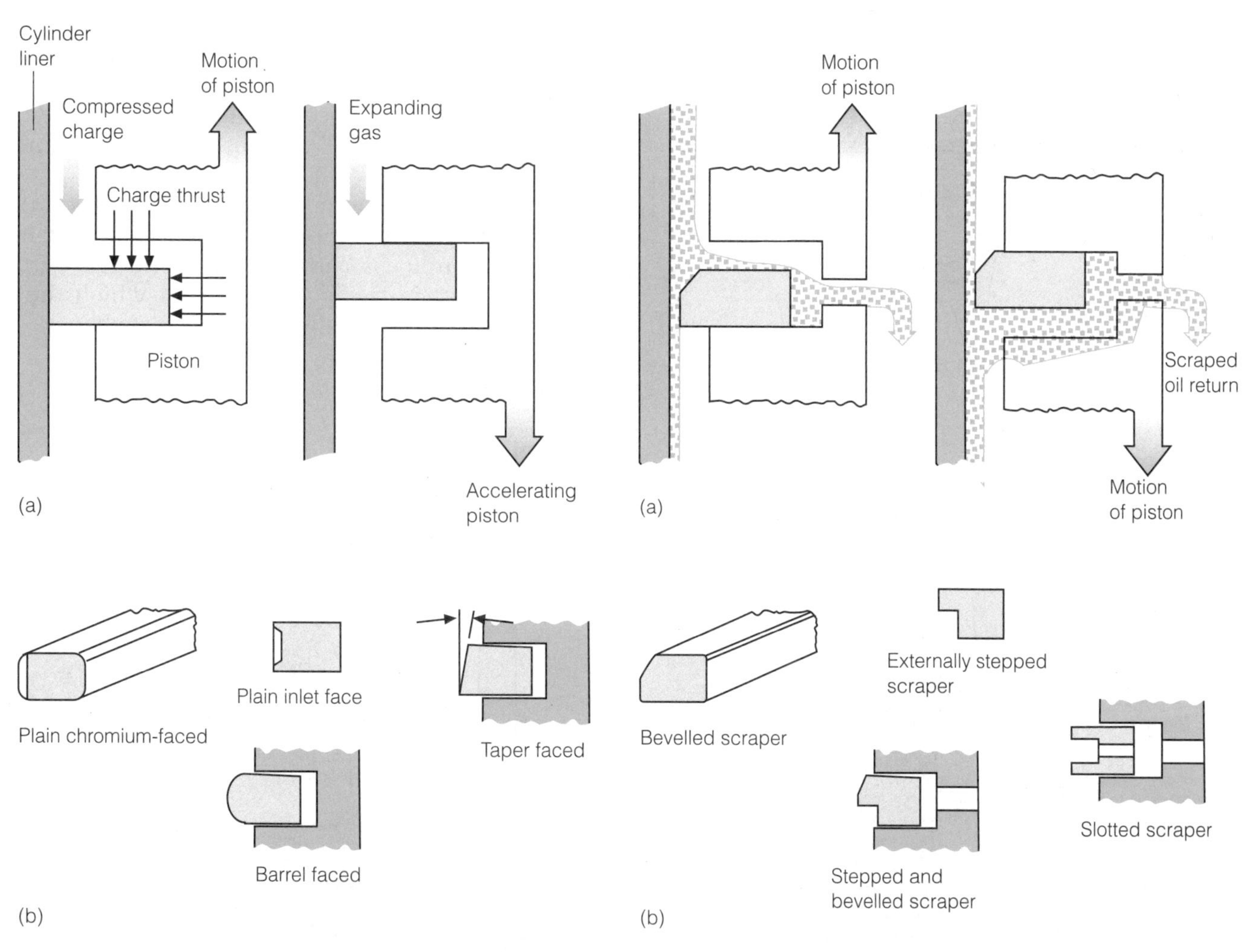

Figure 3.36 Compression rings: (a) principle of action, and (b) some different types of ring.

Figure 3.37 Oil control rings: (a) principle of action, and (b) some different types of ring.

within the manufacturer's tolerances. There will also be a little axial clearance between the ring and the walls of the piston groove, which must also be within tolerance.

When assembling rings onto a piston they must be in the correct position, mounted the right way up, and with the gaps staggered around the circumference. A ring compressor should be used when the piston is entered into the cylinder bore, to avoid breakage.

The connecting rod

> The connecting rod or conrod links the piston to the crankshaft, enabling reciprocating motion to be converted into rotary torque.

It is usually made from a steel forging in the form of an H section to give it strength (Figure 3.38). Where a fully floating gudgeon pin is used, the little end usually has a bronze bush. Alternatively, the bush may be replaced by a clamped eye, when the gudgeon pin moves only in the piston bosses.

The little-end bearing is usually lubricated by splash, but engines with high working temperatures may have oil forced through the conrod or by sprayjets at the base of the cylinder (Figure 3.39). The additional oil also acts as a piston coolant.

At the other end of the conrod is the big-end, which is split to enable fitting to the crankshaft in exactly the same way as the main bearings described earlier. The big-end cap is retained by high-tensile studs or bolts, tightened to a specified torque setting and locked in place. The thin-wall shell bearings are of the same type as the main bearings.

Lubrication of the bearing is by means of the oilways in the crankshaft already described. The bearings have a clearance of as little as 0.01 mm, which under normal working conditions is filled with a film of oil. If this film breaks down, metal-to-metal contact will occur, and bearing failure is inevitable. Dirty oil will also result in damage and failure.

Great care must be taken to avoid any form of damage to the components, and to maintain absolute cleanliness during repair work. The parts must be kept in the positions from which they were removed, especially the bearing shells.

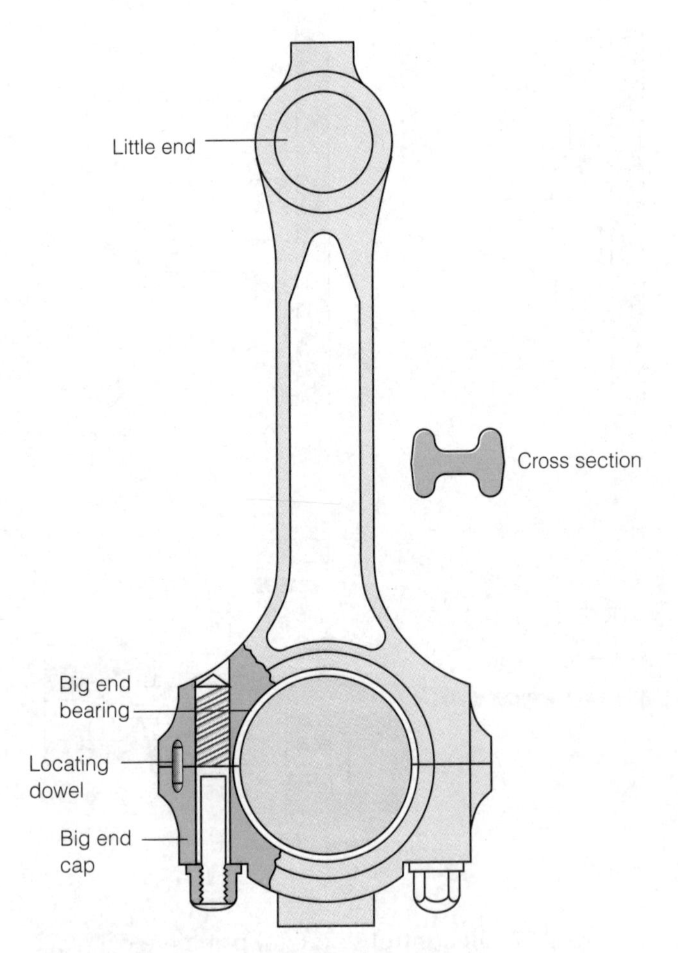

Figure 3.38 Connecting rod (conrod).

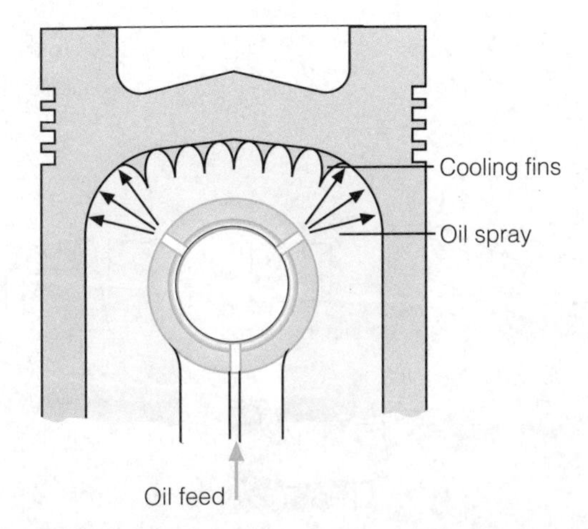

Figure 3.39 Undercrown cooling of a diesel engine piston. Oil is fed through a drilling in the connecting rod to provide lubrication for the little end as well as cooling for the underside of the crown.

Engine balancing

Balance weights are added to the crankshaft to balance the main rotating forces created in the engine. The forces produced by the moving pistons and the connecting rods are known as **secondary forces**, and have a vibration frequency twice the speed of the crankshaft. These forces are completely balanced in six-cylinder in-line and vee engines, but in four-cylinder in-line engines vibration does occur, particularly at certain speeds.

In most cases the vibrations are satisfactorily absorbed by the engine mountings, but in engines above about 2 litres' capacity additional balancing is needed if the engine is to be smooth and quiet. This can be achieved by the installation of a device from the early days of motoring known as the **Lanchester harmonic balancer**.

A modern version of this device is shown in Figure 3.40. The twin balance (or silent) shafts, running at twice engine speed, are positioned on either side of the cylinder block, one a little higher than the other. They rotate in opposite directions, so that their bob-weights counterbalance movement of the engine components.

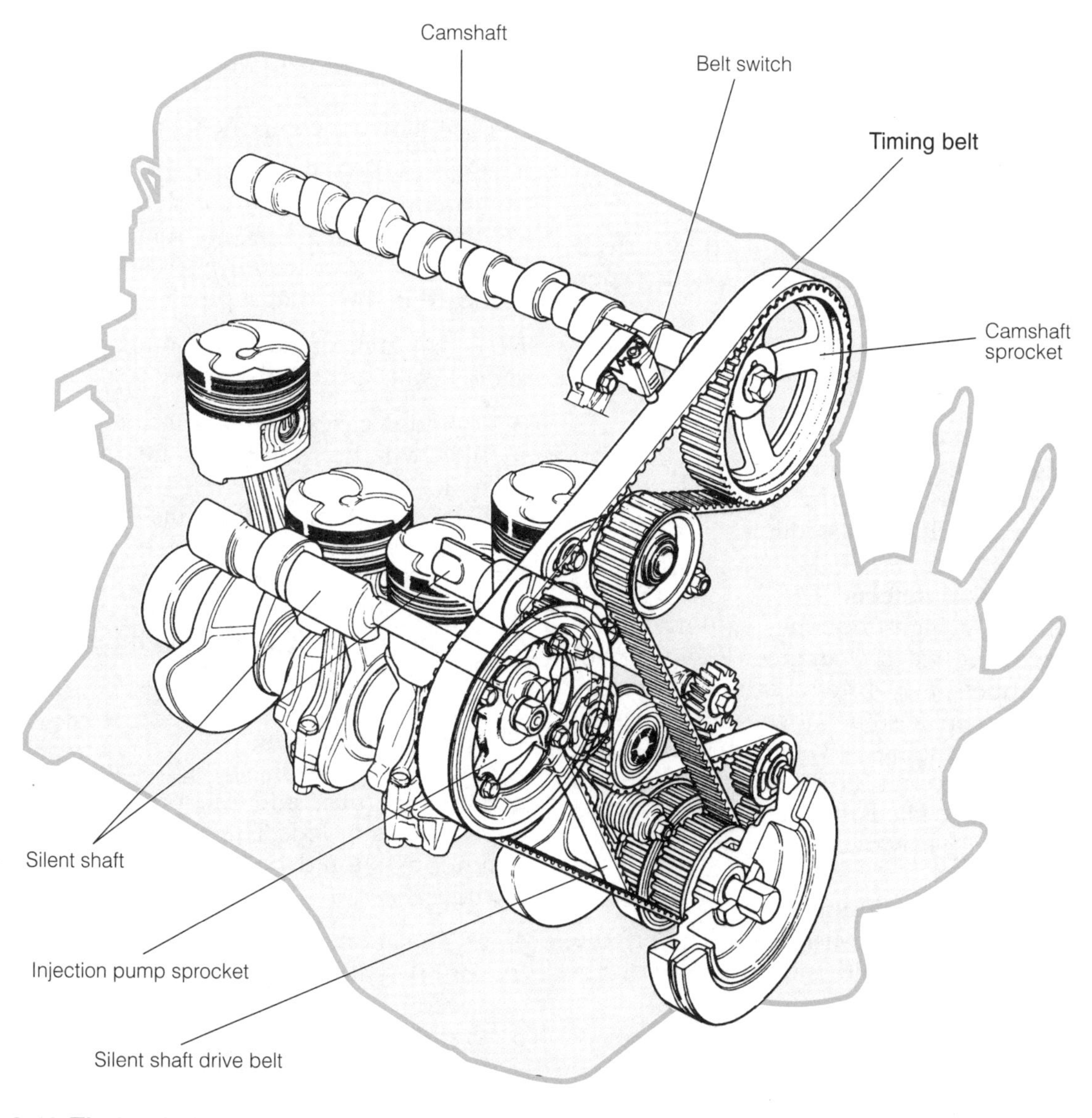

Figure 3.40 Timing belt train.

Fault diagnosis

Running tests

A number of faults can be determined without dismantling, by running the engine or driving the vehicle.

Burning oil
Blue smoke in the exhaust is an almost certain indicator that lubricating oil is being burnt. It will be particularly noticeable when first opening the throttle after allowing the engine to idle for a few minutes. Spark plugs may be fouled with black oily soot, and will certainly be black.

Crankshaft and conrod bearing noise
Faulty big-end bearings are indicated by a sharp, medium-heavy and rhythmic knocking under load. Completely worn-out bearings will knock when the engine is revved up at idle.

A failed little-end bearing is indicated by a lighter, machine-gun type rattle when the engine speed is quickly increased from idle.

Main bearing failure is characterised by a deep rumble, particularly at lower engine speeds, when accelerating under load.

Crankshaft bearing failures may be accompanied by a substantial loss of oil pressure.

Excessive piston clearance
The hollow slapping noise previously referred to is noticeably different from the other sounds, and is most noticeable during fast idling.

Valve mechanism defects
A general, fairly high-frequency rattling sound typifies excessive valve clearance. Engines with hydraulic tappets may briefly exhibit this very loudly on start-up if some of the tappets have drained during standing. A vehicle left idle for a period may need to run for some minutes before all the tappets have filled and are operating. Some modest revving-up may overcome the problem.

Crankshaft thrust problems
An engine that slows considerably when the clutch is depressed could indicate excessively worn thrust bearings.

Oil pressure
Oil pressure on vehicles without a gauge can be tested by attaching one to the oil system. The tests and readings should be in accordance with the vehicle manufacturer's specifications.

Non-running tests

Some tests are carried out by turning the engine over on the starter or when stationary.

Cylinder leakage tests
This is the easiest and most certain way to check for leaking into, or out of, the combustion chamber. It requires no more than an airline adapter welded to the body of an old spark plug. The 'connector' is then screwed into each cylinder in turn and an airline connected to supply at least 6.8 bar (100 lbf/in^2) of 'clean' compressed air. Each cylinder should be at t.d.c. firing stroke and the engine locked to prevent rotation. Putting the vehicle into gear with the handbrake on normally suffices.

The following components are then checked:

1. Inlet valve seat: any leakage can be heard by listening in the air intake with the throttle open and the air cleaner removed.
2. Exhaust valve seat: an escape of air will be heard in the exhaust pipe.

Note that lack of valve clearances may give the same results as both the above tests.

3. Cylinder gases/air leaking into coolant: bubbles will be visible in the radiator header tank.
4. Gasket leaking to the outside: an air escape from the joint. This may need a liquid such as oil to make bubbles apparent.
5. Gasket leaking into another cylinder: an air escape can be heard through the plug hole of the adjacent cylinder.

Compression testing
A compression testing gauge is attached to each cylinder in turn, and the pressure at cranking speed is recorded. The vehicle manufacturer's conditions should be met. These will normally include:

1. engine at operating temperature;
2. battery fully charged for normal cranking speed;
3. throttle wide open;
4. ignition system neutralised;
5. sufficient time allowed to reach speed and pressure.

The pressures, and more particularly the variations between cylinders, will be specified in the workshop manual.

CHECK YOUR UNDERSTANDING

- The cylinder in its simplest form is a tube of circular cross-section, closed off at one end.
- A piston fits closely inside the cylinder so that it can move smoothly up and down.
- Piston rings provide a seal for the combustion gases and the engine oil.
- The piston is connected to the little end of the connecting rod (conrod) by a swivelling gudgeon pin. The big-end of the conrod is attached to the crankshaft.
- The crankshaft is the main shaft of the engine, and is carried in bearings in the crankcase.
- The camshaft is driven from the crankshaft at half engine speed, and opens the poppet valves.
- Poppet valves are fitted in the cylinder head to control the incoming mixture and the exhausting burnt gases.
- The four basic elements of internal combustion engine operation are induction, compression, power, and exhaust.
- There are two basic cycles of operation: two-stroke and four-stroke.
- In the two-stroke engine all four 'elements' occur in one crankshaft revolution.
- In the four-stroke engine two revolutions are needed for the Otto cycle.

PROJECTS

Undertake the following tasks under supervision:

1. Using the correct tools and a suitable engine, check and adjust the valve clearances to manufacturer's specifications. Take care to observe all the requirements of conditions and sequence; fit new seals and/or gaskets as appropriate on completion.
2. Carry out a cylinder compression test, using the correct equipment and the workshop manual for the vehicle.
3. Carry out a cylinder leakage test on, if possible, a defective engine. Observe any requirements of the vehicle manufacturer.

REVISION EXERCISES AND QUESTIONS

1. Label the components identified in Figure 3.42 (see page 42).
2. What is meant by internal combustion?
3. Name the *four* strokes of the Otto cycle.
4. How can you identify the inlet valve from the exhaust valve on a particular engine?
5. What is the speed of the camshaft compared with that of the crankshaft?
6. What is meant by the term *valve overlap*?
7. What is meant by the *swept volume* of an engine?
8. What determines the stroke of an engine?
9. Why must there normally be a clearance between the end of a valve and its operating mechanism?
10. What is the most common method of driving the camshaft on modern light vehicle engines?
11. Why are multiple cylinders used instead of a single large cylinder?
12. Name the parts of the piston in Figure 3.41.
13. State the major operating difference between two-stroke and four-stroke engines.
14. Give the meaning of the term *crankcase compression*.
15. What is the probable cause of bubbles in the coolant when carrying out a cylinder leakage test?

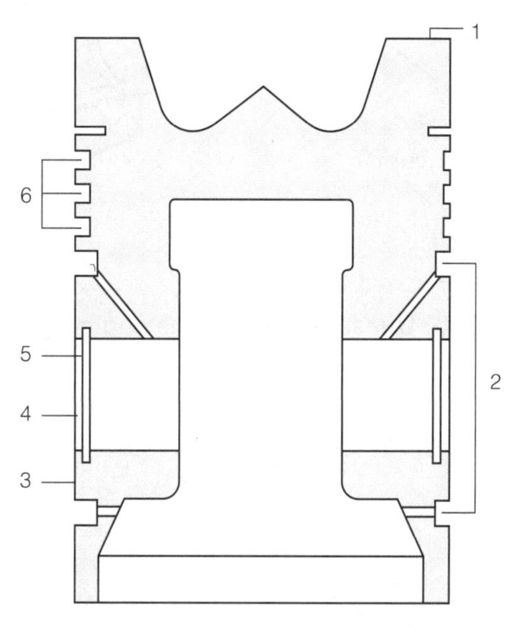

Figure 3.41 Question 12: name the parts of the piston.

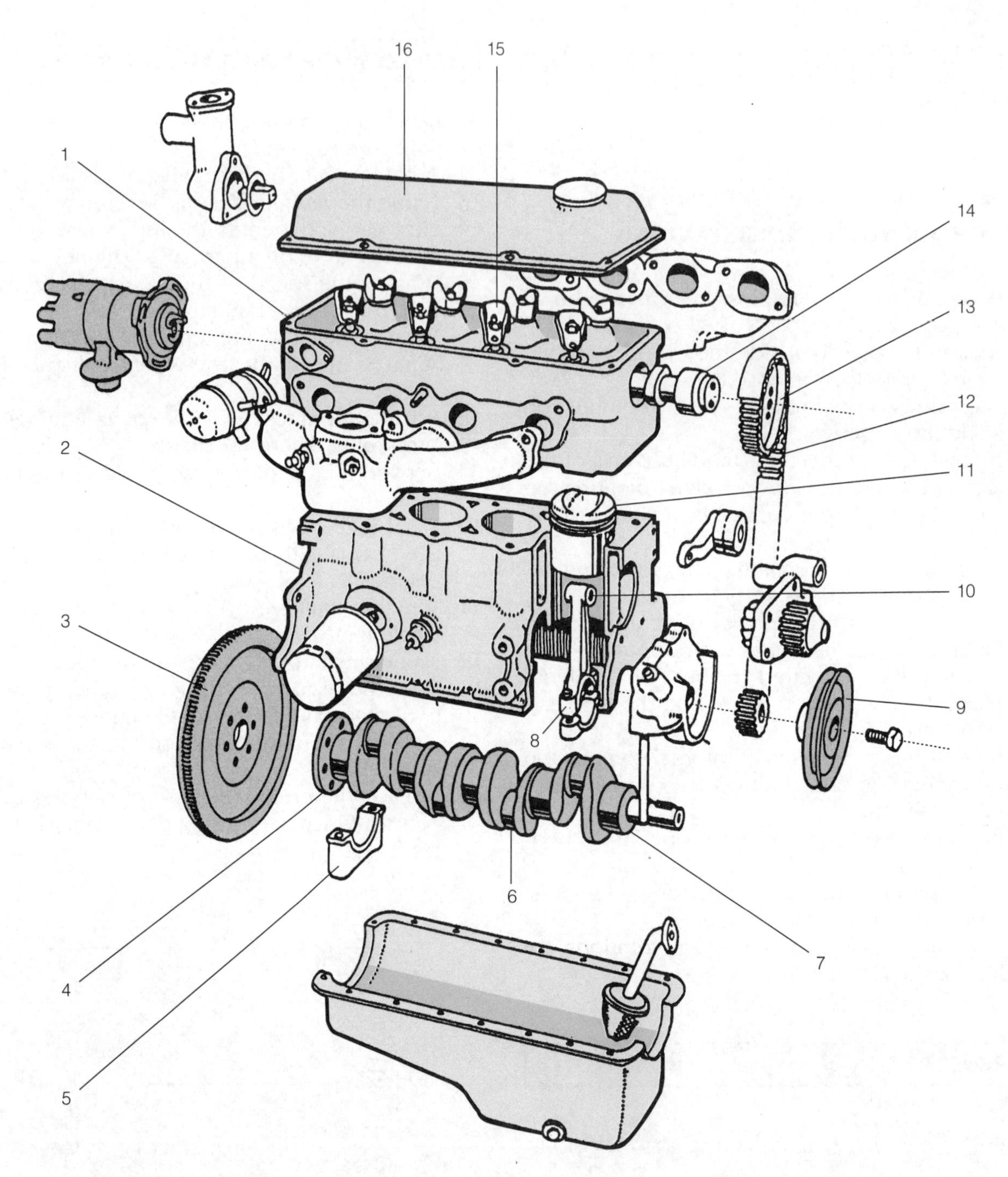

Figure 3.42 Question 1: name the engine components.

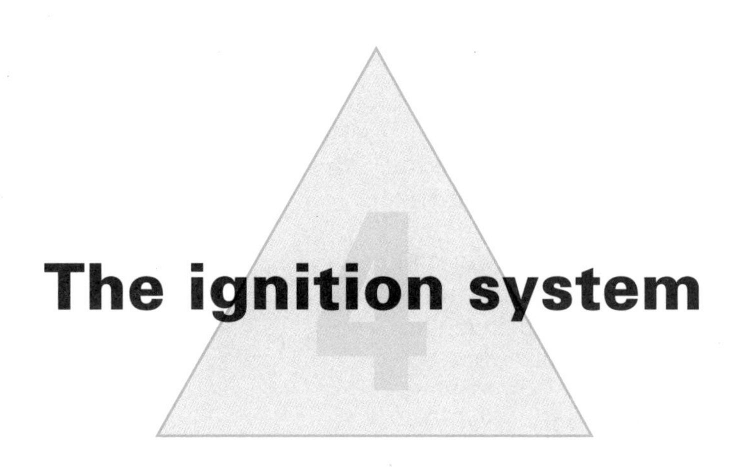

The ignition system

Introduction

On the induction stroke a mixture of petrol and air is drawn into the engine cylinder. Once the mixture has been compressed, some means of igniting it is needed.

> It is the purpose of the ignition system to create the electric spark in the engine combustion chamber at exactly the right time in order to ignite the mixture.

A basic coil ignition system

Look at Figure 4.1 to see the basic parts of a typical system. Put simply, the function of each component is as follows.

The **battery** supplies electrical power.

The **keyswitch** controls the system (and acts as an anti-theft device) by cutting off or switching on the supply of current from the battery.

The **coil** transforms the low battery voltage to the very high voltage essential to jump the spark plug gap and ignite the mixture.

Driven at half engine speed, the **distributor** distributes high-voltage current from the coil to each spark plug in turn, and at the precise moment it is required. The distributor also houses several other important ignition components, which will be looked at in detail later. These are the contact breaker points, a condenser (or capacitor), and the advance and retard mechanism to alter the timing of the spark.

The **spark plugs** are screwed into the cylinder head, and protrude slightly into the combustion chamber. Each provides a gap across which the high-voltage current must jump to create a spark,

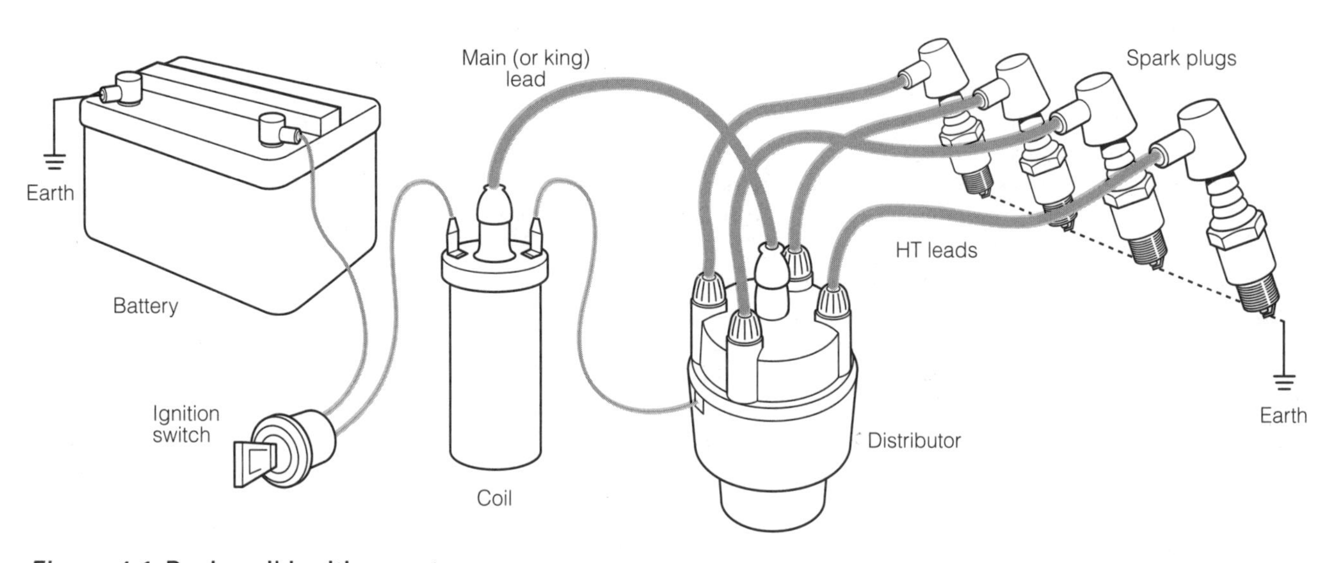

Figure 4.1 Basic coil ignition system.

and so ignite the mixture. A high voltage is necessary not only to jump the gap, but also to force its way through the hot, high-pressure gases in the combustion chamber.

The **low-tension (LT)** and **high-tension (HT) leads** (cables) are different in that the LT cables are thin and the HT cables are much thicker. This provides an important clue to the fact that the ignition system contains two circuits.

The LT battery supply needs only relatively light insulation. It normally operates at only about 12 V, and there is little chance of electric shocks from it. A more scientific name for this circuit is the **primary circuit**.

The HT cables connect the coil, distributor and spark plugs. The heavy insulation is necessary to prevent current leakage, or giving you a strong electric shock of anything up to 20 000 V if you touch the wrong place! The other name for this part of the system is the **secondary circuit**.

Magnetism and induction

Before exploring the operation of the ignition system we need to understand a little about the principle of magnetic induction.

> When an electric current flows through a conductor, such as a cable or wire, it creates a magnetic field around that conductor.

You can prove this yourself by doing a simple experiment, as shown in Figure 4.2. Place the compass next to the conductor, switch on the circuit, and you will notice that the compass needle moves as the magnetic field created by the current flow acts upon it.

The reverse is also true. When a moving magnetic field crosses a conductor it induces a current in that conductor. To prove this you need a sensitive instrument, such as a galvanometer or ammeter, to measure the current flow, and a strong magnet, as seen in Figure 4.3. Move the magnet across the cable quickly. You will see from the movement of the galvanometer needle that when the magnetic field produced by the magnet crosses the cable a small current is **induced** (created).

Our experiment produces only a very small amount of electrical current, which is why we need a very sensitive meter to measure it. However, this current could be vastly increased in three ways:

1. by increasing the speed of movement;
2. by increasing the strength of the magnetic field;
3. by increasing the amount of cable (or conductor) passing through the magnetic field.

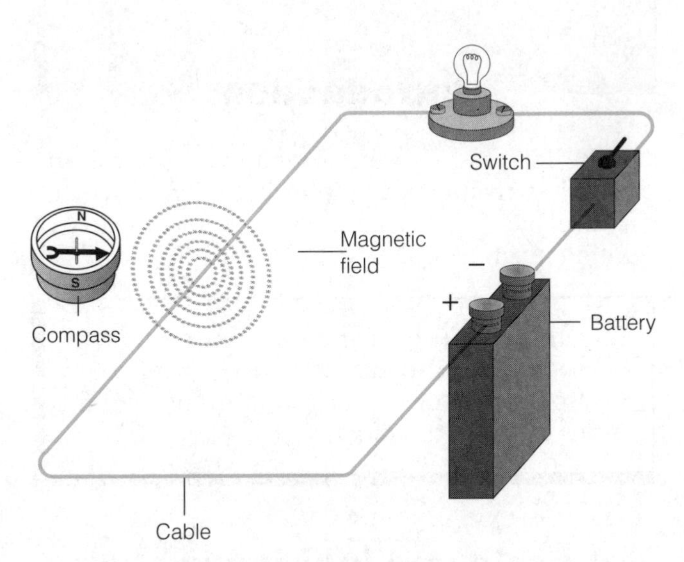

Figure 4.2 Simple demonstration of induced magnetism.

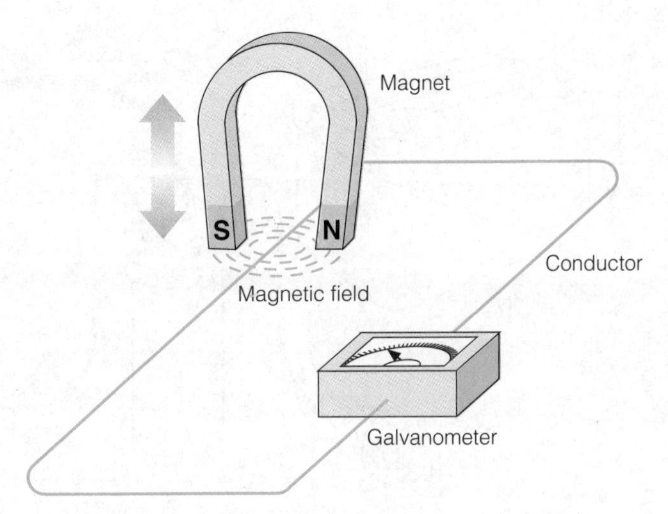

Figure 4.3 Simple demonstration of induced current.

Increasing the speed of movement and the strength of the magnetic field may both be done electrically. Increasing the amount of cable is done simply by forming it into coils of many turns of thin wire. By wrapping the coils around a soft iron core, the strength of the magnetic field is further increased.

Coil primary winding function

> The purpose of the primary circuit is to create and break (or collapse) a concentrated magnetic field.

When the ignition is turned on and the contact breaker is closed, supply current flows from the battery through the primary coil across the contact breaker points and so to earth and back to the battery. This current flow creates a magnetic field around the primary coil. As the engine rotates, the contact breaker is opened by the cam. At this point the circuit is broken, supply current stops flowing, and the magnetic field collapses. Thus while the circuit is in operation and the engine is turning, there is the repeated creation and collapse of a magnetic field (Figure 4.4).

Coil secondary winding function

> The purpose of the secondary winding is to provide a sufficiently high-voltage current that a spark is able to jump across the electrode gap of the spark plug.

The secondary winding is wound inside the primary winding. If we regard the primary circuit as an electromagnet in which current flows and is interrupted, we can see from what has been said

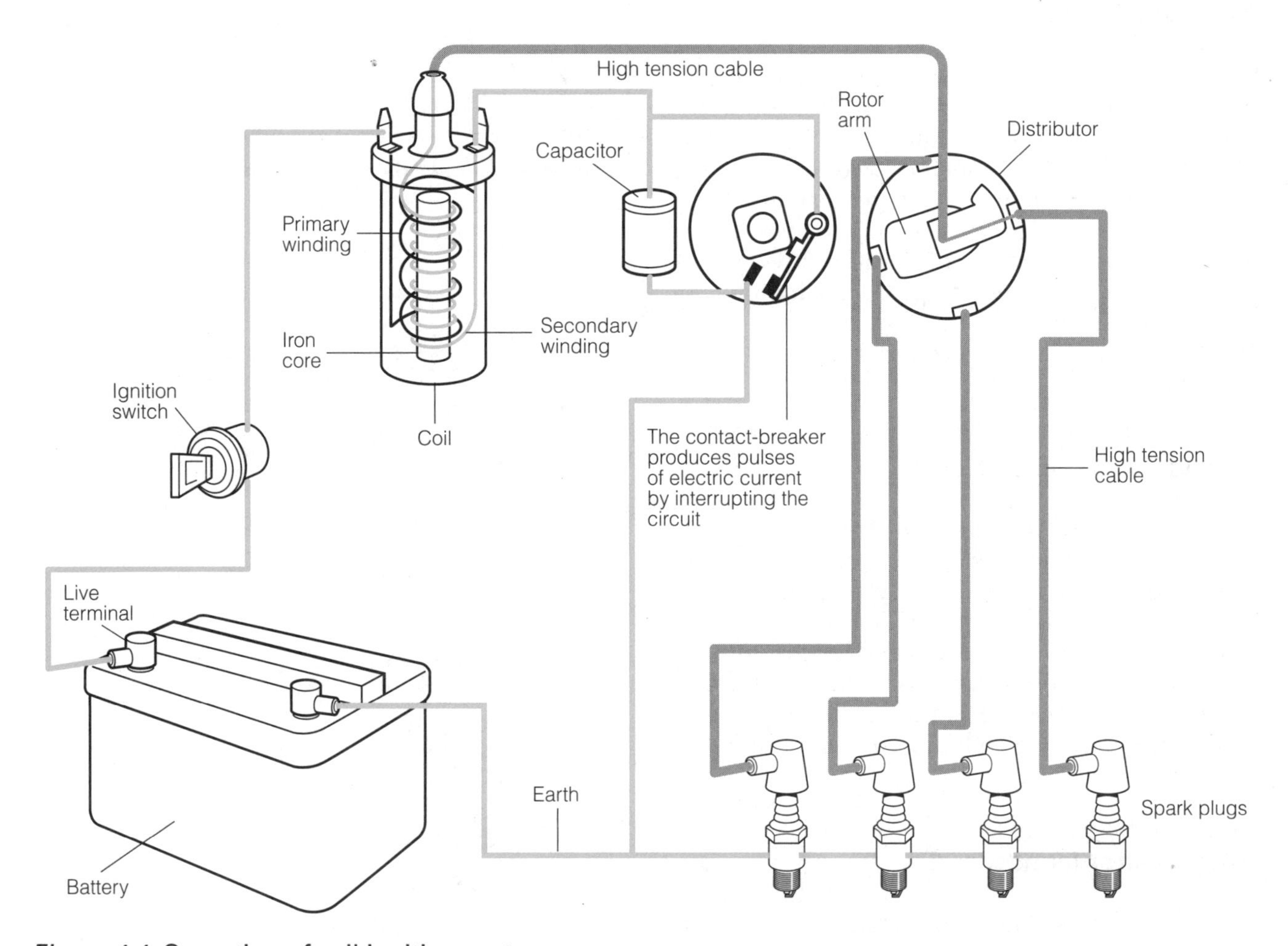

Figure 4.4 Operation of coil ignition system.

about induction that a current will be induced in the secondary circuit every time the primary circuit is broken. This is because the magnetic field collapses towards the soft iron core and, as it does so, crosses the secondary coil, inducing current in it.

By making the primary coil of a few hundred turns of wire and the secondary of thousands of turns, a relatively high voltage can be induced. This high voltage is then transferred to the spark plug, where it is powerful enough to jump the gap to create a spark. If the secondary coil contains 100 times the number of turns in the primary coil, the induced voltage will be 100 times greater. The increase in voltage is balanced by a proportionate decrease in the amount of current flow.

Operating principles of the ignition system

Primary (LT) circuit

The simplest primary circuit consists of a battery, an ignition switch, the contact breaker (an automatic switch), and the primary coil with a soft iron core. When the contact breaker is closed, supply current at battery voltage (usually 12 V) flows through the primary windings across the contact breaker to earth. This current flow creates a magnetic field around the primary windings. As the crankshaft turns so too does the cam in the distributor, opening the contact breaker. At this point the supply current ceases to flow.

Secondary (HT) circuit

Stopping the flow of supply voltage causes a collapse of the magnetic field. This collapse induces a high voltage in the secondary winding, which forces a current along the HT lead to the rotor arm. The rotor arm then transfers the current to a segment in the distributor cap and along the HT lead to the spark plug. Here it jumps the gap and creates the spark, which ignites the mixture in the cylinder.

The capacitor (condenser)

The capacitor is fitted in parallel connection across the contact breaker. In other words, it provides an alternative path for current flow when the contact breaker opens. This enables the capacitor to provide two benefits:

1. It can reduce arcing at the contact breaker points by storing current as they open.
2. Because it does this, current flow to the coil stops immediately. This abrupt shut-off ensures a rapid collapse of the magnetic field in the coil, and therefore a higher secondary voltage.

Contact breaker gap or dwell angle

In the past, the method of measuring the contact breaker gap was to rotate the cam until the gap was at its widest. The gap between the contacts was then measured with feeler gauges and adjusted as required. Because modern engines need a very accurate setting, the use of feeler gauges is inadequate.

> The alternative is to measure the **dwell angle**, the period when the contact breaker is *closed*, using a dwell meter. This setting is determined by the vehicle manufacturer.

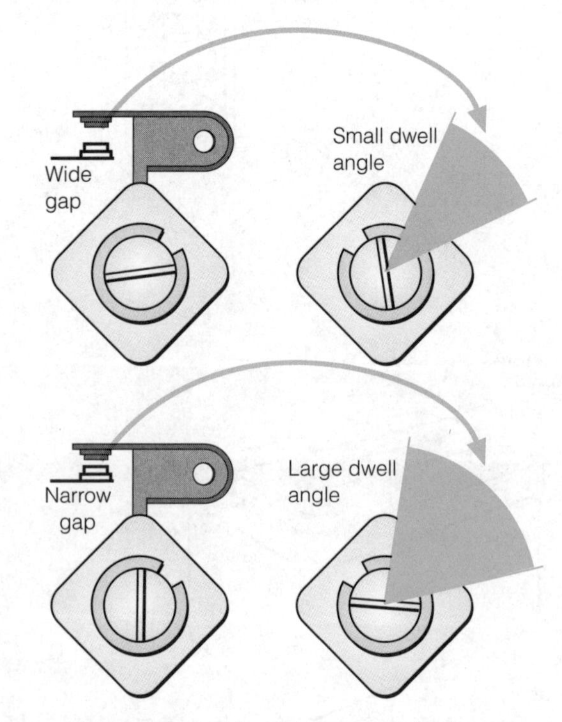

Figure 4.5 Dwell angle: (a) too small; (b) too large.

If the dwell angle is too small (Figure 4.5a), the coil does not have sufficient time to build up the magnetic field to maximum strength. This results in a small HT voltage and a weak spark. Too small a dwell angle also advances the ignition timing, and may cause pinking (see below). A dwell angle that is too small is the same as a contact breaker gap that is too large.

When the dwell angle is too large (Figure 4.5b) the opposite occurs. At low engine speeds the coil becomes over-saturated, which may overload the capacitor and cause the contact breaker to burn away prematurely. It will also retard the ignition timing, which can result in misfiring and loss of power. A large dwell angle is caused by a contact breaker gap that is too small.

Automatic ignition advance and retard devices

> When the engine is running, ignition timing must vary because the speed of the engine varies, but the time (a few milliseconds) that it takes the air/fuel mixture to burn and develop full gas expansion remains very nearly the same.

The maximum pressure in the cylinder needs to be created just after the piston has passed t.d.c. (top dead-centre). At idle, the piston travels relatively slowly in the cylinder, and the mixture can be ignited with a firing point just a few degrees (of crankshaft rotation) before the t.d.c. position.

At faster engine speeds, the piston takes much less time to travel in the cylinder, but because the mixture needs just as much time to burn, it must be ignited long before the piston is near t.d.c. The spark may be needed as much as 40° before t.d.c. (b.t.d.c.).

To obtain ignition at the correct point, two devices are usually fitted to the distributor to vary – within certain limits – the timing of the spark:

1. a mechanical centrifugal advance device, which progressively advances the ignition timing as engine speed increases (Figure 4.6);
2. a vacuum advance device (Figure 4.7), which advances the ignition timing when the engine is under light load, for example when cruising at part throttle. This is needed because under conditions of light load the mixture is relatively weak and requires a longer burning

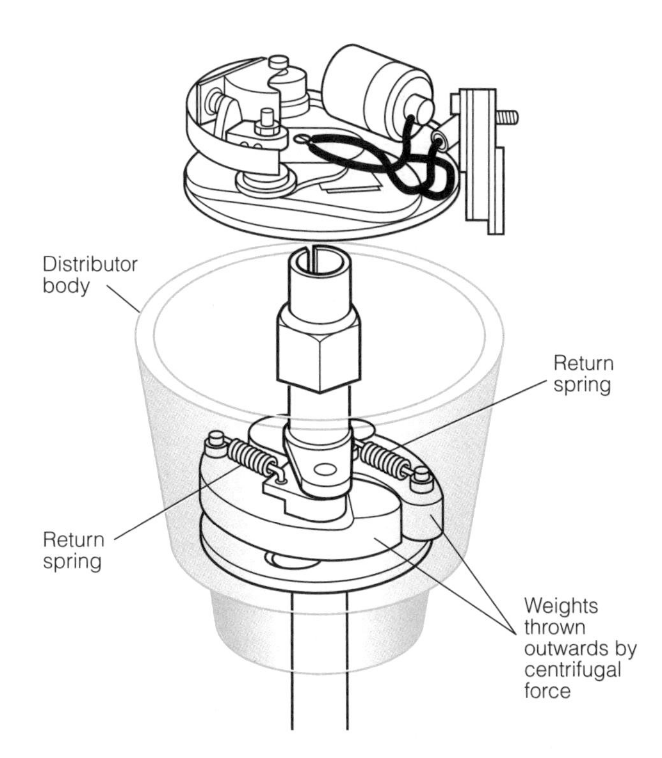

Figure 4.6 Centrifugal ignition advance system. Two pivoted weights are thrown outwards as engine speed increases. They turn the cam, causing the points to open earlier.

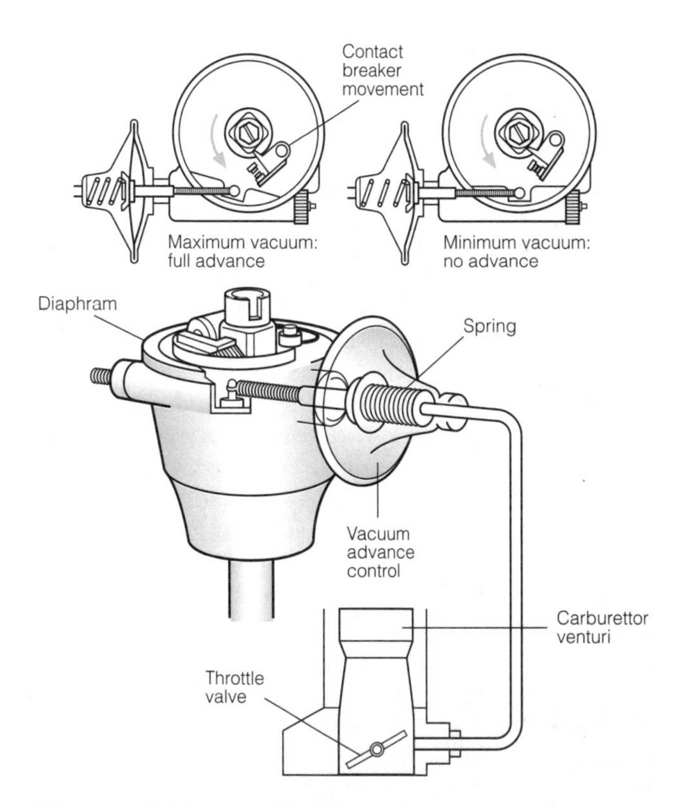

Figure 4.7 Vacuum ignition advance system.

time. The device is operated by the varying depression created in the inlet manifold.

A further refinement of the vacuum advance device is that it also retards the ignition timing when the engine is operating in one of two ways:

1. on over-run, for example when the vehicle is travelling down a steep hill and the engine (via the transmission) is acting as a brake;
2. when the engine is under heavy load, for example at full throttle but at a low engine speed.

The amount of advance varies with the type of engine, its purpose, and the fuel it uses. The settings are determined by the vehicle manufacturer, and must be accurately set.

Although the mechanical advance mechanism can 'sense' engine speed it cannot determine the load on the engine. This means that the maximum advance is usually restricted to avoid what is known as **pinking**. This is a condition that occurs when the spark is ignited too early, causing a rapid rise in pressure to occur before the piston has reached t.d.c. This pressure rise also increases the temperature to the point where the flame spreads through the unburnt mixture at the speed of sound, which can be heard as knocking. This condition puts undue stress on the piston, and could cause severe damage.

The spark plug

Figure 4.8 shows the construction of a typical spark plug. The central electrode, usually made of a nickel-steel alloy, is embedded in the centre of the insulator. The insulator is made from a ceramic material such as fused aluminium oxide. The plug body, which retains the centre electrode and the insulator, screws into the cylinder head and has the earth electrode or electrodes attached to it. The thread is usually 10 mm or 14 mm diameter, although other sizes may be used.

Although the spark plug is of simple construction, it must operate efficiently under pressure and at high temperatures. It must stay gas-tight under these conditions and deliver up to 50 or more sparks each second. The plug must operate at a temperature high enough to burn deposits from the electrodes to stop it from fouling, but not so high that it might ignite the mixture before the spark and so cause **pre-ignition**. Pre-ignition is caused by excessively high temperatures igniting the fuel before the spark occurs. The plug should ideally operate between 800 and 850 °C. As the conditions vary between engine types, each engine design has its own grade of spark plug.

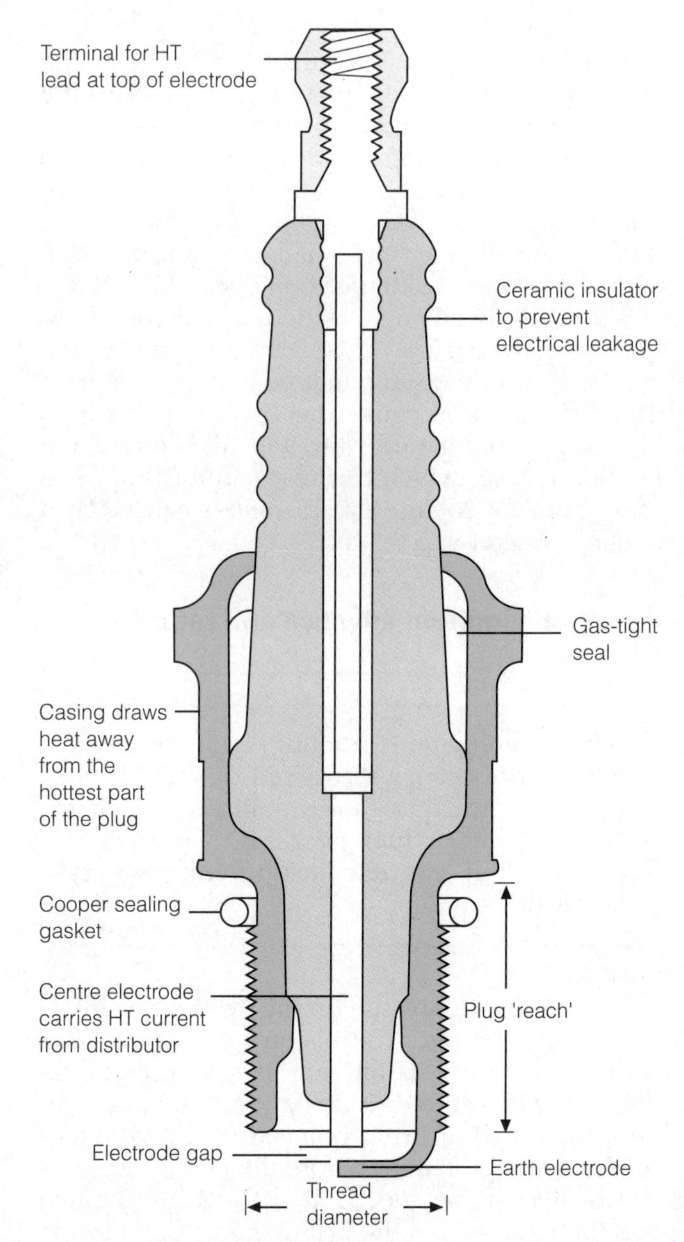

Figure 4.8 Typical spark plug.

> It is very important that the correct grade of plug is fitted to the engine, and that the gap between the electrodes is correct. An incorrect plug or plug gap may cause the engine to run inefficiently, and may possibly cause mechanical damage.

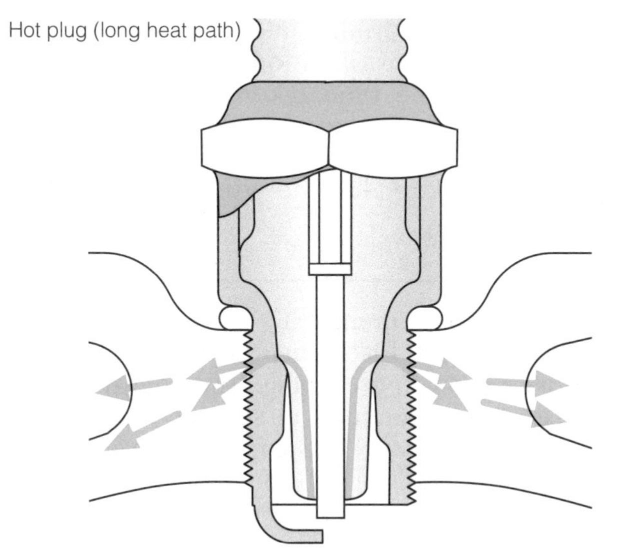

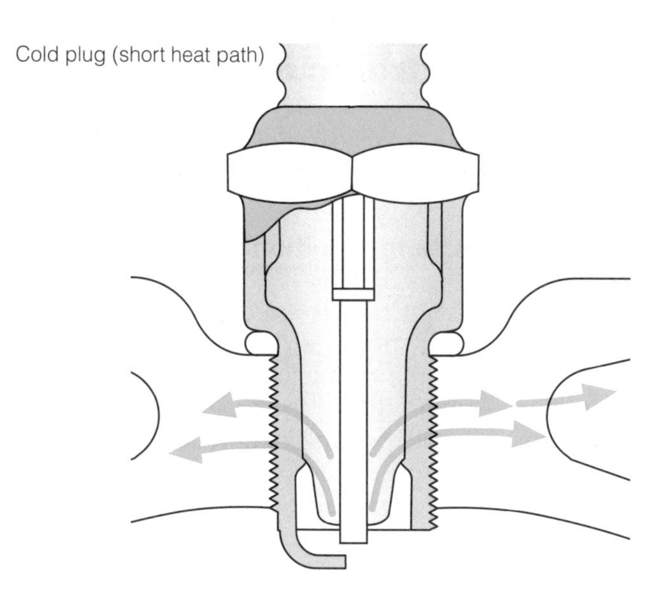

Figure 4.9 Hot and cold plugs.

Spark plug heat range

Spark plugs tend to be categorised as **hot** or **cold** (Figure 4.9). A hot plug has a long insulator tip at the firing end. The heat has to travel a long path before it can flow into the cylinder head, and therefore more heat is retained by the plug. Hot plugs tend to be fitted to cold-running engines.

The cold plug has a shorter insulator tip and retains less heat. Cold plugs are used in engines that run with higher combustion temperatures.

Ballast resistor ignition system

> This is a refinement of the basic ignition system, which gives a better spark for improved cold starting.

It uses a low-voltage coil (approximately 6 V) and a ballast resistor. The resistor is fitted in the primary feed between the battery and the coil.

During engine cranking with the starter, the high load on the battery greatly reduces the effective voltage supplied to the ignition system. At this time the ballast resistor is bypassed, allowing the full voltage available to reach the ignition coil. With its normal working voltage available the coil can provide full secondary voltage. As soon as the engine starts, full battery voltage is restored. To prevent damage to the low-voltage coil, the ballast resistor is brought into the circuit to limit the voltage supply to the level needed by the coil.

Disadvantages of the basic coil ignition system

The basic ignition system has some inherent disadvantages:

1. In time, the contact breaker points erode. Similarly, the gap between the contact points alters in use and, as it does, the dwell angle and the ignition timing change slightly.
2. At high engine speeds there is a tendency for the contact breaker to bounce, reducing the coil output.
3. Because the system is mechanically operated, wear occurs at the contact breaker cam, drive spindle and in other moving parts. This results in an alteration of the ignition timing and the dwell angle. In some cases the cam lobes wear at differing rates, resulting in dwell and timing variance between individual cylinders.
4. The mechanical and vacuum advance and retard devices are a compromise. They do not give precise ignition timing over the engine's full speed and load range.
5. The system requires regular servicing to keep it operating properly and the timing correct.

Although the basic system has been in use for many years, the need for improved fuel economy and the concern over environmental pollution demand improvements in ignition timing control, which the basic system cannot meet. For such reasons manufacturers now fit electronic ignition systems to their vehicles.

Electronic ignition

Electronic ignition systems may be categorised as **capacitor discharge** or **inductive**.

Capacitor discharge ignition system

This system is not widely used, and differs considerably from the standard and inductive systems. One of the problems with using a coil to provide the high voltage is the time required to build up and collapse the magnetic field before a spark can be produced. On eight- or twelve-cylinder engines this can be a major problem.

> In the capacitor discharge system the supply to the coil is stored in a capacitor inside an electronic control unit. An electronic 'trigger' releases the charge stored in the capacitor to the primary winding of the coil.

In operation, an inverter converts the a.c. (alternating current) supply to d.c. (direct current) and feeds it to a step-up transformer to provide the 400 V needed by the capacitor. When a spark is required, the trigger releases the energy from the capacitor to the coil by activating a thyristor (an electronic switch). The sudden discharge of high-voltage electrical energy causes a rapid build-up of the magnetic field around the coil, and induces around 40 000 V in the secondary windings. This results in a spark of high intensity but short duration. Voltage transformation time is about one hundredth of the time taken by the standard system. This allows a much higher rate of sparks per second. However, the short duration of each individual spark renders the system unsuitable for most engines.

> ▲ Do not attempt to test or repair a capacitor discharge system unless you know what you are doing. The energy produced is high enough to severely shock or possibly kill you. The capacitor may also hold its charge for 24 hours or more after switching off.

The inductive system

This is a widely used type of electronic ignition system (Figure 4.10). It is similar to the conventional system in that a current has to flow through the primary winding of an ignition coil, in order to produce a high voltage in the secondary winding when the current is interrupted.

> The big difference is that the primary current is switched on and off by a **transistor** (an electronic switch) or other electronic device. It therefore eliminates the problems associated with contact breaker points.

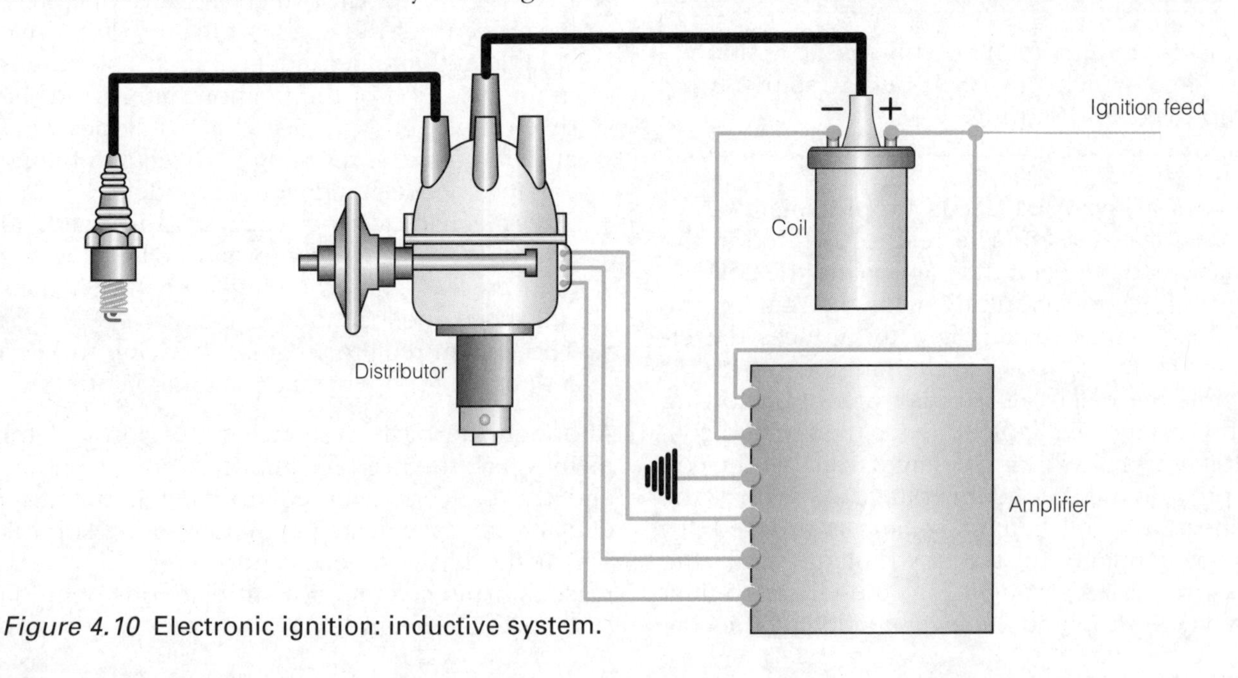

Figure 4.10 Electronic ignition: inductive system.

The system does, however, still use the mechanical centrifugal advance mechanism to sense engine speed, and a vacuum advance to sense engine load. The limitations of these types of timing control mentioned earlier also apply to this system.

Fully electronic ignition system

To further improve the control of the ignition system a powerful microcomputer called an **electronic control unit** (ECU) is used. This system is similar to the electronic system outlined above. The main difference is that the ignition timing is controlled by the ECU instead of the centrifugal and vacuum advance mechanisms.

The ECU operates as a preprogrammed computer. It gathers information from a variety of sensors, interprets that information, and adjusts the ignition timing accordingly (Figure 4.11).

The system consists of the following major components.

Electronic control unit (ECU)

Its two main functions are to control the ignition timing electronically using information from sensors, and to control the ignition coil output.

Crankshaft sensor

This determines the crankshaft speed and position. As the crankshaft rotates, the sensor produces pulses, which are fed to the ECU. From this the ECU can determine the t.d.c. position and the engine speed. These inputs are used by the ECU to calculate basic ignition timing.

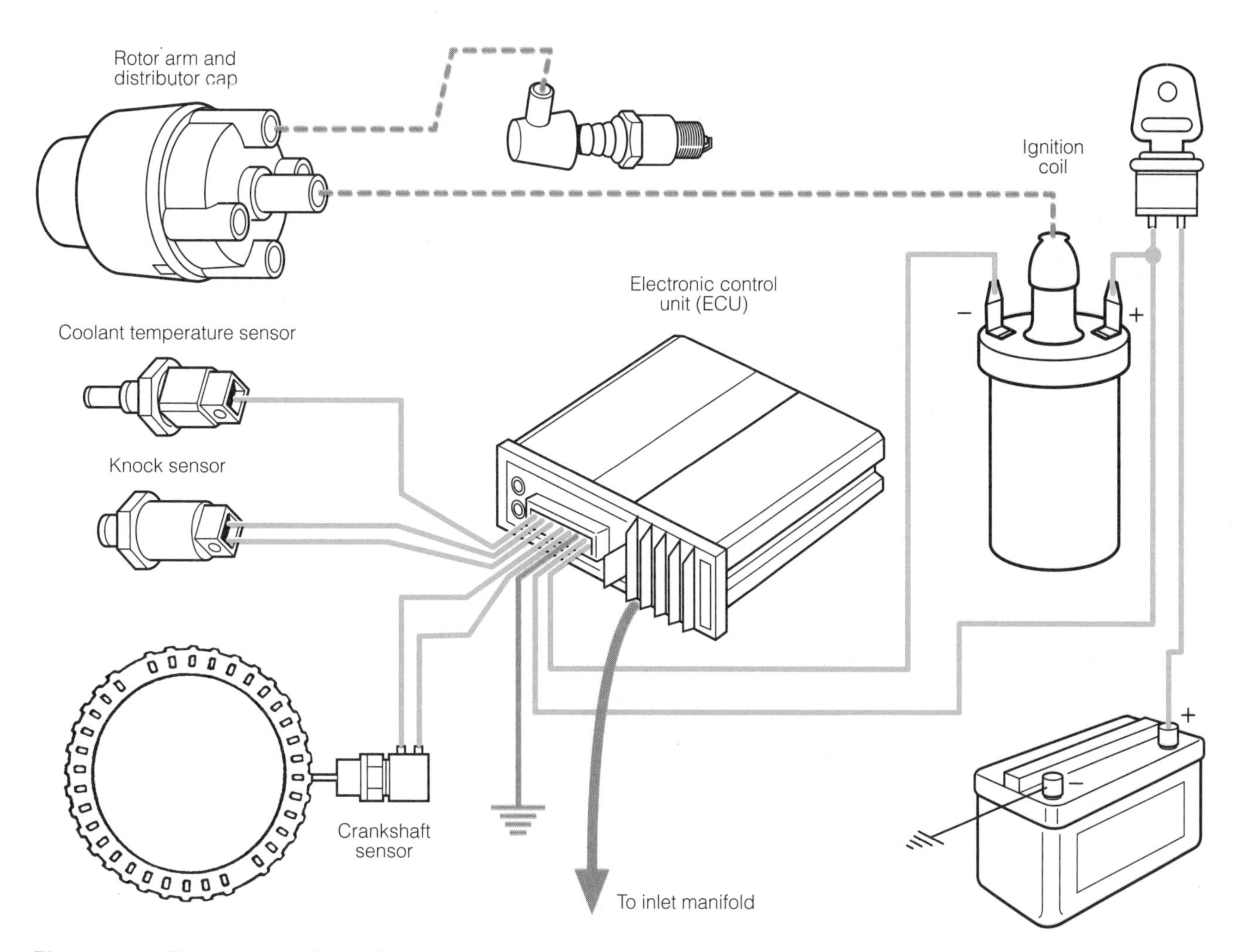

Figure 4.11 Programmed ignition system.

Coolant temperature sensor
The ECU uses this information to adjust ignition timing for engine condition.

Knock sensor
This provides a small input voltage to the ECU, which is proportional to the vibration sensed in the engine block. The vibrations set up by combustion detonation are detected by the sensor, and the information is fed to the ECU. The ECU responds by retarding the ignition timing until the knocking stops. The timing is then advanced again, in steps, up to the setting programmed into the ECU. This process of sensing and adjusting is carried out for each individual cylinder all the time the engine is running. It enables the engine to be run with the maximum possible advance setting to give optimum efficiency, without the risk of damage caused from detonation.

Ignition coil
This acts very like a normal coil; the only difference is that the primary resistance has been lowered in order to ensure that the HT output is reached faster, and is maintained constantly throughout the speed range. It is important that the correct coil is used, as a coil from a contact breaker type of ignition system is *not* suitable.

Rotor arm and distributor cap
These are fitted to distribute the HT output as usual. The unit to which they are fitted will vary, however. An apparently conventional distributor may be fitted on the side of the engine, or there may be a differently shaped component mounted on the end of the camshaft, for example.

Typically, in such a unit the rotor arm is mounted on a stub shaft, which is pressed into a vibration-absorbing bush on the end of the camshaft. A normal distributor cap then covers the rotor.

Variations
Coils for individual or pairs of cylinders, mounted above or adjacent to the spark plugs, are another variation. Individual coils are usually mounted directly above the plug, resulting in no HT leads. Where a coil supplies a pair of cylinders, as in a vee engine configuration, there can be a spark on every crankshaft revolution, the unused spark occurring during the valve overlap period.

Where the ignition system is part of full engine management, the information from the various sensors will be used by the ECU to control fuel supply, as well as the ignition. The coolant sensor input, for example, provides essential information for mixture formulation and the Lambda probe (emission control) sensor.

There are also sensors to monitor inlet air flow volume and air temperature, which, although not directly linked to the ignition system, may result in changes to ignition system operation as the ECU monitors and controls all the engine functions.

Fault finding and maintenance

Basic coil ignition defects

See Table 4.1.

Electronic ignition defects

These are limited to component failure. On many systems, should a component fail, the system

Table 4.1 Basic coil ignition defects

Symptom	Possible cause
• Engine backfires when starting • Engine 'pinks' under load • Rough running and lack of power	Excessive advance: reset ignition timing
• Lack of power • Engine runs hot	Excessive retard: reset ignition timing
• Lack of power • Rough running • Engine runs on when the ignition is switched off	Pre-ignition due to combustion temperature being too high: check ignition timing, spark plug type and correct grade of fuel used
• Engine starts but runs erratically under throttle load; investigation reveals weak spark (at the plugs) and arcing at the contact breaker	Faulty capacitor: replace capacitor and contact breaker

resets itself to operate in a 'fail-safe' or 'limp-home' mode. This allows the driver to continue the journey with limited engine performance.

A major disadvantage of any electronic ignition system is the need for dedicated equipment to carry out fault diagnosis. In the case of programmed engine management systems, special equipment may be needed to reprogram the settings for the vehicle.

Routine maintenance

The contact breaker should be inspected every 10 000 km or so, and cleaned and adjusted if necessary. Take care when lubricating the moving parts to avoid an excess of oil or grease reaching the contacts. This would cause pitting or burning, resulting in faulty running or breakdown.

The insulated surfaces such as the distributor cap and the top of the coil should be cleaned, as dirt and dampness can cause short-circuits.

Spark plugs should be removed and cleaned at the same time as the contact breaker. Generally, the electrodes should be sandblasted to clean them. Once they are cleaned, the gap must be reset to its correct measurement. It is also important that the insulator and threads are clean and undamaged.

Spark plugs and contact breakers are usually changed at major services.

CHECK YOUR UNDERSTANDING

- In the basic ignition system the contact breaker points make and break the circuit between the battery and the ignition coil primary windings. They are opened and closed mechanically by a cam, timed to the engine crankshaft. When the points are *closed*, a current of approximately 5 A flows through the coil primary winding, building up a strong magnetic field, which surrounds both the primary and secondary windings.
- It takes a few milliseconds for the magnetic field to reach its maximum. When the contact breaker *opens*, the current flow ceases abruptly and the magnetic field collapses. As it does so, the magnetic force cuts across the secondary winding, inducing a momentary surge of thousands of volts in the many turns of wire. This high voltage is taken to the spark plugs.
- In electronic ignition systems the contact breaker is replaced by an electronic switch, which provides greater accuracy and reliability.
- Programmed electronic ignition systems also have a microcomputer, which carries out the functions of the mechanical and vacuum advance mechanisms. The ECU uses the input from sensors to calculate dwell and timing, based on data programmed into it by the manufacturer. The ECU can make constant changes to the ignition timing, and is very accurate. To meet new exhaust emission control regulations all new vehicles will soon be fitted with these systems.

REVISION EXERCISES AND QUESTIONS

1. Why are the leads from the distributor cap much thicker than the other cables in the system?
2. Which component changes the low-voltage battery current into the high voltage required at the spark plug?
3. Why is a high-voltage current needed at the spark plugs?
4. Which components sense speed and load conditions in the basic ignition system?
5. What is the purpose of the contact breaker points?
6. What does the term *dwell angle* mean?
7. What is the major advantage of electronic ignition, and how does it differ from the basic system?
8. What advantages does the programmed ignition system have over the basic electronic system, and how does it differ from it?
9. What is the difference between a 'hot' and a 'cold' spark plug?
10. What would be the symptoms of:
    i) over-advanced ignition timing
    ii) over-retarded ignition timing?

5 The petrol engine fuel supply

Introduction

This chapter examines the function of the components that make up the fuel supply system for a petrol engine (Figure 5.1). The fuel supply system consists of:

1. a storage tank;
2. a fuel pump or pumps;
3. a fuel filter;
4. delivery pipes.

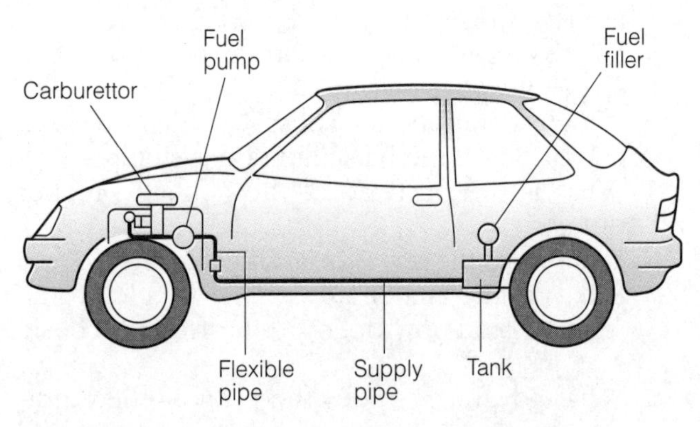

Figure 5.1 Main parts in a carburettor fuel system.

The fuel tank

The fuel tank stores the vehicle's fuel supply, and is nearly always at the opposite end of the vehicle from the engine for reasons of safety, space and weight distribution. This means that for most cars it is at the rear.

The tank has traditionally been made from mild steel sheet pressings, with welded joints and seams (Figure 5.2). Plastic is now in general use, which has the advantages that it is lighter, and it does not corrode. Plastic tanks can also be moulded into complex shapes that allow them to be fitted into uneven spaces, such as that between the rear axle and the body. This position provides additional protection from damage during accidents. Most tanks hold sufficient fuel to enable the vehicle to travel 500 km without refuelling.

Large tanks contain internal baffles to reduce fuel surge when the vehicle is cornering or braking hard. The energy in 50 litres of surging fuel could upset vehicle stability. Cars fitted with a catalytic converter must run on unleaded fuel, and they have a small-diameter inlet pipe to prevent the entry of a leaded petrol pump's filling nozzle.

Each tank has a small-bore outlet pipe leading to the engine, and a mounting point for the fuel level indicator. There is often a gauze filter on the outlet pipe pick-up. On many modern vehicles the fuel pump may be immersed in the petrol tank inside a **swirl pot**, which also has a filter screen.

The tank must be vented to allow atmospheric pressure to force the fuel through the outlet pipe and to prevent the tank from collapsing. On many vehicles the vent is in the filler cap. However, legislation in many countries now demands that no fumes or fuel should be able to escape from the tank to the atmosphere. As a result, fume control systems are fitted to capture the petrol fumes and feed them to the engine at suitable times for burning. Valves permit the entry of air to the tank, but they close to prevent fume leakage or petrol escape if the vehicle overturns.

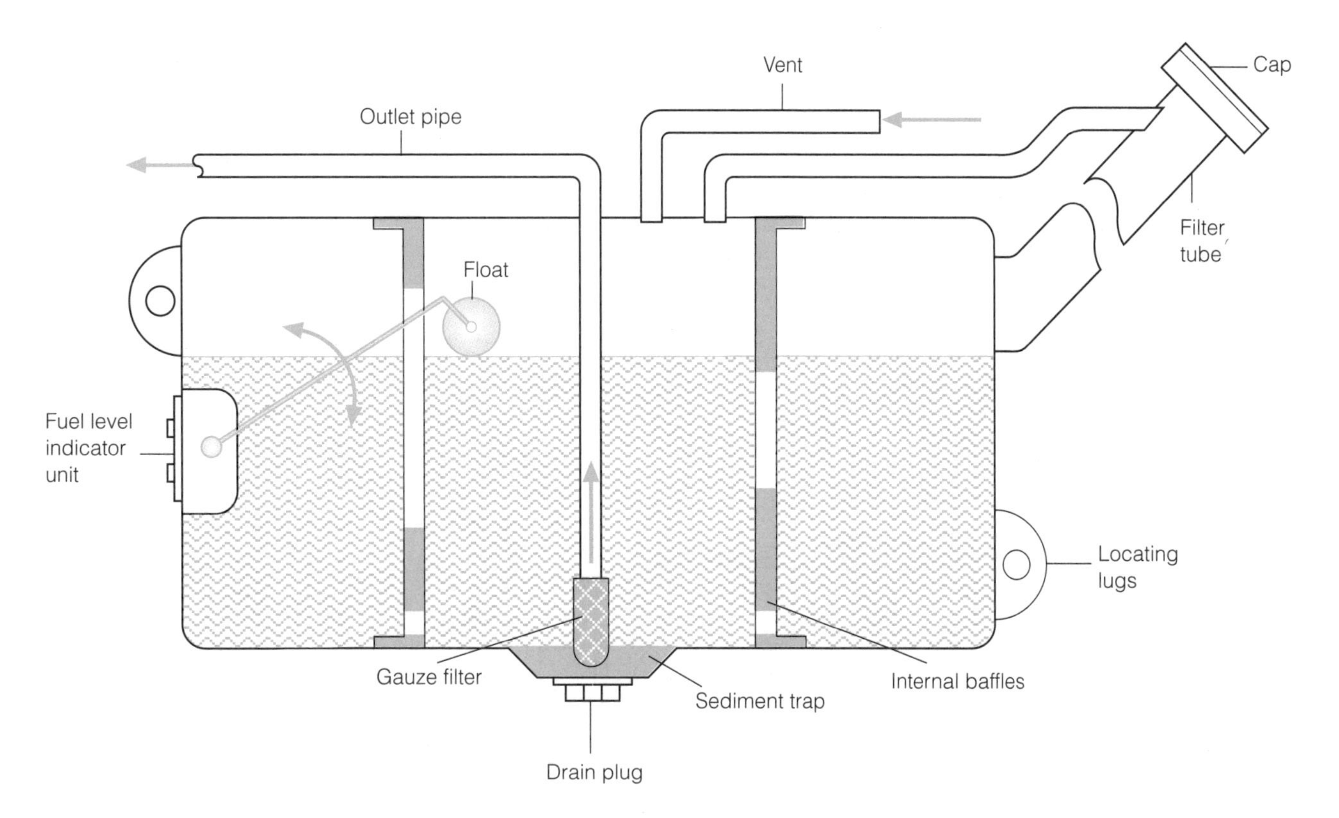

Figure 5.2 Detail of fuel tank construction.

The fuel pump

> The fuel pump transfers fuel from the tank to the carburettor or the fuel injection system.

There are two basic types of fuel pump: **mechanical pumps** operated by the engine itself, and **electric pumps**.

Mechanical fuel pumps

> Most cars with carburettors use this type of pump (Figure 5.3). It is driven directly by the camshaft or an auxiliary shaft, and is bolted to the outside of the engine.

The pump is made from a die-cast aluminium alloy in two main parts. Under a removable cover there is a fine gauze filter and sediment chamber, through which the fuel must pass.

An eccentric lobe on the engine camshaft actuates the operating arm of the pump, which moves the diaphragm up and down. On the downward movement of the diaphragm a depression is created in the upper pumping chamber. Petrol, under atmospheric pressure, flows into the chamber. As the eccentric rotates it allows the return spring to force the diaphragm upwards. As it does so, the inlet valve closes, the outlet valve opens, and petrol is forced into the carburettor float chamber.

The arm is in two parts; the bell-crank lever is held in contact with the eccentric by a small return spring. The inner part transmits the force from the bell-crank to the diaphragm spindle. Having two parts enables the diaphragm to remain stationary when the float chamber is full, but permits the bell-crank lever to continue moving up and down. When fuel is used and the coil spring moves the diaphragm upwards, the driving faces will again make contact, and pumping action resumes.

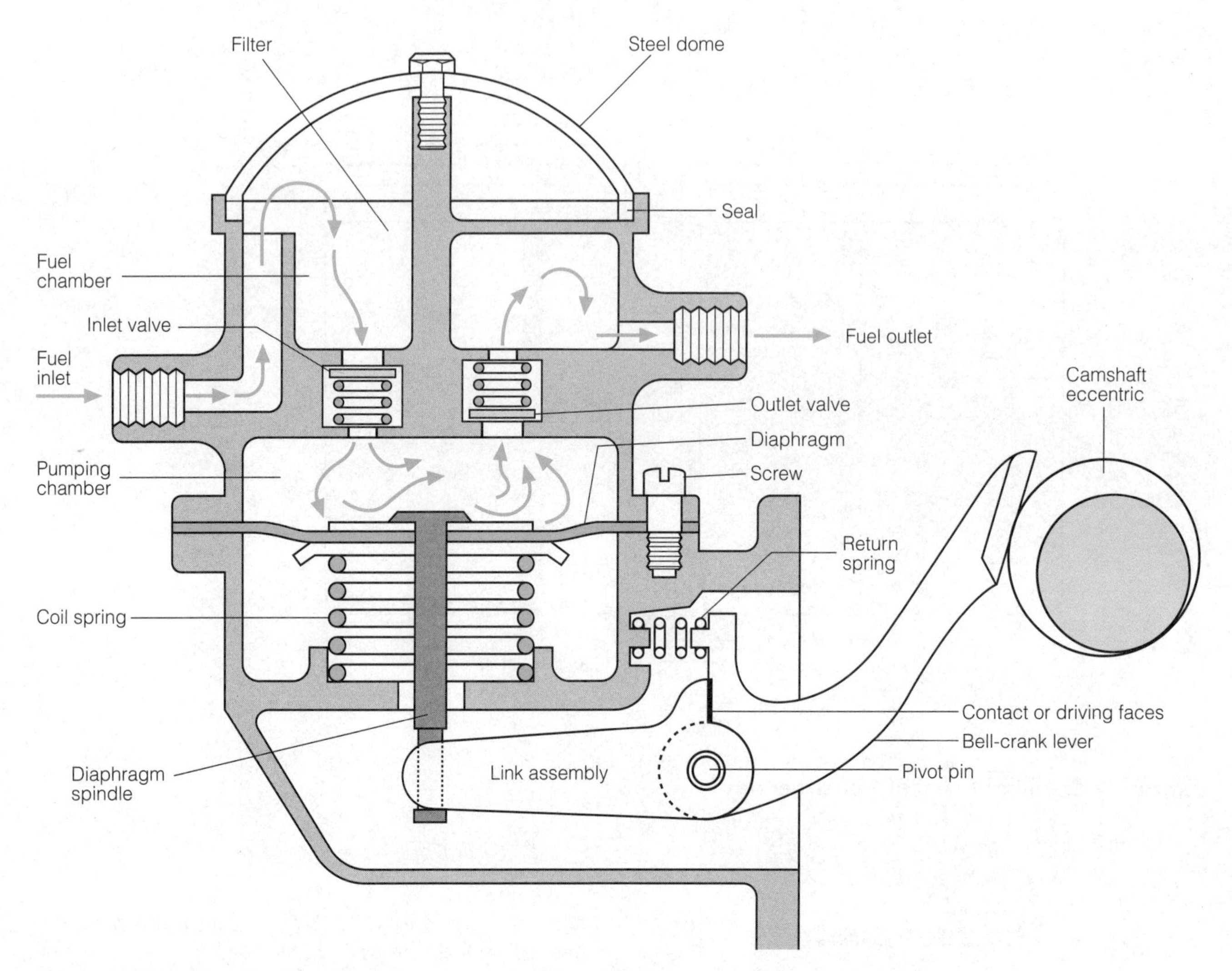

Figure 5.3 Mechanical fuel pump.

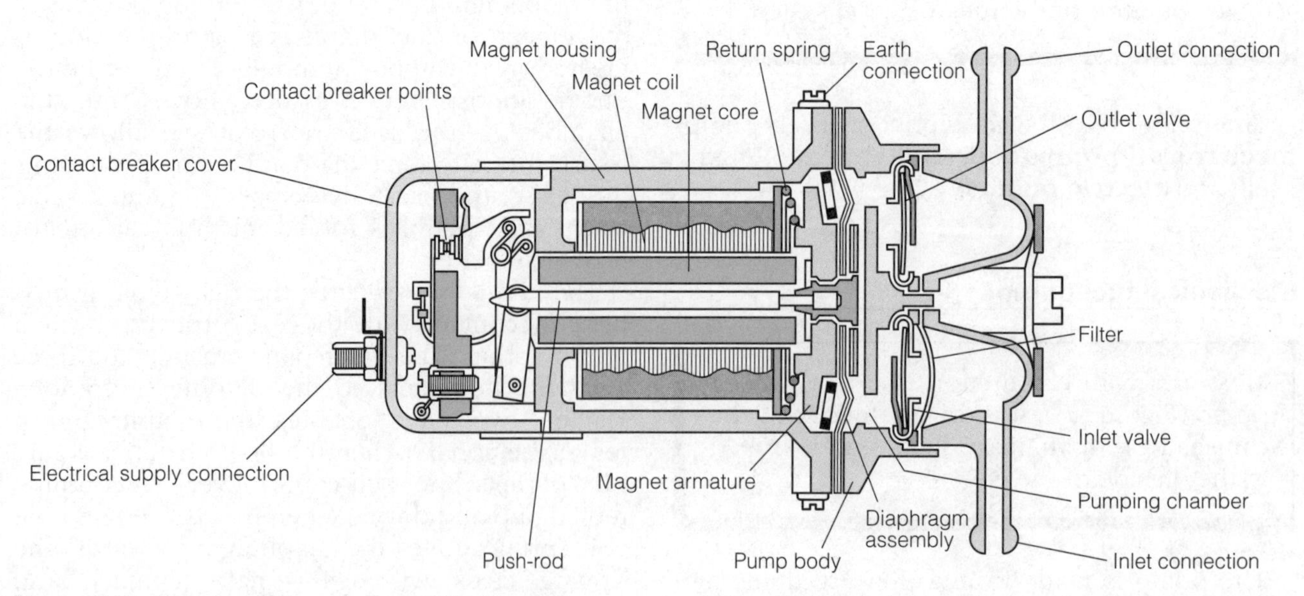

Figure 5.4 Cross-section of electric fuel pump.

Electric fuel pumps

The electric pump for use with carburettors was at one time very popular, as it could be fitted in almost any position between the tank and the engine (Figure 5.4). But it is more expensive and less reliable than the mechanical pump.

The pumping chamber is similar to that in the mechanical pump. The pump body contains an electric solenoid, which receives current from the ignition switch through a pair of contact breakers in the pump. One of the contacts is stationary, and the other is connected to the diaphragm by a control rod. When the contacts are closed, current flows through the solenoid and creates a magnetic field, which attracts an iron disc called an **armature**. This disc is attached to the underside of the diaphragm. When the disc is attracted to the solenoid the diaphragm is also drawn inwards; the volume in the pumping chamber is increased, and so fuel flows from the tank to fill the space. During this time the control rod has moved with the diaphragm and has opened the contacts. The solenoid is no longer activated. The diaphragm return spring now forces the diaphragm outwards, expelling fuel through the outlet valve to the carburettor. The control rod moves back with the diaphragm and closes the contacts: thus the whole cycle is repeated.

If no fuel is needed by the float chamber the diaphragm remains in a mid-position. When the spring has pushed all the fuel out of the chamber the contacts are again 'made' and pumping resumes.

Immersed electric fuel pumps

On fuel-injected engines an inexpensive, hydrodynamic electric fuel pump is often used, and may be installed in the fuel tank (Figure 5.5). The pump is totally immersed in fuel, and as petrol is not combustible in these conditions, there is no danger of fire.

The pump is located on one end of the motor. The pump body is eccentric to the rotor, which gives a variable space (Figure 5.6). Metal rollers

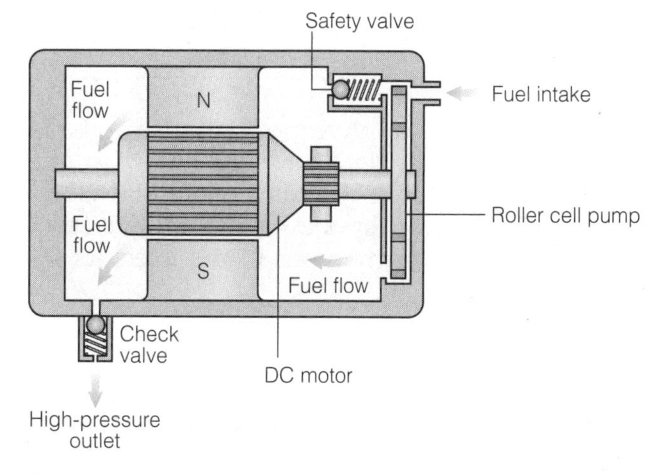

Figure 5.5 Hydrodynamic fuel pump.

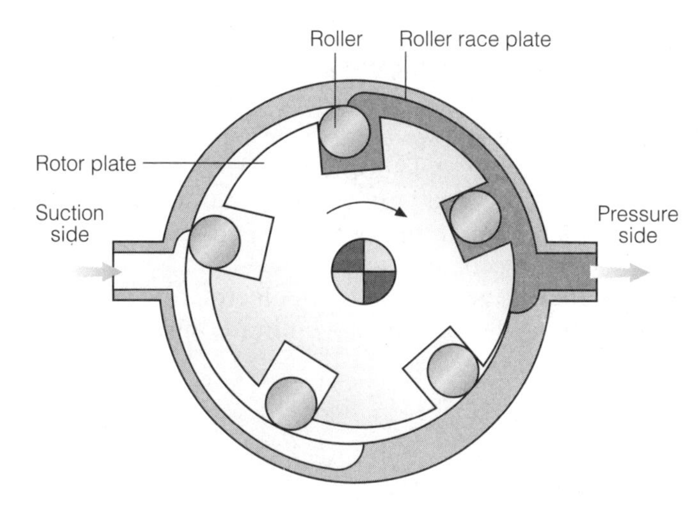

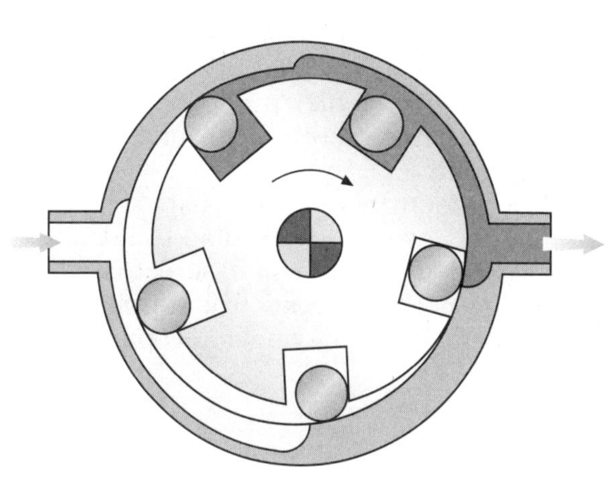

Figure 5.6 Roller cell pump.

located in the rotor are free to move and fly outwards under centrifugal force. Fuel from the inlet is trapped in the spaces between the rollers. As the rotor turns, the spaces reduce adjacent to the outlet, and fuel is forced out of the pump.

Pipelines

Both copper and tin-plated steel pipes have been used for fuel piping, but these have largely given way to plastic materials. The piping used must be rigid enough to retain its shape under atmospheric pressure, and must be capable of being connected without risk of leaks from system pressure. Many countries have requirements for fire and wear resistance.

Where a rigid supply pipe is used a flexible link must be provided for connection to the engine to allow for engine movement and vibration. Fuel injection systems use braided (protected), flexible supply pipes to the injectors for the same reason.

Fault finding and maintenance

Here are a few important points:

1. If the engine will not start, and lack of petrol is suspected, the first step is to check that there is fuel in the tank.
2. Sometimes more than one pump is fitted. When diagnosing fuel supply problems on any modern vehicle check the supply system specification; a fuel pump outside the tank does not necessarily mean that there is not one inside!
3. Most modern petrol pumps are reliable. They are not usually repairable, and must be renewed if faulty. Make sure that the tank venting is correct, and that supply voltage is adequate, before buying a new pump.
4. Where filters are fitted, ensure that they are clean or are passing a full flow of fuel. The filter in the tank, or even the tank itself, may need cleaning if dirty fuel has been used.
5. Pipe blockage or a loose connection on the suction side may both cause low or non-existent fuel delivery.

Petrol is highly flammable. Never use naked lights or smoke where there is petrol or petrol fumes. The fumes in a petrol tank are very dangerous.

CHECK YOUR UNDERSTANDING

- The fuel supply system consists of a tank, pipes, a pump or pumps, and a carburettor or fuel injection system.
- Two types of fuel pump are available: mechanical and electric.
- Fuel tanks and pipes are commonly made of plastic on modern vehicles.
- The fuel pump works on the principle of pressure difference. Many use a diaphragm to alter the volume of a chamber and therefore the pressure.
- The pumping pressure on diaphragm pumps is created by the spring below the diaphragm.
- Hydrodynamic electric pumps rely on an eccentric rotor enlarging and reducing chambers to create the pressure difference.
- Petrol is highly flammable; do not use a naked light, smoke or weld where there is petrol or petrol fumes present.

REVISION EXERCISES AND QUESTIONS

1 Why is it necessary to use a flexible pipe to connect the fuel supply system to the engine?
2 Why is the fuel tank vented to atmosphere?
3 Which component determines the fuel pump's delivery pressure?
4 State *one* advantage of an electric fuel pump.
5 Why is the fuel tank venting controlled on a modern vehicle?

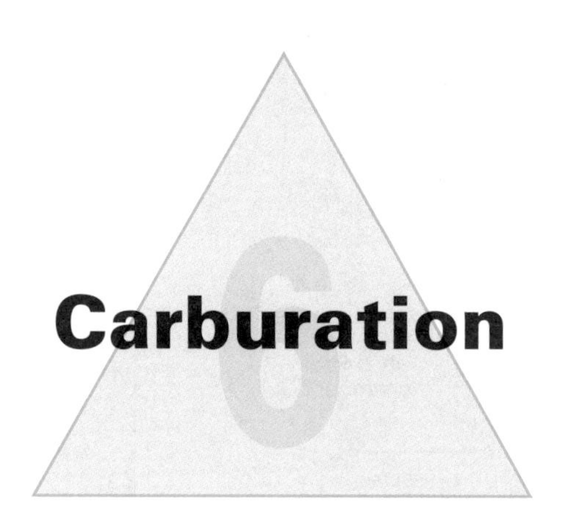

Carburation

Introduction

Petrol will not burn without the oxygen contained in air. The function of the carburettor is to control the quantity and proportion of petrol and air entering the engine cylinders, to control power output and speed. The carburettor is also required to atomise the petrol into a fine spray of very small droplets that will readily vaporise into a consistent, combustible mixture.

This chapter explores the working principle of the carburettor. It is not the intention to describe the precise details of any one make of carburettor, but rather to help build up an understanding of the basic operating principles.

Combustion of petrol

The carburettor must:

- atomise the petrol into a very fine spray to ensure complete mixing with the air, under a variety of engine speed/load conditions;
- provide the correct air/fuel mixture for all operating requirements, including cold starting and full acceleration, with maximum fuel economy;
- allow the engine to idle smoothly, and have no flat spots when the throttle is opened;
- be adjustable to suit different climatic conditions, and meet local exhaust emission regulations.

The proportions of fuel and air are considered in terms of their mass. The reason for measuring the mixture strength by mass is that mass is constant, whereas volume varies with temperature as air and petrol expand and contract with temperature change, and weight varies with pressure changes caused by altitude or atmospheric conditions.

The mass of air per kilogram of fuel is called the **air/fuel ratio**. Although an engine would run on a wide range of different ratios, it would not run economically, or with maximum efficiency. The chemically correct ratio for complete combustion is 14.5 kg of air to 1 kg of fuel. More air than this would make a **lean mixture**, and less air would result in a **rich mixture**. Table 6.1 lists some typical mixture ratios for the basic type of carburettor that this chapter is examining. Note that lean burn engines (see later) may run on leaner mixtures.

Modern engines, particularly those with engine management systems and catalytic converters, run on mixtures that can be either slightly weak or a little rich, depending on circumstances. In general, however, it is still true that a weak mixture makes an engine run hot, while a richer mix makes for cool running and increased fuel consumption. Both conditions may cause some power loss.

The ratio of the mixture entering the engine will affect the combustion process and also, therefore, the composition of the exhaust gases. Legislation regarding exhaust emissions has led to increasingly complicated carburettors, which will allow the vehicles to which they are fitted to pass quite stringent emission tests.

Table 6.1 Typical air/fuel ratios

Stage	Engine function	Ratio
1	Cold starting	9 : 1
2	Idling	10 : 1
3	Economy	16 : 1
4	Acceleration	12 : 1
5	Maximum power	12 : 1

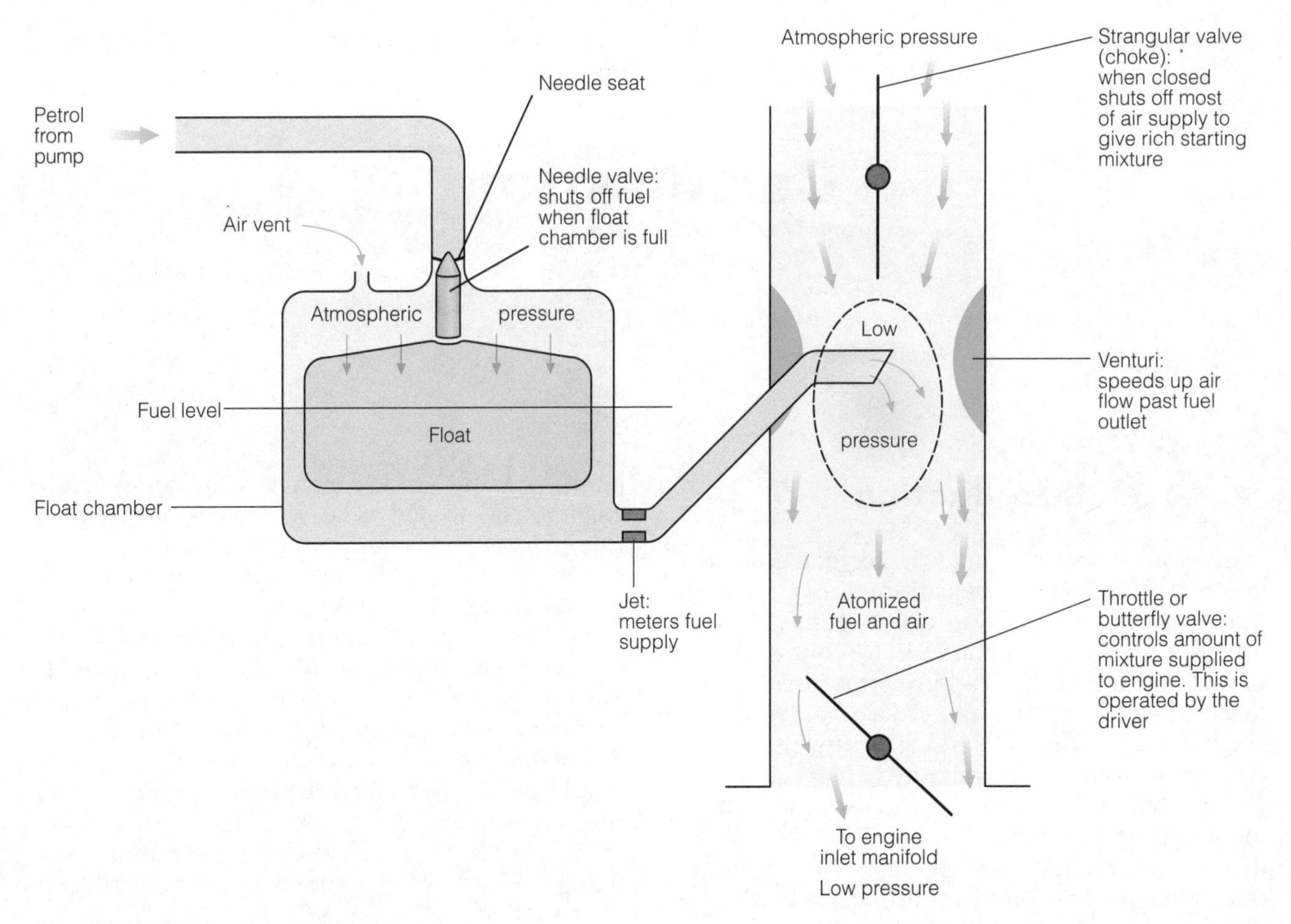

Figure 6.1 Basic simple jet carburettor.

The basic carburettor

The basic carburettor consists of two main parts: a **float chamber** to supply the fuel, and a **choke tube** in which the fuel is mixed with air (Figure 6.1).

The level in the float chamber is controlled by a **float**. When the fuel pump operates, fuel enters the float chamber through the needle valve, and as the fuel level rises, so does the float. The float lifts the needle until it closes the supply. The correct level of fuel is always below the level of the fuel outlet. An air vent allows the float chamber to fill and atmospheric pressure to act upon the petrol in the float chamber.

When the engine is turned, the pistons move downwards on their induction strokes and create a depression in the inlet manifold. Air flows into the manifold through the carburettor's choke tube, passing through a specially shaped restriction called the **venturi**. In the venturi the air speed increases, resulting in a depression at this point.

The outlet from the float chamber is placed in the middle of this depression. Atmospheric pressure forces fuel from the float chamber into the depression in the venturi. As the fuel is hit by the high-velocity air flowing through the venturi it is atomised into a fine spray, before it is drawn into the inlet manifold. **Atomisation** is a term used to describe the process whereby the liquid fuel is broken up into extremely small droplets. In the inlet manifold it is vaporised (it becomes a vapour or gas), and it passes into whichever cylinder has an inlet valve open.

The amount of air/fuel mixture drawn into the cylinders depends on how far the throttle valve is opened. On a vehicle with a basic carburettor this is controlled by the **accelerator pedal**.

The simple carburettor will provide a correct mixture for only one air speed through the choke tube. Because of the different flow characteristics of petrol and air, it will provide a rich mixture at high speeds, when a high quantity of air is passing through, and a weak mixture at low speeds, when a small amount of air is flowing (Figure 6.2). To overcome this disadvantage and give efficient carburation on a variable-speed engine, some form of **compensation** must be used.

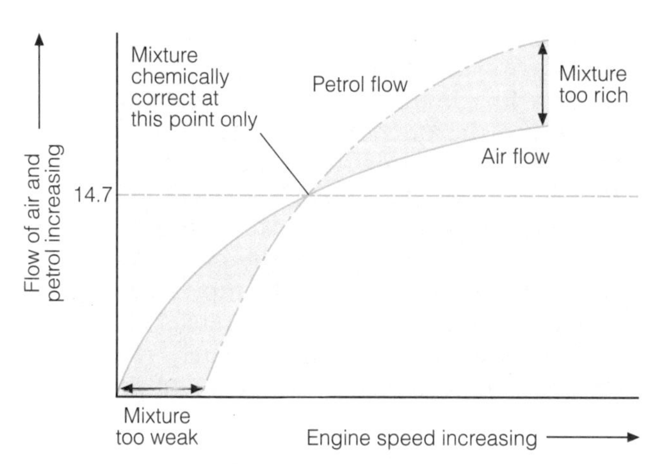

Figure 6.2 This graph shows what would happen if a simple single-jet carburettor was fitted to a variable-speed engine.

Fixed-jet carburettors

Compensation enables a fixed-jet carburettor to supply a mixture of air and fuel to the engine, in the correct proportions for proper combustion, under all conditions of load and speed.

Compensation may be achieved in various ways:

1. by using air bleeds;
2. by using fuel-metering jets;
3. by supplying metered quantities of fuel to the point of highest depression in the choke tube.

Both air and fuel are **metered** or measured by passing them through accurately sized drillings of various sizes. These metered drillings are usually in the form of removable, screwed inserts made from brass.

Main jet operation

In the air-bleed type of carburettor, petrol flows through the **main jet** and gathers in the spray tube at the same level as in the float chamber (Figure 6.3). The openings at the top of the spray tube are subject to engine intake depression. Inside the spray tube is the **emulsion tube**, which has a series of openings, and an **air correction jet** at the top.

As engine speed increases the fuel well is emptied of liquid fuel by the increasing depression. The fuel mixes with air flowing into the air correction jet and through the openings in the emulsion tube. These openings are uncovered as the fuel is used, allowing increasing amounts of air into the fuel, and weakening the mixture.

As further fuel flow is restricted by the main jet, the air/fuel ratio will gradually weaken as engine speed and air flow increase.

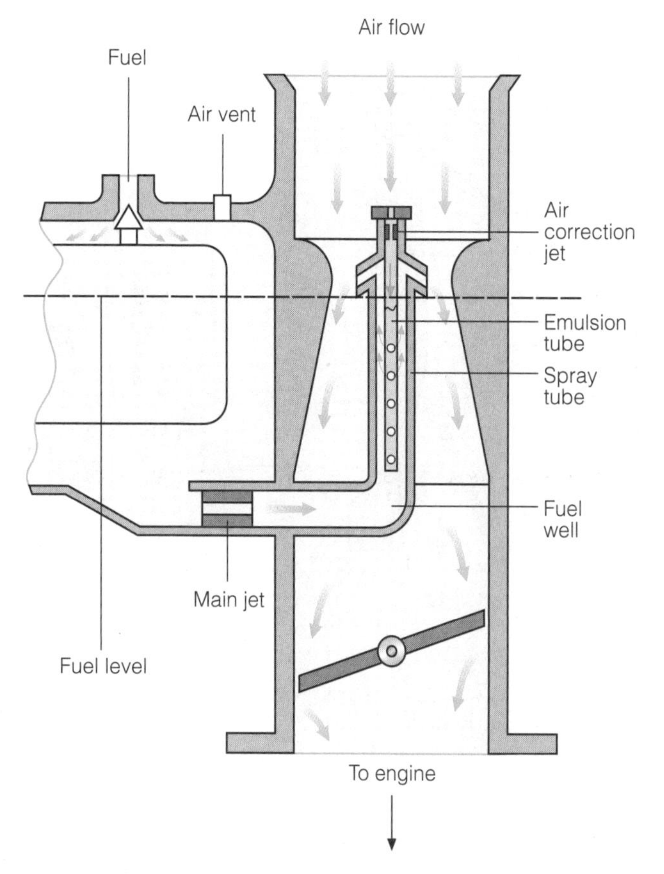

Figure 6.3 Air-bleed system of compensation.

Cold starting

When starting from cold there are two problems:

1. The air speed is very low, causing the mixture to be weak.
2. A proportion of the atomised fuel condenses onto the cold surfaces inside the intake manifold, instead of being vaporised to improve combustion.

As a result, the normal air/fuel ratio of about 15 : 1 would be too weak for normal combustion, and a method of enrichment must be used.

This often takes the form of a **choke butterfly valve** or **strangler** (Figure 6.4). It consists simply of a butterfly valve, which restricts the air flow into the carburettor. It may be manually controlled or fully automatic. Invariably the choke is linked to the throttle so that when it is operated the throttle is opened slightly.

Automatic chokes are set by opening the throttle before starting to permit the mechanism to operate. The choke is controlled by a bimetallic spring, which closes the butterfly when the engine is cold and opens it fully when it is at operating temperature.

The spring is heated, either electrically when the ignition is turned on, or by the engine coolant.

Bypass starting device

An alternative to the choke valve is an independent air/fuel supply inside the carburettor, which is also controlled manually or automatically. Mixture is supplied from a separate petrol jet and air passage to an outlet on the manifold side of the throttle valve. A typical method of control is by a rotary disc valve.

Cold-start system requirements

It is very important that cold-starting devices are returned to the off position as soon as possible. With cold-starting air/fuel ratios as low as 9 : 1, excessive use of the system will result in an over-rich mixture, resulting in poor running or even stalling, and unburnt fuel in the cylinders. As the inlet manifold begins to warm up, fuel that has condensed onto the interior surfaces will evaporate, making the condition much worse. An excess of fuel can also wash away lubricant and contaminate the engine oil, a condition shown by an increasing oil level. This is typical of vehicles on intermittent, short-journey work.

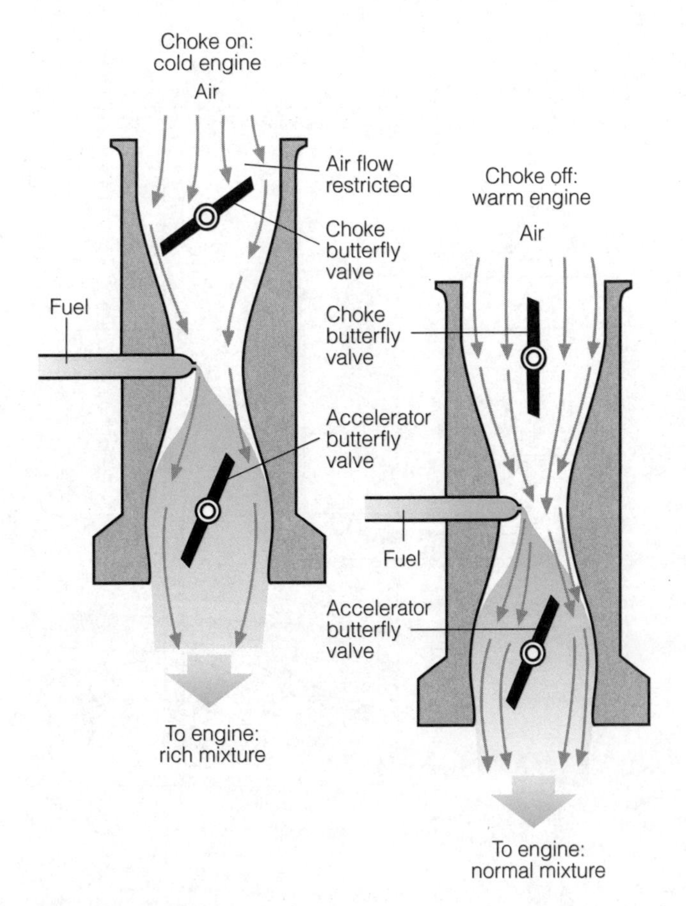

Figure 6.4 Choke operation.

Idling system

When the engine is idling, air speed through the venturi is not fast enough to create sufficient

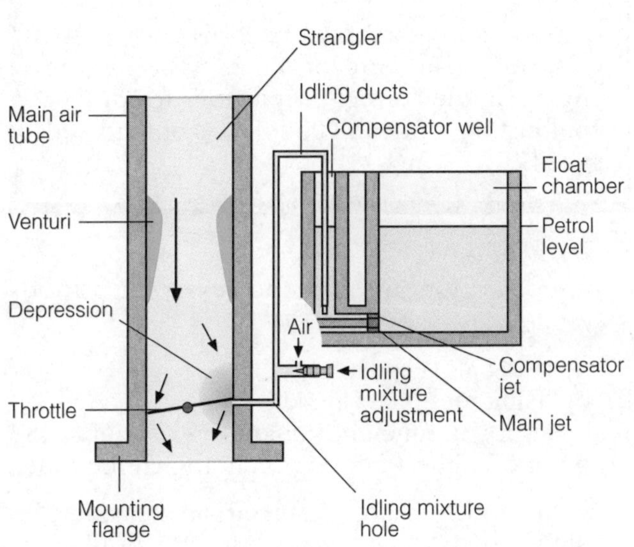

Figure 6.5 Slow-running jet.

depression for fuel to flow from the spray tube. But the speed of air around the slightly open throttle does create a high depression, and the idling outlet is situated just below the gap in this area (Figure 6.5).

This system operates in the same way as the main jet, supplying just enough fuel to keep the engine ticking over. On a basic carburettor there is an adjusting screw to vary the idling air/fuel ratio, the amount of mixture supplied to the engine being set by the throttle opening.

Progression system

The first increase of engine speed above idle does not raise the depression in the choke tube to the level of the spray tube outlet. Without more fuel the engine would not run properly, and a **flat spot** – an engine hesitation – would occur.

To overcome this problem, a fuel outlet is provided a short way up the choke tube in a position where it is influenced by depression only when the throttle is slightly open (Figure 6.6). This system supplies extra fuel to increase engine speed above idle, until the depression rises to the spray tube and the main jet can operate.

Accelerator pump

Drivers demand that their vehicles accelerate rapidly and smoothly. If the throttle is opened suddenly there will be an instant increase in the flow of air. Because of the difference in flow characteristics between fuel and air, the fuel will not be immediately available and, as before, a flat spot will result.

> To overcome this sudden weakening of the mixture a charge of fuel is injected into the air stream from a device called the **accelerator pump**.

Figure 6.7 shows one of several designs. In this example a loose-fitting plunger is connected to the throttle. Sudden opening of the throttle will push the plunger rapidly down its cylinder, forcing fuel past the delivery valve and into the venturi. This sudden injection will provide sufficient fuel to raise the engine speed. During gentle operation of the throttle, fuel is able to escape past the loose plunger, and no enrichment takes place. The cylinder is recharged whenever the throttle is released.

Full load enrichment

Some engines are designed to be used at maximum engine revolutions. At such speeds the air/fuel ratio normally weakens, and prolonged high-speed use could result in engine overheating.

To provide a little enrichment at these speeds many carburettors have a metered fuel supply outlet in the top of the choke tube, where the depression will be felt at high speed. Alternatively,

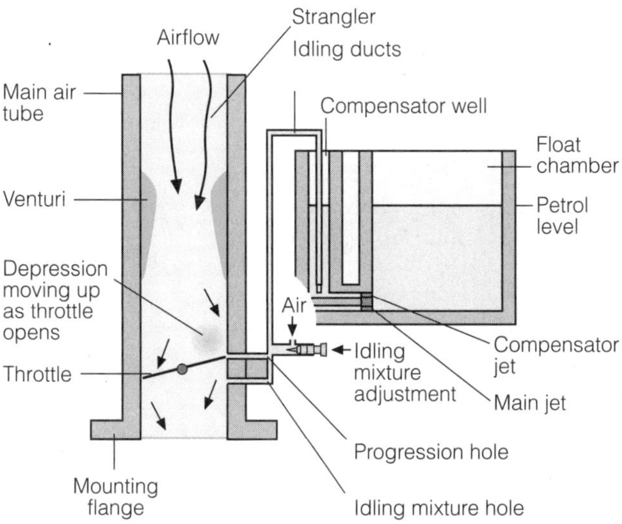

Airflow
Strangler
Idling ducts
Main air tube
Compensator well
Float chamber
Venturi
Petrol level
Depression moving up as throttle opens
Air
Idling mixture adjustment
Compensator jet
Throttle
Main jet
Progression hole
Mounting flange
Idling mixture hole

Figure 6.6 Progression jet.

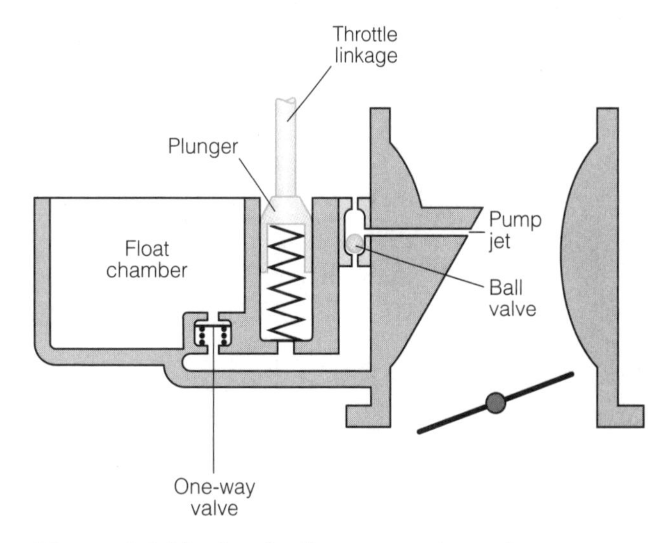

Figure 6.7 Mechanically operated accelerator pump.

there may be a system controlled by mechanical linkage.

The use of weak mixtures

Weak mixtures in general give less power than the correct or optimum mixture of 14.5 : 1. Under conditions of full throttle weak mixtures could cause engine damage. This is because a weak mixture burns at a slower rate and causes residual gases to become hotter.

Under cruising conditions with a part-open throttle and light engine load, the petrol engine can run on a weaker mixture with no danger of overheating, and any power loss is not noticeable. A weaker mixture produces no carbon monoxide, and improves the vehicle's fuel consumption. Modern engines have to meet stringent exhaust emission laws, and this has resulted in manufacturers developing what are known as **lean burn** engines. Under normal driving conditions it is rare for the driver to require maximum power from the engine. Lean burn engines make use of the benefits of a slightly weaker mixture without causing the engine to overheat.

Economy devices

Most carburettors are fitted with some form of economy device. The device in Figure 6.8 is influenced by manifold depression, which increases as the throttle opening decreases. The device works by allowing more air to 'bleed' into the jet outlet, and weakening the mixture at part-throttle openings.

Constant-vacuum carburettors

An alternative method of providing compensation is by providing a constant vacuum or depression (Figure 6.9). In this type of carburettor the choke or venturi area is variable and is controlled by a movable piston, as in the illustration (or sometimes by a pivoting 'plate').

The piston, or the rubber diaphragm attached to it, is subjected, through a small orifice, to the venturi depression on its upper surface, and to atmospheric pressure below. The piston and its spring are lifted by the difference between these pressures, and the piston takes up a position of equilibrium where its weight is balanced by the depression at the venturi. The piston therefore rises and falls as necessary to maintain a constant depression at any engine speed or throttle opening. If the venturi depression increases,

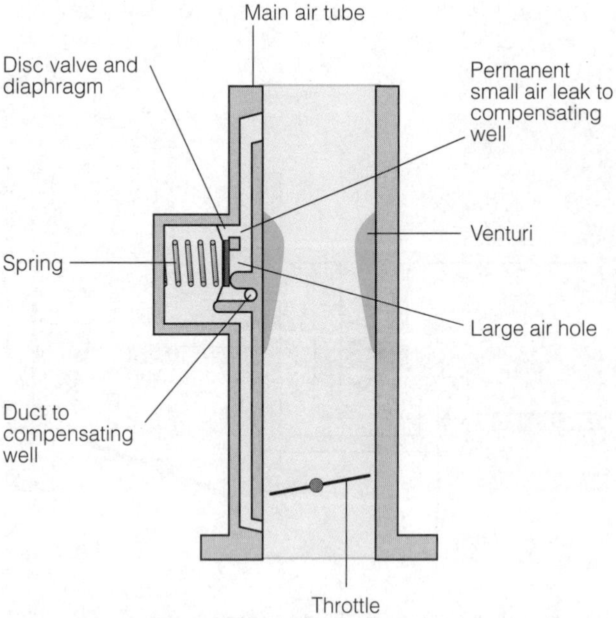

Main air tube
Disc valve and diaphragm
Permanent small air leak to compensating well
Venturi
Spring
Large air hole
Duct to compensating well
Throttle

Figure 6.8 Economy device.

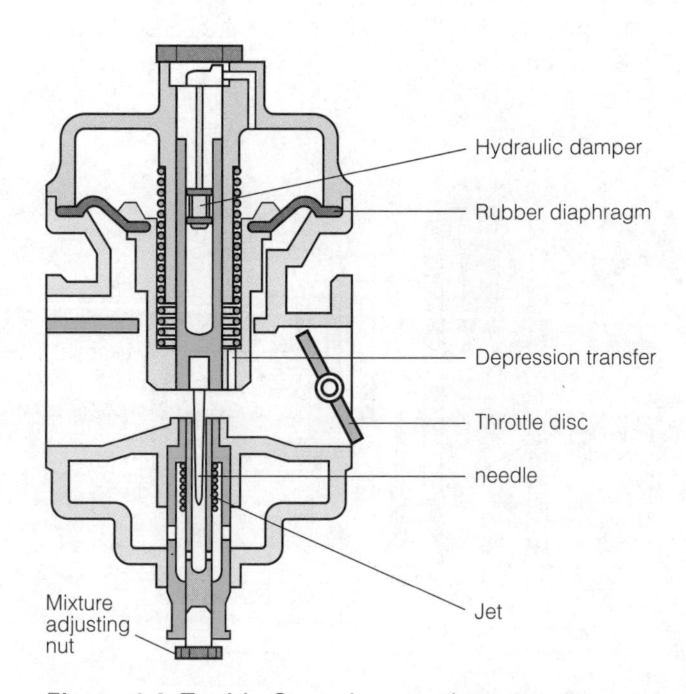

Figure 6.9 Zenith–Stromberg carburettor.

atmospheric pressure will lift the piston, enlarging the venturi as it does so and reducing the depression, until a state of balance is achieved.

This provides conditions similar to the simple carburettor in that there is a constant air speed and depression over the fuel jet. Here, however, the venturi area is increasing and decreasing to adjust the amount of air entering the intake. The jet area must also be regulated to suit the varying venturi size to give a constant mixture strength. This is achieved by having a tapered needle attached to the bottom of the piston and moving inside the jet. As the needle rises it increases the size of the jet opening and increases the amount of fuel that can enter the air stream. In this way it maintains a constant mixture strength.

Cold starting

The simplest method is achieved by lowering the jet. The jet movement is controlled by a pull cable.

When starting, the engine turns over at about 500 rpm, resulting in low air speed and very little depression. Because there is little difference between the pressure above or below the carburettor piston, it remains at the bottom of its chamber. Only a small quantity of air is able to mix with an increased amount of fuel, so enriching the mixture.

Carburettor and manifold layout

Attempts have been made to improve the efficiency of the engine by making the inlet ports and passages between the carburettor and the cylinders as short as possible. It does not matter whether the choke tube is horizontal, vertical or at an angle in between, as long as the float chamber is vertical. Many different carburettor versions have been used in the past, but the downdraught type has been favoured in recent years because the air/fuel mixture is assisted by gravity to enter the manifold, and a larger venturi can be employed. Figure 6.10 shows three layouts.

Manifold systems

To improve volumetric efficiency the inlet manifold must be designed to distribute the mixture as evenly as possible and assist vaporisation.

Inlet manifolds are usually made of cast iron, aluminium alloy or, more recently, plastic. The bore of the manifold should be the same diameter as the inlet port. It should have no sharp bends, as this would cause some momentum of the

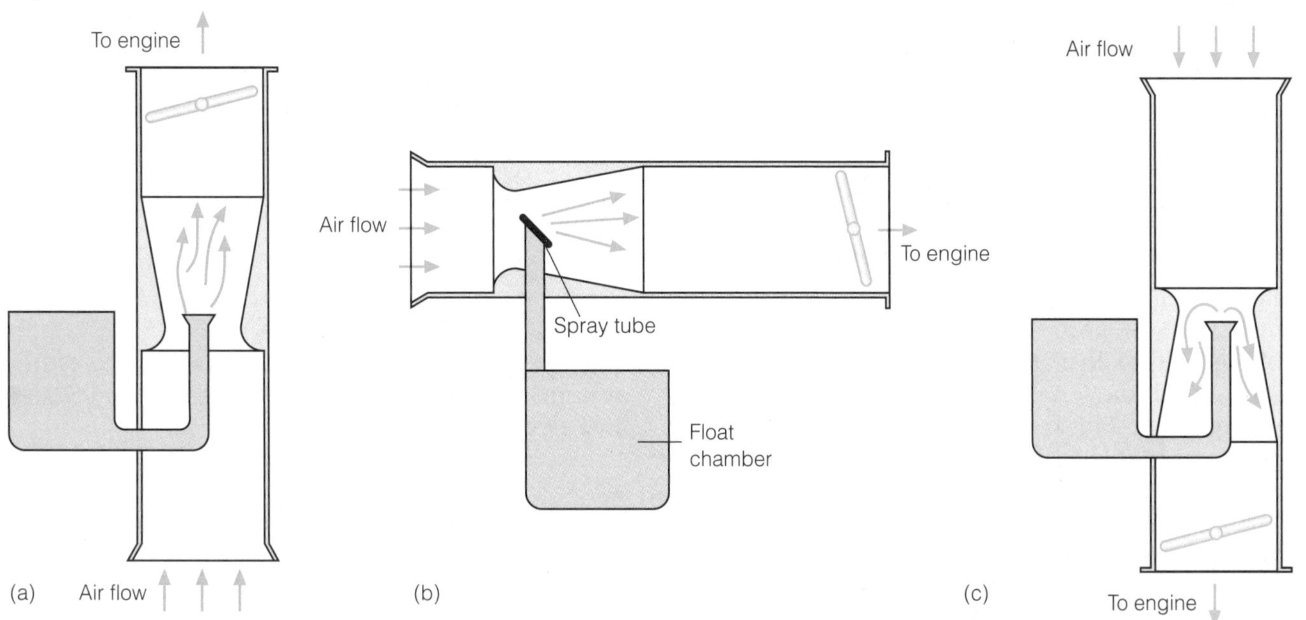

Figure 6.10 Carburettor layouts: (a) up-draught; (b) side-draught; (c) down-draught.

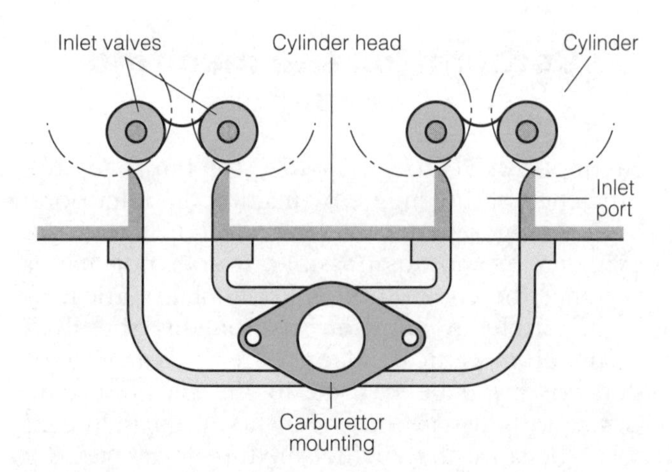

Figure 6.11 Inlet manifold for four-cylinder engine.

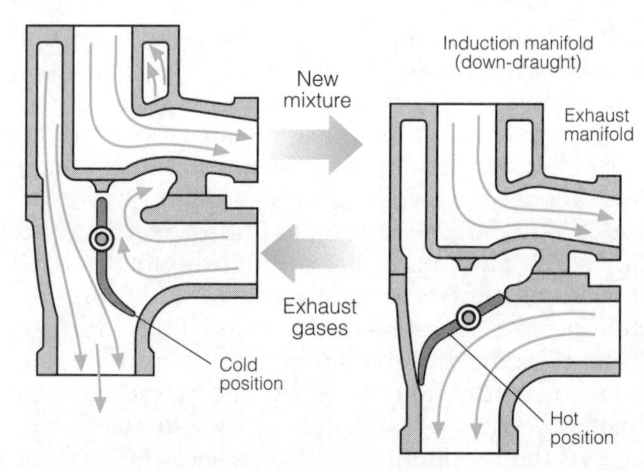

Figure 6.12 Use of exhaust gases to heat the inlet manifold.

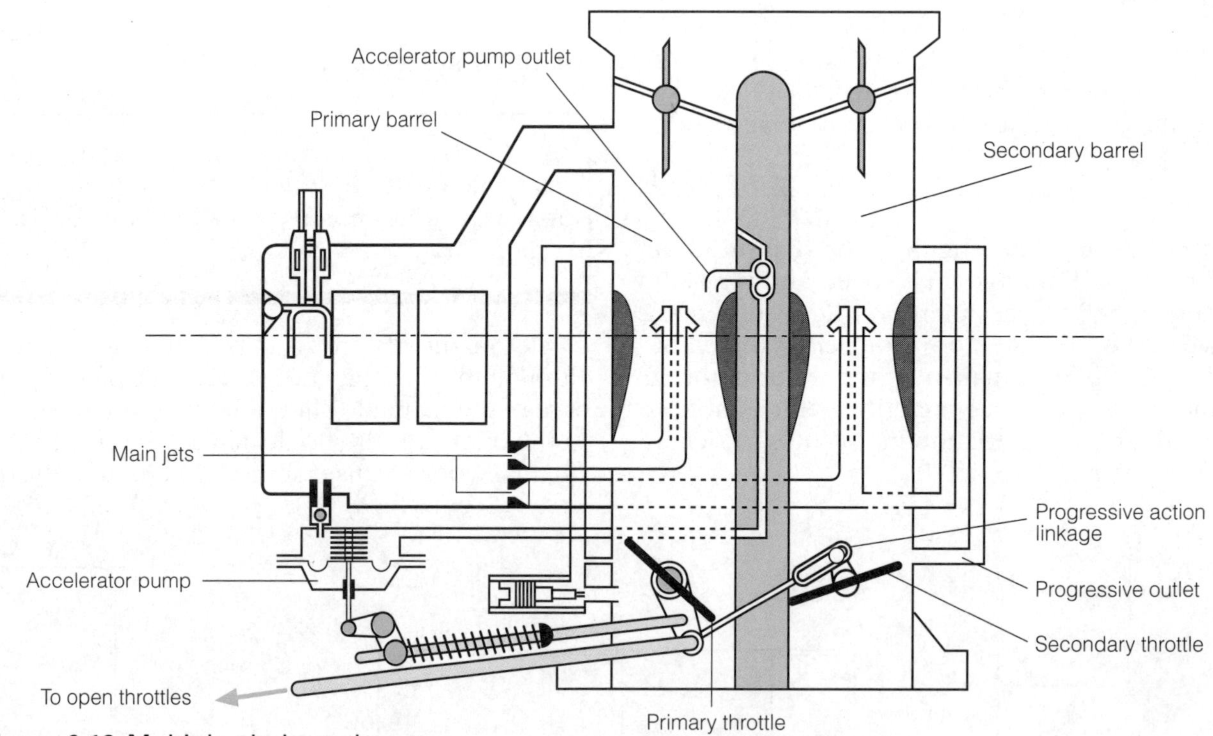

Figure 6.13 Multiple-choke carburettor.

mixture to be lost, fuel would condense on the bends, and uneven mixture distribution would be exaggerated. Figure 6.11 shows an example of inlet manifold layout.

To assist vaporisation as soon as possible after starting, some inlet manifolds are heated by the exhaust gases (Figure 6.12). This is called a **hot spot**, and is controlled by a valve to prevent overheating of the mixture, and consequent loss of density and volumetric efficiency, when the engine reaches operating temperature. Other systems include heating with the cooling water and electrical heaters.

Multiple carburettors and multiple-choke carburettors

To increase volumetric efficiency it is possible to increase the size of the choke tube and venturi, thus allowing more air and fuel to enter the engine cylinders. Unfortunately, this is not as good an option as it appears to be, as a large-diameter choke tube leads to poor atomisation and rough running at low engine speeds because of poor depression at the venturi. Manufacturers have to find the optimum size of choke for their engines, or fit multiple carburettors, or a single carburettor with multiple chokes to increase efficiency and output.

To improve volumetric efficiency, power output and economy, high-performance engines may have multiple carburettors: the usual arrangement is for a four-cylinder engine to have two and six-cylinder units to have three. Although advantageous, such installations are expensive, and require expert tuning.

> To save space and reduce costs, manufacturers now fit multiple-choke carburettors with two, three or four chokes (Figure 6.13). Each choke has its own jet system drawing fuel from a common float chamber. Four choke units may be used on six- or eight-cylinder vee engines.

Air filtration

Engines consume large amounts of air, and that air is often heavily contaminated with dust. If the dust was allowed to enter the engine, considerable wear would take place. Tests have shown that the wear on the cylinder walls can increase tenfold on engines working in dusty environments without air filters.

> Modern air filters serve three important functions:
>
> - They remove dust and other particles from the air before it enters the carburettor.
> - They silence the sound of the air entering the intake.
> - They act as a flashback arrester when a cold or poorly tuned engine 'coughs' a flame back through the carburettor.

Although there are many different designs, the two types shown in Figures 6.14 and 6.15 are the most common.

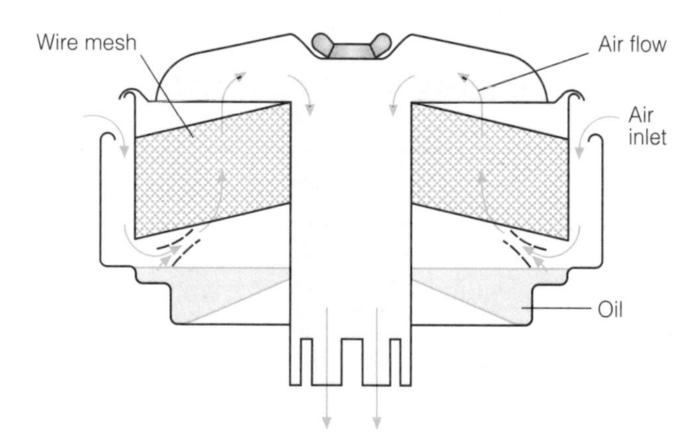

Figure 6.15 Oil bath air cleaner.

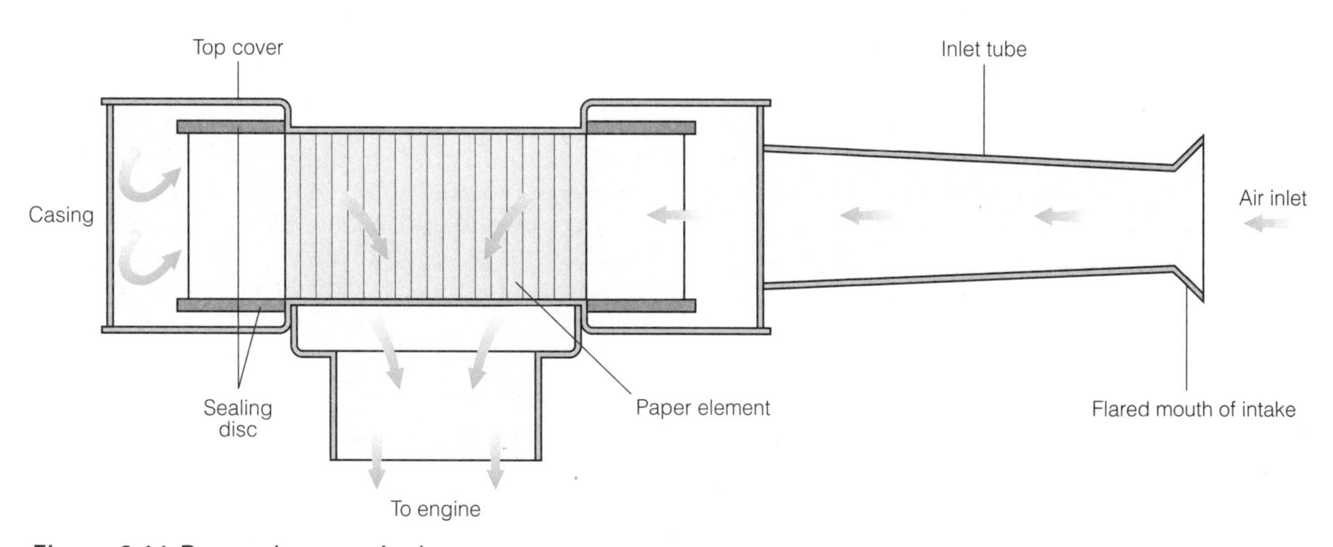

Figure 6.14 Paper element air cleaner.

Paper element air cleaner
This is used on light vehicles. A replaceable paper element, designed so that it does not restrict air flow, is fitted in a pressed steel or plastic housing, which is usually mounted on top of the carburettor. The element must be replaced when dirty, or at the specified service intervals.

Oil bath air cleaner
This is very effective in dusty conditions. Air flows into the filter through an oil tray and then through an oil-impregnated, fine wire filter before entering the engine. Most of the dirt is trapped in the oil tray, then the air reverses direction to flow upwards, when the remainder is trapped in the oiled wire mesh. The oil requires changing, and the mesh needs to be cleaned at regular intervals. Apart from renewing the oil, this type of filter requires no replacement parts.

Fault finding and maintenance

> There is very little to go wrong with the modern carburettor; defects are generally due to dirt or wear. Because of strict exhaust emission regulations, carburettor adjustment points are sealed to prevent tampering. It is only when there is an obvious carburettor defect that any attempt should be made to adjust the original settings, and then only when the correct data and equipment are available.

All the other engine settings must be correct before you make any attempt to adjust idling settings and the exhaust emission reading. Do not overlook such factors as a properly working fuel supply system and the correct type of carburettor for the vehicle.

Excessive fuel consumption

First, check that the problem really does exist, by carefully measuring the precise amount of fuel being used against a true mileage. As already mentioned, check all engine settings before undertaking detailed work on the carburettor. If fuel consumption is heavy, this may be caused by:

1. carburettor flooding resulting from
   a) defective needle valve, or a dirty or damaged needle seat,
   b) punctured float,
   c) high fuel-pump pressure,
   d) leaking jets or gaskets inside the carburettor;
2. other causes:
   a) fuel level set too high,
   b) worn or damaged jets,
   c) cold-start device sticking on,
   d) dirty air filter.

Do not overlook external causes, such as:

1. engine running too hot;
2. spirited, high-speed or low-gear driving;
3. excessive load, or loaded roof rack;
4. brakes binding.

Popping back

This is a term given to the phenomenon of a flame spitting back through the carburettor. It is caused by too weak a mixture, but may result from a number of defects:

1. trying to start a cold engine without the choke;
2. a leaking gasket in the intake system (check by squirting oil on the joints to see where it is drawn in);
3. retarded ignition timing;
4. defective inlet valve seat, or valve not closing properly.

Hunting

This term is used when the engine runs in a series of surges at idle. It is caused by too rich a mixture, and provided there is no deep-seated cause, it can be corrected by adjustment. Emission control carburettors should only be adjusted if a carbon monoxide (CO) gas analyser is available. Correct adjustment on cars with an emission carburettor but without a catalytic converter will be shown by a light grey colour inside the exhaust tailpipe.

Other problems

Although carburettors are usually reliable, like other components they can fail after prolonged service. Here are some problems that may occur:

1. Constant-vacuum carburettor; poor starting and loss of power. A diaphragm puncture can cause these problems, because the fuel needle will not rise correctly, and the mixture will be too weak.
2. Hesitation or popping back when trying to accelerate briskly. If the carburettor has a diaphragm-type accelerator pump it may be punctured and failing to pump extra fuel.
3. Poor starting when hot, low power output, high fuel consumption and, possibly, black exhaust smoke. This is usually caused by a choke sticking on. A manually operated choke will need attention to the cable link. An automatic choke may have a loose housing or defective bimetallic spring.

Faults and their possible causes are listed for fixed-choke and constant-vacuum carburettors in Tables 6.2 and 6.3 respectively.

CHECK YOUR UNDERSTANDING

- The function of the carburettor is to mix petrol and air in the correct ratio, as needed by the engine, and to atomise it into a fine spray for vaporisation.
- The driver uses the throttle valve to vary the quantity of mixture supplied to the engine to regulate speed and power output.
- Complete combustion of 1 kg of petrol requires 14.5 kg of air.
- Engines need a richer mixture for cold starting and initial acceleration but a weaker mixture for economical cruising.
- There can be six stages in effective carburation: choke, idling, progression, main jet, accelerator pump, and full load enrichment.
- The two main types of carburettor are the fixed-jet or fixed-choke unit, and the constant-vacuum, variable-choke unit.
- The carburettor is mounted on the inlet manifold, which distributes the mixture to the inlet ports.
- The air filter extracts dust from the air, acts as a silencer, and arrests any flashback.

REVISION EXERCISES AND QUESTIONS

1 Which part of a carburettor maintains a constant level of fuel?
2 How does the throttle valve control the engine speed and power output?

Table 6.2 Faults and possible causes for fixed-choke carburettors

Fault	Possible cause
Poor starting from cold	• Choke not operating correctly • Manual: check fully closed when on
Erratic slow running	• Idle incorrectly set • Slow-running jet partially blocked
Hesitation during acceleration	• Progression jet blocked • Accelerator pump not working
Loss of power	• Blocked jets • Throttle not opening fully • Low fuel level in float chamber
Poor hot starting	• Rich mixture • Fuel level too high in float chamber • Float chamber flooding • Fuel pump pressure too high

Table 6.3 Faults and possible causes for constant-vacuum carburettors

Fault	Possible cause
Erratic running, stalling at low engine speed, lack of power, and high fuel consumption.	Sticking piston due to • dirty piston or suction chamber • jet out of centre • bent needle • punctured diaphragm • oil too thick in damper
Hesitation when accelerating	• Low oil damper level • Oil too thin in damper

3 What is the purpose of the venturi?
4 Why is a rich mixture needed for cold starting, and what part of a fixed-jet carburettor fulfils this function?
5 What is the difference between a fixed-choke and a constant-vacuum carburettor?
6 Why are so many compensating jets and systems needed in a fixed-jet carburettor?
7 How is the effective size of the jet altered in a constant-vacuum carburettor?
8 What harm is likely to result from running an engine without an air cleaner element?
9 What is the effect on performance of running an engine with a clogged air filter?

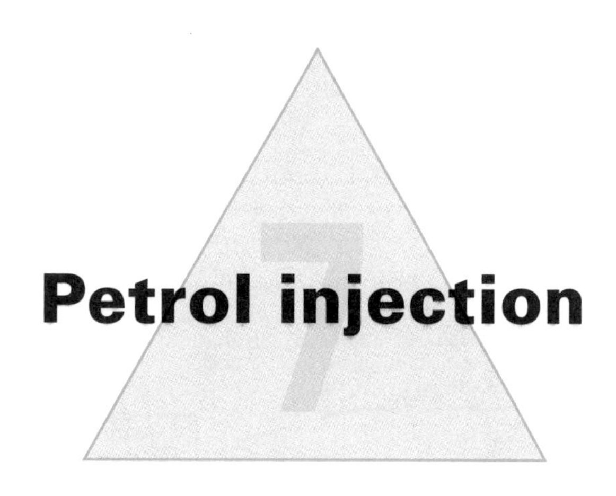

Petrol injection

Introduction

Carburettor-based petrol fuel systems have worked well for many years, but demands for better fuel economy, lower exhaust emissions, increased power output and more flexible engine performance can be met only by more complex carburettors and ancillary systems. Most modern cars now have a fuel injection system, because it is often cheaper and more efficient, and can be readily combined with an electronic engine management system for total control.

The **advantages** that apply to all electronically controlled systems are as follows:

1. better control of the fuel supply to cylinders;
2. higher volumetric efficiency, as there is no venturi to restrict the air flow;
3. better atomisation of the fuel;
4. provision of the correct mixture ratio for all engine conditions, resulting in better economy and higher engine power output.

The more elaborate systems also give the correct quantity of air/fuel mixture to each cylinder on every induction stroke, ensuring smooth and even power output.

The **disadvantages** of petrol fuel injection are as follows:

1. The more elaborate systems are more costly and more complicated.
2. Specialist servicing is required.
3. Failure of a key component could disable the engine.

Fuel injection systems

The fuel injection systems introduced to meet the earliest Californian legislation were fully electronic. These were very expensive, and subsequently a cheaper system with mechanical control was developed for less sensitive markets.

Mechanical management of fuel injection

This system uses a mechanical fuel-metering distributor to control the air/fuel ratio (Figure 7.1). A throttle butterfly controls the air inlet, and the fuel injectors atomise the fuel by spraying it into the inlet valve port on each cylinder (Figure 7.2a).

Operation

As the throttle butterfly is progressively opened the flow of air increases. The incoming air lifts the air flow sensing plate (Figure 7.1). The wider the throttle is opened, the greater is the air flow, and the higher the plate will be lifted. The plate, through its arm, lifts the control plunger in the fuel-metering distributor, which allows more fuel to flow. The pressure created by the fuel flow opens the lines to the injectors, which continuously spray fuel onto the back of the inlet valve (Figure 7.3). The atomised fuel mixes with the air and vaporises before entering the cylinder when the inlet valve opens.

Mechanical systems have the disadvantage of moving parts that wear, causing inaccuracies in the air/fuel ratio. They are also prone to corrosion from water in the fuel system, and are less sensitive than electronically controlled systems.

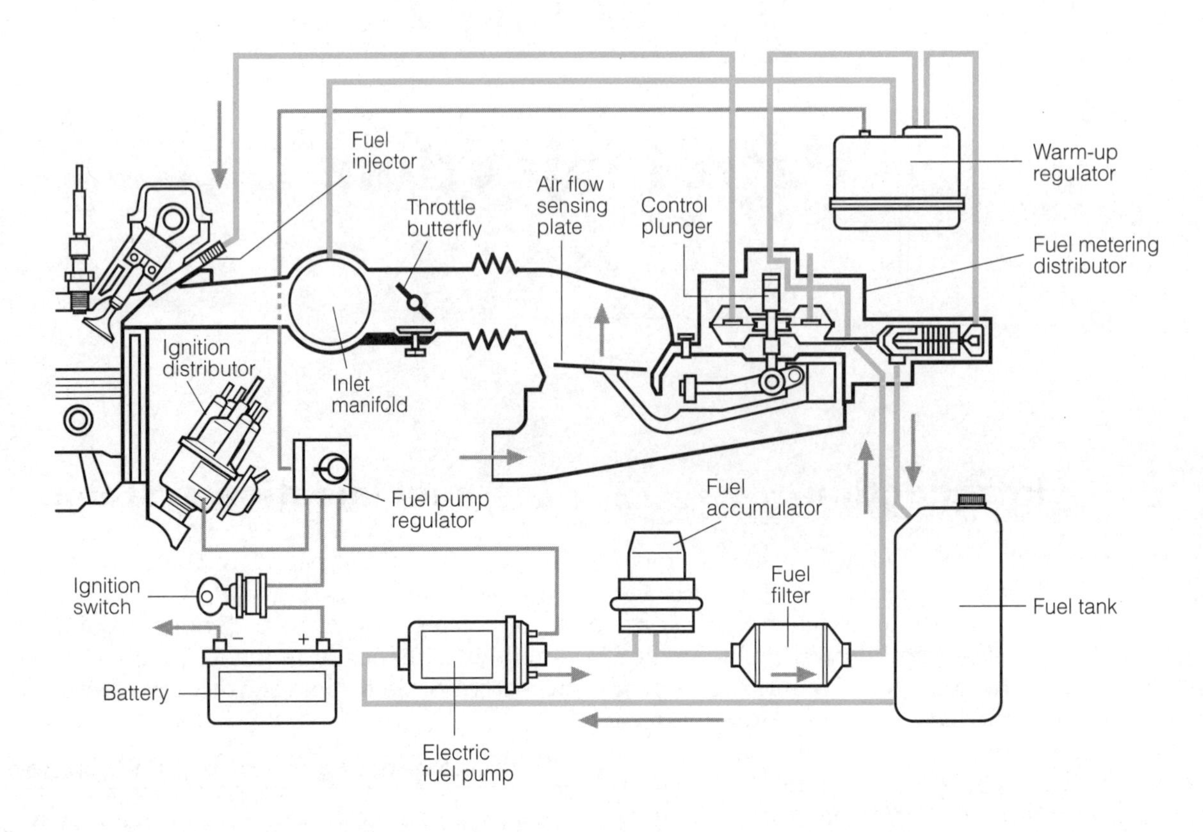

Figure 7.1 Mechanical injection fuel management.

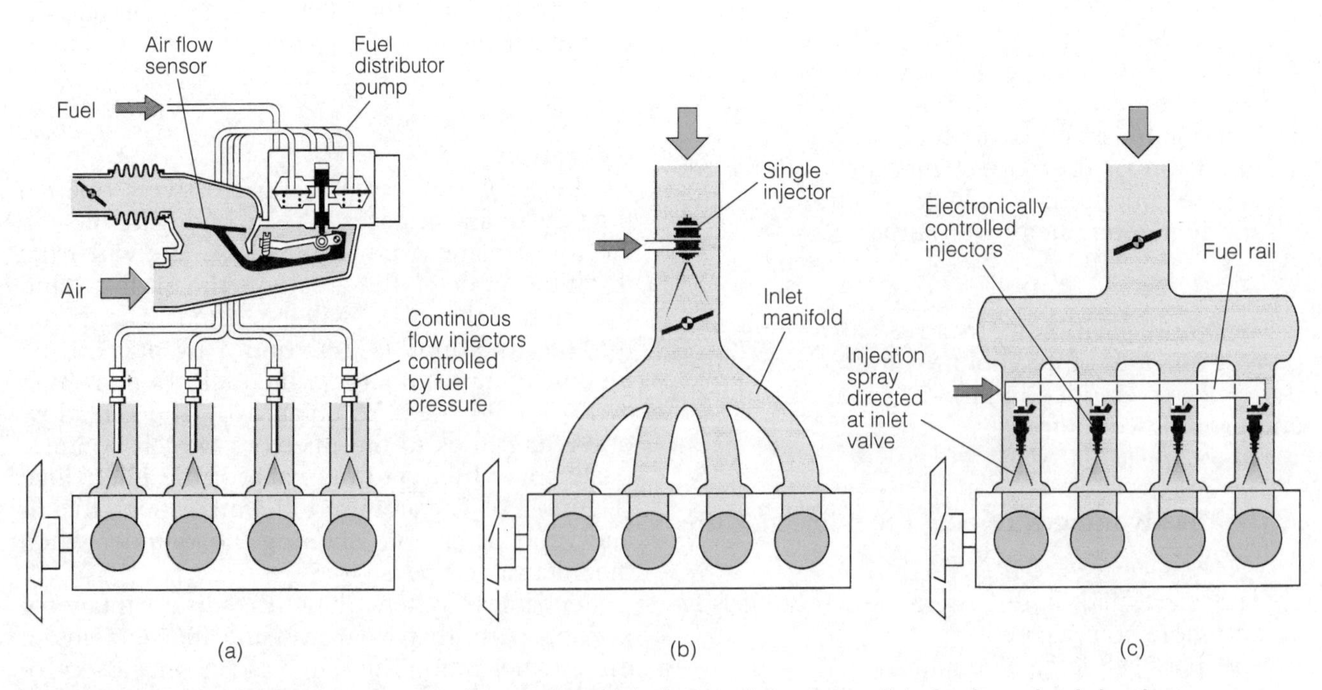

Figure 7.2 Petrol injection systems: (a) mechanical electronic system; (b) single-point injection; (c) multi-point injection.

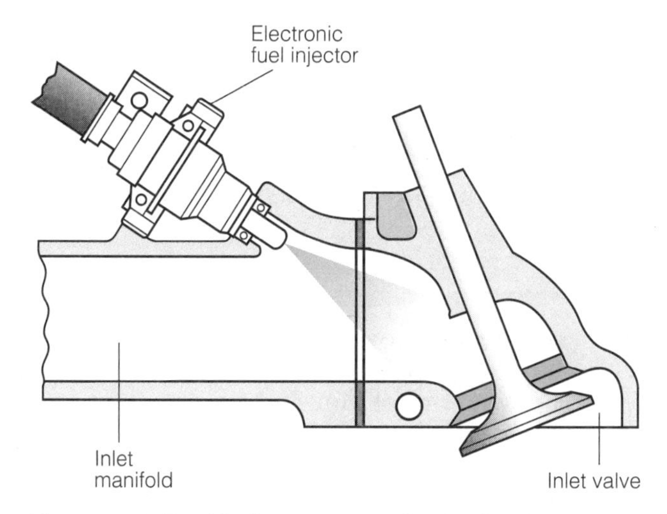

Figure 7.3 Fuel being sprayed in the intake port towards the inlet valve.

Electronic fuel injection management

The management of the fuel system is carried out by an **electronic control unit (ECU)**, which is a specialised microcomputer (Figure 7.4).

In present-day systems the ECU usually controls all aspects of engine management. Such systems have the advantage of being able to monitor engine speed and load more accurately, as well as being able to gather and use other information such as engine temperature and ignition timing conditions.

All petrol fuel injection systems rely on a rotary electric fuel pump or pumps to supply a circuit of piping with fuel, pressurised and regulated to a predetermined figure. On ECU-controlled systems the injectors are basically spray 'taps', which are opened for varying periods of time to allow pressurised fuel to escape into the air stream. The injector valves are opened and closed accurately by solenoid valves inside them (Figure 7.5).

There are two main types of electronic fuel injection: single-point and multi-point (Figure 7.2b, c).

Single-point injection has a single large injector mounted in the usual place for a carburettor. This is a relatively cheap system for small, mass-produced vehicles. It has full electronic control, but has the same drawback as carburettors in that

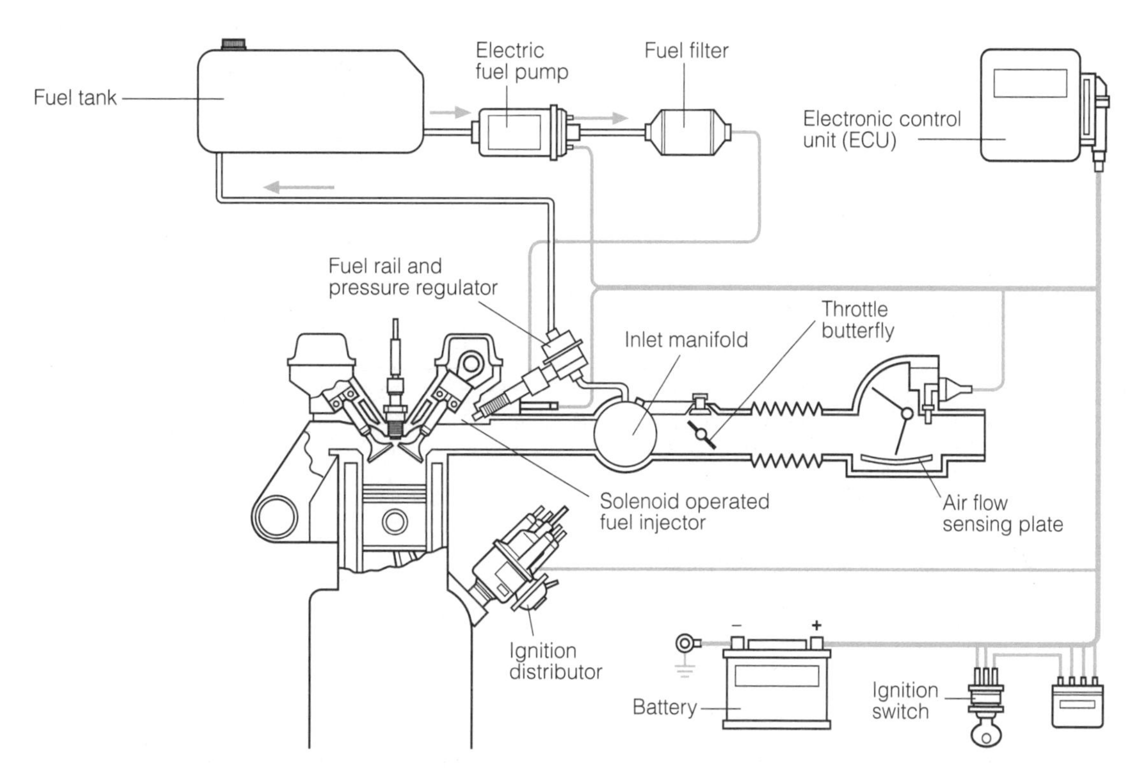

Figure 7.4 Electronic fuel management.

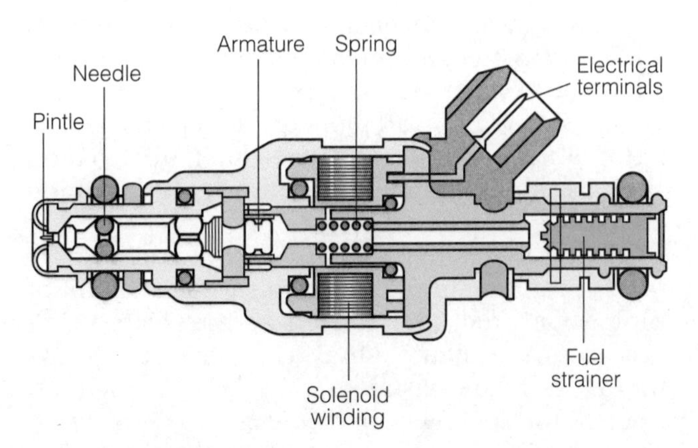

Figure 7.5 Fuel injector.

the cylinders do not receive exactly equal amounts of mixture. **Multi-point injection** has an injector for each cylinder, so ensuring the very best mixture distribution.

The ECU monitors a whole series of sensors that supply its inputs, one of which is the throttle position, and another the air flow entering the engine. This information is compared with the data stored in the ECU's memory, and all the outputs are then activated to control the engine. These include setting the period of injection, to ensure that the appropriate amount of fuel is supplied for the quantity of air and the conditions.

Air flow

Measuring the air flow is done by an air flap, as with the mechanical system, or by the more recent hot wire or hot film sensors.

Flap-type air flow sensor

The air flow sensor measures the volume of air passing through the chamber and into the engine (Figures 7.4 and 7.6). Movement of the sensor flap varies a voltage, which is fed to the ECU as one of its inputs.

Hot wire and hot film sensors

There are several versions of these sensors, but they work on the same basic principle, differing

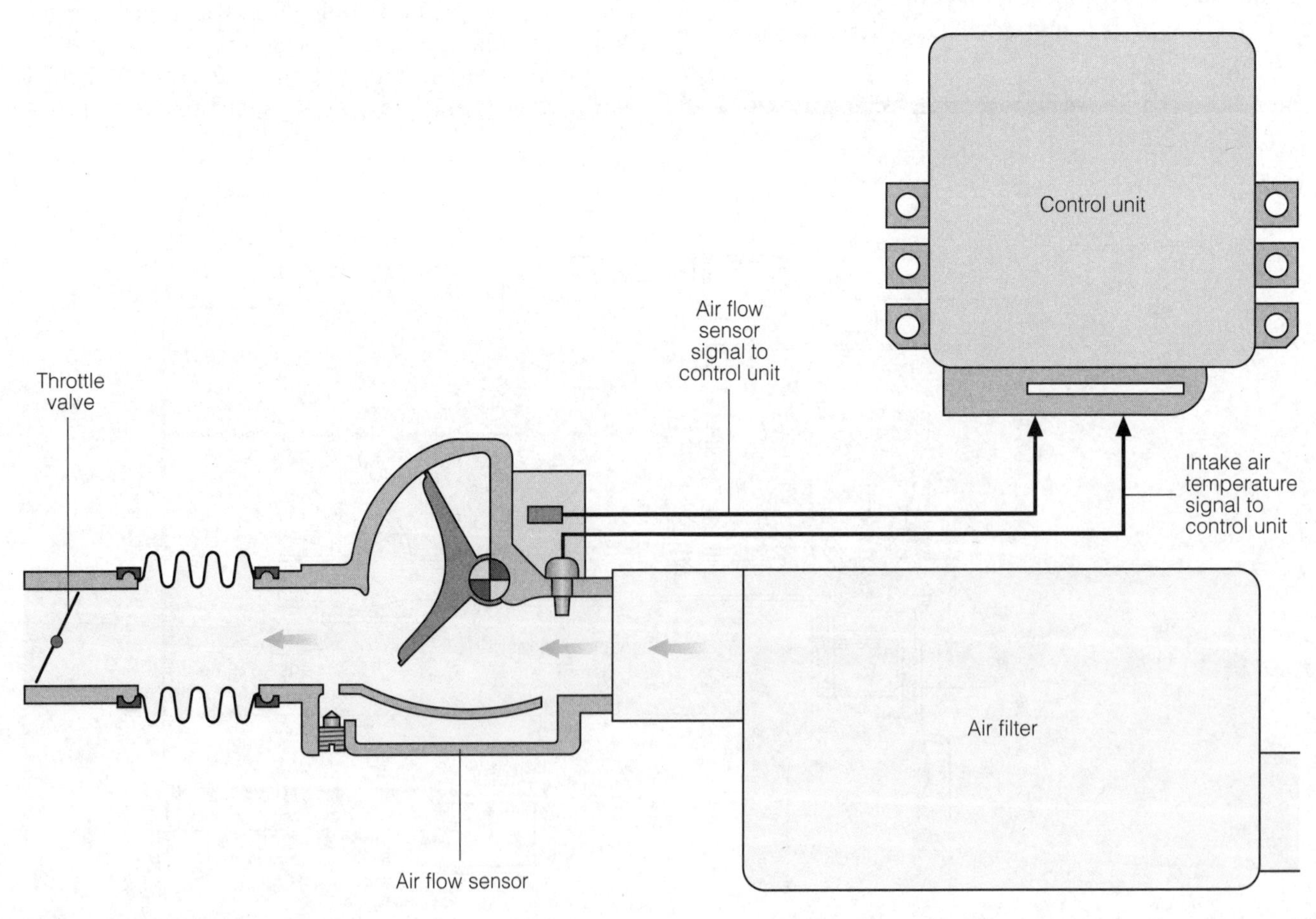

Figure 7.6 Air flow sensor.

only in details of construction and operation. A wire or film resistance is heated above air temperature (Figure 7.7). The incoming air flow takes heat from the resistor. The control circuit increases the voltage to maintain the temperature, which it measures against another reference resistor. The voltage increase is a true measure of the quantity of air and also of its temperature.

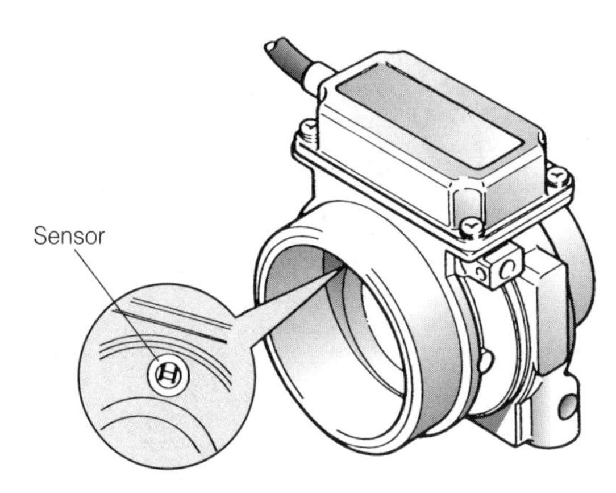

Figure 7.7 Bypass hot wire sensor.

Pressure sensors

Manifold pressure sensor

Engine load is also measured by the manifold pressure sensor on some systems. This sensor, which may be incorporated into the ECU itself, is connected to the manifold by a small pipe. The depression in the manifold is converted into an electrical signal for use as an input.

Fuel system pressure

The quantity of fuel injected is determined by the length of time for which the injectors are opened. The timing by the ECU is extremely accurate. The fuel quantity itself can be accurate only if the pressure is held at a constant figure for all the injectors. This is ensured by having a delivery rail (or fuel distributor tube), with an integral pressure regulator, attached to all the injectors (Figures 7.8 and 7.9).

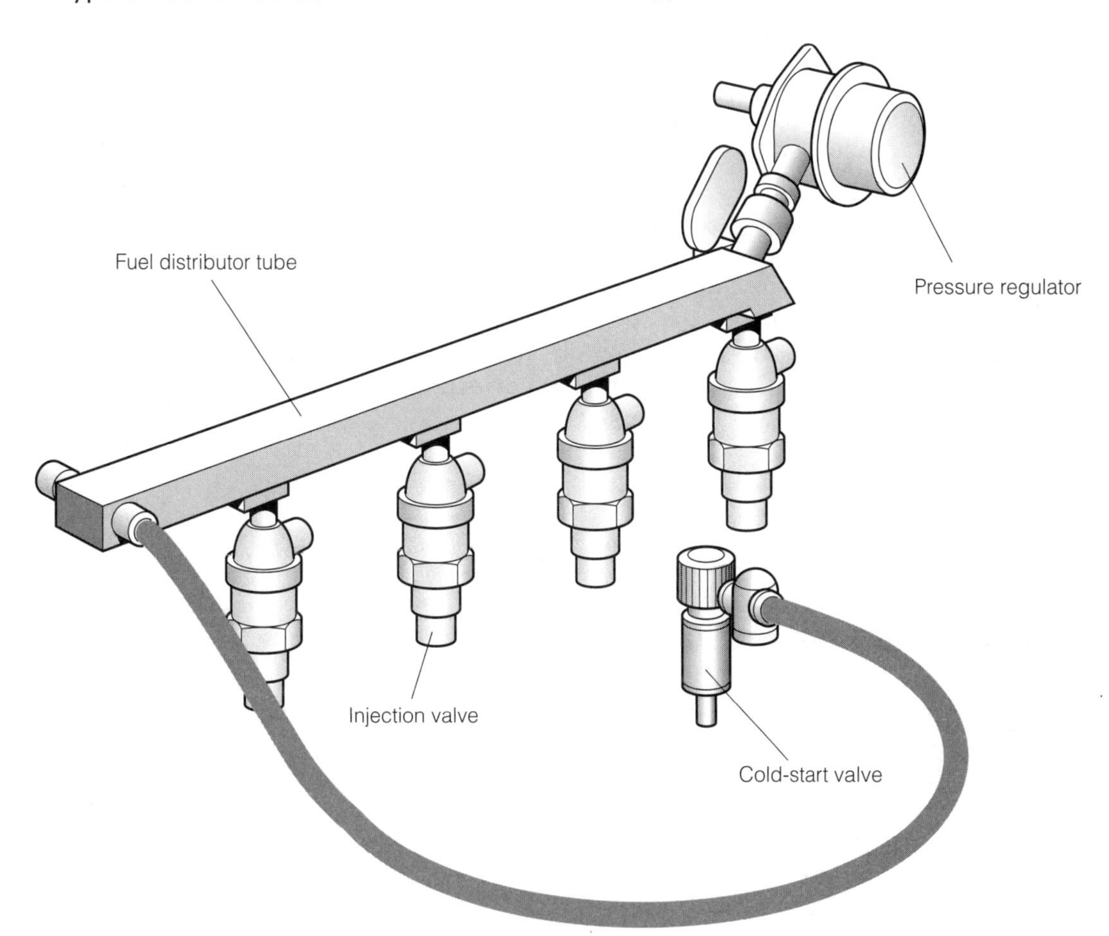

Figure 7.8 Fuel layout for electronic fuel injection system.

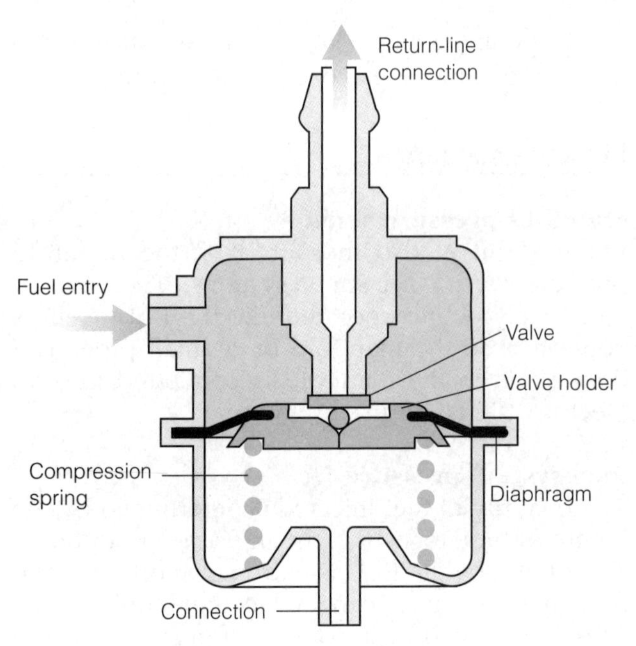

Figure 7.9 Fuel pressure regulator.

Engine position and speed sensors

> Two of the most important sensors are those providing an input for cylinder 1 t.d.c. position, and for engine speed.

Indicators on the flywheel or a timing pulley change a magnetic field around a sensor to provide a voltage signal (Figure 7.10). This information determines when injection should start, and, for a full engine management system, is also used to control the ignition timing.

Figure 7.11 shows a simplified flowchart of fuel injection control.

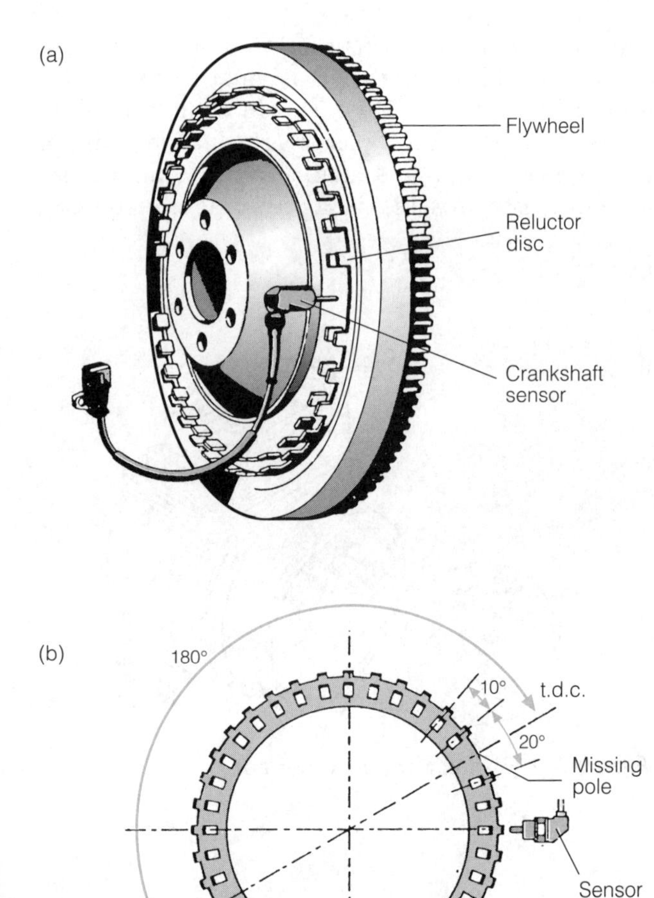

Figure 7.10 Crankshaft position and speed reluctor disc and sensor: (a) assembly; (b) reluctor disc details. The two missing teeth correspond to two t.d.c. positions.

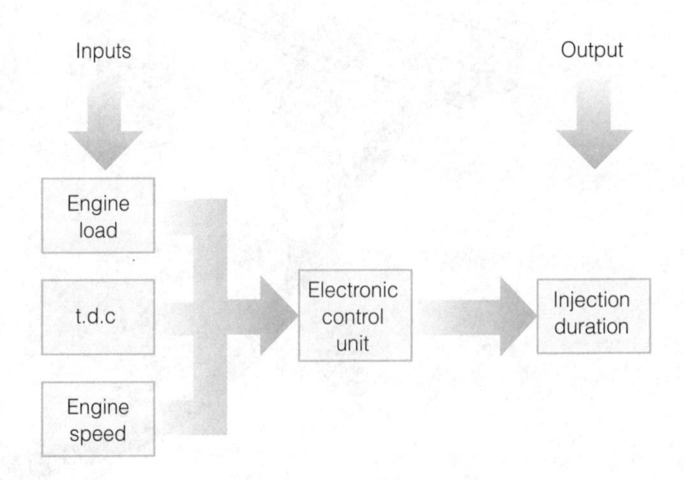

Figure 7.11 Simplified flowchart of fuel injection control.

CHECK YOUR UNDERSTANDING

- Fuel injection has the following advantages over a petrol supply system using a carburettor: higher volumetric efficiency, as there is no restriction to intake air flow; better atomisation of the fuel; electronic control providing the correct mixture ratio for all engine conditions, resulting in better economy and higher power output; better distribution of the air/fuel mixture into the cylinders on multi-injector systems.

- Fuel injection systems are required to increase engine output, yet at the same time reduce pollution and save fuel.
- The function of the electronic control unit (ECU) is to monitor the engine load, deliver and atomise the fuel, and control the air/fuel ratio.
- The ECU depends upon information from sensors monitoring engine load, air temperature, cylinder 1 t.d.c. position, and engine speed.
- The data is compared with information in the ECU, and the outputs are activated accordingly.

REVISION EXERCISES AND QUESTIONS

1 In the mechanical fuel injection system, which items
i) control air flow
ii) control fuel injection?
What atomises the fuel?

2 How is
i) the air flow controlled
ii) the air intake measured
on an electronically controlled fuel injection system?

3 What is different about fuel injector opening times on mechanical and ECU-controlled fuel injection systems?

4 How does an ECU control the quantity of fuel injected?

5 What are the *two* main types of electronically controlled fuel injection system?

6 In what respect is single-point injection no better than a carburettor?

8 Compression ignition (diesel) engines

Introduction

The name **diesel** comes from Rudolf Diesel who, in 1892, took out a patent covering the operation of an engine in which ignition was achieved by high compression.

The name **compression ignition** (CI) describes the process of combustion. The basic difference from a petrol engine is that in the CI engine no spark is needed to ignite the mixture. Air alone is drawn into the cylinder during induction, and it is compressed so that its temperature is raised to the point where ignition of the diesel fuel occurs as soon as it is injected.

The temperature increase of the air in the cylinder basically depends on two things: the speed of compression, and the extent of compression (that is, the final pressure).

Diesel engines have compression ratios of between about 12 : 1 and 24 : 1; most petrol engines have compression ratios below 10 : 1. The high compression ratios used in CI engines are sufficient to heat the air inside the cylinder to around 1000 °C. As diesel fuel has a **flash point** (the temperature at which the vaporised fuel ignites) of around 400 °C, it will ignite as soon as it is injected. This occurs without any need for an ignition system, although some diesels have glow plugs to heat the air for cold starting.

Physically, CI engines are usually constructed more robustly than petrol engines, but apart from that there is little difference in the main components and their functions. There are both two-stroke and four-stroke CI engines.

Types of CI engine

Four-stroke CI cycle

The CI engine employs the same four strokes of induction, compression, power and exhaust as the spark ignition cycle.

Induction
The piston moves down the cylinder, creating a larger volume and lower pressure (Figure 8.1a). Air flows into the depression through the open inlet valve until the piston reaches the bottom of its stroke and the valve closes. The cylinder is full of air.

Compression
With both the inlet and exhaust valves closed, the piston moves up the cylinder, compressing the air to between 3000 kPa and 5000 kPa and raising its temperature to around 1000 °C (Figure 8.1b). Just before t.d.c. a finely atomised spray of fuel is injected into the hot air. The droplets vaporise, combine with the oxygen in the air, and ignite.

Power
The burning gases cause a very rapid temperature increase to around 1500 °C, which raises the pressure to around 7000 kPa (Figure 8.1c). This high pressure forces the piston down the cylinder on its power stroke, producing a turning force or torque on the crankshaft.

Exhaust
As the piston reaches the bottom of the cylinder the exhaust valve opens and the piston returns up the cylinder, pushing the exhaust gases out

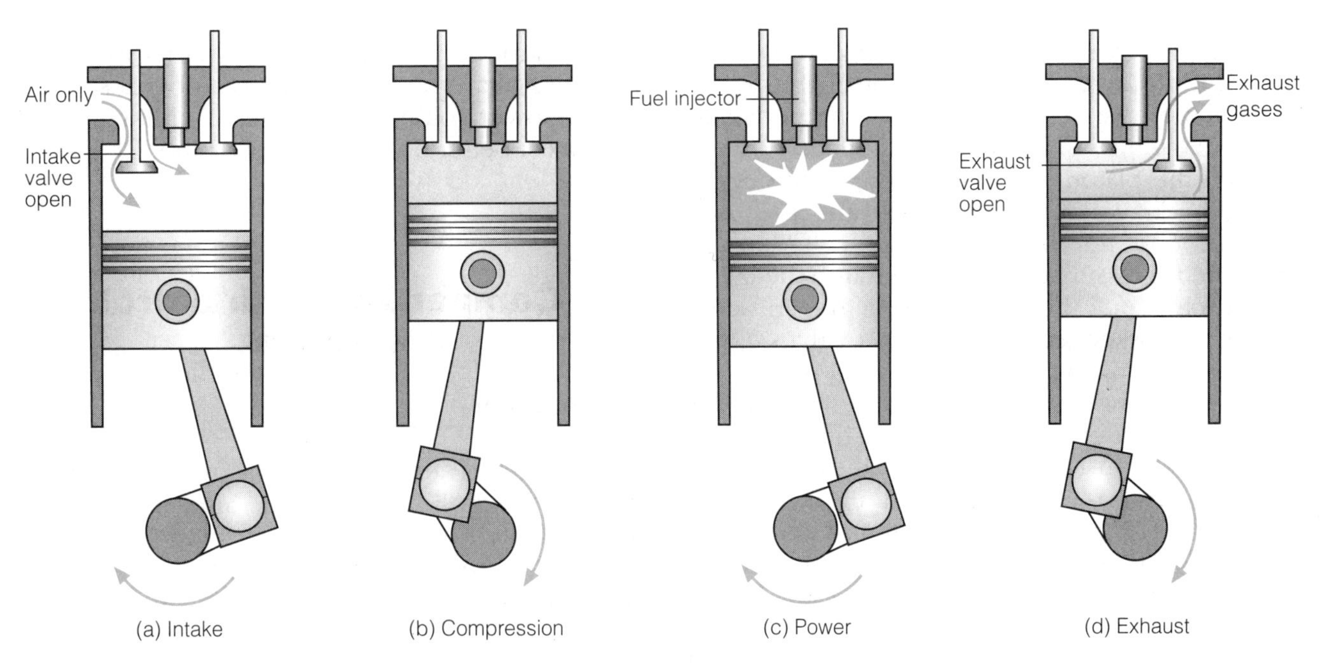

Figure 8.1 Four-stroke compression ignition (CI) cycle.

through the exhaust port (Figure 8.1d). When the piston nears the top of its stroke the inlet valve begins to open as the exhaust begins to close.

The cycle repeats with the inlet open and the piston descending the cylinder on induction.

Two-stroke CI cycle

In the CI two-stroke engine the complete cycle of operations takes place in two strokes of the piston (that is, one crankshaft revolution), in a similar manner to that of the petrol engine. However, where petrol engines often rely on crankcase compression to transfer the air/fuel mixture to purge the cylinder, CI engines usually rely on some form of charger or blower.

There are two basic types of CI two-stroke engine: **uniflow**, using inlet ports and exhaust valves; and **valveless**, using inlet and exhaust ports.

Uniflow CI two-stroke engine

This engine employs normal poppet-type exhaust valves at the top of the cylinder, opened by rockers operated by a camshaft (Figure 8.2). Instead of inlet valves there are inlet ports cut into the cylinder walls at the lower end of the cylinder. The ports

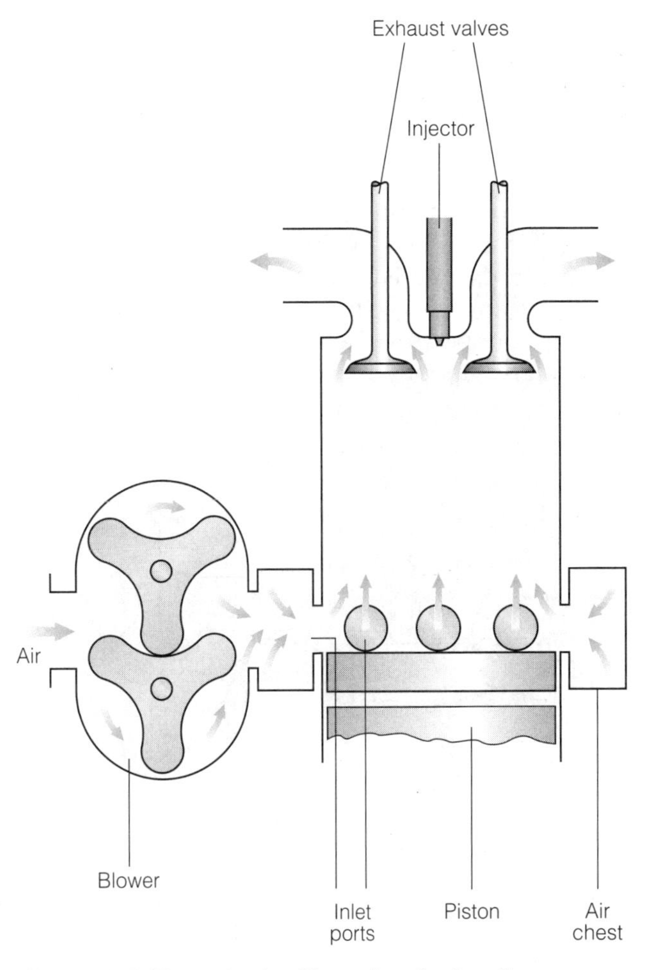

Figure 8.2 Two-stroke CI engine (valved).

are supplied with air under pressure from a mechanical blower. The movement of the piston controls the opening and closing of the ports and therefore the flow of air into the cylinder.

When the piston is at the bottom of the cylinder, the exhaust valves are open and the inlet ports around the bottom of the cylinder are uncovered. Pressurised air is blown into the cylinder, forcing out the burnt gases in a process known as **scavenging**. The exhaust valves close, and the rising piston shuts off the inlet ports.

The charge of fresh air trapped in the cylinder is compressed by the rising piston, gaining heat in the process. Just before t.d.c., diesel fuel is injected into the hot, compressed air and begins to burn. There is a rapid rise in temperature and expansion of the gases, which force the piston down the cylinder on the power stroke. At the bottom of its stroke the piston uncovers the inlet ports, and the exhaust valves open, repeating the full operating cycle in just two strokes.

The design is called *uniflow* because of the single-direction flow of air through the cylinder.

Valveless two-stroke CI engine

The valveless CI engine uses ports for both inlet and exhaust (Figure 8.3). In this unusual type of engine the opposed pistons come together in the centre to form the combustion chamber, and are forced apart on the power stroke. The centre crankshaft is driven by the rocking arms and connecting rods. Air is blown in at one end of the cylinder, and the exhaust gases are forced out through the ports at the other end. This engine is particularly smooth in operation.

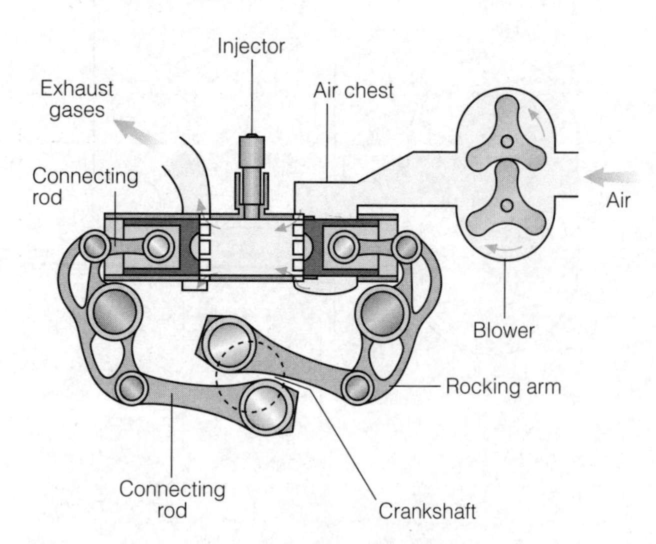

Figure 8.3 Two-stroke CI engine (ported).

Two-stroke CI engines have a higher fuel consumption than the four-stroke type because they have a lower volumetric efficiency, although they do have a better power-to-weight ratio.

Comparison with petrol engines

Combustion

In the petrol engine a uniform combustible mixture is supplied through the induction system, and is ignited by a spark when it has been compressed in the cylinder. At part-open throttle the petrol engine does not convert the fuel energy very effectively because the cylinder is only partly full of air.

In the CI engine the mixing of the fuel and air is done inside the cylinder. This is achieved by using a very high-pressure spray of fuel and considerable air turbulence in the cylinder. However, the CI engine is particularly economical on fuel at part-open throttle positions because fuel energy conversion is very efficient; a little fuel is injected into a full cylinder of air.

There are two types of injection: **direct injection** is into the cylinder itself, while **indirect injection** is into an ante-chamber, which is connected by passage to the combustion chamber.

Power and torque

CI engines in general develop their maximum torque and power at lower engine speeds than the petrol engine, although recent developments have brought the engine types much closer together. Typically a small high-speed CI engine will reach its maximum revolutions at a little over 5000 rpm, compared with the petrol engine's 6000 rpm or higher. Large six- or eight-cylinder CI engines may reach their maximum at as little as 2000 rpm. Low engine speeds and robust construction give the advantage of a longer engine life.

Construction

The high compression ratio and the resulting high compression pressures of a CI engine call for sturdy, heavy construction. The cylinder head, cylinder block, crankshaft and bearings have to be stronger than in the petrol engine to resist the greater forces. In addition, the fuel injection pump and injectors are manufactured to very fine tolerances, adding to production costs. Although extensive use is made of light alloys, the power-to-weight ratio is lower than for similar-sized petrol engines.

Cylinder block and crankcase

The smaller, high-speed CI engines used in motor vehicles are similar to the petrol-powered versions, but some larger CI engines have separate cylinder blocks. The cylinder block may be made up of groups of cylinders bolted to a separate crankcase (Figure 8.4). There are several reasons for this:

1. The parts can be made from different materials.
2. Cylinder blocks cast individually or in groups can be used in multiples for different sizes of engine, saving production costs.
3. In case of damage or wear it is cheaper to replace one part than to buy a complete cylinder block and crankcase unit.

Most CI engines – and some petrol engines – use cylinder liners made of a different material from that of the cylinder block. Such liners are of two types: wet and dry.

Wet liners have thick walls, and are in direct contact with the coolant (Figure 8.5a). They are a push fit into the block. Coolant leakage is prevented by seals at the bottom and gaskets at the top. The liner is pressed down and held in place by the cylinder head. If damage or wear occurs removal is easy, and service repair is comparatively cheap.

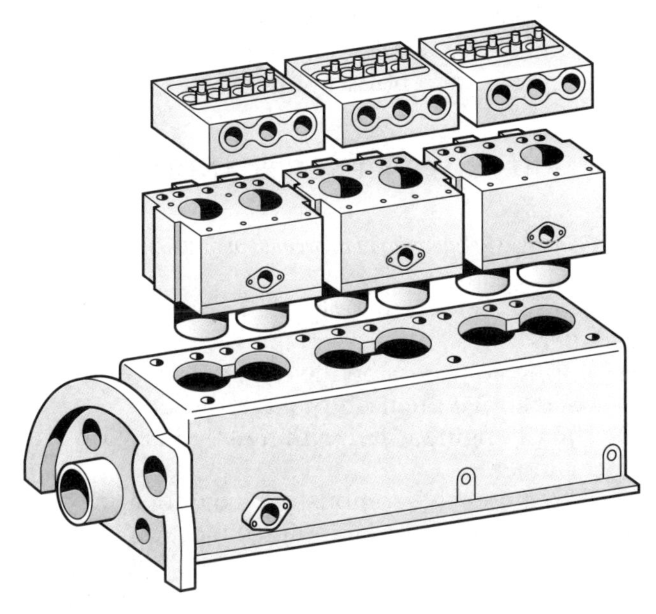

Figure 8.4 CI engine cylinder block and crankcase.

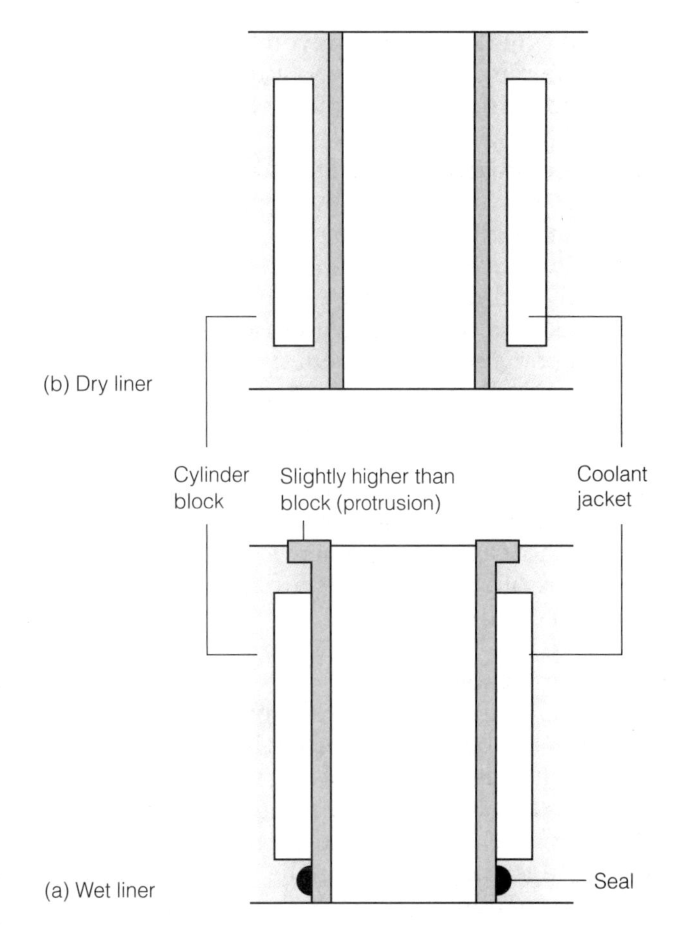

Figure 8.5 Cylinder liners.

> Never turn over such an engine with a cylinder head removed without first clamping down each cylinder liner, as they can push upwards with piston movement.

Dry liners can be of two types: press fit or push fit (Figure 8.5b). **Press** or **interference fit liners** are pressed into the block with a press. The operation sometimes calls for heating of the block to expand it, or freezing of the liner to reduce its size. Once fitted they may require machining to an exact internal diameter. The major disadvantage with interference fit liners is that the cylinder block, or even the entire engine, has to be removed to carry out the work.

Push fit liners can be pushed or tapped in and out of the cylinder block. They are pre-finished and therefore need no additional work once fitted. They are held in position by a lip, which fits into a recess at the top of the block, similar to the wet liner. Once the cylinder head is fitted they are trapped, and cannot move. Care should also be exercised that these liners are not disturbed when working on a partly dismantled engine.

Although the fitting of liners increases the initial cost of the engine, this cost is more than compensated for by reduced maintenance and longer engine life. Liners are usually made from better, wear-resistant material than that of the cylinder block, and can be machined to finer tolerances. Examples of such materials are high-quality alloy cast iron or alloy steel.

Cylinder heads

Compared with the petrol engine, the CI cylinder head has to be more robust with, usually, more head bolts fastening it to the block. Accurately machined holes and mounting points are provided for the injectors and heater plugs. Unlike spark plugs, the injectors are usually clamped into place. Depending upon the design, the combustion chamber may be formed in the cylinder head or in the crown of the piston.

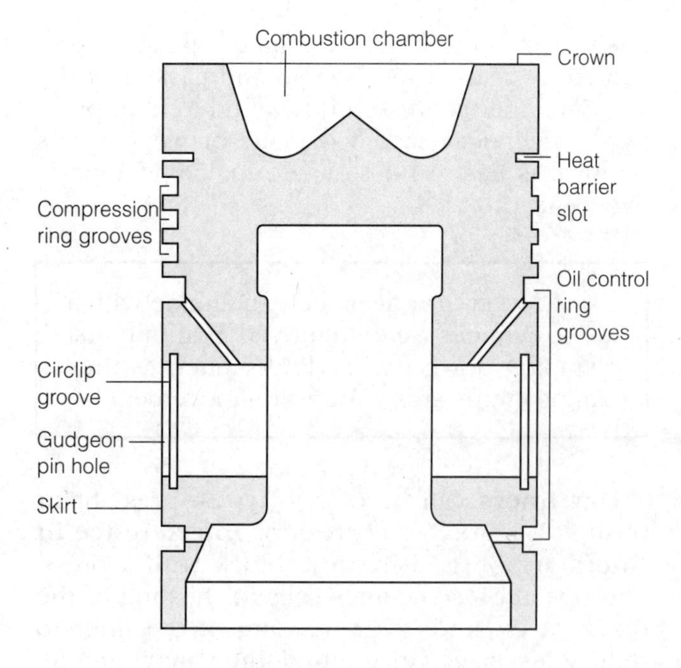

Figure 8.6 CI engine piston.

Pistons

Pistons must be more robust than those used in petrol engines, and they usually have three compression rings and two oil control rings. A longer piston skirt minimises piston slap, and the gudgeon pin is usually stronger. The piston crown often forms part of the combustion chamber, and is shaped to create turbulence (Figure 8.6).

Advantages and disadvantages of the CI engine

Among the **advantages** are the following:

1. CI engines have the advantage of a greater thermal efficiency and better fuel economy because of their high compression ratio.
2. Diesel fuel in many countries is cheaper than petrol, and it has a much reduced fire risk.
3. Engine torque is usually greater at low engine speeds.
4. Maintenance is decreased.
5. Longer engine life can generally be expected.
6. The exhaust gases emitted by a CI engine are generally less harmful to people than the fumes emitted by an equivalent petrol-engined vehicle.

Disadvantages include the following:

1. Their construction is heavier and more costly.
2. A slower rate of acceleration is usual compared with a similar size of petrol engine.
3. They are often noisy in operation.

CHECK YOUR UNDERSTANDING

- CI engines have compression ratios between about 12 : 1 and 24 : 1.
- During induction only air is drawn into the cylinder.
- During compression the temperature of the air is raised above the flash point of diesel.
- The CI engine is fed with fuel by injection into the cylinder.
- Two types of combustion chamber may be used: direct injection or indirect injection.
- Advantages of CI engines include: better thermal efficiency; lower servicing requirements; good torque at low rpm; long service life; less pollution than petrol engines; lower fuel fire risk.

- Disadvantages include: noisy idling; heavy construction; an expensive, high-pressure fuel injection system; lower power-to-weight ratio; sometimes need an air-heating cold-start system.

REVISION EXERCISES AND QUESTIONS

1 List *three* advantages of the CI engine.
2 Unlike the two-stroke petrol engine, CI two-stroke engines do not use crankcase compression to breathe. How is air introduced into the cylinders?
3 How is the fuel ignited in a CI engine?
4 Explain the term *wet liner.*
5 List *three* differences between diesel and petrol engines.

9 CI engine combustion chambers

Combustion

When engine efficiency and the combustion process are at their best, the exhaust gas is virtually colourless. If combustion is incomplete or too much fuel is being injected the engine 'smokes'. How cleanly the fuel and air mixture burns depends on many factors: the design of the combustion chamber, the type of injector and even the direction of fuel spray all play a part.

The combustion process takes a certain amount of time, and is divided into three phases (Figure 9.1):

1. ignition delay period;
2. flame spread;
3. direct burning.

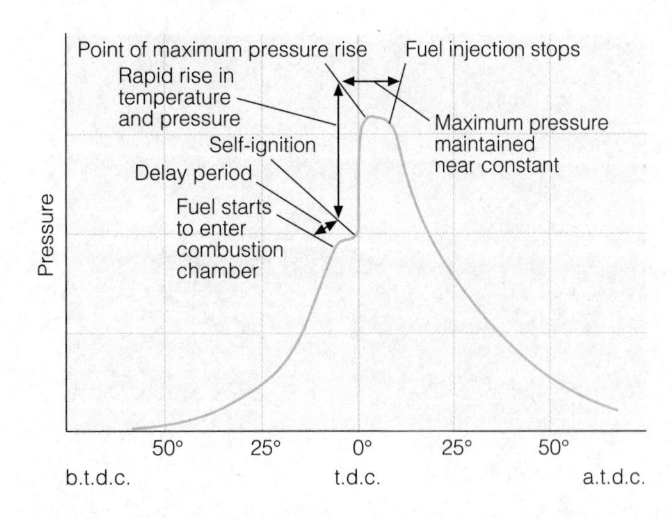

Figure 9.1 Diagram of pressure versus crank angle.

Ignition delay period

The period from the start of injection until the time combustion begins is known as the **ignition delay period**. Injection commences just before t.d.c. when fuel is sprayed into the cylinder and, during this period, mixes with the hot air under very high pressure. Combustion does not occur immediately; the droplets of fuel go through a period of heating and vaporisation.

This delay phase occupies some 12° of crankshaft rotation, during which there is no change in cylinder pressure.

Flame spread

Sufficient fuel has now vaporised and mixed with the air to cause it to ignite, and the flame spreads through the mixture: the heat creates a rapid rise in cylinder pressure to about 6500 kPa.

This sudden increase in cylinder pressure is heard as **diesel knock**, the typical noise of diesel engines. This phase takes 10°–15° of crankshaft rotation.

Direct burning

During this phase the last of the fuel is injected, and is ignited immediately by the burning mixture.

Combustion is completed, and the expanding gases force the piston down the cylinder on the power stroke. The rate of combustion in this phase is directly controlled by the quantity of fuel injected into the cylinder.

Other factors

The design of the combustion chamber, the properties of the fuel such as its **cetane number**, the pressure and temperature of the air during compression, and the rate at which the fuel is injected, are all factors in deciding the length of the delay period and the rate of pressure rise in phase 2.

Combustion chamber design

During the short period of injection the fuel and air must be completely mixed. For this to occur the air has to be moving around the combustion chamber at the time of injection. This air turbulence, sometimes referred to as **swirl**, is to a large extent determined by the shape of the combustion chamber. To ensure that a CI engine performs and operates efficiently and effectively, combustion chamber design is very important. A good design will ensure that the following conditions are promoted:

1. The air and fuel in the combustion chamber are thoroughly mixed.
2. The fuel absorbs sufficient heat during the compression stroke to self-ignite and start the combustion process.
3. The actual combustion of the air/fuel mixture is evenly distributed around the combustion chamber, to prevent localised hot spots from forming and causing pre-ignition.
4. The pressure rise inside the cylinder is rapid although gradual, to avoid excessive stress on the mechanical components of the engine.
5. The actual metallic surface area of the combustion chamber is kept to a minimum, to avoid undue heat loss. This is especially important when starting from cold.
6. All the burnt gases are efficiently removed from the combustion chamber as soon as possible on the exhaust stroke.

Although there are many combustion chamber designs, they can be divided into two groups: **direct injection** and **indirect injection**.

The combustion chamber includes both the piston crown and cylinder head. The choice of design depends upon the purpose for which the engine is intended and, increasingly nowadays, how other controls can be combined with the engine to provide a wide torque band and good exhaust emission control.

Direct injection

The fuel is injected directly into the combustion chamber, which is usually formed in the crown of the piston, the cylinder head being flat.

To achieve thorough mixing, the fuel is injected into swirling air. The swirl or 'squish' effect is created by the shape of the piston crown, the rising movement of the piston, or by masked inlet valves and sometimes by inlet port design (Figure 9.2). A multi-hole injector is usually used in such designs.

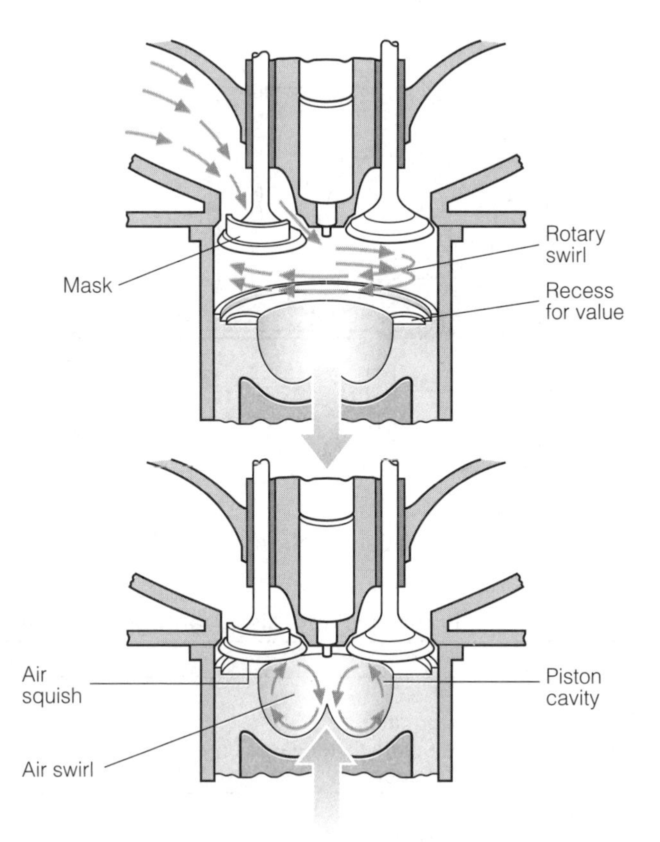

Figure 9.2 CI combustion chamber: direct injection type.

Direct-injection engines generally start readily from cold and do not usually need starting aids. Although they tend to run more roughly, particularly at low engine speeds, they have a high thermal efficiency, which produces a good torque output and makes them more economical than indirect-injection types. Later versions with full electronic engine management control have achieved a smoothness of performance that permits their use in luxury cars.

Indirect injection

This may sometimes be referred to as the pre-combustion chamber type (Figure 9.3). The combustion chamber is separated from the cylinder by a short connecting passage or 'throat'.

During compression, air is forced through this passage at high speed by the rising piston. This produces air swirl in the small pre-combustion chamber to promote good combustion.

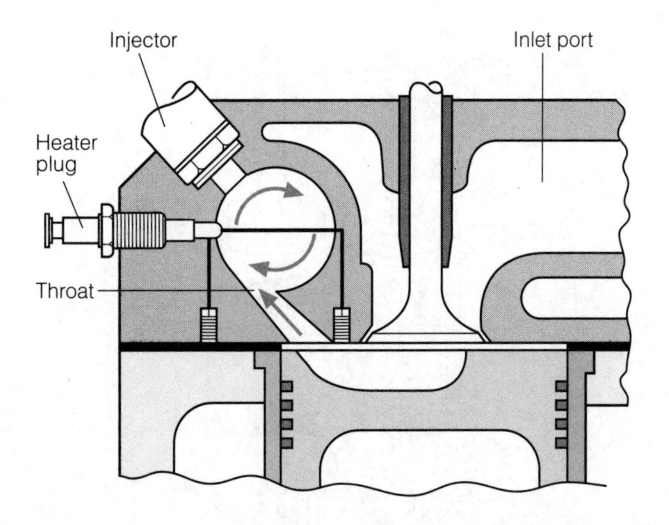

Figure 9.3 CI combustion chamber: indirect type.

The fuel is injected into the chamber by a single-hole injector, which produces a conical spray. When the mixture ignites, the burning and expanding gases spread from the chamber and produce turbulence and pressure in the cylinder, forcing the piston downwards on its power stroke.

Because there is a larger surface area with the indirect-injection engine, there is more heat lost from the combustion space. To overcome difficult cold starting a heater plug is fitted into each pre-combustion chamber.

This design is smooth running and causes less pollution, but its lower thermal efficiency means that it is less economical than direct-injection engines.

Compression ratios

CI compression ratios are higher than those of a comparable petrol engine. An indirect CI engine would normally have a compression ratio of between 22 : 1 and 24 : 1, compared with a direct-injection engine ratio of between 12 : 1 and 17 : 1.

Advantages and disadvantages

The advantages and disadvantages of direct and indirect injection are listed in Table 9.1.

CHECK YOUR UNDERSTANDING

- The three phases of combustion are: ignition delay, flame spread, and direct burning.
- Combustion chamber design is important to ensure that the air and fuel trapped inside the combustion chamber are burnt completely.

Table 9.1 Advantages and disadvantages of direct and indirect injection in CI engines

Advantages	Disadvantages
Direct injection	
Lower compression ratio	Poor natural turbulence on most engines
No electrical cold-start aids (on large engines)	High injection pressure required
Good thermal efficiency	Noisy in operation
Indirect injection	
Good swirl characteristics	Higher compression ratio
Smooth running and operation	Greater heat loss
Higher rpm possible	Cold-starting aids required

- CI combustion chambers can be classified into direct injection and indirect injection types.
- To ensure that the air and fuel mixes thoroughly, combustion chambers are designed to promote swirl or turbulence.

REVISION EXERCISES AND QUESTIONS

1 Give *two* desirable characteristics of CI combustion chamber design.
2 List *three* main advantages of a direct-injection CI engine compared with an indirect-injection unit.
3 List *three* advantages of an indirect-injection CI engine compared with a direct-injection unit.
4 Why is an electrically operated cold-start device needed on an indirect-injection CI engine?
5 State a typical compression ratio for
   i) a direct-injection engine
   ii) an indirect-injection engine.

10 CI engine fuel supply

Introduction

The CI engine fuel supply system consists of a fuel storage tank, low-pressure pipelines, fuel lift pump, filters, fuel injection pump, high-pressure pipelines, fuel injectors, and leak-off pipes (Figure 10.1).

Fuel tank

On a light vehicle the fuel tank will be the same or similar to its petrol counterpart. Heavy vehicles normally have a large-capacity tank, which is cylindrical or rectangular in section. As a heavy vehicle may travel as little as 1.8 km per litre of diesel fuel, the tank must be strong enough to hold quantities in the order of 250 litres. Vehicles travelling long distances may be fitted with a larger tank, or possibly two tanks.

Internal baffles limit the surging of fuel inside the tank caused by vehicle movement. There will be a tank unit to operate the fuel gauge, or, on older vehicles, a gauge may be fitted to the tank itself. To prevent dirt from entering the tank there may be a mesh filter inside the filler neck.

Fuel supply pump

The function of this pump, which may also be called the lift, transfer or feed pump, is to move fuel from the tank through the filters and into the high-pressure fuel injection pump. Separate pumps may be operated by the engine's camshaft, but others will be mounted on, or may even be an integral part of, the injection pump itself.

There are three basic types in use:

1. diaphragm;
2. plunger;
3. vane.

Diaphragm pump

These are similar in action if not always in shape to those of the petrol engine (see Chapter 5), but external diesel lift pumps always have a lever for priming (Figure 10.2). This enables the system to be 'bled' by hand if air has entered the pipelines.

Plunger pump

This type of pump is usually mounted on the fuel injection pump, and is driven by the pump's internal camshaft. It works on a similar principle to that of the diaphragm pump, except that a plunger is used instead of the diaphragm, and both the top and bottom of the plunger are used to transfer fuel (Figure 10.3). A spring holds a cam follower in contact with the cam.

In operation the plunger follows the cam profile of the injection pump camshaft, which moves the plunger up and down in its cylinder. As the plunger moves downwards, the volume of the pump fuel chamber increases, and the pressure drops in the chamber. This causes the outlet valve to close and the inlet valve to open (Figure 10.3a). Atmospheric pressure in the fuel tank forces fuel into the chamber above the plunger. At the same time, fuel below the plunger is forced out to the filters and the injection pump by the tension of the plunger return spring.

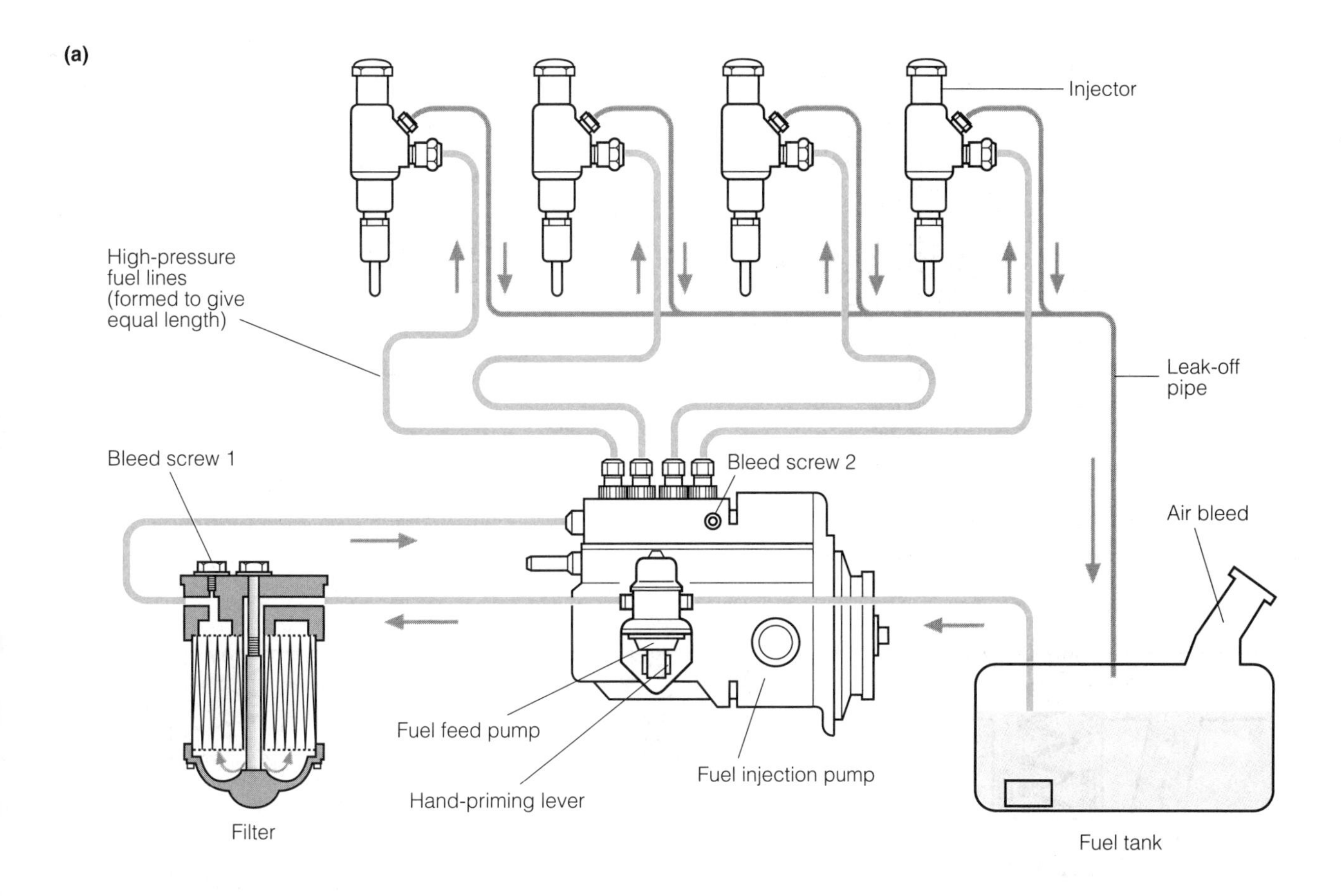

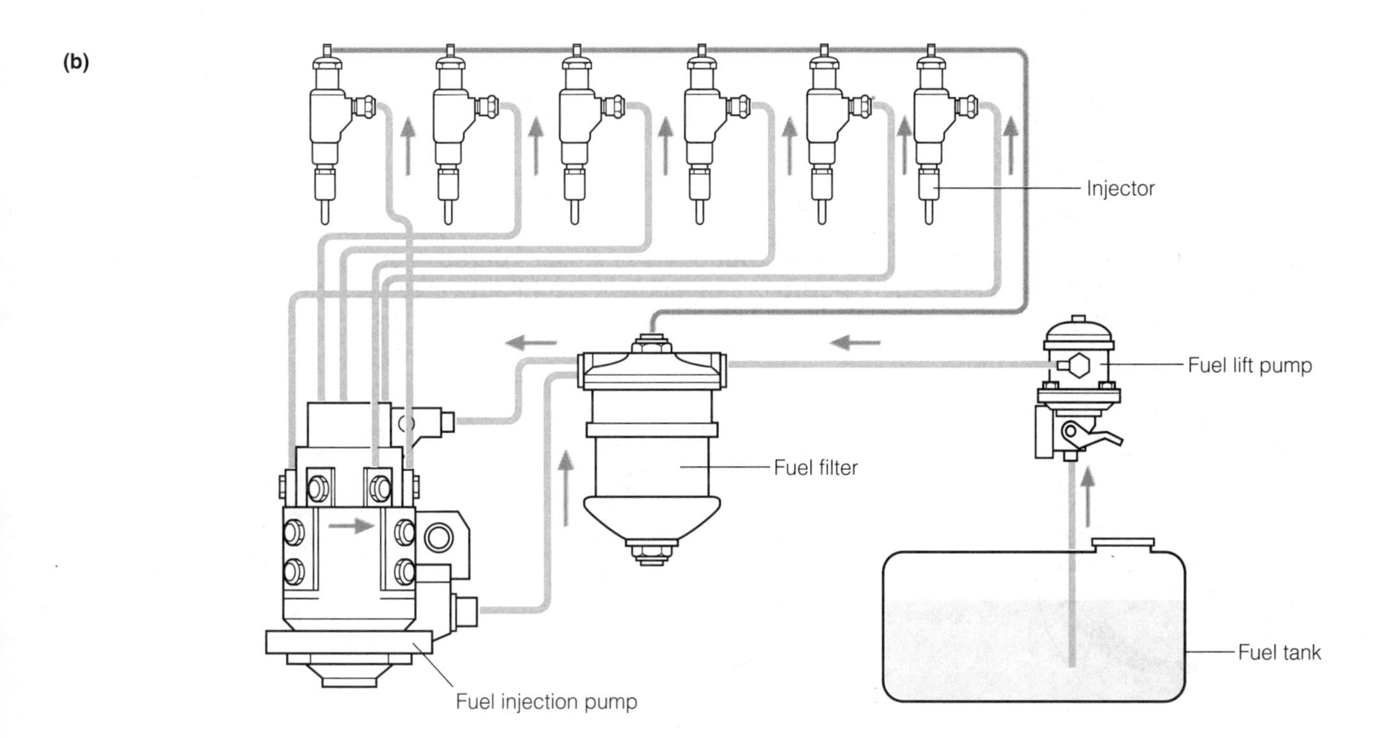

Figure 10.1 CI engine fuel injection systems: (a) in-line fuel pump; (b) distribution-type fuel pump.

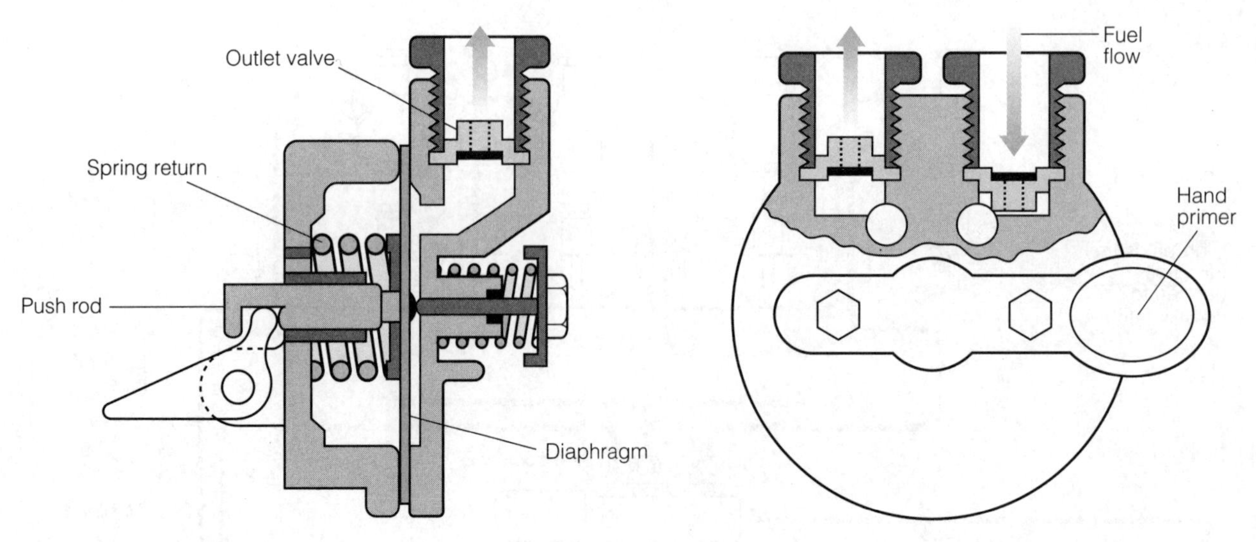

Figure 10.2 Diaphragm-operated lift pump.

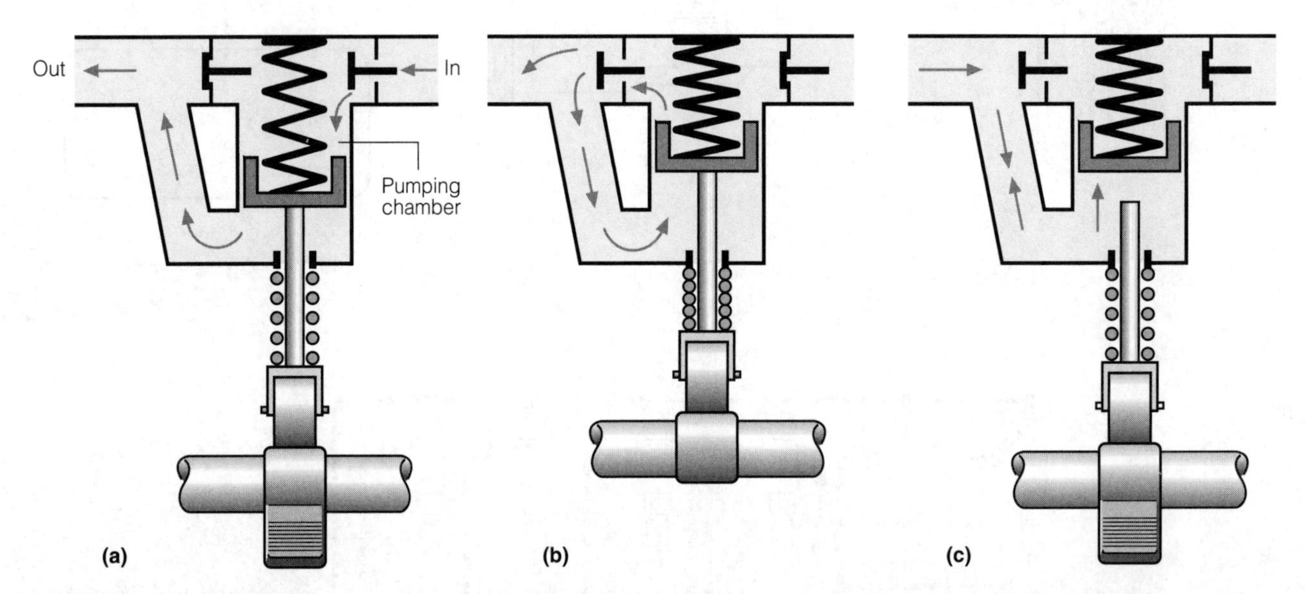

Figure 10.3 Plunger pump. (a) Inlet valve open, outlet valve closed; pump is spring actuated (plunger). (b) Inlet valve closed, outlet valve open; pump is cam actuated. (c) Inlet valve closed; outlet valve closed; self-regulating.

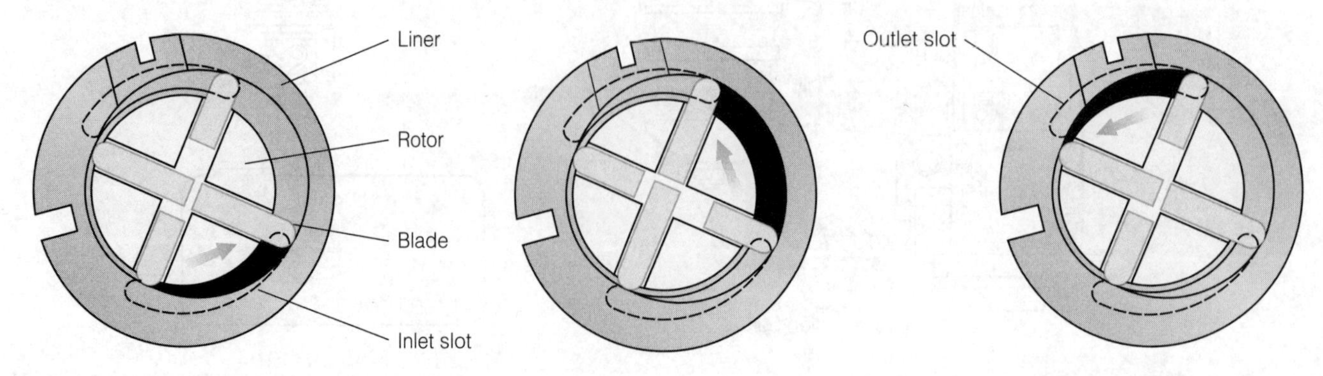

Figure 10.4 Vane-type transfer pump.

As the camshaft continues to turn, the plunger moves upwards, creating pressure on the fuel above the plunger. This closes the inlet valve and opens the outlet valve, when fuel is forced both into the outlet pipe and into the chamber below the plunger (Figure 10.3b).

Once the plunger has been pushed to the top of its travel, the cam follower returns to its base position, when the plunger return spring again pushes the plunger downwards (Figure 10.3c). The pressure in the supply side of the system is governed by the tension of the spring; if little fuel is being used the plunger will only move downwards when the spring can overcome the pressure.

Vane pump

The vane pump is an integral part of a distributor-type fuel injection pump. An off-centre rotor carries vanes mounted in slots (Figure 10.4). As the rotor rotates, the vanes slide in and out to follow the shape of the chamber. The increasing cavity is at the inlet to allow atmospheric pressure to push fuel into the chamber. Further rotation carries the fuel to the outlet port, where the cavity reduces in size, forcing the fuel into the body of the pump at a modest pressure.

Fuel filters

> The fuel delivered to the injection pump must be perfectly clean. Even minute particles of dirt entering the injection pump can cause very rapid wear.

The pump is manufactured to the exceptionally close tolerances of 0.004 mm or 0.0001 in. This is because it has to meter and inject very precise amounts of fuel into the cylinder, at exactly the right moment, and at extremely high pressure. Any wear in the system could cause excessive fuel to be delivered and make the engine run inefficiently.

The fuel system is therefore fitted with a series of filters, which remove any fuel contamination, including water, before it reaches the injection pump. The filters must be able to remove particles as small as 3 μm (0.003 mm) in diameter. For comparison, the finest human hair is around 30 μm in diameter. Why not check it for yourself: you will need a metric micrometer, carefully zeroed, and a hair from your head.

Filters fitted between the fuel tank and the lift pump are known as **primary filters**. These are designed to remove relatively large particles of dirt, and any water that is present, usually by sedimentation. Because fuel is lighter than water, it floats, and the water sinks to the bottom, together with any sediment (Figure 10.5). The water must be drained off periodically: on the latest vehicles a switch is triggered that automatically opens the drain when the water level rises.

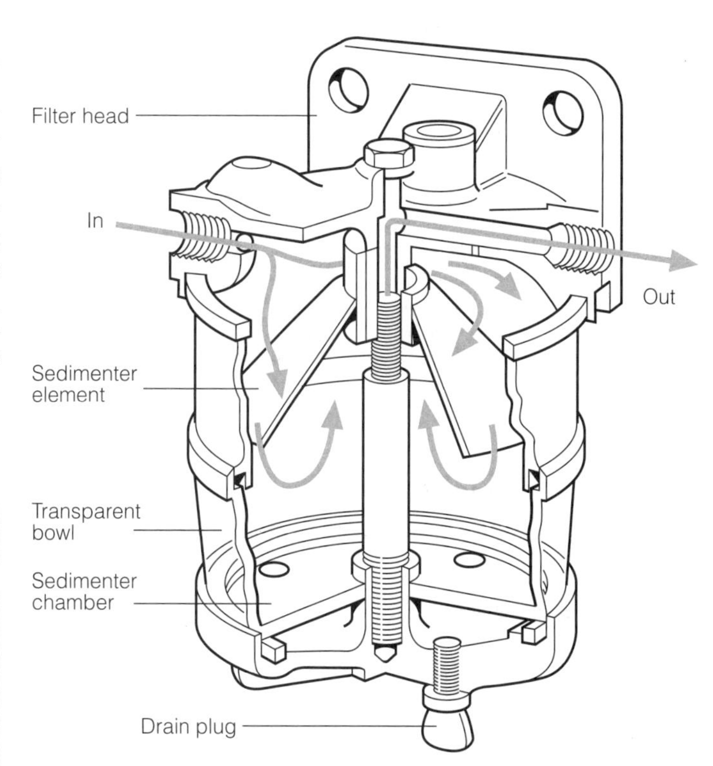

Figure 10.5 Sedimenter.

On vehicles with a separate supply pump, the **main filter** is fitted between the lift pump and the injection pump; modern commercial vehicles often have more than one filter. Distributor-type injection pumps with an integral supply pump rely on atmospheric pressure to force the fuel through the main filter.

Some filters incorporate a sediment chamber, in which case they are called **agglomerators** (Figure 10.6).

Filters now generally have replaceable elements.

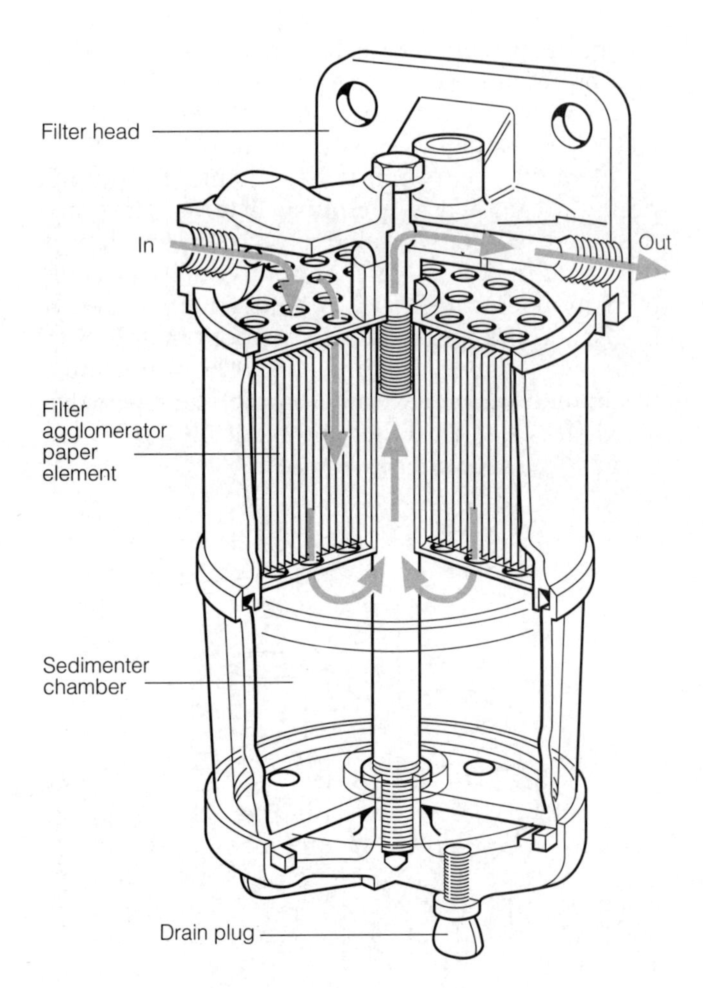

Figure 10.6 Agglomerator filter.

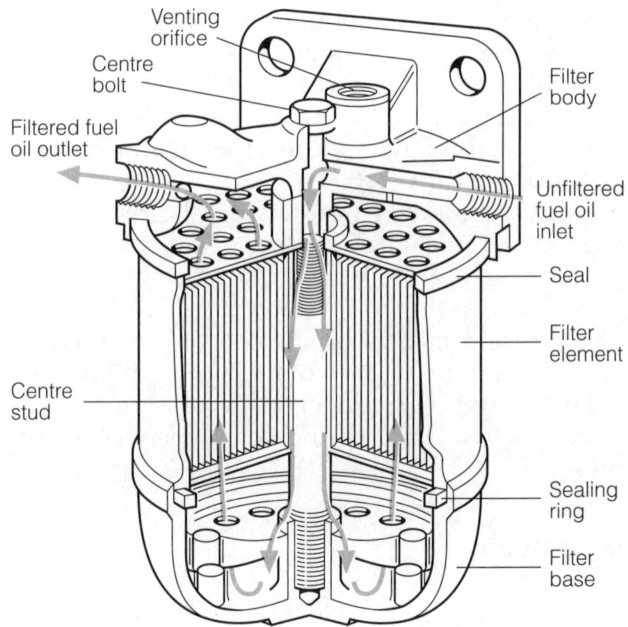

Figure 10.7 Conventional filter.

Filter elements

The filter element may be made of pleated paper, cotton or felt.

Pleated paper element

Special resin-treated paper is used to give it high strength when wet. It is formed round a metal core in a series of vee-shaped coils. This greatly increases the surface area of the filter, and enables its service life to be extended (Figure 10.7).

Cotton and felt

Once common, cotton and felt are seldom used in modern filters. Although they have the disadvantage of being able only to filter out particles down to a size of around 20 μm, they did have the advantage that, in many cases, they could be cleaned and reused.

Filter changing

> All filters must be sealed to prevent air from entering and fuel from leaking out.

This is achieved by ensuring that all unions are correctly tightened, and that sealing rings are placed between all the mating surfaces. These seals should be changed whenever the filter is replaced or cleaned.

Pipes

The system uses two types of pipe (Figure 10.8): **low pressure** and **high pressure**.

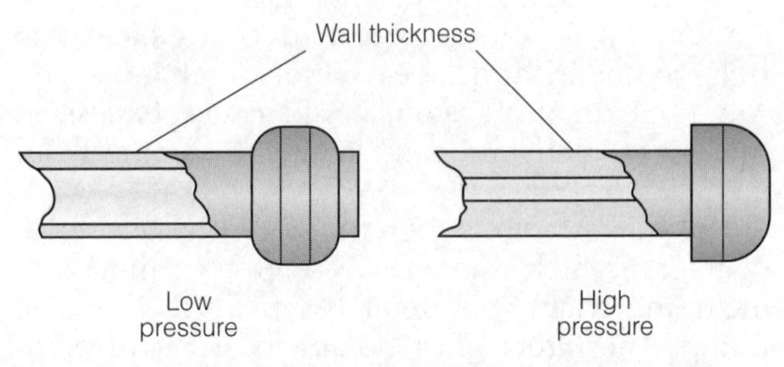

Figure 10.8 Low-pressure and high-pressure pipe.

Low-pressure pipe

Low-pressure pipe is used from the tank to the filters, lift pump and injection pump; and similarly for the leak-off pipes to return fuel from the injectors to the tank. These pipes are usually about 10–12 mm in diameter, and are made from mild steel or, more commonly now, plastic.

High-pressure pipe

High-pressure pipe is used between the injection pump and the injector. Because of the high pressure, these pipes are made of high-quality mild steel tubing with walls usually 2.5 mm thick, and with a bore of 1.0 mm. They either have brazed nipples, or the end is flared to provide a perfect, pressure-tight seal.

All the pipes should ideally be of the same length to prevent fuel surge, and should be securely clamped to prevent vibration and subsequent fracture. It is also very important that the pipe ends sit neatly into their locations on the pump and the injector without any tension.

CHECK YOUR UNDERSTANDING

- CI fuel injection systems consist of a large-capacity, low-pressure fuel supply pump, fed from a fuel tank through primary filters. External supply pumps deliver fuel at a relatively low pressure through one or more secondary filters to the injection pump.
- Where there is an integral supply pump, fuel is forced by atmospheric pressure through the secondary filters.
- Because of the very small operating clearances of the injection equipment, efficient filtration is essential to remove water and any particles of dirt.
- Air must be excluded from the system, so screws are fitted to allow the fuel lines to be bled after reassembly, or if the tank is allowed to run dry.

PROJECTS

Before working on CI fuel systems it is important to remember that **cleanliness is essential**; this cannot be overstressed. Take care to ensure that dirt or fine particles of dust do not contaminate the system, as this will cause damage to the injectors and injection pump.

Servicing filters

For any particular engine with which you are familiar, find the instructions for filter servicing. Note the number, type and position of all the fuel filters, and how often they need to be serviced and the procedure. If possible – and under supervision – carry out the filter changes.

Bleeding the low-pressure system

The system will not work properly if air is in any part of it. Although some modern diesel fuel systems are self-bleeding, most need bleeding if they have been completely drained of fuel, or if the filters have been changed.

For the same engine as the filter-servicing project, find out the procedure for bleeding the low-pressure system. Again, if possible, carry out the work.

REVISION EXERCISES AND QUESTIONS

1. Name the basic units of the CI engine fuel system.
2. What is a vane pump, and where is it usually located?
3. Why are filters so important in the system?
4. How are water, and some dirt, filtered out of the system?
5. Why are external lift pumps fitted with a hand-operating lever?

11 CI injection equipment

Introduction

The primary functions of a compression ignition (CI) fuel injection pump are:

- to deliver the correct amount of fuel under all conditions of engine load and speed;
- to deliver the correct amount of fuel at the correct time;
- to raise the pressure of the fuel so that the injectors can break up (or atomise) the fuel into a fine mist.

There are two types of fuel injection pump that are commonly fitted to IC engines: the **multi-element** or **in-line injection pump**, and the **rotary** or **DPA-type injection pump**.

Multi-element (in-line) fuel injection pump

This type of pump is located on the side of the engine block, and is driven by the engine. It is called an in-line pump because the pumping elements are mounted in line as shown in Figure 11.1.

The pump consists of a hollow aluminium casing, which contains the same number of **pumping elements** as the engine has cylinders; above each element is a delivery valve. Each pumping element consists of a plunger and a barrel, which have been precisely machined to form a mated pair. The plunger is machined with a **helix**: that is, a curved cutaway along the plunger's body.

The barrel has two ports drilled into its body, the **inlet port** and the **spill port**, which align with the fuel gallery supplying all the pump's elements.

The plungers can twist or rotate within their barrels, and this movement is controlled by the control rack, which is itself controlled by both a governor unit and the accelerator pedal. The rotation of each plunger alters the position of the helix relative to the spill port, which regulates the amount of fuel delivered by each pumping element.

Operation

When each of the plungers is at bottom dead-centre (b.d.c.) (Figure 11.2a), pressurised fuel enters through the inlet port and fills the space immediately above the plunger and the cutaway formed by the helix. Any remaining fuel passes through the spill port and into the common fuel gallery.

As the pump camshaft lifts the plunger, it reaches a point where both the inlet and the spill ports are cut off from the fuel gallery (Figure 11.2b). Further upward movement causes the fuel trapped above the plunger to be pressurised and forced past the delivery valve (not shown here) towards the injector. To vary the amount of fuel that each pumping element is capable of delivering, each plunger is rotated by means of a toothed control rack. This rotation varies the amount that each plunger can deliver to its attached injector (Figure 11.2c and d).

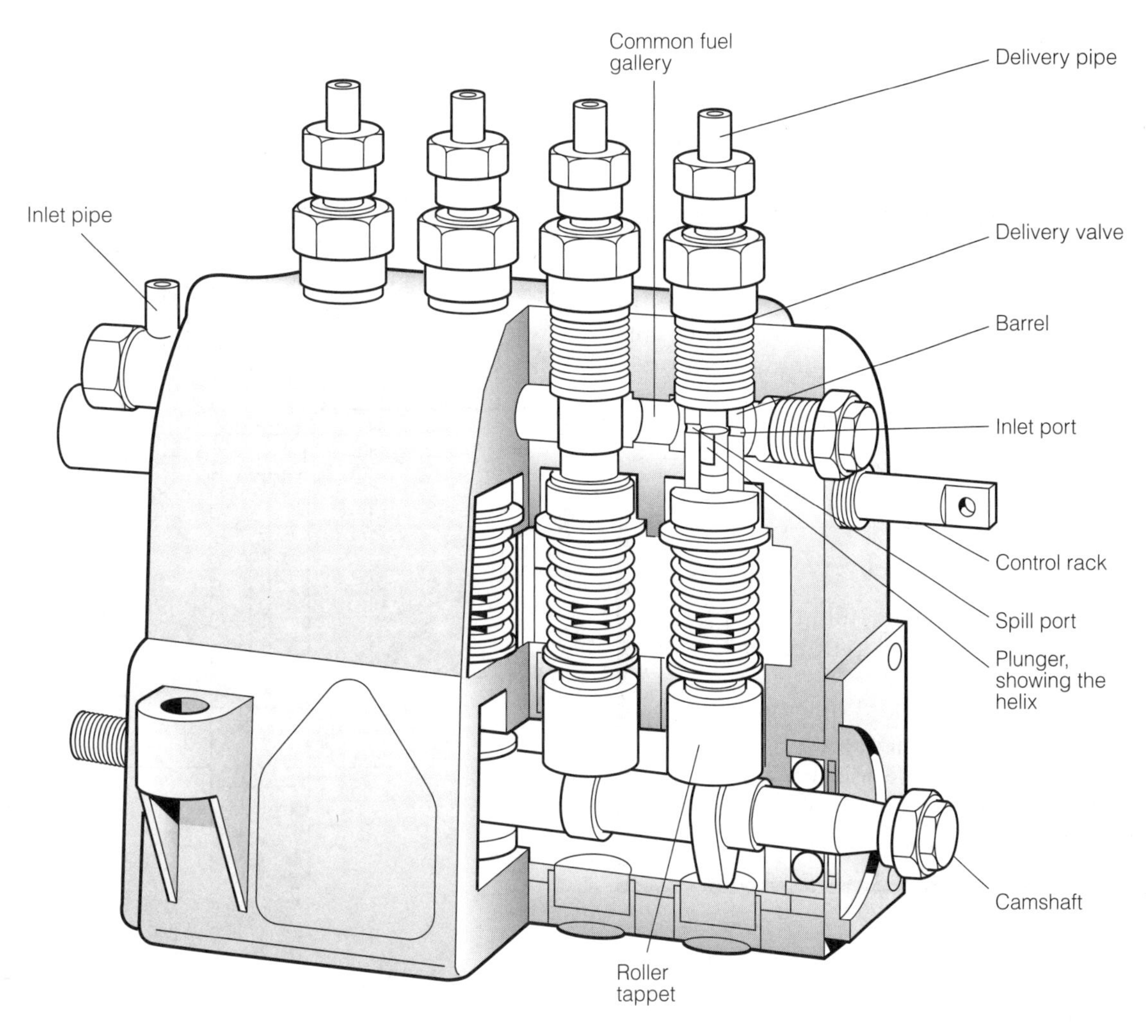

Figure 11.1 In-line fuel injection pump.

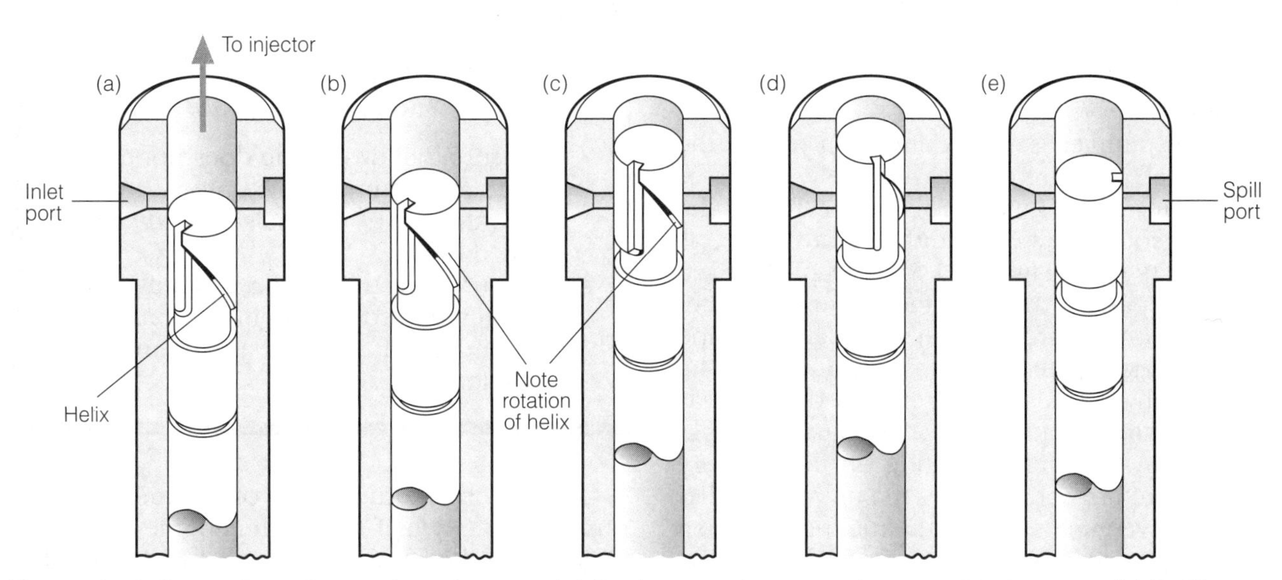

Figure 11.2 Operation of pumping element. (a) Recharge: plunger at bottom dead-centre. (b) Spill cut-off position. (c) End of injection: maximum power. (d) End of injection: low power. (e) Stop position: slot in line with spill port.

Engine stop control

To prevent a CI engine from running, the injection pump includes a fuel cut-off device.

When the device is operated, the control rack rotates all the plungers so that their slots line up with the spill ports (Figure 11.2e). This prevents the upward-moving pumping elements from pressurising the fuel.

Delivery valve

The main functions of a delivery valve are:

- to prevent fuel from running out of the injector pipe when the plunger is on its downward stroke;
- to ensure that a residual line pressure is maintained in each injector delivery pipe;
- to stop dribbling at the injector nozzle by ensuring a rapid collapse of pressure at the end of the injection phase.

A delivery valve is fitted above each pumping element. It consists of a spring-loaded valve (face and seat) and a volume-reducer guide machined to give a perfect fit. The valve face is tapered, and matches up with a similarly shaped valve seat machined onto the main body of the valve guide.

Operation

When the plunger is on the injection phase, the rise in fuel pressure pushes the delivery valve upwards inside its guide. This action forces the unloader collar upwards, and the valve face is lifted off its seat (Figure 11.3). The pressurised fuel then passes through the volume-reducer guide and on towards the injector delivery pipe and the appropriate injector. At the end of the injection phase, the plunger moves downwards towards bottom dead-centre. This causes a rapid reduction in the pressure acting on the delivery valve. The return spring forces the unloader collar into the valve guide, sealing the fuel return. Then further slight downward movement of the delivery valve as it closes produces a very small space in the pipeline, which cause a sudden pressure drop, and prevents the injector from dribbling.

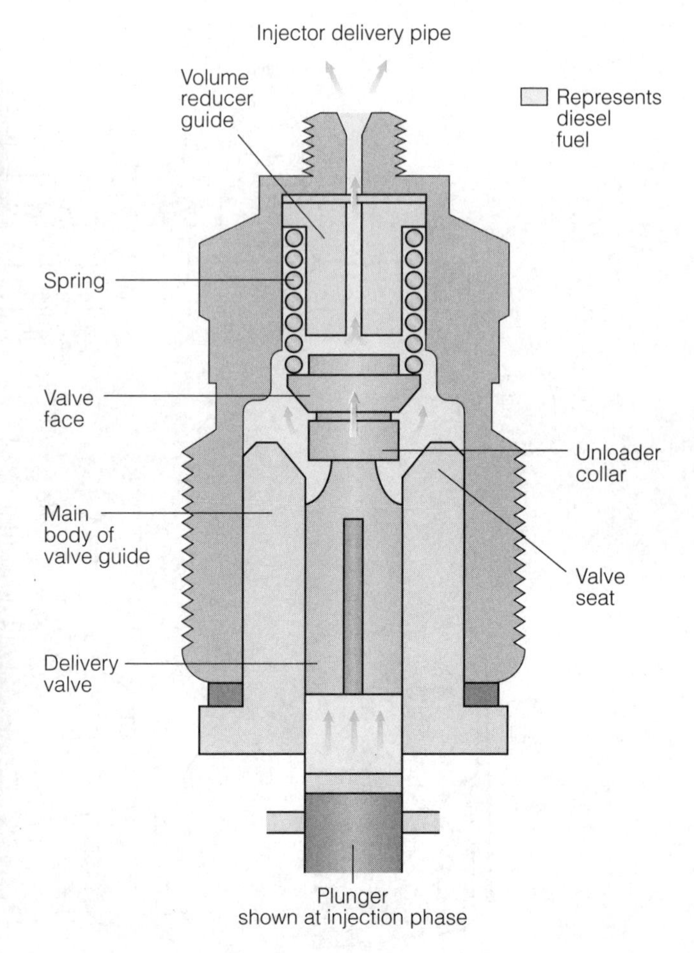

Figure 11.3 Delivery valve operation.

Governors

The main functions of a governor unit are:

- to ensure that an engine does not exceed its safe maximum rpm setting;
- to control the engine's speed within defined limits;
- to ensure that the correct amount of fuel is injected into the combustion chamber under all engine speed and load conditions.

On a CI engine the speed of the fuel injection pump is exactly half that of the engine. So, as the engine speed increases, more fuel is delivered to the engine. This, in turn, causes a further rise in the speed of the engine. Unchecked, this could cause serious engine damage.

The three main types of governor unit that are commonly fitted to an in-line injection pump are:

1. pneumatic;
2. flyweight mechanical;
3. leafspring mechanical.

Pneumatic governors

This type of governor consists of a **venturi flow control unit**, which is fitted to the inlet manifold, and a pneumatic unit fitted to the injection pump. Connecting the venturi flow control unit to the pneumatic governor are two suction pipes. These enable the variation of the depression in the venturi, created by the progressive opening or closing of the butterfly valve, to influence the pneumatic governor (Figure 11.4).

When the engine is stopped, the spring loading on the diaphragm moves the fuel control rack to the maximum fuel position for starting. When the engine is running, the high depression in the venturi is felt in the diaphragm chamber, and this allows atmospheric pressure to push the diaphragm back to the idling position. This action limits the amount of fuel delivered to the engine.

When the accelerator pedal is depressed, the butterfly valve progressively opens up, and the depression reduces. As the depression is not so great, the control spring can force the control rack in the direction of increased fuel until the spring balances the atmospheric pressure on the vented side of the diaphragm. This limits control rack movement and governs the engine speed.

Maximum fuel (maximum engine speed) is controlled by a stop at the other end of the control rack.

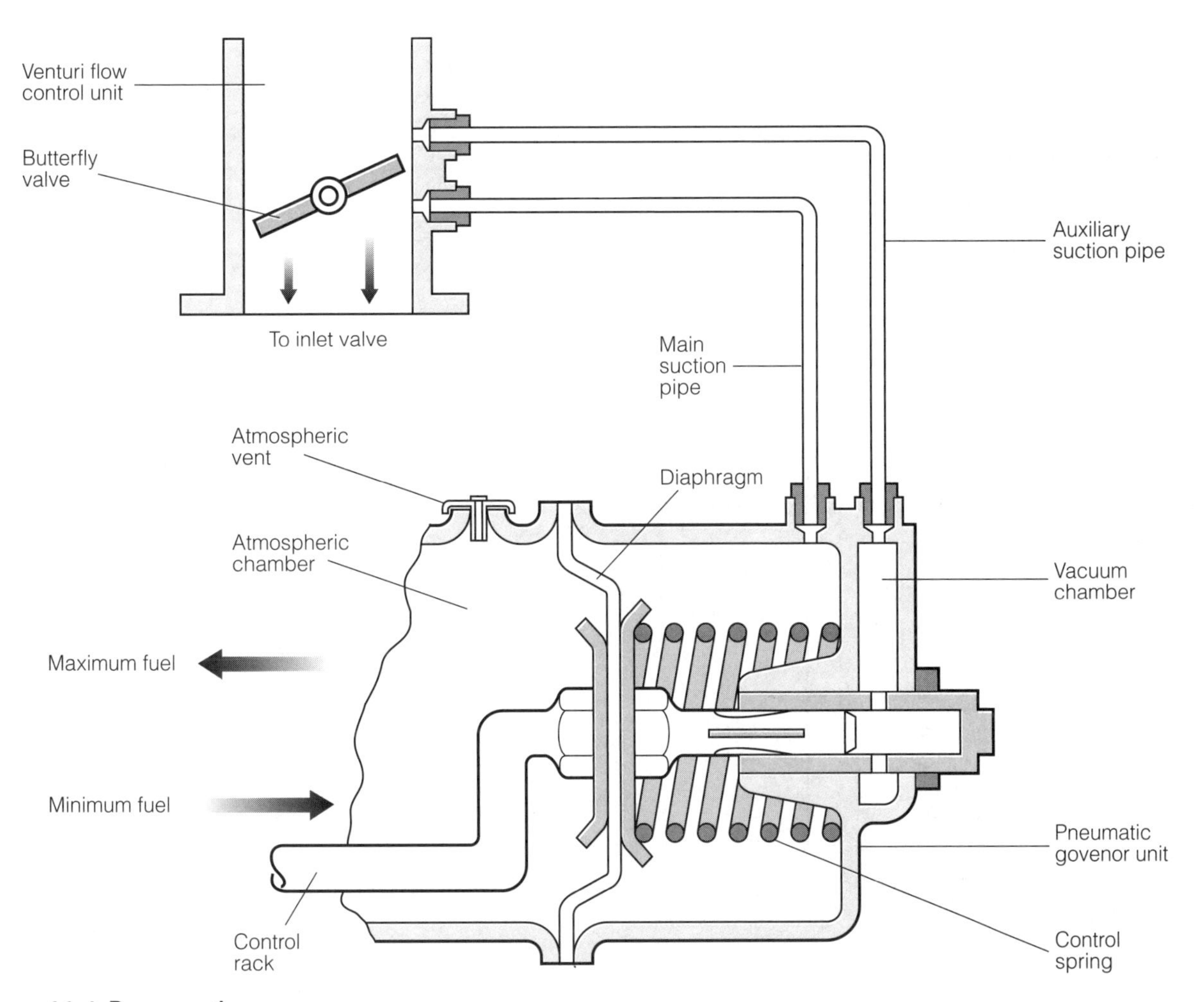

Figure 11.4 Pneumatic governor.

Flyweight mechanical governor

> In this type of governor a set of balancing (governor) weights are mounted on the pump's driveshaft. When these are subjected to a centrifugal force, a reaction occurs that limits the movement of the control rack.

The main components of a flyweight mechanical governor are:

1. an adjustable throttle lever;
2. a pivoted control arm, which moves the control rack between its minimum and maximum settings;
3. a governor spring, which connects the throttle lever to the control arm;
4. a fuel control rack, which alters the position of each of the pump's plunger elements;
5. a thrust sleeve located on the pump's driveshaft, which is operated by the centrifugal action of the governor weights.

At idling speed, the control rack moves towards the minimum fuel position. This results in the engine's running at a constant idling speed (Figure 11.5). To prevent the engine from stalling, an adjustable idling screw is fitted to the control rack. This limits the amount of movement of the control rack when in the minimum fuel position.

When the accelerator pedal is operated, the tension on the governor spring increases, and this causes the control rack to move towards the maximum fuel position. As more fuel is delivered, the speeds of both the engine and the injection pump driveshaft increase. The governor weights fly outwards, because of the increased centrifugal force, which moves the thrust sleeve and the control rack back towards the minimum fuel position. This action continues until a state of balance is reached where the engine runs at a governed speed.

Leafspring mechanical governor

> This type of governor has many similarities to the flyweight unit, the main differences being the use of:
>
> - a shaped governor spring;
> - a roller assembly;
> - a shaped ramp.

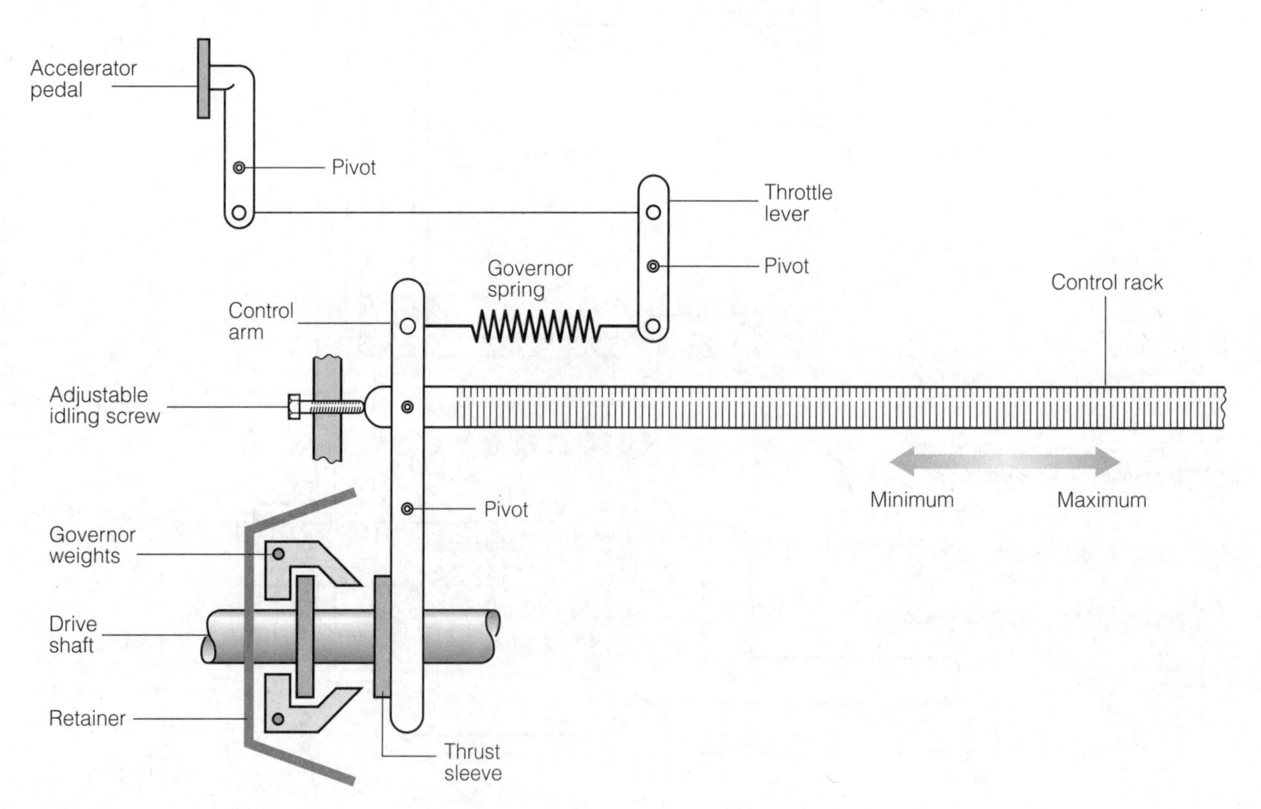

Figure 11.5 Flyweight mechanical governor.

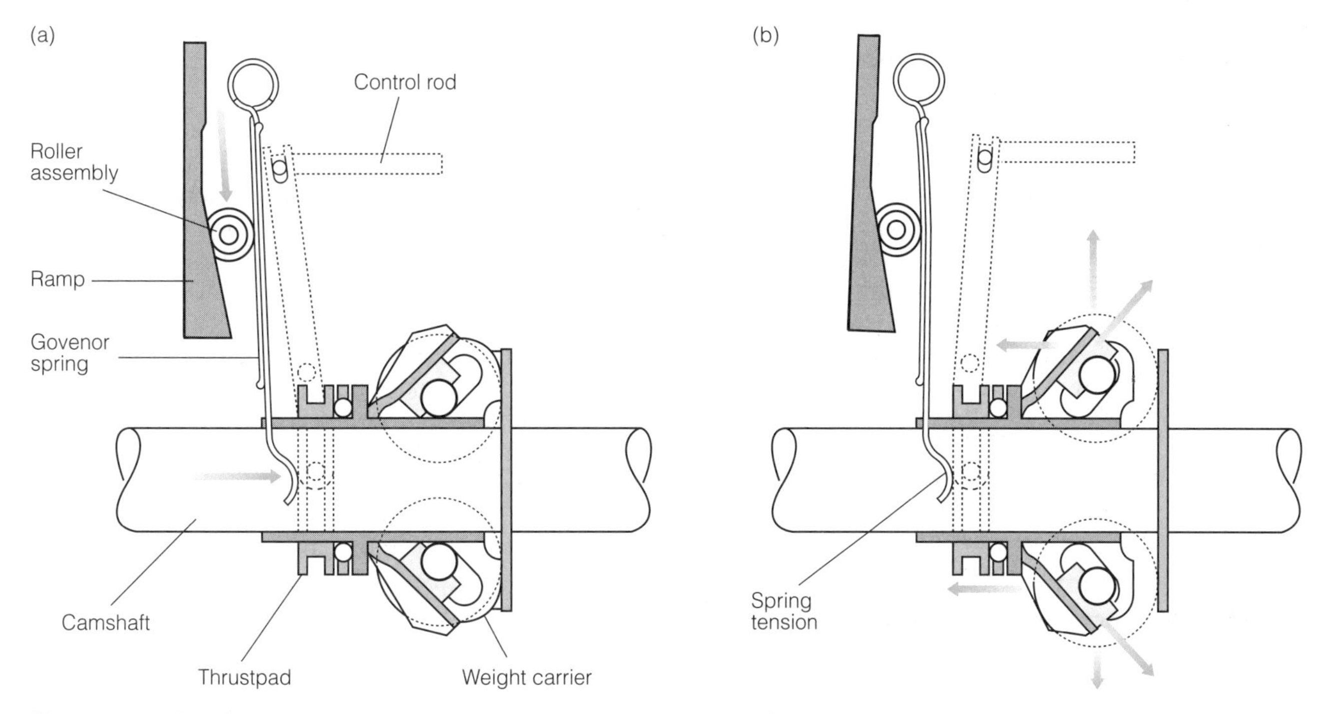

Figure 11.6 Leafspring mechanical governor: (a) maximum fuel position; (b) minimum fuel position.

These items are jointly used to control the engine speed.

As the accelerator pedal is operated, the tension on the governor spring increases. This causes a set of rollers to be pushed down between both the ramp and the governor spring, thus forcing the control rod towards the maximum fuel position (Figure 11.6a). The increased centrifugal force acting on the governor weights creates an opposing force on the thrust pad, and thus moves the control rod towards the minimum position (Figure 11.6b). It is the balancing of the centrifugal force created by the rotating weights, and the tension force held in the leafspring by the roller assembly, that holds the thrust pad and control rod in the governed engine speed position.

Maximum and minimum speeds are determined by control rod stops.

Phasing and calibration

Phasing is a term used to describe the timing interval, measured in degrees, between each successive injection of fuel from the injection pump.

On a four-cylinder CI engine the injection phases should be every 90° of pump driveshaft rotation, while for a six-cylinder engine they are every 60°. The phasing of an in-line injection pump needs to be periodically checked because, after a high mileage, the internal components of the pump suffer from wear and tear.

Calibration is the term used to describe the procedure of adjusting the quantity of fuel that each pump element delivers to each particular injector.

The injection pump needs to be calibrated to ensure that each pumping element delivers exactly the same quantity of fuel.

Phasing and calibration adjustment

To check that a pump's phasing and calibration settings are within specified tolerances, a specialist piece of test equipment called a **diesel pump test bench** is used.

Injection pump repairs are usually carried out by specialist service personnel.

Distributor-type injection pumps

The distributor-type injection pump is usually called the **rotary** or **DPA** (distributor pump application) injection pump. The main parts of the pump are shown in Figure 11.7. The DPA pump has a set of plungers located within a centrally mounted rotor shaft, which is driven by and timed to the engine. Behind the plungers is a set of rollers, which are mounted on a cam ring.

> The main purpose of the **rotor** is to transport fuel towards the plungers, and then to distribute the fuel to each of the injector outlet ports in the appropriate sequence.

The cam ring has a number of cam lobes machined at equally spaced distances from each other. The recess between each lobe is known as the **retraction curve**. There are as many cam lobes as the engine has cylinders.

The main steel body of the DPA pump is called the **hydraulic head**. This contains a set of internal drillings, which allow the fuel into the pump; then, in conjunction with the rotor, the pressurised fuel is distributed to each of the injector outlet pipes in the appropriate sequence. To control and regulate the pressure of the fuel accurately, a **transfer pump** and **regulator valve** are fitted inside the injection pump. These two components ensure that the line pressure of the fuel is kept within specified tolerances. To measure the quantity of fuel entering the injection pump precisely under all operating conditions, a **metering valve** is built into the pump (Figure 11.8).

In order to provide the pump with a means by which the fuel injection phase can be progressively advanced or retarded with engine speed and load changes, an automatic advancement mechanism is fitted (Figure 11.9).

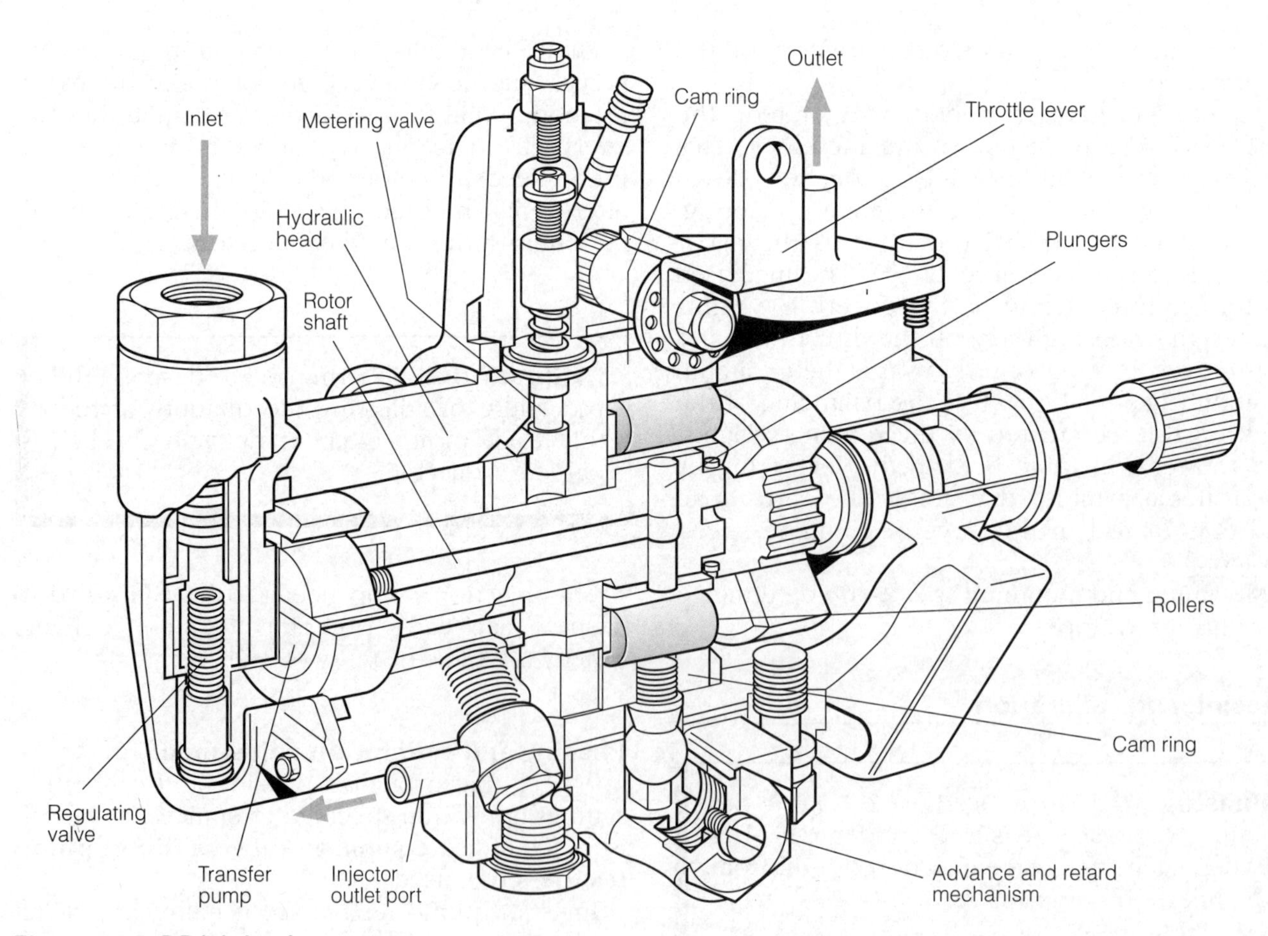

Figure 11.7 DPA injection pump.

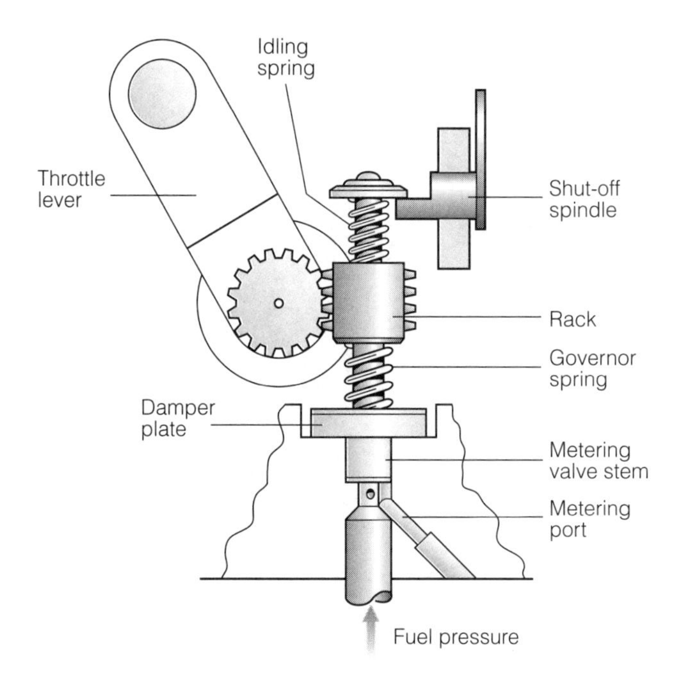

Figure 11.8 Metering valve controlled by a hydraulic governor.

Operation

When the fuel is delivered to the DPA injection pump by the fuel lift pump, a sliding vane-type transfer pump raises the fuel's pressure still further (Figure 11.9). The purpose of the transfer pump is to create a transfer pressure, so that the injection pump can supply all of the engine's fuel requirements under varying operating conditions. To prevent the transfer pressure inside the pump from exceeding certain design tolerances, a spring-loaded regulator valve is fitted.

The position of the fuel-metering valve is controlled by a combination of throttle lever movement and the action of the governor. From the metering valve, the pressurised fuel is transferred to the metering port in the hydraulic head. When the charging port on the rotor aligns with the metering port, fuel is transferred towards the plungers (Figure 11.10). The pressure of the incoming fuel is sufficient to force the plungers and rollers against a cam ring.

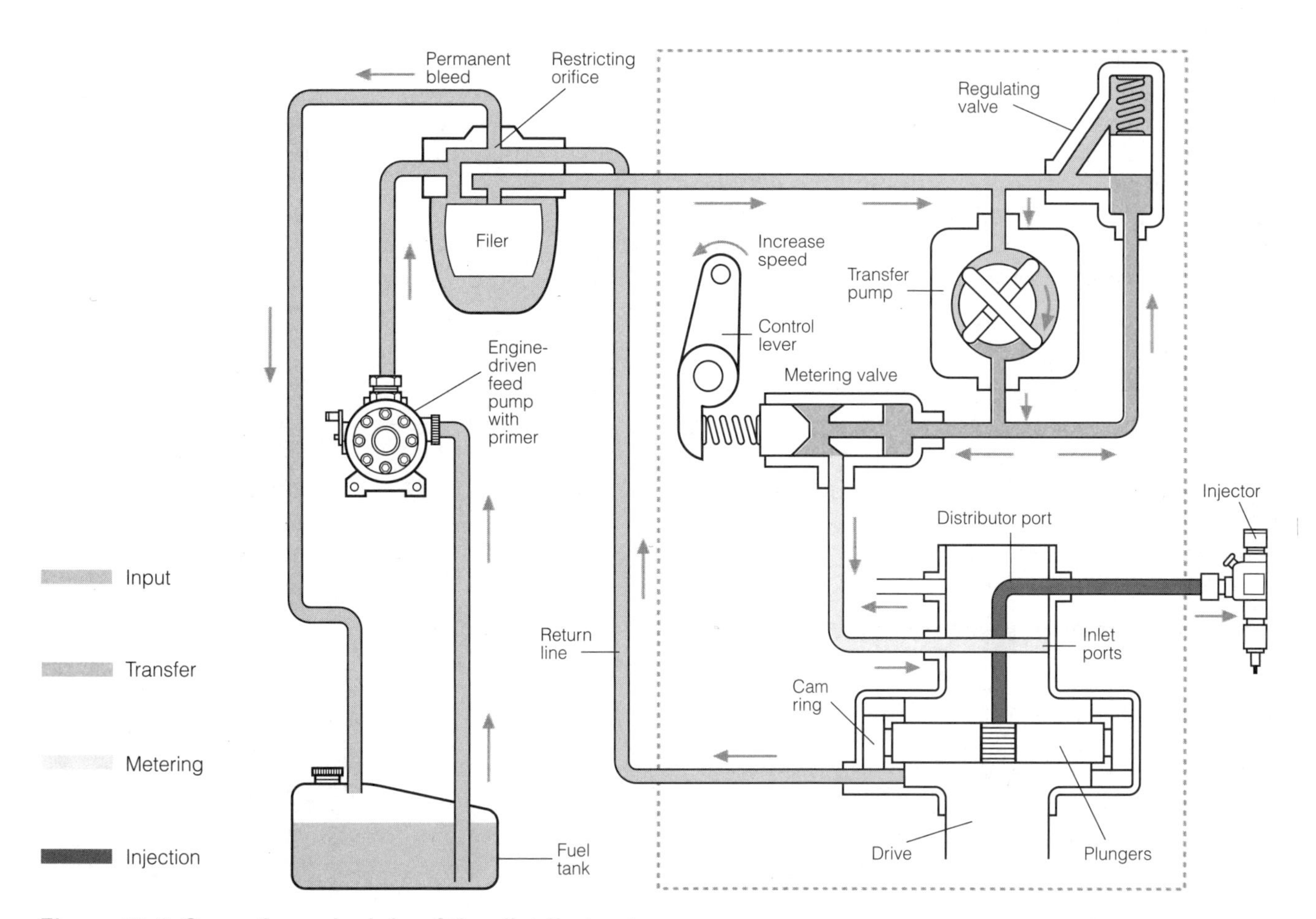

Figure 11.9 Operating principle of the distributor-type pump.

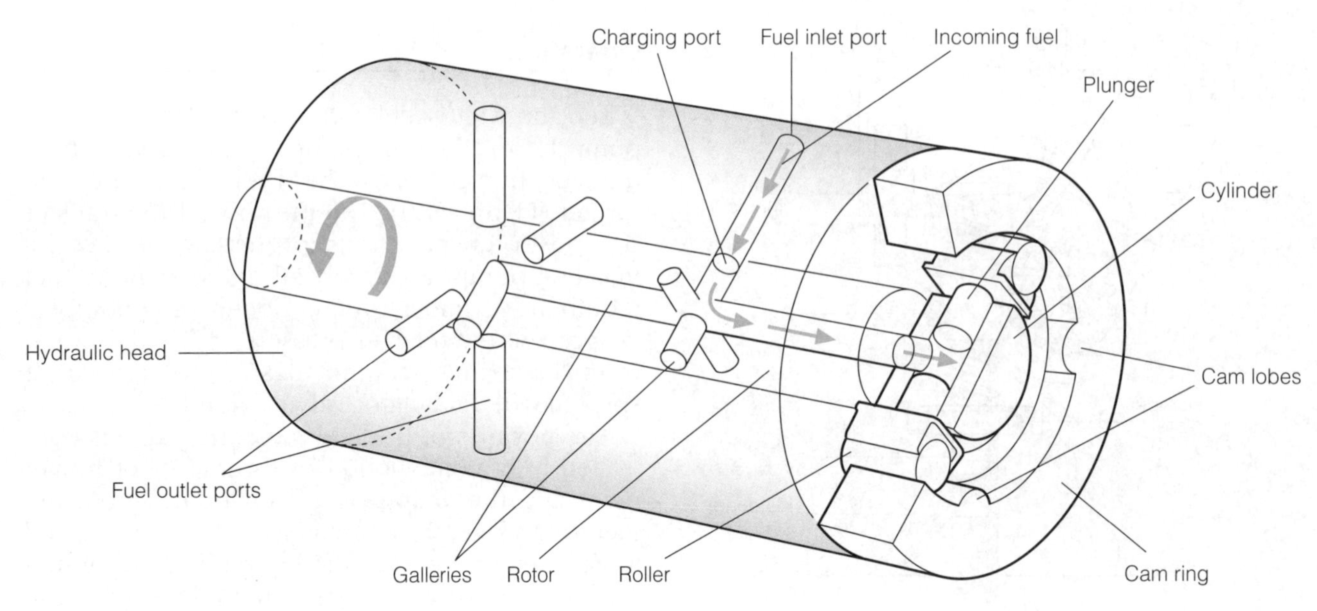

Figure 11.10 Metering valve.

Further movement of the rotor shaft, which is being driven by the timing gears, causes the rollers to rotate and follow the rising and falling contours of the cam ring. As the rollers approach the peaks of the cam lobes, the plungers are forced towards each other and so increase the pressure of the fuel in the internal centre gallery of the rotor. The fuel remains under pressure in the internal gallery of the rotor until the distributor port aligns with one of the fuel outlet ports in the hydraulic head. The pressurised fuel is then transferred to the appropriate injector.

Hydraulic governor

The basic principle of the hydraulic governor is that moving the metering valve alters the effective area of the metering port and therefore the quantity of fuel delivered to the engine.

The position of the metering valve is dependent upon both the governor spring pressure and the pressure created by the transfer pump. The pressure of fuel acting on the base of the metering valve is counteracted by the governor and idle springs until an equilibrium position (or state of balance) is achieved (Figure 11.11). When the accelerator pedal is operated, the metering valve is pushed downwards inside its guide. This downward movement causes more of the metering port to be uncovered, allowing a greater quantity of fuel to be delivered to the hydraulic head and plungers, and so the engine speed increases. The transfer pressure also increases and causes the metering valve to be pushed upwards inside its guide against the governor spring pressure until a state of equilibrium is reached.

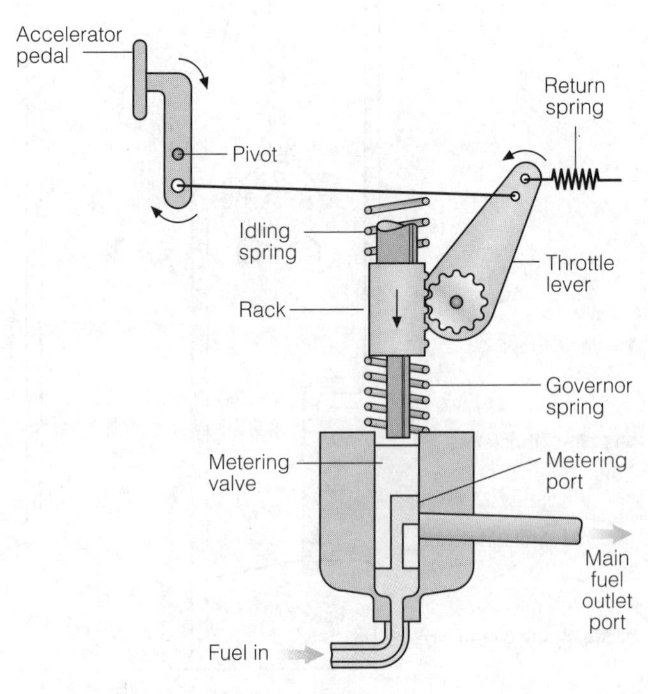

Figure 11.11 Hydraulic governor.

Automatic speed advance device

> Because both the engine's speed and load are variable, an automatic advance mechanism must be fitted to a DPA pump to advance or retard the fuel injection phase.

The automatic speed advance unit is located at the base of the injection pump, and consists of a cylinder which has two pistons. Located between these two pistons is a ball-shaped lever, which is screwed into the cam ring (Figure 11.12). One of the pistons is fitted with a double-action return spring, which pushes the cam ring towards the fully retarded position. During engine operation a small drilling behind the second piston allows fuel under transfer pressure to oppose the spring pressure acting on the first piston. As the speed of the engine increases, the transfer pressure acting behind the second piston increases, and so rotates the cam ring towards the fully advanced position. This rotation enables the plungers to be forced together at an earlier period than otherwise would be the case. As the engine speed reduces, the transfer pressure falls, and the cam ring returns to the retarded position under the influence of the return spring.

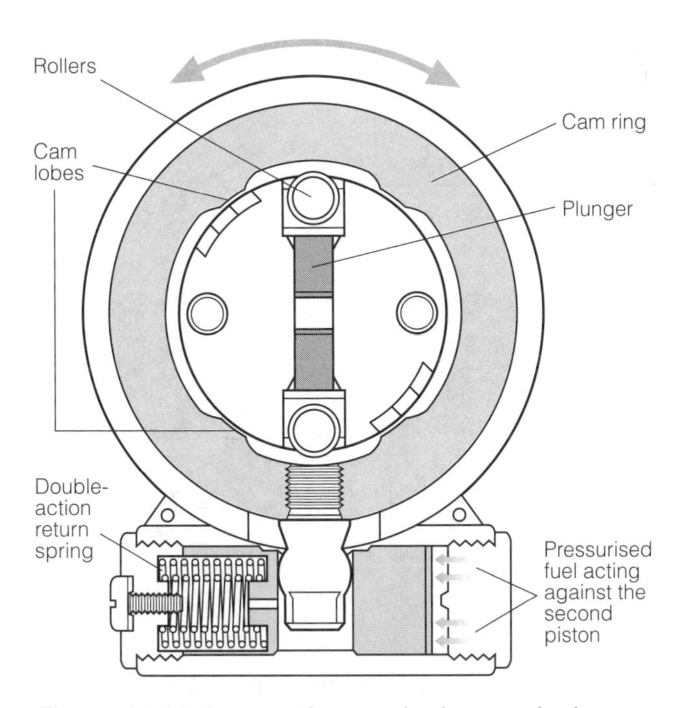

Figure 11.12 Automatic speed advance device.

Fuel shut-off device

> The fuel shut-off device prevents a CI engine from running.

It consists of a shut-off spindle that, when operated, causes the metering valve to be lifted upwards to a 'no fuel' position (Figure 11.8). In such a position, the metering valve prevents the fuel from reaching the hydraulic head or injectors.

Advantages of the rotary pump over an in-line pump

The rotary injection pump has grown in popularity in recent years. It has a number of technical advantages over more traditional in-line pumps:

1. It is generally smaller, lighter, and more compact, and can be fitted in a variety of convenient locations on the engine block.
2. Since the diesel fuel lubricates all the moving internal components, it requires no separate lubrication supply, and so little periodic maintenance is necessary. An in-line pump requires a separate oil supply to lubricate the internal camshaft.
3. It has fewer moving components, and therefore there is a lower risk of mechanical failure.
4. It does not need phasing and calibration, because the phasing is pre-specified by the manufacturer and is set by the position of the cam lobes, while the calibration is determined by the metering valve. An in-line pump requires phasing and calibration testing periodically and adjustment if necessary.
5. It is less expensive to make.

Diesel fuel injectors

For a CI engine to work at its most efficient and achieve complete combustion, the diesel fuel must be changed from a liquid state (which cannot be easily ignited) into a fine, atomised spray (which will readily burn).

The main functions of a CI fuel injector are:

- to ensure that the diesel fuel is injected into the engine's combustion chamber at the correct pressure, and to form the correct spray pattern;
- to stop the injection of the fuel as soon as the injection pump pressure drops below a pre-set level.

Injector operation

Inside a CI fuel injector nozzle is a needle valve, which has been machined to very fine tolerances. The needle valve is held tight on its seat by an injector spring and spindle (Figure 11.13). Directly below the needle valve and seat is the nozzle tip, which directs the fuel into a predetermined spot within the combustion chamber. When the fuel pressure is low, the needle valve is held tightly onto its seat by spring pressure.

As injection pump pressure rises, highly pressurised fuel enters the injector through the inlet union. The fuel is directed towards the shoulder of the needle valve by a small drilling in the body of the injector. When the fuel pressure, acting on the shoulder of the needle valve, exceeds the injector's spring pressure, the needle valve lifts off its seating, and fuel is forced through the spray hole in the nozzle tip as a finely atomised spray. In contrast, when the fuel injection pressure falls below that of the injector spring pressure, the needle valve is forced back onto its seat. This prevents any more fuel from being injected.

There are four types of fuel injector that may be fitted to CI engines:

1. single-hole injector;
2. multi-hole injector;
3. pintle-type injector;
4. pintaux injector.

Examples of each are shown in Figure 11.14.

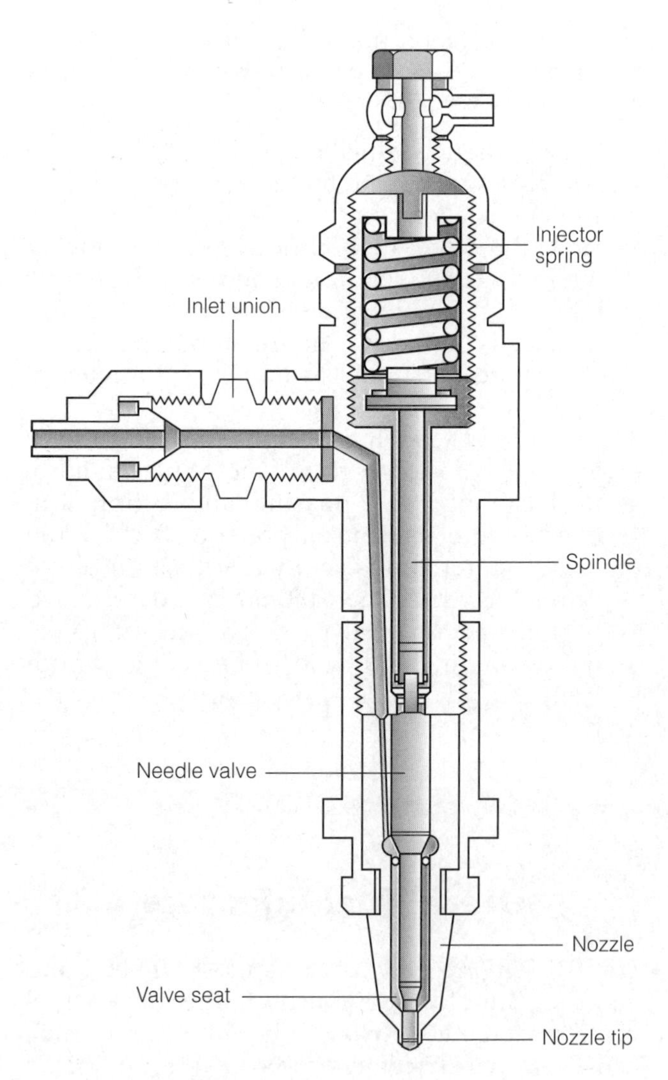

Figure 11.13 Typical CI fuel injector.

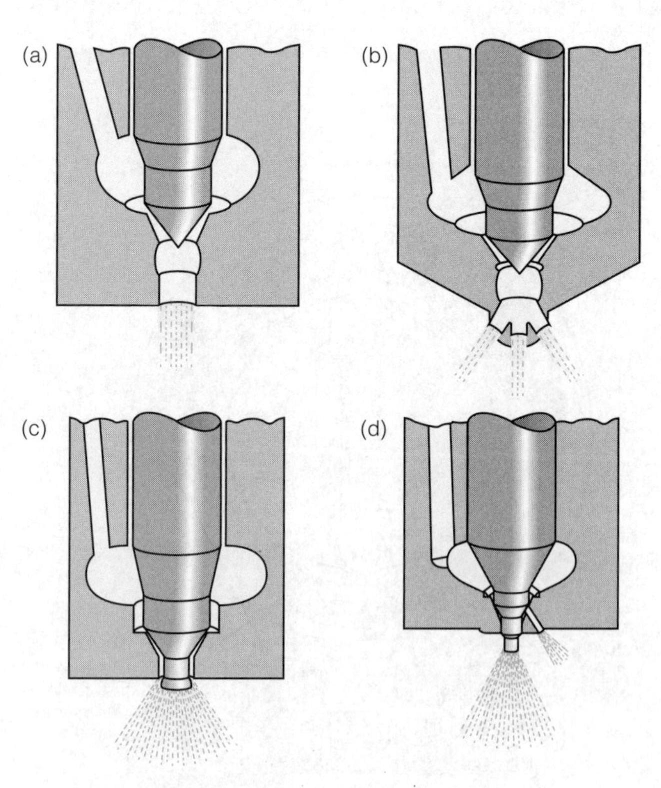

Figure 11.14 Injector nozzles: (a) single hole; (b) multi-hole; (c) pintle; (d) pintaux.

Single-hole injector

> The single-hole injector (Figure 11.14a) has a single spray outlet drilled centrally through the end of the injectors nozzle tip, which allows the atomised fuel to be directed into the engine's combustion chamber.

Single-hole injectors are simpler and cheaper than other types. One of their main disadvantages is that they give a relatively poor spray pattern. This often results in unburnt fuel escaping in the exhaust gases, giving heavy fuel consumption. For this reason they are seldom fitted to modern CI engines.

Multi-hole injector

> The multi-hole injector (Figure 11.14b) has a number of spray holes drilled into its nozzle tip (usually four).

This type of injector is often fitted to direct-injection CI engines, because it ensures a more precise distribution of the atomised fuel. The main advantages of a multi-hole injector over a single-hole injector are:

1. improved atomisation of the fuel;
2. better distribution of the fuel in the combustion chamber;
3. a reduction in the amount of unburnt fuel.

Pintle injector

> With an indirect-injection CI engine in which the atomised fuel is sprayed into the antechamber (rather than the actual combustion chamber), a pintle-type injector may be used (Figure 11.14c).

The end of the injector needle valve is extended to form a **pintle**, which protrudes through the single spray hole. By modifying the size and shape of the pintle, the injector's spray pattern can be changed to suit different engine requirements.

Pintaux injector

> The pintaux injector (Figure 11.14d) is a variation of the pintle type, but it has an auxiliary hole in the injector's nozzle to assist engine starting from cold.

When the engine is being turned over by the starter motor, the pressure of the fuel is only sufficient to raise the needle valve slightly. This movement is enough to uncover the auxiliary spray hole, which directs most of the fuel towards the hottest part of the combustion chamber, usually where the **heater plugs** are situated.

During normal engine operation, the more rapid build-up of fuel pressure lifts the pintle faster, and directs most of the atomised fuel through the main spray hole and into the combustion chamber. In practice approximately 10–12 per cent of the fuel continues to be sprayed through the auxiliary hole, even when the engine is running at its normal operational speed. This is to ensure that the auxiliary spray hole is kept free from a build-up of carbon deposits.

Injector maintenance

One of the problems with CI fuel injectors is that their efficiency deteriorates with prolonged usage. This makes it necessary to have the injectors serviced at regular intervals. The frequency of such maintenance depends upon:

1. the engine's normal operating conditions;
2. the quality of fuel used;
3. the efficiency of the fuel-filtering system.

To ensure that the injector both atomises the fuel and forms the correct spray pattern, it is necessary to check the opening or **cracking** pressure of the injectors periodically. The opening pressure is measured in bars or atmospheres (1 atmosphere = 14.7 lbf/in^2 or 101.3 kPa). For most injectors, the opening pressure will be in the range 125–175 bar.

Injector testing

The opening pressure of an injector can be tested using a hand-operated test unit, sometimes called a **pop tester** (Figure 11.15). The basic tester

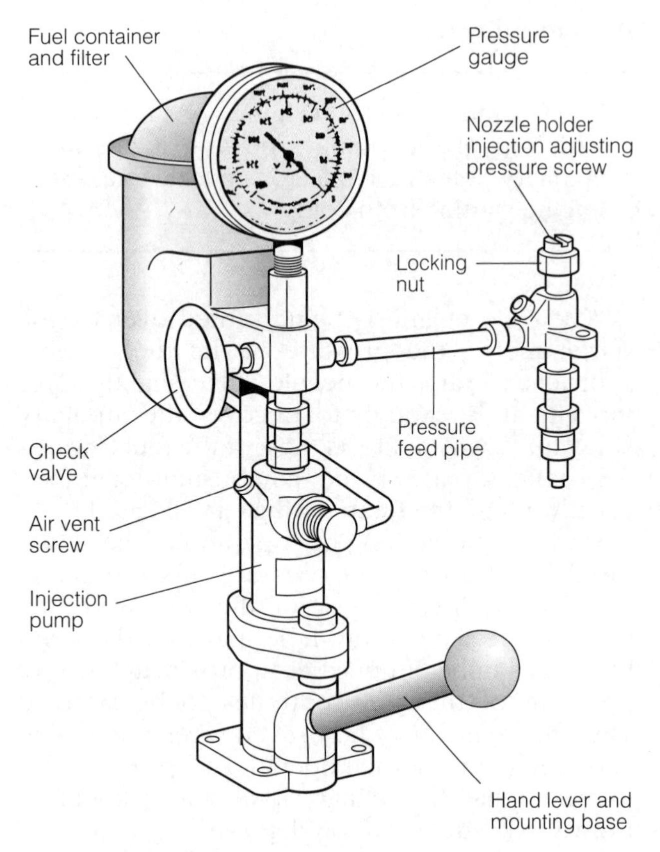

Figure 11.15 Nozzle tester.

shown consists of a reservoir containing test fluid, a hand-operated hydraulic pump, and a calibrated pressure gauge. By operating the tester, the injector opening pressure can be measured. If the injector pressure is incorrect, it can be adjusted by varying the tension of the injector spring.

> ▲ If atomised fuel or test fluid at high pressure is directed towards the human body it will pass right through the skin and cause severe injury.

Main injector tests

After checking the opening pressure of the injector, three additional tests should be carried out to assess its serviceability:

1. **Leak-back test** to check for excessive leaking back of fuel from between the needle valve and the nozzle body. A pressure drop from approximately 150 bar to 100 bar in less than 6 seconds indicates that either the needle valve and nozzle, or the injector spring, should be renewed.
2. **Nozzle seat test**. The injector pressure is raised to just below opening pressure, and held there for approximately 10 seconds. Any dribbles or drips present on the tip of the injector nozzle indicate that the needle valve and nozzle require regrinding or renewing.
3. **Atomiser operation**. A visual check of the injector spray pattern should show it to be uniform and even throughout. Any abnormal pattern may be caused by carbon build-up in the nozzle holes.

Injector fault chart

See Table 11.1.

Table 11.1 Injector fault chart

Main injector faults	Probable causes
Excessive leak-off	● Worn valve ● Nozzle cap nut incorrectly tightened ● Dirt between needle and seat
Nozzle blued	● Faulty fitting i.e. excessive tightening of holder ● Poor cooling
Opening pressure too high	● Needle valve seized ● Spray hole blocked ● Injector spring too tight
Opening pressure too low	● Injector spring broken or weak ● Too little spring tension
Nozzle dripping	● Sticking valve ● Carbon deposits on nozzle ● Seat or needle damaged
Spray pattern distorted	● Spray holes partly blocked ● Carbon deposits on the tip of the needle ● Pintle damaged

Cold-start devices

CI engines operate by generating enough heat during the compression stroke to cause the air/fuel mixture to self-ignite. In a cold CI engine, it can be difficult to raise the air temperature inside the combustion chamber to a level where it can ignite the atomised diesel fuel. To help overcome this problem, a cold-starting device must be fitted.

Heater plugs

One of the most common cold-starting devices is the **heater plug** or **glow plug**.

Looking rather like a spark plug, the tip of the heater plug protrudes slightly into the combustion space. The tip, though, is a heavy-duty electrical element. When the driver operates the cold-start switch, battery current is fed to the plug, which causes the element to glow red hot. This heats the air, helping to make it hot enough to ignite the fuel spray from the injector. A double-coil heater plug is shown in Figure 11.16.

Excess fuel device

On direct-injection CI engines the excess fuel device is often controlled by a button or cable that, when operated, causes the control rack stop to be pushed to one side (Figure 11.17). This allows the control rack to pass beyond the usual maximum fuel position and deliver an extra quantity for cold starting. When the engine has started, the control rack stop springs back into its original position, and the excess fuel control is released.

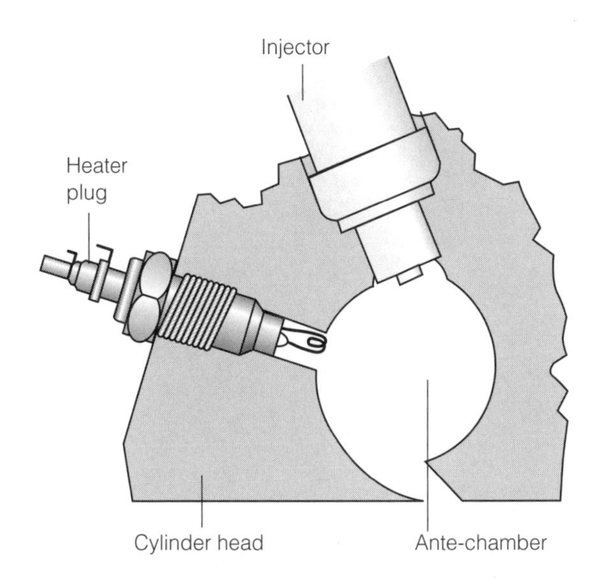

Figure 11.16 Double-coil heater plug.

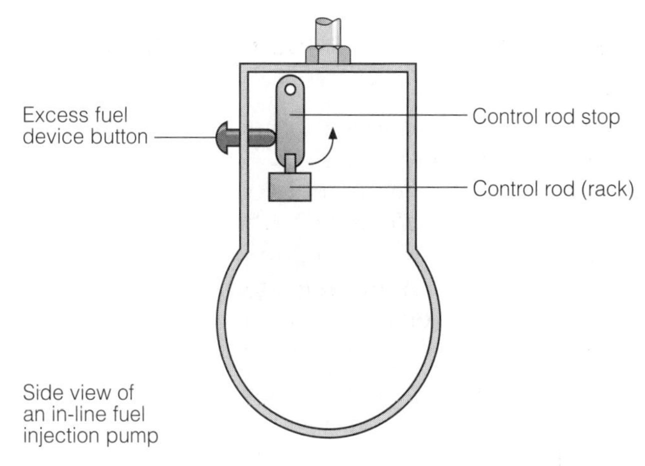

Figure 11.17 Excess fuel device.

CHECK YOUR UNDERSTANDING

- CI ignition engines are normally fitted with one of two types of fuel injection pump, known as in-line or DPA (rotary) pumps. The purpose of the fuel injection pump is to deliver highly pressurised diesel fuel to each injector sufficient to cause atomisation.
- The phasing and calibration of an in-line pump should be periodically checked. Phasing is the timing sequence for each of the pump's pumping elements. Calibration is the amount of fuel that each pumping element delivers.
- The purpose of a governor unit is to control the engine's maximum speed within defined limits. The main types of governor are pneumatic, flyweight mechanical, leafspring mechanical, and hydraulic.
- To ensue that the diesel fuel will burn easily inside the combustion chamber it must be atomised into a very fine mist spray.
- A common type of cold-start device fitted to CI engines is the heater plug or glow plug. For direct-injection engines an excess fuel device is commonly used.

REVISION EXERCISES AND QUESTIONS

1 Briefly state the primary functions of a CI fuel injection pump.
2 What are the main functions of a governor unit? State the *three* types that can be fitted to an in-line fuel injection pump.
3 What do the terms *phasing* and *calibration* mean in relation to a fuel injection pump?
4 On a multi-plunger rotary-type injection pump (DPA), what is the purpose of the metering valve?
5 State the main advantages of a rotary fuel injection pump.
6 On a Pintaux fuel injector, what is the main purpose of the auxiliary spray hole?
7 State *three* tests that are carried out on an injector tester.
8 What is the purpose of fitting a cold-starting device?

12 The exhaust system

Introduction

The function of the exhaust system is:

- to direct the burnt gases of combustion away from the vehicle and into the atmosphere;
- to reduce the noise of the exhaust gas flow.

One of the principal components of exhaust gas is carbon monoxide (CO). It is a poison, and at the very least may cause drowsiness.

The exhaust system is connected at its forward end to the exhaust manifold flange or outlet. It may be bolted or clamped into position to provide a gas-tight seal (Figures 12.1, 12.2). A simple system consists of steel pipes, possibly a catalytic converter, and one or more silencers. It is attached to the underbody or chassis by flexible mountings, often of rubber.

Components and operation

Exhaust system mountings

The flexible mountings allow for engine movement relative to the body, and for the considerable expansion and contraction of the system that takes place. The system must be sturdy and secure if leaking exhaust gas is not to be drawn into the interior of the vehicle.

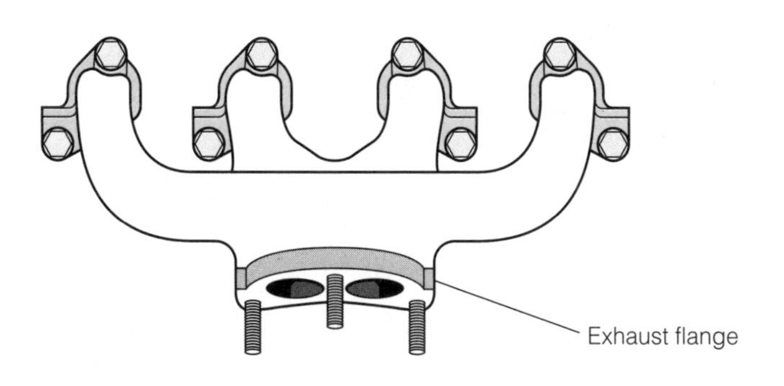

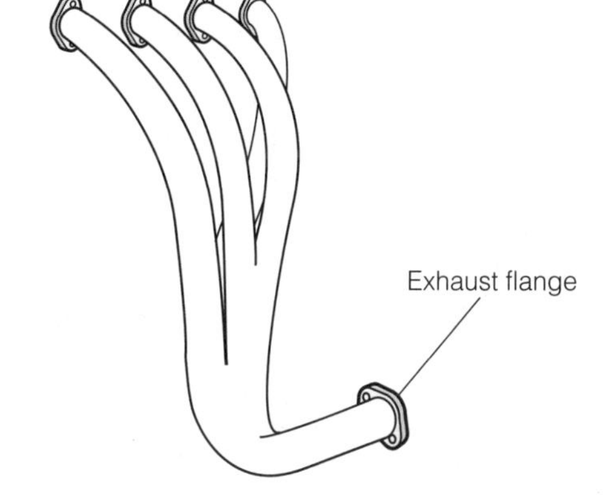

Figure 12.1 Typical exhaust manifolds.

Flexible mountings are also very important in preventing vibrations and resonance from the system being transmitted to the body (Figures 12.2 and 12.3).

Exhaust system materials

> Exhaust noise is caused by the necessarily high-speed escape of the burnt gases from the cylinder. These gases produce sound waves, which have to be damped or absorbed to a level that is acceptable to the law, to the passengers, and to the general public.

To increase the service life of exhausts, particularly on new vehicles, the system may have a corrosion-resistant aluminised coating. It is also possible to obtain stainless steel replacement exhaust systems, and some vehicle manufacturers now fit them as original equipment. They are expensive, but extremely long-lasting.

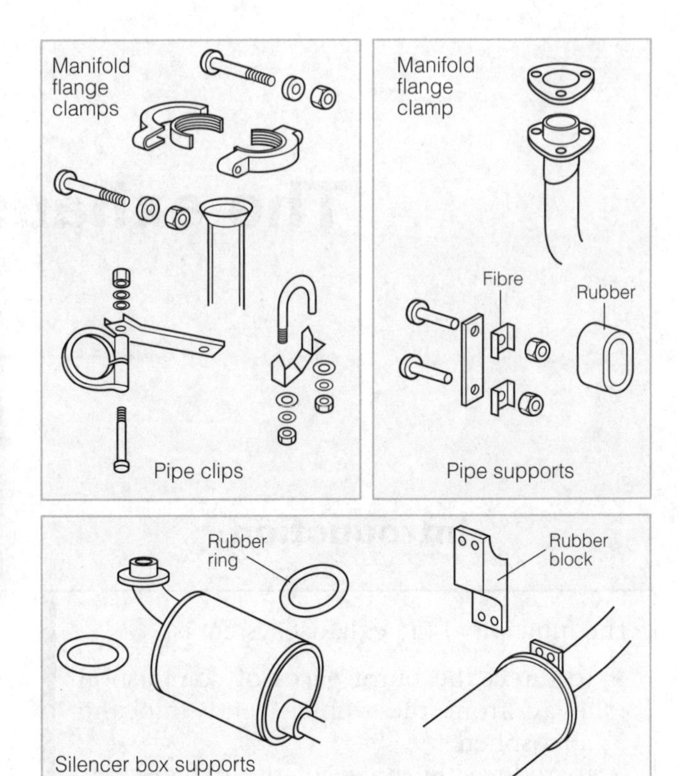

Figure 12.2 Typical exhaust clamps, box and pipe supports.

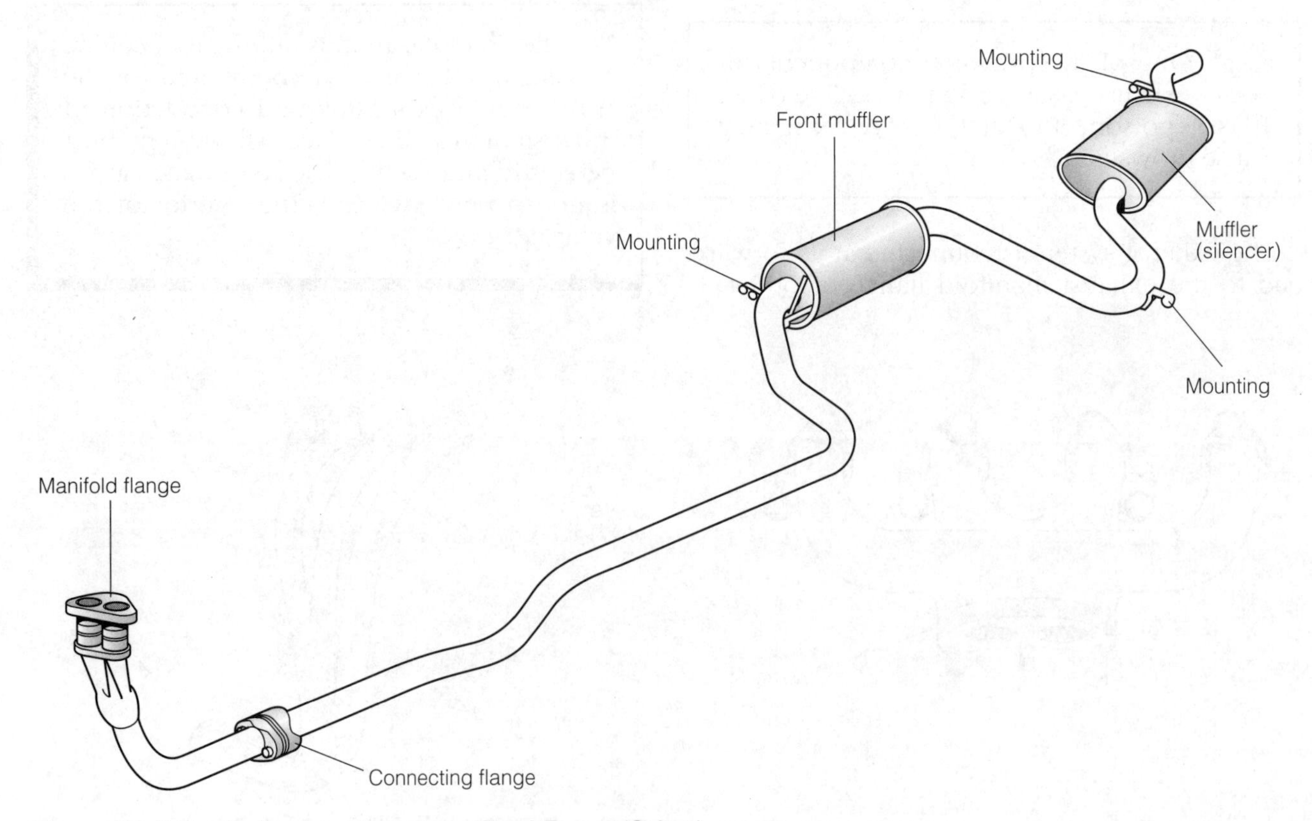

Figure 12.3 Typical exhaust system (Ford Escort/Orion).

Silencers

Exhaust systems are usually made from mild steel. This material is cheap, strong and easy to work, but corrodes easily. The inside is attacked by the acids and water created during combustion; the outside is attacked by water, dirt and stones thrown up under the vehicle. All this, plus the extremes of temperature, reduces the system's life considerably.

There are two main ways in which sound is controlled:

1. by causing the gas to pass along narrow passages and thereby to expand in a controlled manner, when much of their sound energy is lost (Figure 12.4a);
2. by surrounding the pipe with sound-absorbing material (Figure 12.4b).

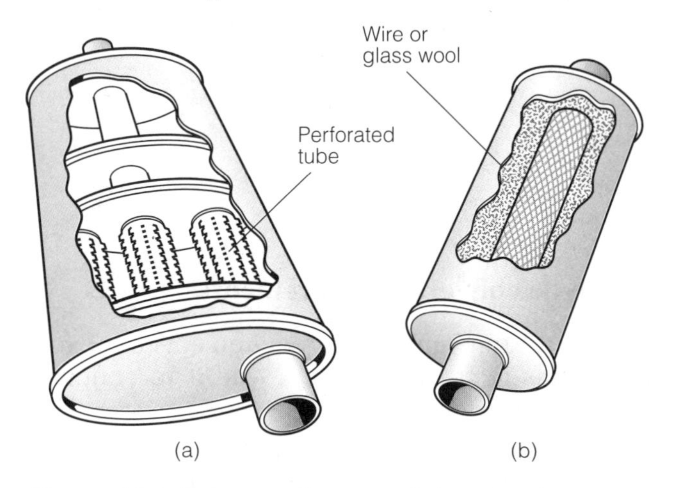

Figure 12.4 Exhaust silencers: (a) expansion silencer; (b) absorption silencer.

Catalytic converters

The need to care for the environment is a major requirement in many countries, and laws regarding exhaust emissions are commonplace. As a result, vehicles are often equipped with **catalytic converters** to convert the pollutants produced by the engine into non-toxic substances.

This is achieved by using **catalysts**, which are substances that can aid chemical change without themselves being changed. The catalytic converter is positioned close to the front of the exhaust system (Figure 12.5).

There are two-way and three-way converters, but the most efficient is known as a **three-way converter** with **closed-loop Lambda control**.

Construction and operation

The principle of operation is based on two chemical processes: oxidation and reduction. **Oxidation** is the addition of oxygen to a chemical compound or (more generally) any reaction involving the loss of electrons from an atom.

It is always accompanied by **reduction**, which is a reaction in which an electron is added to an atom or ion. Typical reduction reactions are the removal of oxygen from a molecule, and the liberation of a metal from its compounds.

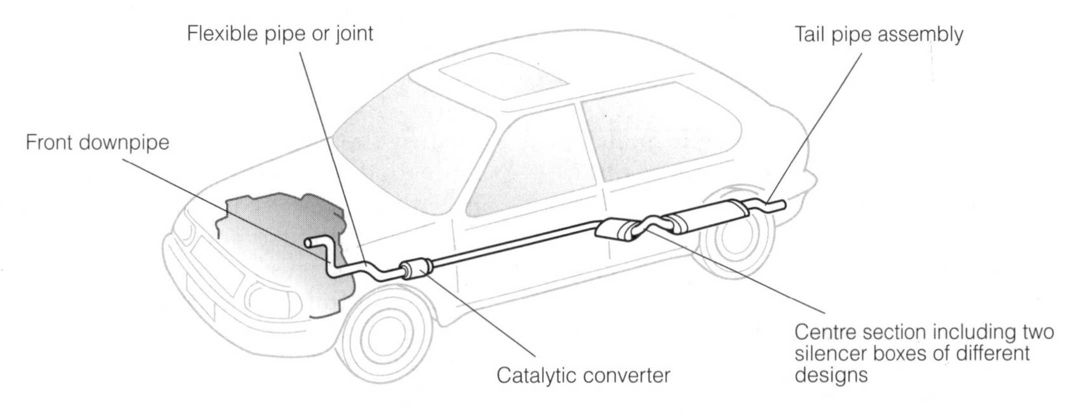

Figure 12.5 Location of catalytic converter.

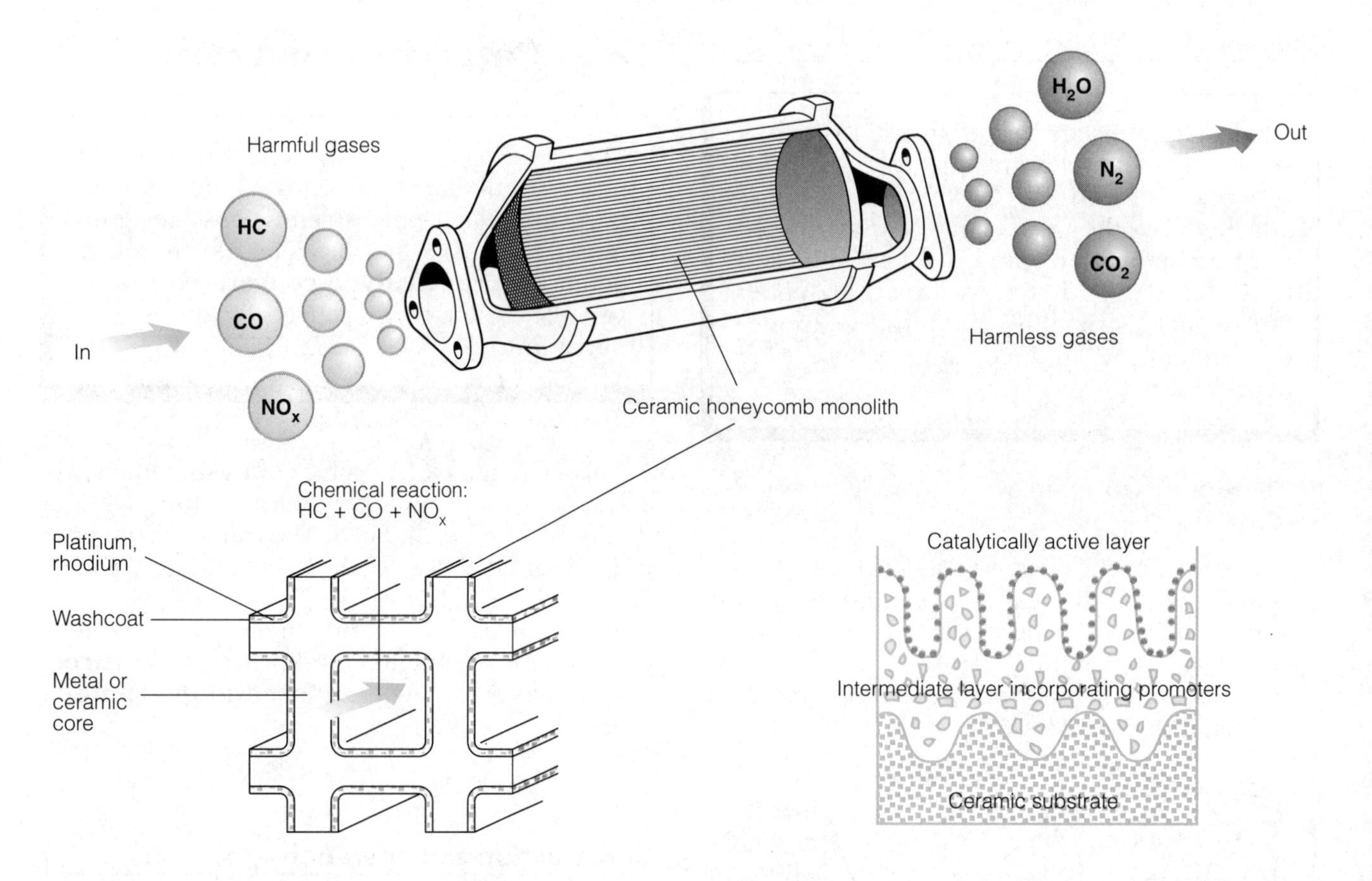

Figure 12.6 Operation of the catalytic converter.

In the three-way converter the necessary reactions are achieved by having a ceramic honeycomb monolith, which is given a washcoat of aluminium oxide to increase its effective surface area 7000 times, to about the size of two football pitches (Figure 12.6). This surface is then coated with the tiniest traces of the noble metals platinum, rhodium and palladium.

The exhaust gases are changed as they flow across these metals: carbon monoxide (CO), nitrogen oxide (NO_x) and the hydrocarbons (HC) become carbon dioxide (CO_2), nitrogen (N_2) and water (H_2O).

There is, however, one peculiarity with catalytic converters that cannot be avoided: they often produce a 'rotten egg' smell before they reach operating temperature.

The close control of the exhaust gases in a three-way system is enabled by the use of an oxygen sensor called a **Lambda probe**. This unit is mounted in the exhaust gas entry to the catalytic converter, and is wired into the engine management system.

Catalytic converter requirements

There are some important requirements to be met and faults to be avoided if a 'cat' is to continue functioning effectively.

1. In order to do its work the 'cat' must be at a temperature of at least 250 °C and, preferably, between 400 °C and 600 °C. At 1000 °C and above, however, the ceramic monolith will be damaged and may even melt.
2. A persistent misfire will melt the ceramic monolith.
3. Burnt engine oil in the exhaust will also destroy the monolith.
4. Unleaded fuel *must* be used in a vehicle with a 'cat'; the use of leaded petrol will coat the catalysts with lead and render them ineffective.
5. The ignition system must be accurately controlled for full effectiveness.
6. The Lambda probe exhaust gas sensor must be functioning correctly.
7. A vehicle equipped with a 'cat' must never be bump started.

CHECK YOUR UNDERSTANDING

- The purpose of the exhaust system is to transport the toxic gases away from the vehicle, and to reduce the noise created by the exhaust gases to an acceptable level.
- The system is supported on flexible mountings, which prevent vibrations and noise from being transmitted to the vehicle body, and allow for engine movement and for expansion and contraction.
- The system is usually made from mild steel, and given a corrosion-resistant coating. Stainless steel systems are available for longer life.
- Many vehicles are now equipped with catalytic converters to reduce pollution, and must be run on unleaded fuel.

PROJECT

Using a suitable vehicle, inspect the exhaust system, noting the information as you go.

1. List the details of the vehicle: its make, model, and year of manufacture.
2. How is the front exhaust pipe secured to the engine?
3. What types of mounting are used to secure the system to the underside of the vehicle?
4. How many separate sections are there in the system?
5. Check the condition of the downpipe, catalytic converter (if fitted), silencers, pipes, and mounting brackets.
6. Check the tightness of the manifold and pipe joints.
7. Check the exhaust for leaks by momentarily blocking the tailpipe with a wad of rag.

A concentration of only 3 per cent of carbon monoxide in the air is fatal; always run engines where there is adequate ventilation. A catalytic converter will not reduce the level of toxicity until it has reached operating temperature.

REVISION EXERCISES AND QUESTIONS

1. What is the cause of exhaust noise?
2. What safety precaution should be taken when running a vehicle in a confined space such as a closed garage?
3. Which material is most often used to make exhaust systems?
4. Which material can be used to extend the service life of the exhaust system?
5. Name the toxic gas emitted with unconverted exhaust gas.
6. State the purpose of a catalytic converter.
7. Which noble metals are used as catalysts in a catalytic converter?
8. What precautions should the user of a vehicle take to ensure that the catalytic converter will continue to function correctly?

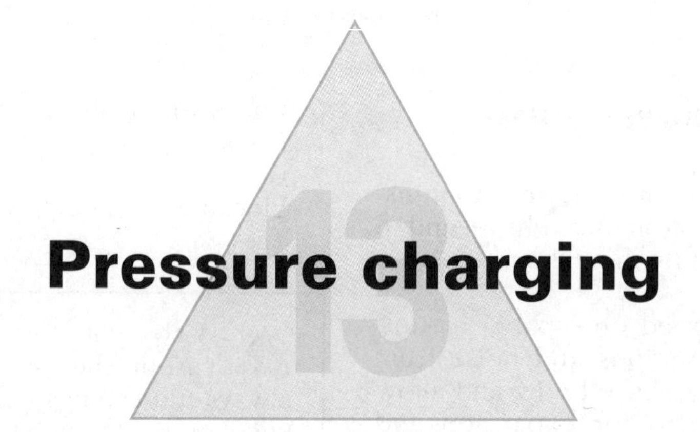

Pressure charging

Introduction

Engines that rely solely on atmospheric pressure to fill the cylinders are known as **naturally aspirated engines**. Others have some form of fan (or air 'pump') to create intake air pressure. There are two types of pressure charger in use: **superchargers**, which are mechanically driven, and **turbochargers**, which are powered by exhaust gas.

The power of an engine is proportional to the air throughput (volumetric efficiency). Because air throughput, in turn, is proportional to air density, the power of an engine can be increased by compressing the air before it enters the cylinders. This is done by pressure charging, which increases the amount of air in the cylinders and in this way raises the volumetric efficiency.

Advantages claimed for pressure charging are:

1. a greater power output for a given size of engine;
2. improved fuel consumption;
3. a wider torque band;
4. reduction of harmful emissions.

Superchargers

The mechanically driven supercharger has not been used much on vehicles because of its high manufacturing cost, but it does have definite advantages.

Advantages and disadvantages

Advantages

Mechanically driven superchargers do not heat the air entering the cylinder, which is therefore cooler and denser.

Superchargers respond immediately to changes in engine load, and are effective at slow engine speeds.

Disadvantages

The principal disadvantage, apart from cost, is that the mechanically driven supercharger imposes an extra load on the engine.

Types of supercharger

Rotor supercharger

The two symmetrical rotors operate without directly contacting each other or the housing (Figure 13.1). External gears drive and synchronise the motion of the two rotors.

Eccentric or sliding-vane supercharger

An eccentrically mounted rotor drives the centrally mounted sliding vanes. As the rotor revolves, the vanes move in and out of their slots, and the compartments increase and reduce in volume. Air enters on the expanding movement, is compressed by the reducing space, and is released into the outlet (Figure 13.2).

Orbiting spiral pressure charger

A belt drives a central eccentric, and there is a second belt to rotate an eccentric shaft to one side of the main chamber (Figure 13.3a). These eccentrics rotate at the same speed.

Within the chamber, the main eccentric forms the spindle for a disc on which are two perpen-

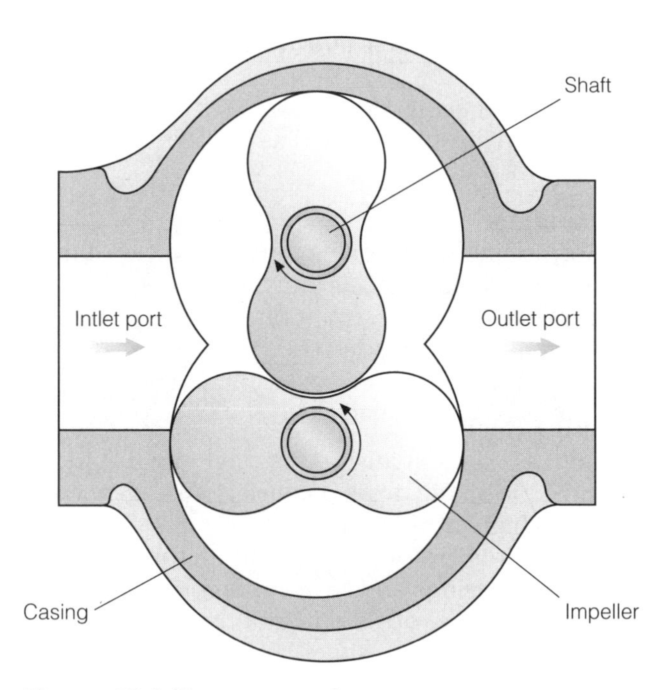

Figure 13.1 Rotor supercharger.

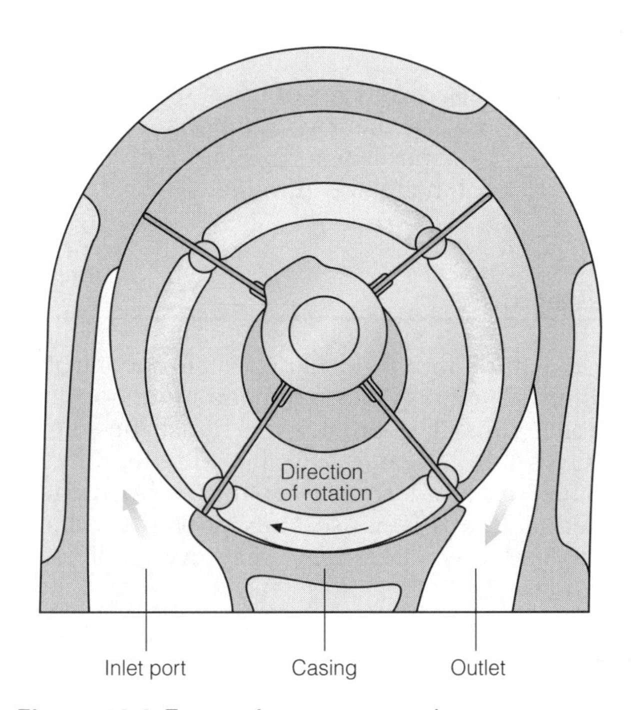

Figure 13.2 Eccentric vane supercharger.

dicular plates forming two spiral-shaped walls, mounted opposite to each other. Standing between them but fixed firmly to the opposite casing are two similar spiral walls (Figure 13.3b).

Rotation of the shaft and eccentric causes the spiral walls on the disc to move up and down between the fixed spiral walls. This changes the spaces between them. At the same time, the second eccentric rocks the disc from side to side by means of the connecting arm.

As the walls are enclosed at the top and bottom, two spiral passages are formed. The orbiting and wobbling motion traps the air in the entry side of each passage and, as the walls close together and rock, forces air through the spiral passages until it is squeezed into the outlet.

The advantage of this unit is that less power is needed to drive the small rotating shafts, particularly at high speeds, where its power loss compares favourably with that of a turbocharger. But, unlike a turbocharger, it provides rapid response at low engine speeds.

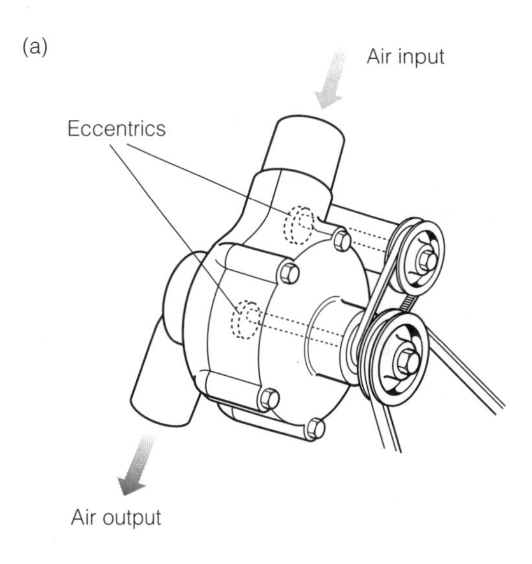

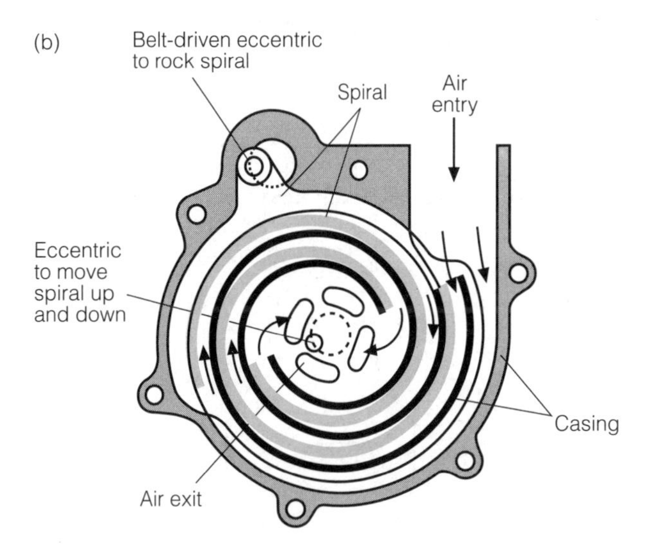

Figure 13.3 Orbiting spiral pressure charger: (a) exterior view; (b) cross-section.

Turbochargers

Exhaust-driven turbochargers are the most popular form of charge air pressurisation, and are used on both petrol and diesel engines (Figure 13.4). The discharged exhaust gases drive a fan acting as a turbine. A fan on the other end of the turbine shaft acts as a compressor, forcing air into the engine's intake.

The turbine housing is invariably cast iron, while the compressor is often mounted in an aluminium housing. The shaft bearings, usually fully floating, are fed with oil from the engine lubrication system. The high temperatures created by the exhaust gases and speeds of between 70 000 rpm and 180 000 rpm mean that lubrication and cooling are of the highest priority. The high temperatures that this unit may reach are one reason why some manufacturers recommend that vehicles that have been driven at high speed for some time are allowed to idle for a minute or so to allow initial cooling before the ignition is switched off.

A major disadvantage of the turbocharger is that of **lag**. This is a time delay after acceleration commences, particularly at slow engine speeds, before the exhaust gases give sufficient impetus to the turbocharger to affect engine charging. Recent developments such as variable intakes and electronic control have largely minimised this.

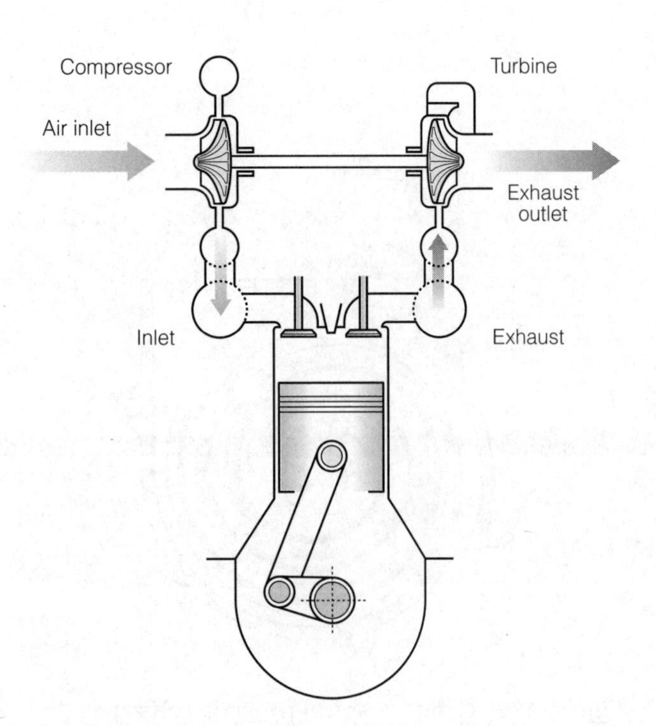

Figure 13.4 A turbocharged engine.

Advantages and disadvantages

The advantages and disadvantages of the turbocharger may be summarised as follows.

Advantages

1. Considerable increase in engine power output.
2. Improved exhaust gas emissions.
3. Improved fuel consumption.
4. Moderate production cost.

Disadvantages

1. Because the exhaust gases drive the turbine, it must be made from materials that can withstand high temperature.
2. It requires pressure lubrication for the high-speed bearings and to act as a coolant.
3. Basic designs do not respond immediately to changes in engine speed and load.
4. It tends to heat the air as it passes through, reducing its density.
5. It must be controlled within the engine's capabilities.

Two of the disadvantages of the turbocharger are commonly overcome by additional fittings: a wastegate to control overboosting, and an intercooler to cool the intake air.

Wastegate

By its nature, the turbocharger is an uncontrolled turbine, which provides more and more boost the faster it runs. The greater the boost the engine receives, the greater will be the quantity of exhaust gas and the faster the turbocharger's speed. If the driver uses this power in an uncontrolled way, the engine may eventually self-destruct.

To control the boost a device called a **wastegate** is used (Figure 13.5). This simply wastes some of the exhaust gas by causing it to bypass the turbocharger turbine.

The wastegate employs a spring-loaded, engine-type valve, controlled by a pneumatic bellows or diaphragm, to open or close a bypass. This unit is normally an integral part of the turbocharger.

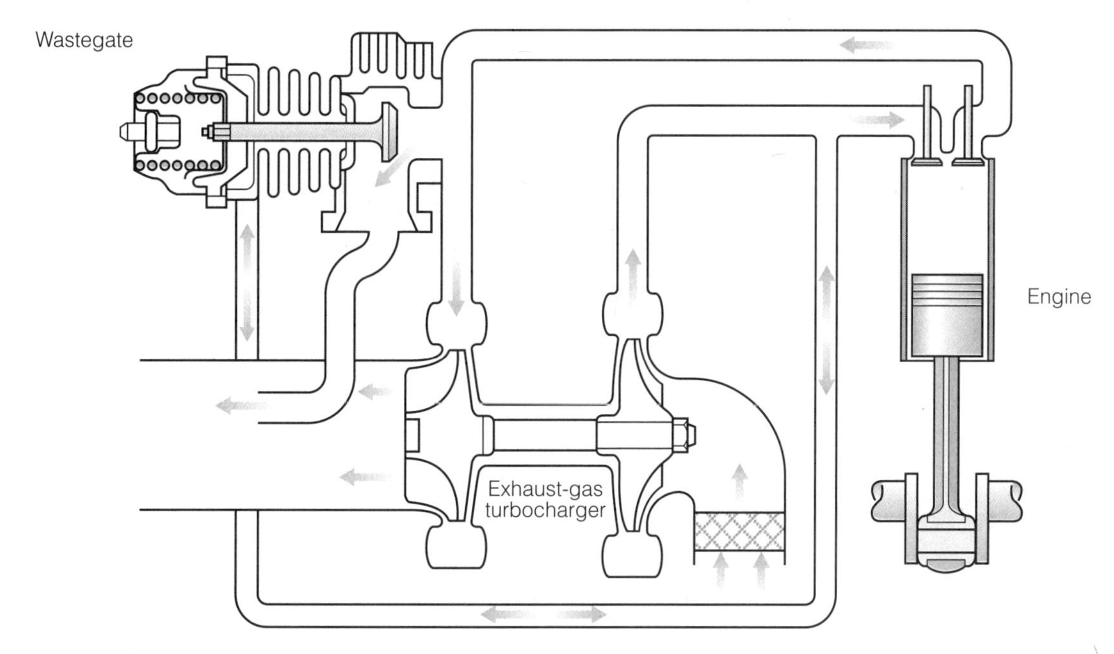

Figure 13.5 Wastegate.

Intercooling

> The intake air temperature increases considerably as a result of turbocharging and, as a result, expands and becomes less dense. Cooling the air to increase its density is known as **intercooling**.

After leaving the turbocharger, intake air is fed to a cooling radiator or heat exchanger, called an **intercooler**, before it enters the engine intake (Figure 13.6).

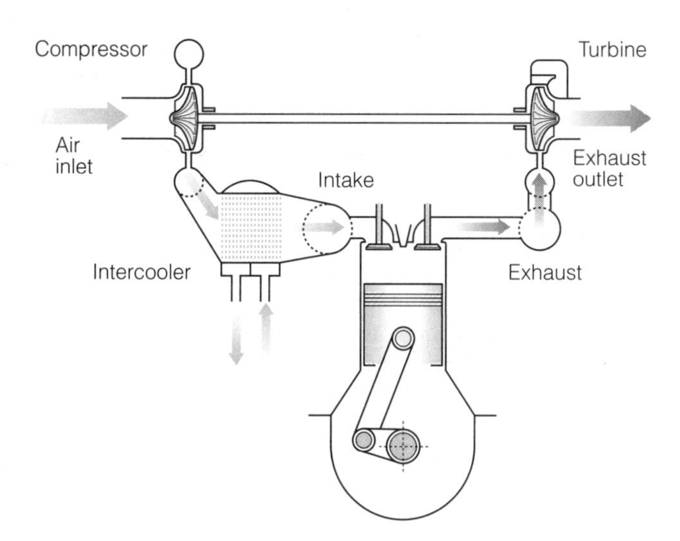

Figure 13.6 A turbocharged engine with intercooler.

CHECK YOUR UNDERSTANDING

- Pressure charging increases the power output, torque and fuel economy of an engine.
- There are two main types of charger: mechanically driven, and those powered by exhaust gas.
- Mechanically driven units are generally called superchargers.
- Exhaust-driven units are known as turbochargers.
- The charging effect of turbochargers must be restrained by a wastegate.
- To increase the effect of pressure charging the air is sometimes cooled, before it enters the engine, by an intercooler.

REVISION EXERCISES AND QUESTIONS

1 What purpose does a pressure charger serve on an engine?
2 What is the main advantage of the turbocharger over a supercharger?
3 What is the main advantage of the supercharger over a turbocharger?
4 What is the purpose of a wastegate?
5 What is the purpose of intercooling?

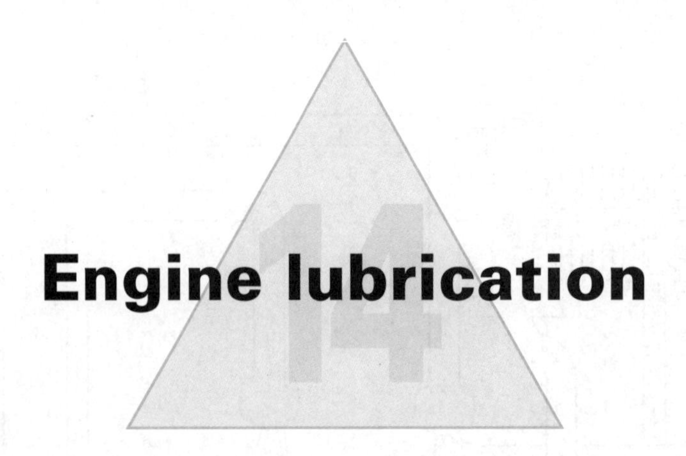

Engine lubrication

Introduction

Friction is the resistance that occurs when two substances move over one another. Even the smoothest engine component will have a 'rough' surface when looked at under a powerful microscope. Look at the sketch in Figure 14.1: the magnified surfaces look like a range of mountains. If they move across each other the tips of the rough surface will take all the pressure; they will become hot, and would soon wear away.

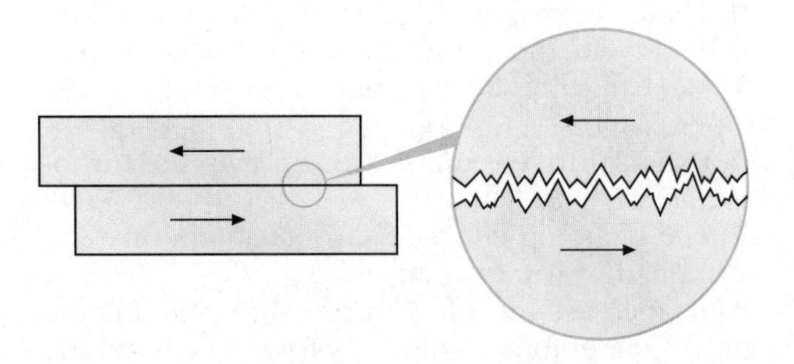

Figure 14.1 Friction.

Friction is used in motor vehicles to very good effect: in clutches and brakes, for example. But it can also be a disadvantage. Every engine contains numerous metal components that constantly rub one another. If excessive friction was allowed to occur heat would be generated, causing the parts to expand, whereupon rapid wear would take place with eventual seizure. So it is essential that friction is minimised by ensuring that the moving parts are constantly covered with lubricating oil.

The purpose of the engine lubrication system is to:

- reduce friction and wear between the moving parts as much as possible;
- reduce noise;
- dissipate heat by carrying it away from the working surfaces;
- clean the engine.

Engine oil

Oil is the lifeblood of the engine. It is generally refined from crude oil extracted from the earth's crust. This is known as a **mineral oil**, but it is increasingly being supplemented or even replaced by **synthetic oil**, which is formulated from chemical substitutes to give excellent lubricating properties.

Properties of oil

To cope with the arduous conditions inside the engine, the quality of basic oil is improved by adding to it other substances called **additives** to improve its specific properties. The quality of the oil is determined by the American Petroleum Institute Classification (API), and by specifications issued by equivalent bodies or the vehicle manufacturers.

Some of the important additives and their functions are as follows:

1. **Film strength agents** reduce the wear on areas such as the cylinder walls and cams, by strengthening the oil film to prevent metal-to-metal contact.
2. **Corrosion inhibitors** provide protection from the acids that seep into the crankcase as a result of the combustion process in the cylinders.
3. **Oxidation inhibitors** protect the metal surfaces from an acid lacquer that results from high-temperature sludge created by the high engine temperature and constant churning of the oil.
4. **Low-temperature sludge inhibitors** reduce oil degeneration resulting from incomplete combustion and crankcase condensation.
5. **Anti-foam agents** are needed because foam and froth cannot be pumped by the oil pump, and must be prevented to ensure adequate lubrication.
6. **Detergents and dispersants** hold the minute carbon particles produced during combustion in suspension in the oil. They are then filtered out before they can block oilways or seize the piston rings. These additives are especially important for diesel engines, which tend to produce more carbon particles than petrol engines.

Viscosity

> The measure of an oil's ability to flow is its **viscosity**: the higher the viscosity, the 'thicker' is the oil. When an oil is heated it becomes 'thinner': it loses viscosity.

The relative change in viscosity with temperature is called the **viscosity index**. The internationally accepted standard for defining the viscosity of an oil is that issued by the Society of Automotive Engineers (SAE).

Engine oils can be classified into two groups: single- or monograde, and multigrade. **Monograde oils** are mainly restricted to special applications today.

Multigrade oils contain an additive that alters the viscosity characteristics so that the oil does not thin as much as a comparative monograde when subjected to heating. This allows the use of an oil that has a lower viscosity to make cold starting easier by reducing the turning resistance, but which still has adequate viscosity when hot. For example, a 20w/50 multigrade oil has the virtues of a 20 grade oil when cold, but maintains its body and acts like a 50 grade at high temperatures. This quality enables such oils to be used in many parts of the world throughout the year.

Oil renewal and level

> Oil, like many other substances, deteriorates with time when exposed to the atmosphere and particularly when it comes into contact with the heat, dirt and condensation that occur inside the engine crankcase. It is often recommended that engine oil should be changed on a time and mileage basis, even if the mileage run is very low. If the mileage run by the vehicle is high, the oil may need to be changed more frequently.

The level to which the oil is maintained is also very important. To prevent oil leaks and heavier oil consumption the level should never be above the maximum mark on the dipstick (Figure 14.2). Some manufacturers suggest that the ideal level is between the marks.

Conversely, if the oil level is too low the bearings may be starved of oil. The engine may also run too hot because the cooling action of the oil is reduced.

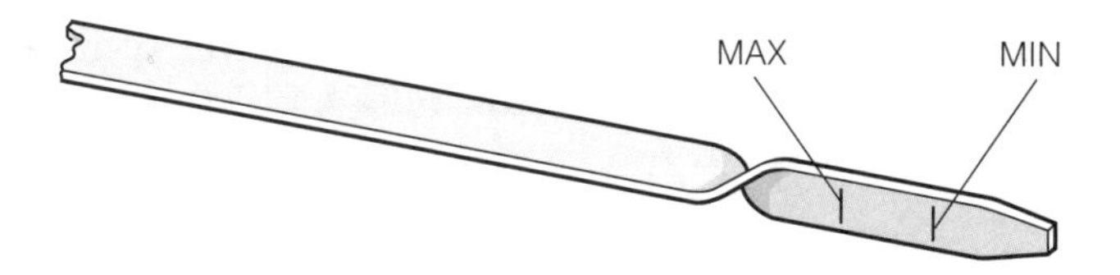

Figure 14.2 The oil level should never be above the maximum mark on the dipstick.

Engine lubrication systems

Splash system

This is still used on some single-cylinder stationary engines, but it is no longer used on motor vehicles (Figure 14.3).

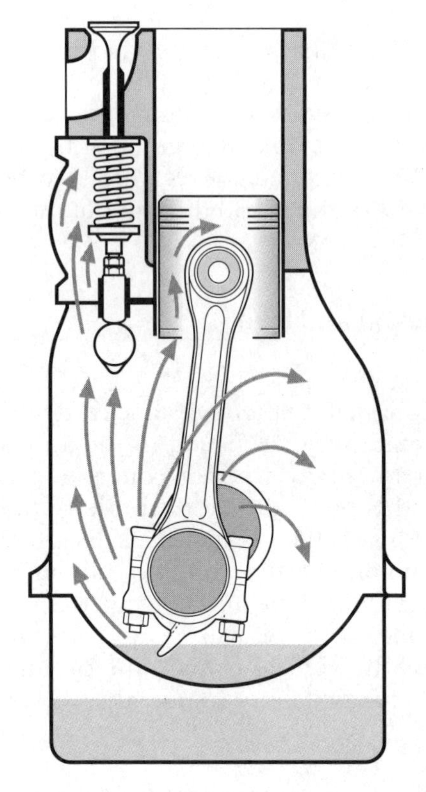

Figure 14.3 Splash lubrication system.

Construction

Splash-lubricated engines have conrods with an extension that dips into the oil as the crankshaft revolves. The 'dipper' feeds the big-end bearing, and splashes oil onto the upper parts of the engine, such as the cylinder walls. The system is adequate for low-power, slow-revving engines, but it is not suitable for high-performance units. This is because the pressure created during combustion tends to squeeze the oil away from the bearing surfaces.

Pressure lubrication systems

To counteract the loss of oil from bearings, modern lubrication systems feed the oil under pressure between the surfaces to keep them apart. There are two main types of system: dry sump and wet sump.

Dry sump has been a popular system on motor cycles for many years. It employs a separate tank to hold the oil, which is fed to the engine and returned through pipes. A principal advantage of the system is that whatever angle the engine may adopt, the oil supply is not interrupted.

The angle of the engine is not of such concern with larger vehicles (although gradients or centrifugal force may momentarily alter the oil level in the engine sump), and **wet-sump** systems are generally used.

Wet-sump lubrication system

The oil is stored in a reservoir known as the **sump** located at the base of the engine (Figure 14.4). A submerged pump, usually driven from a skew gear on the camshaft, pumps oil under pressure around the engine.

The inlet to the pump is protected by a metal mesh strainer known as the **primary filter**. This stops larger particles of dirt from entering the system. The oil is delivered, under pressure, through a finer **secondary filter** into the main oil gallery of the engine.

The oil is fed under pressure to the crankshaft main bearings and then along internal drillings in the crankshaft to the big-end bearings. On some engines, oil may also be pumped to the little-end bearing through an internal drilling in the connecting rod. At the same time, oil is fed up to the camshaft, where it lubricates the camshaft bearings and cams. The oil then drains back to the crankcase and sump.

While the engine is running, oil also splashes around vigorously inside the crankcase. It is this splashing that usually lubricates the cylinder walls and pistons. Some engines with high cylinder temperatures, such as turbo diesels, may have pressure-fed oil jets to lubricate the cylinders.

Oil pressure

It is essential that the oil is forced round under pressure at all times when the engine is running. This ensures that the component parts are separated by a very thin film of oil to prevent metal-to-metal contact and subsequent seizure.

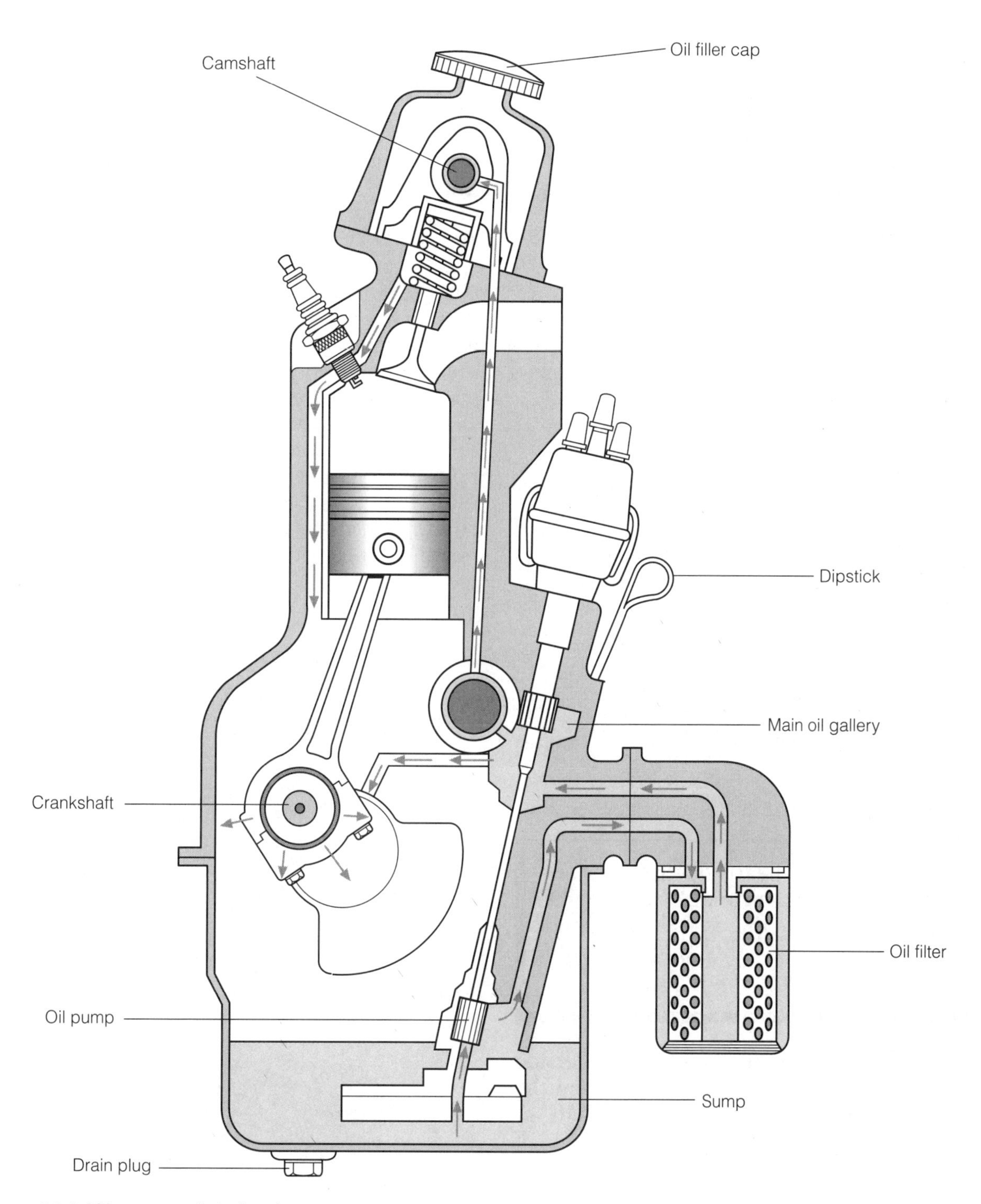

Figure 14.4 Wet sump lubrication system.

In the case of a main bearing, for example, the crankshaft does not touch the bearing when the engine is running, but is floating on the thin film of oil (Figure 14.5). The only friction that occurs is that of the moving molecules in the oil itself, and is called **fluid friction**.

The pressure is created by a pump forcing oil into the lubrication system faster than it can seep out. Oil pressure varies with temperature and engine speed. A cold engine will have a higher oil pressure because of the thicker consistency of the oil (that is, it has a high **viscosity**), and is

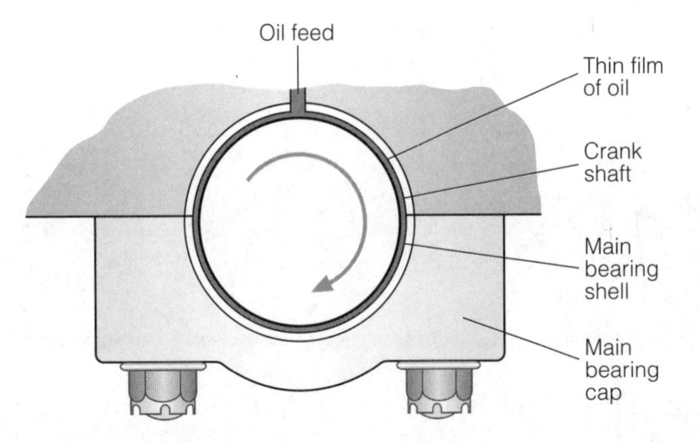

Figure 14.5 When running, the crankshaft floats on a thin film of oil.

slow to bleed out of the lubrication system. When the engine warms up the oil is thinner (it has a lower viscosity), and the pressure is less. A typical oil pressure with an engine at running temperature is 2.5 kgf/cm^2 (= 245 kPa or 35 lbf/in^2).

Lubrication system components

Oil pump

> The pump is the heart of the engine, pumping oil around the various components to keep them working in good order. Should the oil cease to flow the engine would quickly seize and stop running.

The pump is usually mounted on the underside of the crankcase, and is driven directly from the crankshaft or indirectly from the camshaft or another component. The intake to the pump or even the pump itself is submerged in the oil in the sump. A passage connects the pump outlet to the filter and then on to the main oil gallery to be distributed throughout the engine.

> Several types of pump are used, but they all work on the same principle. Oil is drawn from the sump into a chamber that reduces in size, forcing the pressurised oil into the lubrication system.

Gear-type oil pump

The gear-type pump is commonly used. It consists of two spur gears rotating in a close-fitting chamber (Figure 14.6). One of the gears is driven by the camshaft, and this in turn drives the other gear. Oil is drawn into the pump on one side of the housing and is trapped between the casing and the gear tooth cavities. When the gear teeth mesh together, oil is forced through the outlet into the system.

Rotor-type oil pump

This pump consists of a multi-lobed rotor, which is eccentrically mounted inside a ring (Figure 14.7). The ring has recesses of a similar shape but one more in number, and is free to turn in the housing. The driven rotor revolves, turning the ring. Pumping action is obtained by the oil's entering a chamber at its greatest volume and being ejected through the outlet as the space reduces.

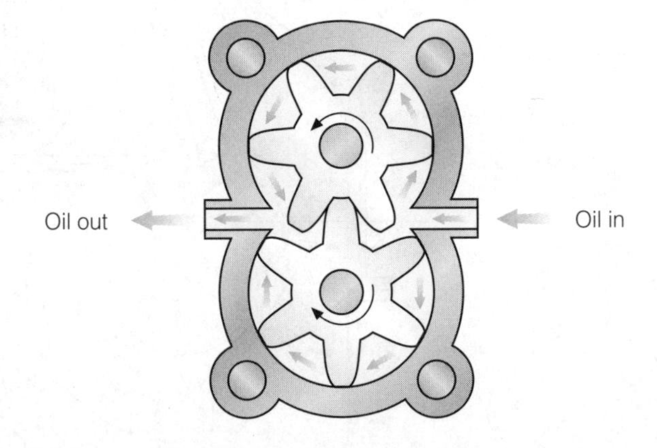

Figure 14.6 Gear-type oil pump.

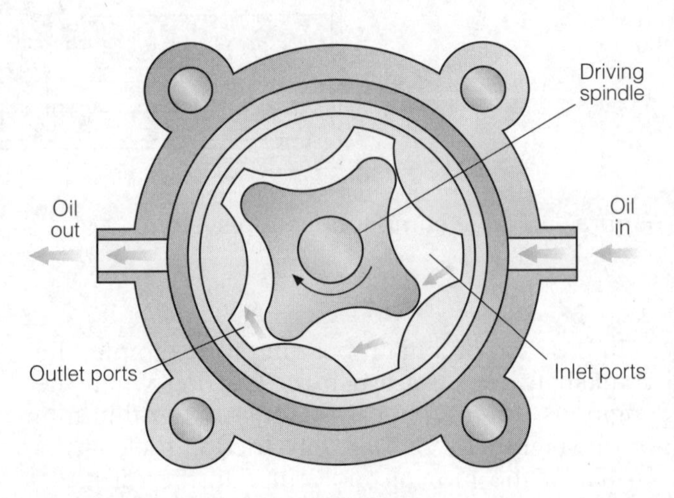

Figure 14.7 Rotor-type oil pump.

The rotor pump is about 25 per cent more efficient than the gear type, and has a longer service life.

Pressure relief valve

The oil pump is designed to provide adequate pressure, even when the engine is idling. At high engine speeds, or when the oil is cold, the pump delivery pressure may be excessively high. This could cause oil leaks around the filter seal and at other seals and joints. It may even cause excessive oil consumption because too much oil is fed to the cylinder walls, where the piston rings are not able to scrape the oil clear. Therefore some means of controlling the pressure is necessary.

Excess pressure is relieved by a **pressure relief valve** installed just after the pump (Figure 14.8).

The valve assembly consists of a metal ball or plunger, held by a spring onto a seat, which closes off an outlet to the pressurised oil gallery. When the oil pressure rises above the spring pressure, the valve is lifted from its seat, and oil can escape into the sump. When the oil pressure reduces, the spring closes the valve.

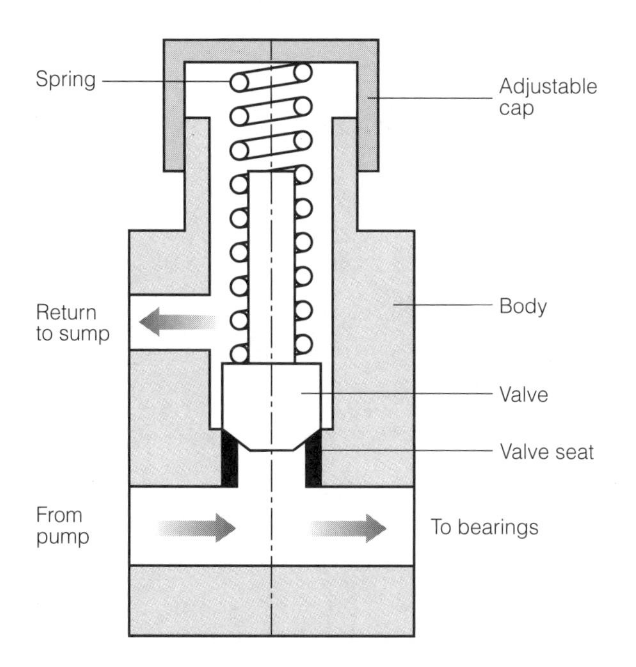

Figure 14.8 Oil pressure relief valve.

Oil filtration

Foreign matter, metal particles and the by-products of combustion all gather in the sump of an engine over a period of time. Wherever possible they should be prevented from entering the bearings of the engine to avoid accelerated wear.

This is typically achieved by a two-stage filter system.

Primary oil filter

The first stage filter, the primary filter, is of fairly coarse wire mesh, and prevents relatively large particles of dirt or swarf from entering the pump. It normally needs no attention between engine overhauls, provided normal cleanliness has been observed in topping up the engine oil. It may become clogged if the engine oil changes have not been carried out at the recommended intervals.

Secondary oil filter

These are much finer filters, and are fitted on the pressure side of the pump. The engine lubricating oil becomes contaminated over a period of time with the by-products of combustion and possibly also by small particles of abrasive material that enter the engine through the oil filler and the engine breather system. In addition, there may be metal particles worn from the engine parts.

Modern engine oils are formulated to carry much of this material so that it can be collected and removed periodically in the disposable filter element, the secondary filter. This prevents these particles from causing excessive wear to engine components.

The filter is usually made from a specially processed paper. The filter surface is folded to enable a large surface area to fit inside a small container. Oil can flow freely through the material, but particles as small as 2 μm in diameter will be filtered out. In comparison, the thinnest human hair is 30 μm in diameter.

Secondary filters are available in bypass or full-flow versions.

The **partial flow or bypass oil filter** is fitted between the main oil gallery and the sump, and is designed to remove very fine particles (Figure 14.9). About 15 per cent of the oil flow from the pump travels through the filter and returns to the sump. The other 85 per cent is sent to lubricate the engine. The filter operates at a low pressure. In modern engines it is recommended that a bypass filter is used only in conjunction with a full-flow filter. In this way, particles that have not been removed by the full-flow filter are removed by the bypass filter, reducing the concentration of very fine pollutants such as particles of soot.

The **full-flow oil filter** is fitted between the pump and the main oil gallery to clean all the oil flowing into the lubrication system (Figure 14.10). It is designed to accept the full flow of oil at pressure. There are two types: replaceable element and renewable cartridge.

The **replaceable element** is the earlier type. It consists of a canister with a replaceable paper element inside (Figure 14.11). The canister is bolted to the filter body, which is itself mounted to the cylinder block.

The modern filter is a case and paper element combined into a single **cartridge** with a built-in

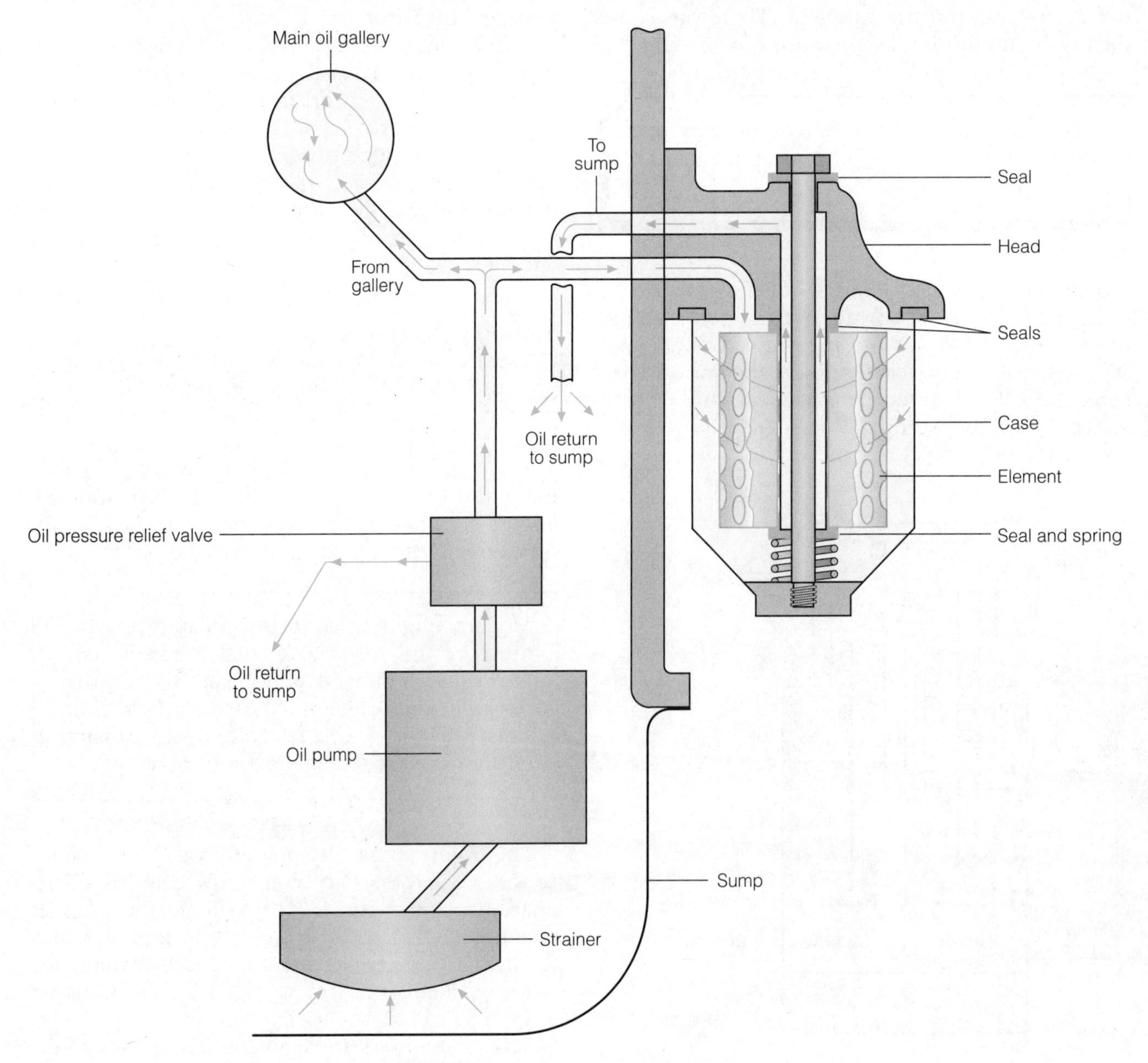

Figure 14.9 Bypass filter.

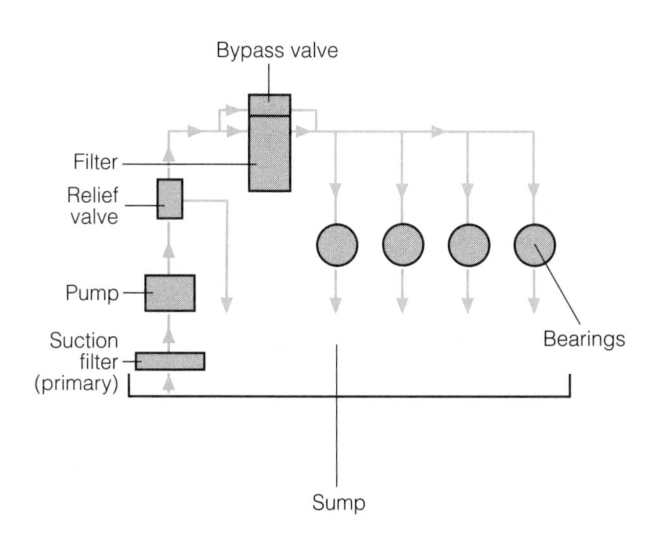

Figure 14.10 Full flow filter, fitted between the pump and the main oil gallery.

seal (Figure 14.12a, b). It screws either onto a housing or directly to the cylinder block. One or two integral valves are also provided.

Bypass valve

A bypass valve is fitted to permit oil to continue to flow and avoid serious engine damage in the event of filter blockage (Figures 14.10 and 14.12a). If the filter becomes blocked the pressure rises and lifts the valve from its seat, when oil can continue to flow. The oil is unfiltered, but that is better than no oil at all!

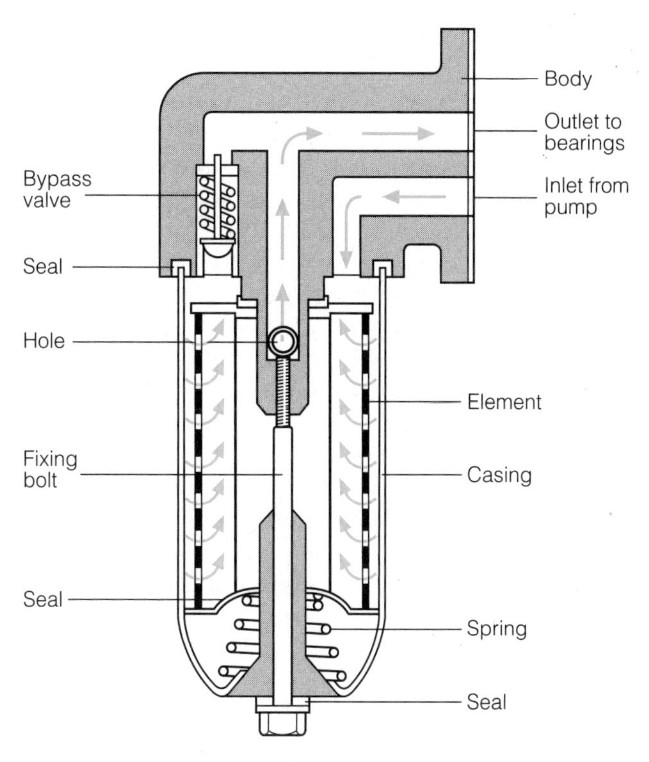

Figure 14.11 Replaceable-element oil filter.

Residual pressure valve

Many filters are now equipped with another valve that holds oil in the system when the engine stops, rather than allowing it to drain away entirely. It is important that the correct filter cartridge is used where an engine is so equipped.

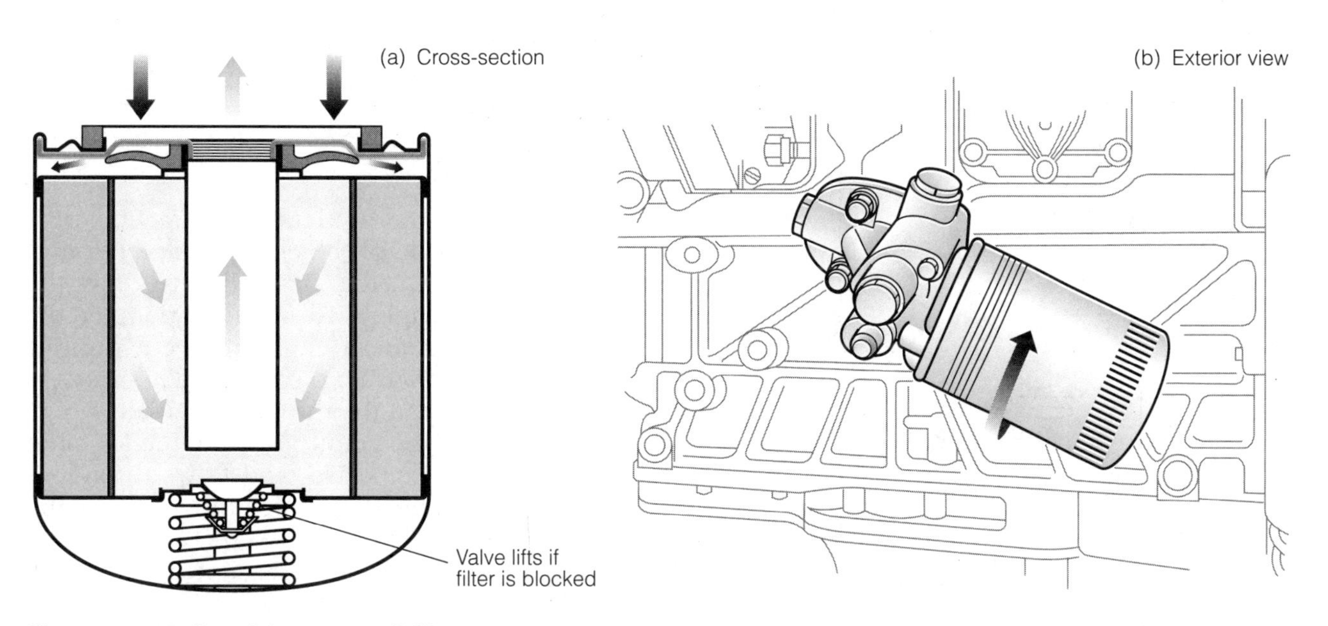

Figure 14.12 Cartridge-type oil filter.

Warning devices

The most common low oil pressure warning device is a red or orange warning lamp in the driver's instrument panel. A pressure switch in the oil gallery is normally closed (Figure 14.13). When the engine is started and oil pressure rises the contacts are broken, extinguishing the light. A typical opening setting for such a switch is 50 kPa (= 0.5 kgf/cm^2 or 7 lbf/in^2).

Some vehicles may have a pressure gauge in place of, or in addition to, the oil warning lamp. Early types of gauge use small-bore copper or plastic pipe to connect the gauge to the main oil gallery. The needle of the gauge is moved in direct response to the pressure. Modern pressure indicators are usually electrically operated by means of a bimetallic transmitter and indicator.

Oil coolers

Oil coolers are miniature radiators or heat exchangers through which the oil is passed for cooling; in so doing, they contribute to the cooling of the engine. The radiator types of cooler give up their heat to the surrounding air, while the heat exchanger versions are incorporated into the engine cooling system.

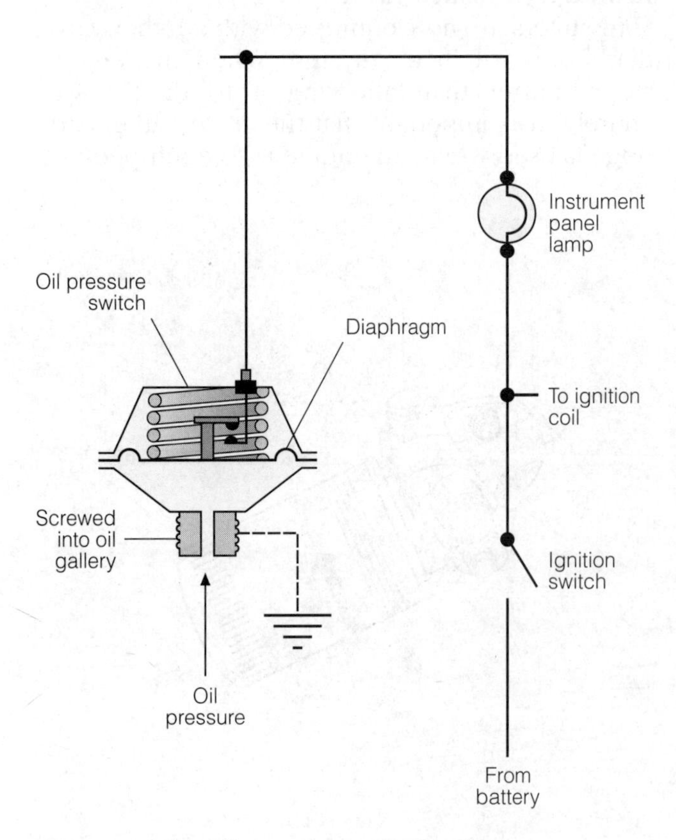

Figure 14.13 Oil pressure warning lamp.

Oil seals

> All the joint faces, such as sump to crankcase, and the moving surfaces of protruding shafts must be made oil-tight to prevent oil loss.

Gaskets are usually made from waxed gasket paper, cork, plastic or other materials that are resistant to heat, oil and water. Revolving shafts are sealed by spring-loaded, synthetic rubber lip seals or felt sealing rings, often in combination with oil deflectors. Examples of these can be seen in Chapter 3.

Crankcase ventilation

There are two reasons for ventilating a crankcase:

1. Rising temperature expands the air trapped inside the crankcase: this, together with gases that have blown past the piston rings, would place excessive pressure on the seals and gaskets. This would result in oil leaking past seals and through gaskets; in extreme cases, gaskets could be blown out.
2. Some of the corrosive gases that are the products of combustion, and which find their way into the sump, could cause rapid deterioration of the oil if they were allowed to stay. Crankcase ventilation prevents the build-up of these contaminants.

Older engines simply had an extraction pipe attached to the side of the engine; the motion of the vehicle through the air tended to draw the gases out of the engine. This method polluted the atmosphere, so modern engines have a positive system of ventilation: a typical system is shown in Figure 14.14a. When the throttle is partially open, air is drawn into the crankcase from the air filter: it ventilates the crankcase, and flows through a valve into the inlet manifold and on into the cylinders to be burnt.

With an open throttle the crankcase is ventilated through the hose into the air intake (Figure 14.14b).

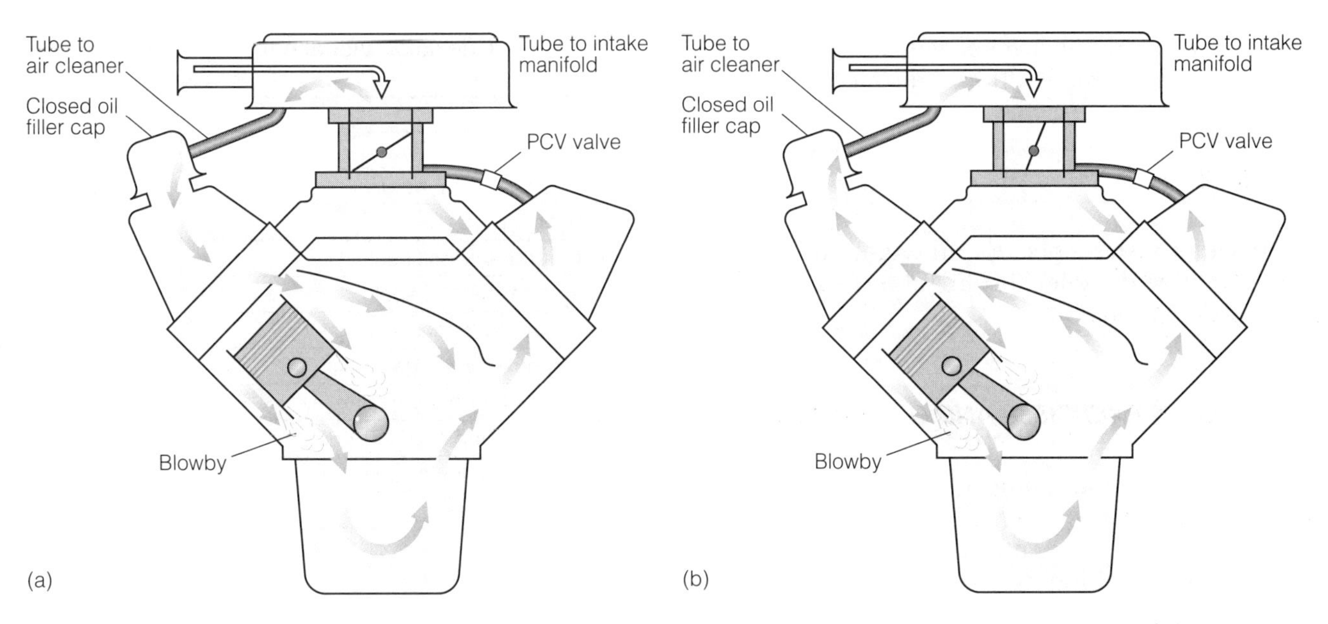

Figure 14.14 Crankcase ventilation air flow: (a) throttle closed or partially open; (b) throttle fully open.

Fault finding

See Table 14.1.

CHECK YOUR UNDERSTANDING

- Good-quality oil of the recommended grade is essential to reduce engine wear to a minimum.
- Always use the correct oil, and change the oil and filters at the recommended intervals. Check and maintain the oil level frequently.
- On wet-sump systems the oil is usually contained in a sump under the engine.
- The oil is circulated around the lubricating system and pressurised by a pump.
- The oil is filtered to prevent dirt from damaging the engine bearing surfaces.
- The crankshaft is internally drilled so that the big-end bearings receive a direct supply of oil under pressure.
- The oil thrown out by the bearings sprays around to lubricate the cylinders and pistons.
- To provide a safety factor the pump normally delivers more oil than the system can accept:

Table 14.1 Engine lubrication fault-finding chart

Fault	Possible cause
Oil pressure warning lamp remains on	• Low oil pressure • Low oil level • Faulty oil pressure switch or circuit
Low oil pressure	• Worn big-end and main bearings • Pump primary filter blocked • Pressure relief valve stuck open • Faulty pump or pick-up
Oil lamp flashes on when cornering or braking hard	• Low oil level
Oil level rises over a period of time	• Petrol in the oil from faulty mechanical pump • Petrol in the oil from short journey use • Water seeping into the sump
Oil level drops rapidly between services with no evident leaks	• Worn piston rings or cylinders causing engine to burn oil • Blocked engine breather causing engine to burn oil

hence the need for a relief valve, which allows the excess oil to bleed off into the sump.

PROJECT

Carry out a visual check of an engine to look for oil leaks. Use the checklist in Table 14.2 to record your observations.

REVISION EXERCISES AND QUESTIONS

1 Why is it important to change the engine oil at regular intervals?
2 What would happen to the oil if the full-flow filter became blocked?
3 What is the purpose of the pressure relief valve?
4 Name *two* types of oil pump in general use.
5 What are additives, and why are they used?
6 What is meant by the term *viscosity*?

Table 14.2 Checklist: visual check of engine for oil leaks

Component	Wet	Dry
Sump drain plug		
Fuel pump to engine gasket		
Oil filler cap		
Distributor shaft oil seal		
Rear crankshaft oil seal		
Camshaft cover gasket		
Timing drive cover gasket		
Oil pump/filter body gasket		
Oil filter sealing ring		
Crankshaft pulley oil seal		
Camshaft oil seal		
Sump gasket		

15 The cooling system, interior heaters, ventilation and air conditioning

Introduction

Although every petrol or diesel engine burns fuel to produce power, if it gets too hot or cold it cannot work at its best. Extremes of temperature could even damage the engine beyond repair.

This is why the engine cooling system is so important. It keeps the engine close to its best temperature for most efficient working. In much the same way, people inside the vehicle work best at temperatures to suit them. In many parts of the world, the waste heat from the engine's cooling system is used to heat the interior of the vehicle.

Ventilation is also important. All vehicles have it (even if it is provided by simply opening the windows), but usually it is combined with the heating system. Both the heat and the ventilation can be controlled. To actually cool the air coming into the passenger compartment needs some form of air conditioning. The power for this comes from the engine, but the air flow is normally via the ventilation system.

The cooling system

A feature of the internal combustion engine is that it creates a large amount of heat as the fuel burns. The temperature in the cylinders can be as high as 2400 °C. To prevent the engine from overheating, a cooling system is required.

The main functions of a cooling system are to:

- control the temperature of the engine within precise limits;
- increase the efficiency of the engine;
- provide heat for other devices such as the interior and manifold heaters, and the automatic choke.

Before looking at cooling systems it is important to understand how heat travels through different substances, such as solids, fluids and gases.

Heat transmission

The heat generated during the combustion process can travel in one of three ways:

- **Conduction**. When the molecules in a solid material such as metal are heated, they vibrate and move. This movement conducts the heat away from its source.
- **Convection**. When the molecules of liquids or gases are heated, they travel faster, which causes expansion. Liquids or gases that have been warmed become less dense, and so rise, producing convection currents. This, too, carries heat away from the source.
- **Radiation**. This is the transmission of heat as electromagnetic waves through transparent solids, gases or a vacuum.

Air cooling

> In this type of cooling system, the air that surrounds an engine is used to reduce its temperature.

Air-cooled engines have cooling fins, which are cast into both the cylinder block and the cylinder head (Figure 15.1). The purpose of the fins is to increase the surface area of the hottest parts of the engine, and to help the flow of heat into the passing air. The deepest fins with the largest surface area are around the combustion chamber, where the most heat is generated.

Sometimes an air-cooled engine is completely enclosed by a cover or cowling. This is to allow an engine-driven fan to circulate air so that the engine is cooled evenly (Figure 15.2). With very few exceptions, air-cooled engines have largely been replaced by liquid-cooled units in cars and commercial vehicles.

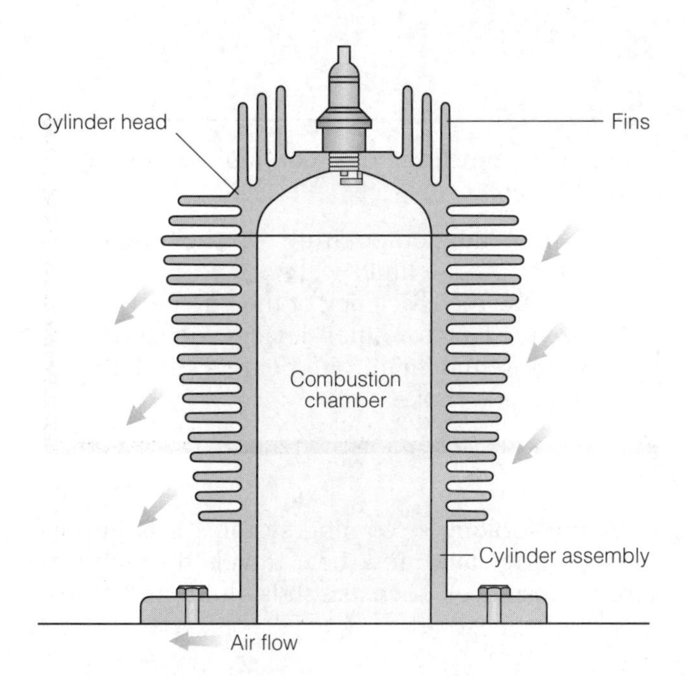

Figure 15.1 Cross-sectional view of a single-cylinder, air-cooled engine.

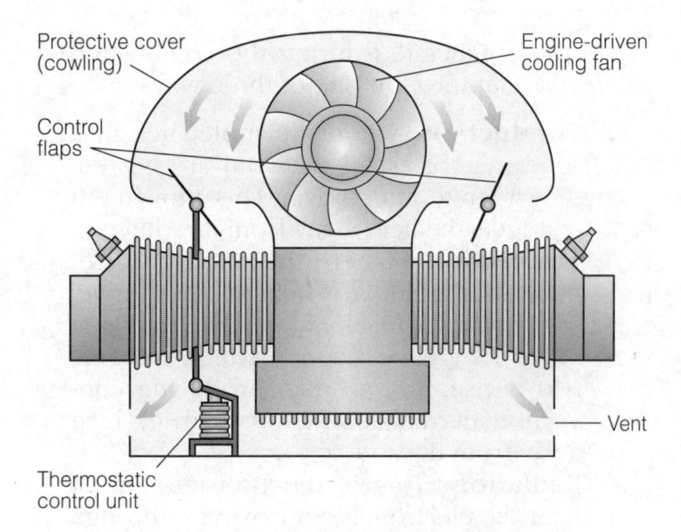

Figure 15.2 Horizontally opposed, air-cooled engine.

Liquid cooling

> For the majority of both light and heavy vehicles, liquid-based cooling systems are now the norm.

They have a number of technical advantages over air-cooled designs:

1. The coolant in the engine water jacket acts as a sound-deadening material, which helps to reduce engine noise.
2. It is possible to maintain a more even temperature across all the cylinders.
3. There is improved control of the engine's thermal efficiency.

The thermosiphon cooling system

This was the earliest type of cooling system. It relied on convection currents to circulate the coolant. As there was no pump, a tall, vertical-

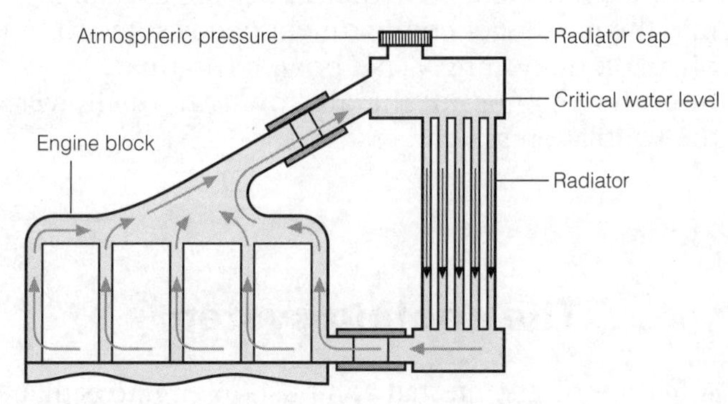

Figure 15.3 Cross-sectional view of a thermosiphon cooling system. Arrows indicate coolant circulation. Note the height of the radiator compared with the engine.

flow radiator was needed (Figure 15.3). Poor circulation often resulted in localised overheating.

The pressurised, pump-assisted cooling system

In this development from the early system, a positive flow of coolant is achieved by some design changes (Figure 15.4).

The main features of this cooling system are the fitting of an engine-driven **water pump** to circulate the coolant, and the provision of both a **thermostat** and a **pressure filler cap**. These ensure that the engine remains at an ideal operating temperature close to the normal water boiling point of 100 °C.

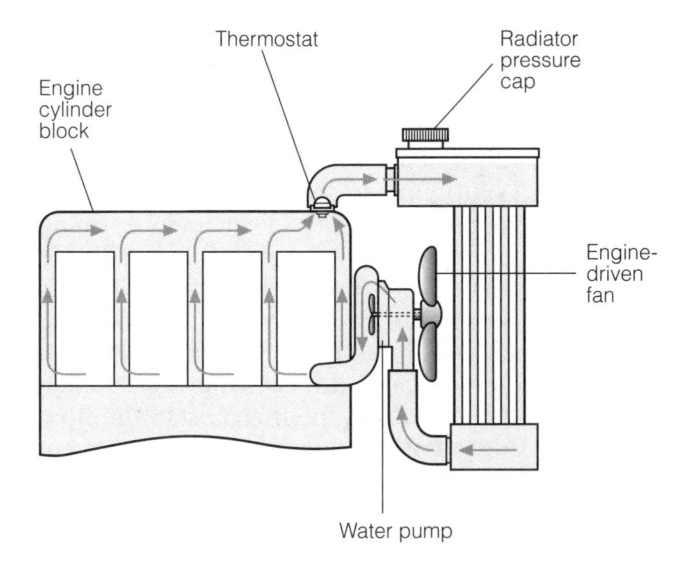

Figure 15.4 Cross-sectional view of a pressurised, pump-assisted cooling system. Arrows indicate coolant circulation.

> By pressurising the cooling system the possibility of steam pockets forming within the water jacket is reduced, and a smaller radiator can be used, which allows a lower bonnet to be fitted. A pressurised cooling system also allows an engine to run at higher operating temperatures, where it is more efficient and gives better fuel economy.

Water pumps

The water pump consists of a belt-driven pulley mounted on a spindle, with an impeller on the other end (Figure 15.5). The spindle is mounted in bearings protected by a seal. As the engine rotates, the drive belt turns the spindle and the impeller, which circulates coolant around the system. It is important to remember that the pump does not pressurise the coolant; this is done by the pressure filler cap.

Thermostats

> A thermostat can be thought of as a temperature-sensitive valve, which regulates coolant temperature and circulation.

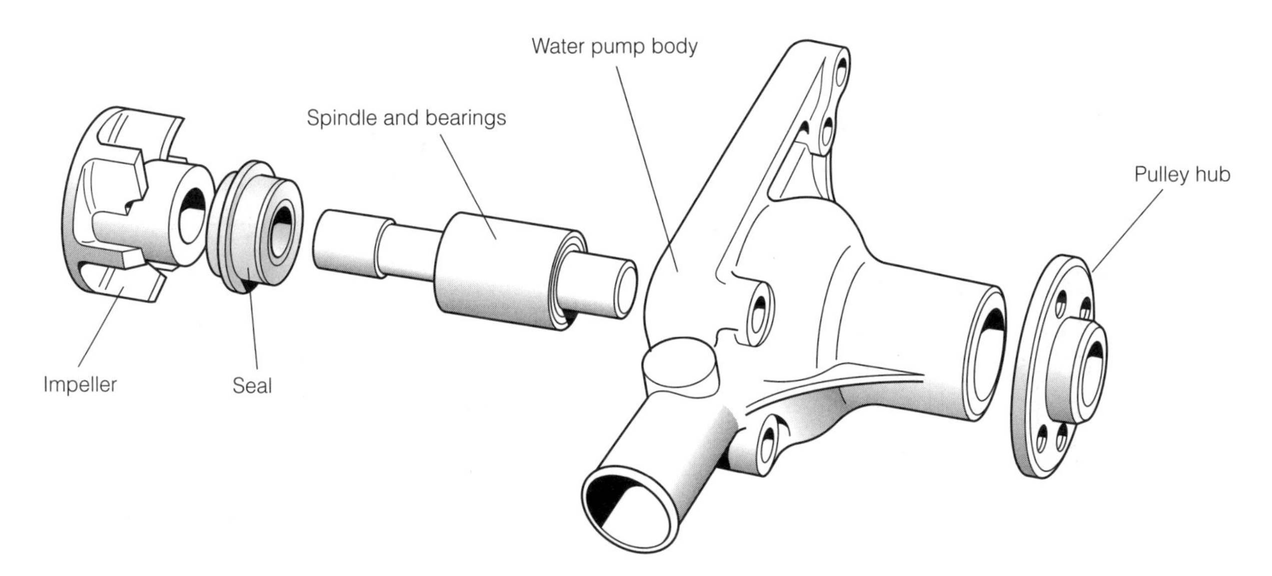

Figure 15.5 Water pump components.

Two of the more important reasons for fitting it are:

1. to ensure that the engine warms up rapidly when starting from cold, by preventing circulation of the coolant through the radiator before the engine reaches operating temperature;
2. to control the rate of circulation around the water jacket. The thermostat helps to keep the engine at a constant operating temperature.

There are two types: the **bellows thermostat** and the **wax element thermostat**.

Bellows thermostat

This is so called because it consists of a sealed brass bellows, which contains a solution of methyl alcohol and water, held in a partial vacuum.

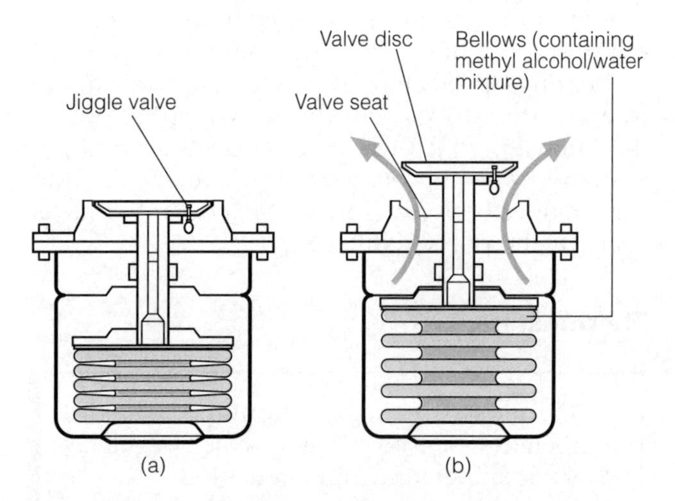

Figure 15.6 Bellows-type thermostat: (a) cold – valve closed; (b) hot – valve open.

An alcohol mixture is used for two main reasons:

1. It has an extremely low freezing point, much lower than that of water.
2. It has a low boiling point, which causes it to expand at a greater rate than the coolant in the cooling system.

When the temperature of the coolant is low, the bellows pulls the valve disc tightly onto its seat (Figure 15.6a). This prevents the flow of coolant from the engine block to the radiator. As the temperature of the coolant rises, the alcohol mixture in the bellows expands. This forces the valve disc off its seat, which allows the heated coolant to escape to the radiator, where it can be cooled (Figure 15.6b). The alcohol mixture in the bellows reduces in volume as the temperature falls, and at a predetermined limit the valve disc is forced back onto its seat once more.

To prevent the possibility of air locks forming when the cooling system is being filled, a **jiggle valve** is also fitted to the thermostat unit. This valve has a small float, which, when the system is empty, opens a small hole. As the cooling system is filled, air can escape through the hole. When the coolant level reaches the thermostat, the float rises and the valve blocks the hole to prevent coolant circulation until the thermostat operates normally.

Wax element thermostat

This thermostat employs a special wax compound, which has been compressed into a copper container.

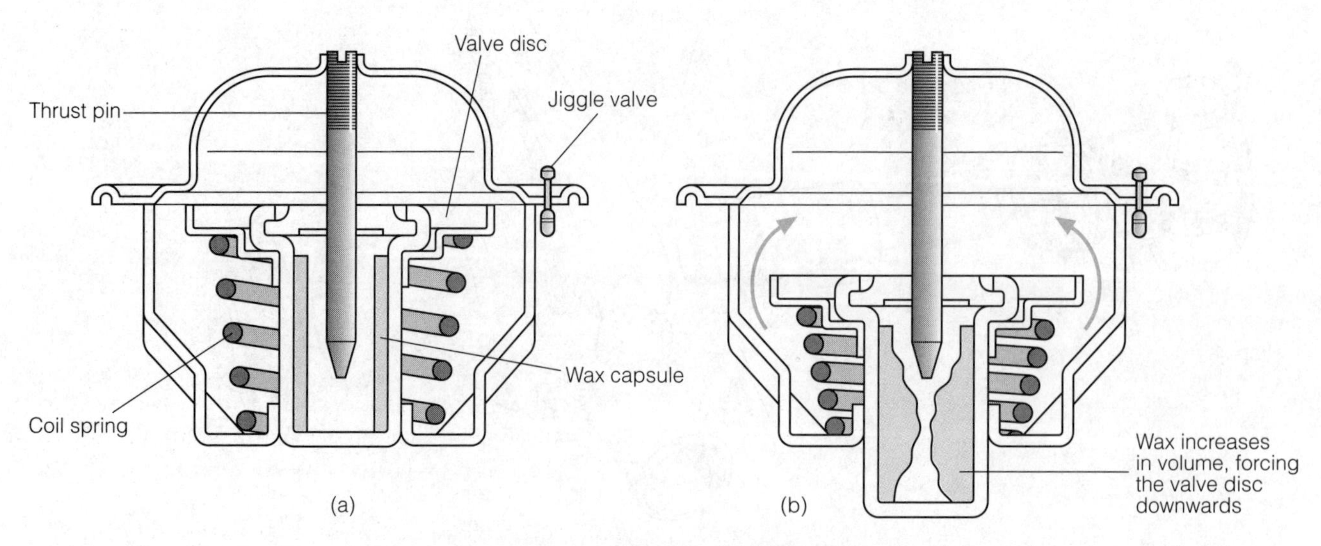

Figure 15.7 Wax-element thermostat: (a) cold – valve closed; (b) hot – valve open.

Although it operates in a similar way to the bellows type, a notable feature of this thermostat is that it is unaffected by cooling system pressure, making it more suitable for use in a pressurised system.

The wax container is sealed except for a small opening through which a tapered needle called a **thrust pin** passes. A rubber sealing cap is also fitted to the container to prevent the wax from escaping past the thrust pin. A heavy-duty coil spring ensures that the valve disc sits tightly on its seat.

When cold, the wax inside the container is solid and exerts no pressure; at the same time the valve disc is held firmly against its seat by the coil spring (Figure 15.7a). This prevents the coolant in the cylinder block from escaping to the radiator. As the temperature of the coolant inside the engine block rises, the solid, heat-sensitive wax starts to turn to liquid and expands. This expansion creates pressure, which acts upon the thrust pin, and the reaction forces the valve disc downwards against coil spring pressure (Figure 15.7b). The open thermostat then allows hot coolant to flow into the radiator to be cooled.

Air-cooled engine thermostats

Although the air-cooling fan is driven by the engine, the amount of cool air blown around the engine may also be regulated by a similar thermostat, which controls flaps in the air passages. It allows the engine to reach normal working temperature before the control flaps are opened to admit full air flow.

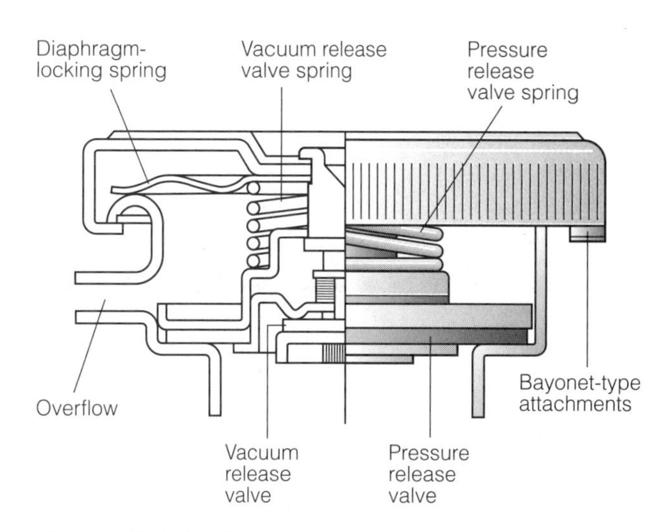

Figure 15.8 Radiator pressure cap.

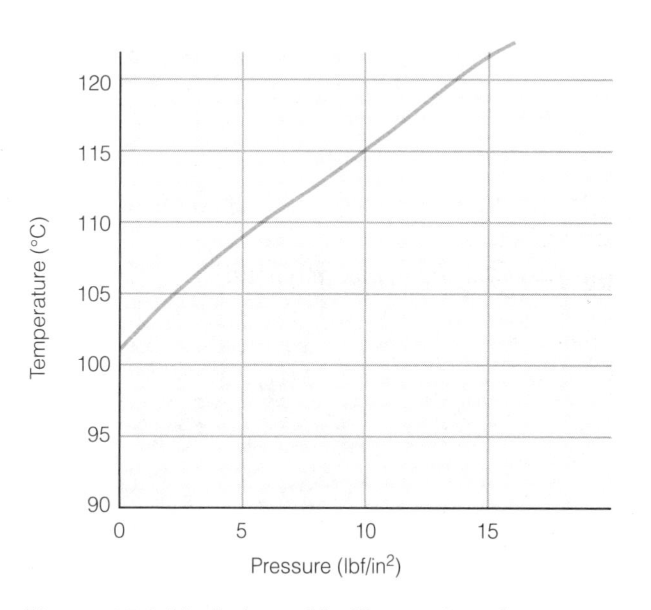

Figure 15.9 Variation of boiling point of water with pressure (1 lbf/in^2 = 6.9 kPa approx.).

Radiator or filler pressure cap

To maintain the pressure of the coolant at a predetermined setting, a pressure filler cap must be used.

The pressure cap consists of a spring-loaded release valve, which increases the overall pressure inside the cooling system (Figure 15.8). This allows the temperature of the coolant to rise above 100 °C without its boiling.

For example, as can be seen from the graph (Figure 15.9), a pressure of 26 kPa (4 lbf/in^2) will raise the temperature at which water boils to 107 °C, while at 103 kPa (15 lbf/in^2) the boiling temperature will be 121 °C. Every 8 kPa increase of pressure will raise the boiling point of water by approximately 1.5 °C.

At a predetermined setting the pressure cap release valve lifts off its seat, and any excess pressure escapes through the overflow. As the coolant temperature reduces, so too does the pressure, and a depression (vacuum) could be created in the cooling system. To prevent this the cap has a small release valve built into it, which allows atmospheric pressure into the system.

Radiators

> The purpose of the radiator is to provide a means of rapidly reducing the temperature of the engine coolant, and so help to prevent the vehicle from overheating.

In many ways a radiator can be thought of as a liquid-to-air heat exchanger. It provides a large cooling area for the coolant, which is exposed to an incoming stream of air at the front of the vehicle.

The basic construction of a radiator consists of two tanks: an upper or header tank, and a lower (or bottom) tank. In addition, there is also a radiator core or matrix, which is attached to the upper and lower tanks (Figure 15.10). The matrix allows the hot coolant to be cooled by the surrounding air as quickly as possible.

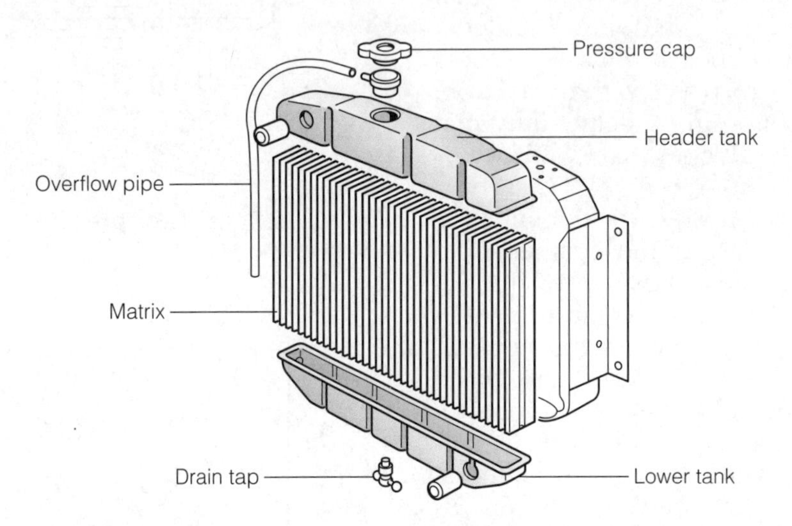

Figure 15.10 Radiator construction.

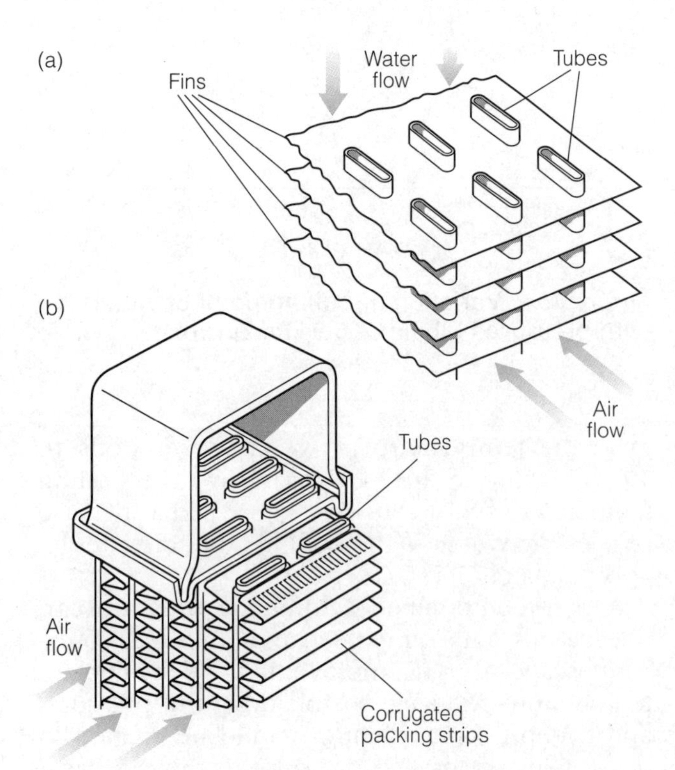

Figure 15.11 Radiator types: (a) tube and fin; (b) pack block.

> Radiators are distinguished by the direction of coolant flow and by the construction of their matrixes. The two main types are the **tube and fin** and **pack block**.

Tube and fin radiator matrix

In this type of radiator the tubes through which the coolant flows are surrounded by fins (Figure 15.11a). This construction permits the air to flow over the tubes and fins to draw off heat in order to reduce the temperature of the coolant.

Pack block radiator matrix

This is of similar design to the tube and fin type, except that corrugated packing strips are used to space out the gaps between the tubes (Figure 15.11b). The extra surface area of the corrugated packing strips provides a quick rate of cooling, as with the fins, but is cheaper to make.

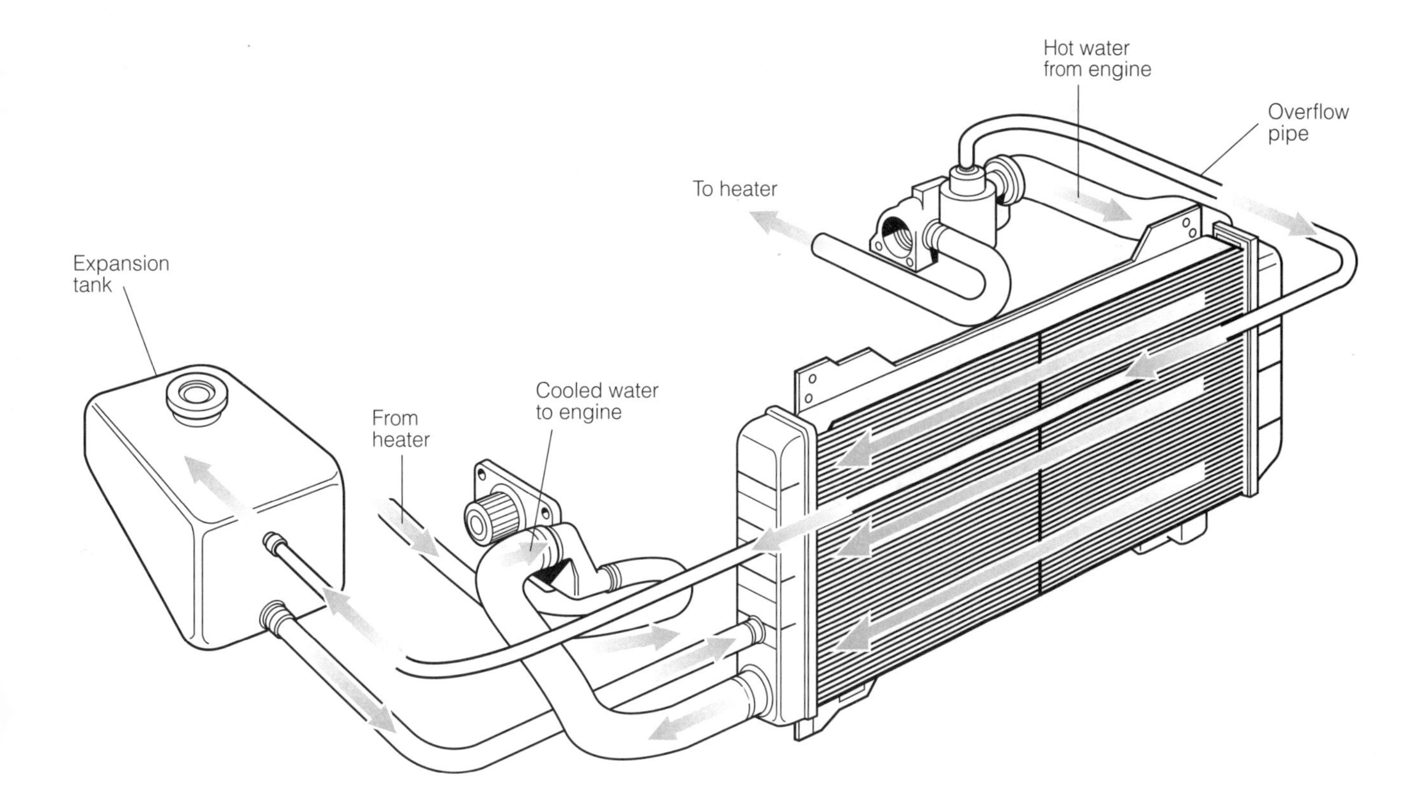

Figure 15.12 Cross-flow radiator.

Vertical-flow radiators

The cooling effect of the matrix results in the coolant's becoming denser, when gravity will cause it to flow naturally to the lower tank. All the radiators shown so far are of this type.

Cross-flow radiators

In this type of radiator, the coolant flows horizontally from the header tank to the outlet pipe located at the lower tank (Figure 15.12). Because of its long horizontal design, the flow of coolant through the matrix provides sufficient time to allow the passing air to reduce its temperature. The front height of the vehicle can be reduced.

Although cross-flow radiators have become a standard fitting on most vehicles, they have a number of disadvantages:

1. It is easier for sediment to form in the tubes and restrict the flow of coolant, which can result in problems of over-heating.
2. It is necessary to fit a more powerful pump to create a **positive circulation**. However, this helps to limit deposits of sediment in the radiator matrix.

Semi-sealed and non-sealed cooling systems

When the coolant becomes hot and expands, the pressure in the system may rise above its designed setting. If this happens in an ordinary, non-sealed system, the pressure release valve in the filler cap lifts off its seat and allows the excess expanded coolant to escape to atmosphere through the overflow pipe. When the temperature of the coolant returns to normal its volume reduces, and a small loss of coolant will have occurred. Over a period of time this loss of coolant could result in the engine having overheating problems.

With a semi-sealed system, an **expansion tank** is fitted to the overflow pipe. This minimises any coolant loss by providing a space for the hot, expanded coolant to flow into as its volume increases (Figure 15.13). When the temperature falls, the excess coolant is drawn back into the radiator to maintain a constant level.

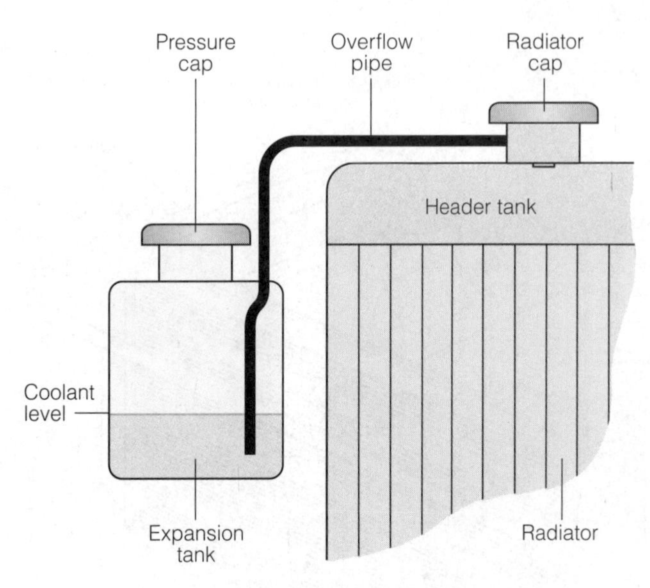

Figure 15.13 Semi-sealed cooling system.

Cooling fans

> The purpose of a cooling fan is to force or draw additional quantities of air through the radiator matrix, to reduce the coolant temperature.

When a vehicle is in motion, the coolant inside the radiator unit is cooled by the passing air. Unfortunately, this does not provide sufficient cooling under all operating conditions, so a cooling fan is normally fitted.

Three of the most popular types of cooling fan are:

1. direct-drive fans;
2. viscous coupling fans, such as the torque-limiting and air-temperature-sensing types;
3. electrically driven fans.

Direct-drive cooling fan

In the example shown (Figure 15.14), the fan is driven by the crankshaft pulley through a vee-shaped belt known as a **fanbelt**. The alternator and water pump, and sometimes the power steering pump, are also often driven by the same fanbelt.

The simple, belt-driven cooling fan has the advantages of cheapness and simplicity, but it also suffers from a number of disadvantages:

1. During cold-starting conditions, the engine is cooled unnecessarily. This often results in excessive use of cold-starting aids such as the choke.
2. There are rising noise levels from the fan blades as engine speed increases.
3. The engine constantly loses some power driving the fan, even when its cooling action is not needed.

To overcome these limitations some vehicle manufacturers have opted for variable-drive fans such as torque-limiting viscous-coupling fans or air-temperature-sensitive fans.

Torque-limiting viscous-coupling fan

This appears to be a simple belt-driven fan, but it has a designed maximum speed. The fan consists of a fluid coupling sandwiched between an inner and an outer drive disc (Figure 15.15).

At first the drive pulley and fan increase speed at the same rate. Then the fan speed increases at a slower rate because of viscous drag or slip

Figure 15.14 Direct belt-driven cooling fan arrangement.

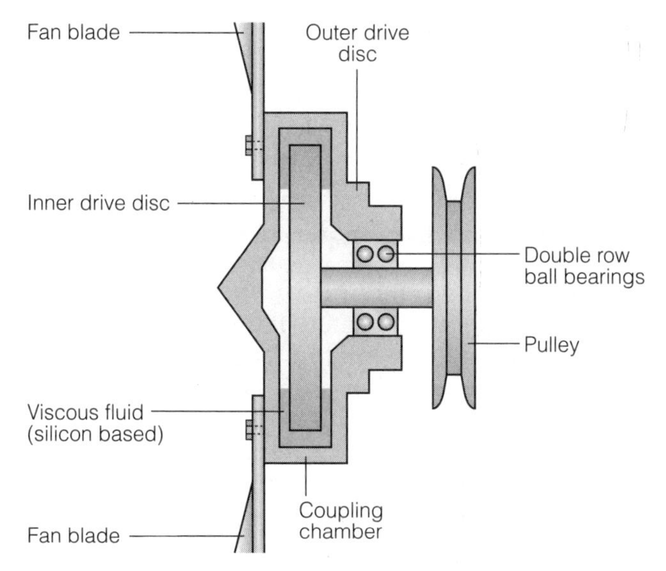

Figure 15.15 Torque-limiting, viscous-coupling fan.

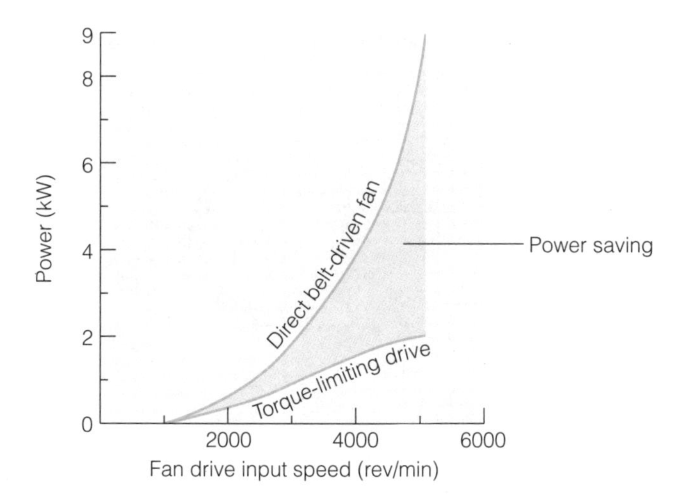

Figure 15.16 Relative power consumptions of a torque-limiting fan and a direct belt-driven fan.

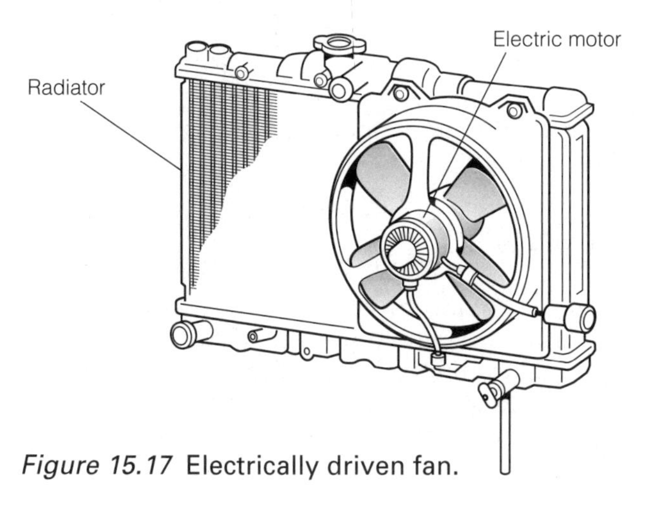

Figure 15.17 Electrically driven fan.

within the unit. The fan reaches its maximum speed when the force of the air flow passing through the fan blades equals the shearing torque of the silicone fluid. This torque limit prevents the fan from rotating any faster when engine speed is increased. The coupling requires no maintenance.

Air temperature-sensing viscous-coupling fan
This fan is similar to the viscous-coupling type in that it has an inner and an outer drive disc separated by silicon-based fluid. The important difference is that it does not operate until the system requires cooling. This is controlled by a bimetallic temperature-sensing device located at the front of the fan unit.

The graph (Figure 15.16) shows the potential power savings that can be achieved by using a torque-limiting fan rather than a direct belt-driven fan.

Electric fan

The now very common electrically driven cooling fan replaces the belt driven unit (Figure 15.17).

To control its operation, a temperature sensor is fitted to the cooling system. When starting and in cold-starting conditions, the sensor detects that the radiator does not require forced air cooling, and the electric fan is inoperative. This enables the engine to reach its normal operating temperature far quicker than an engine equipped with a direct belt-driven cooling fan. Power loss is much reduced. When the coolant temperature exceeds a predetermined setting, the sensor automatically switches on the electric fan to reduce its temperature.

Keep your fingers away from the fan. Even with the engine stopped, it can suddenly start to spin.

Fanbelts

The belt provides a simple means of driving the alternator and water pump, together with some other ancillary units such as a power steering pump, from the crankshaft pulley.

The two most common types of fanbelt fitted to vehicles are the **vee belt** (Figure 15.18a) and the **ribbed vee belt** (Figure 15.18b). They are normally made from a mixture of canvas, rubber and cord material. Interestingly, such belts – even if they do not drive the fan – are often still called fanbelts.

In order to drive the various components properly, the fanbelt must always be correctly tensioned. A fanbelt that is too loose would slip on its drive pulley. In contrast, a fanbelt that is too tight could cause early failure of both the alternator and water pump bearings.

To tension a fanbelt, the alternator is normally pivoted away slightly from the engine block until the recommended tension (approximately $\frac{1}{2}$ inch (12 mm) of movement) is achieved on the longest run of the belt (Figure 15.19).

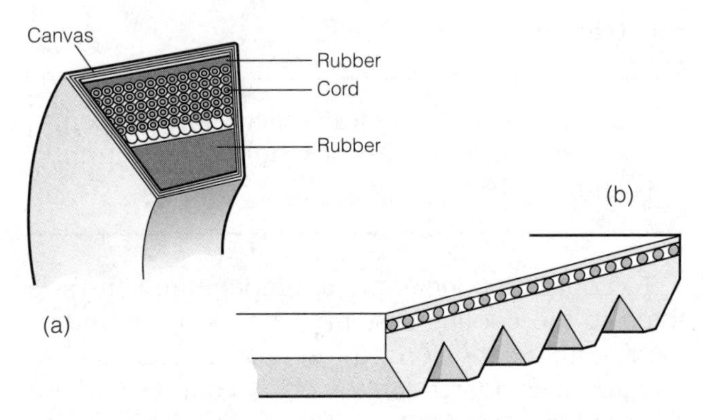

Figure 15.18 Fanbelts: (a) vee belt; (b) ribbed vee belt.

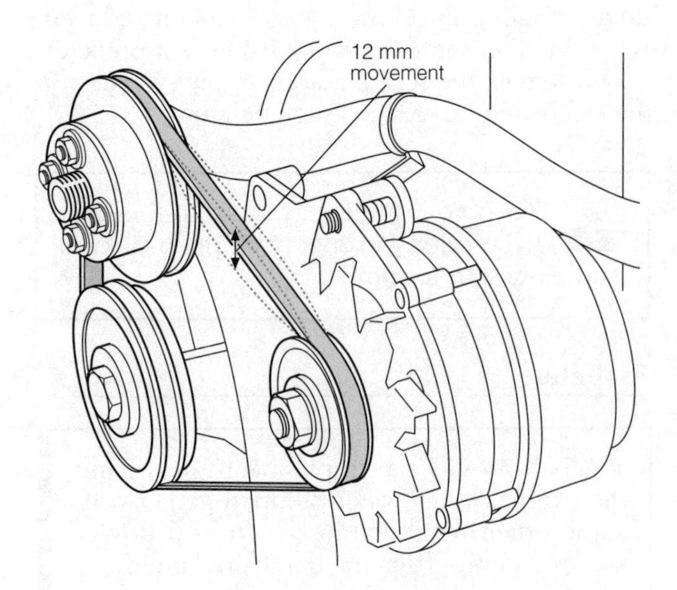

Figure 15.19 Tensioning a fanbelt.

Temperature gauges

> A temperature gauge is an electrically operated measuring device to give visual indication of the engine operating temperature.

The gauge is operated by means of a heat-sensitive sender unit located in the cooling system, either on or near the engine. The electrical resistance value (measured in ohms) of the sender unit progressively changes with variations in operating temperature, so that, for example, high resistance = low temperature; low resistance = high temperature. The two most common types of temperature gauge fitted to vehicles are the **bimetallic** gauge (Figure 15.20a) and the **moving iron** gauge (Figure 15.20b).

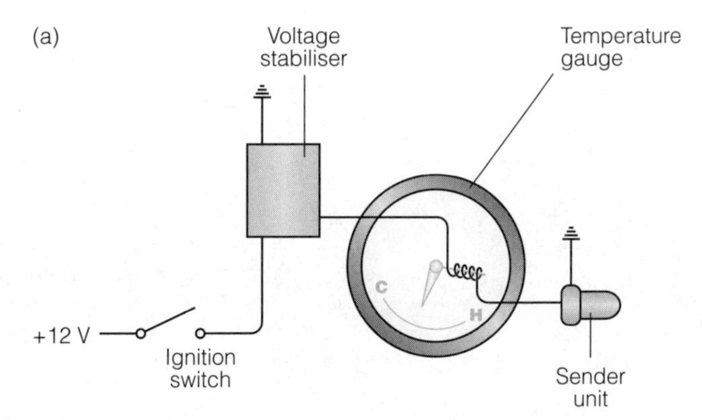

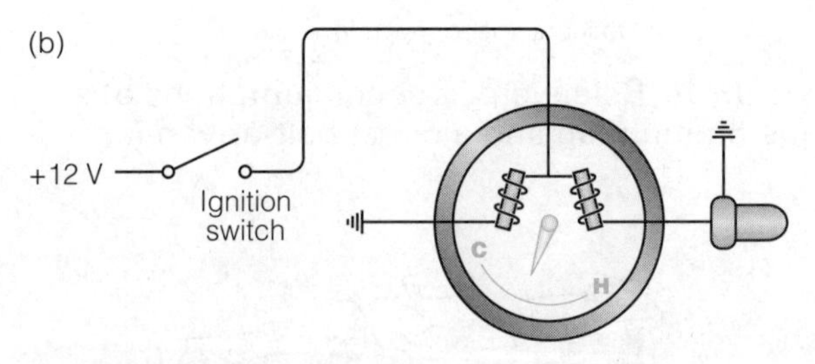

Figure 15.20 Temperature gauges: (a) bimetallic; (b) moving iron.

Core plugs

When an engine block has been cast, the sand that formed its mould must be removed from the water jacket through holes cast in the side. The holes are then capped using a set of core plugs, which prevent the escape of coolant (Figure 15.21).

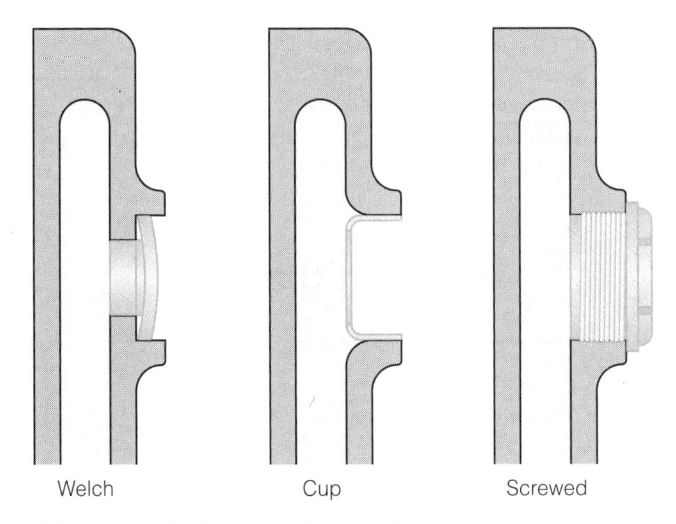

Figure 15.21 Types of core plug.

Cooling system inhibitors

A corrosion inhibitor is a chemical solution (normally sodium based), which prevents the formation of corrosive acids inside the cooling system.

Modern engines are commonly made from a combination of different metals: for example, aluminium for the cylinder head and cast iron for the cylinder block. These dissimilar metals can react with each other in the presence of water, causing corrosion. It is therefore desirable to add some form of corrosion inhibitor to the coolant. Indeed, there are some vehicles in which an approved coolant additive must be used as it also raises the boiling point of the coolant. Anti-freeze solutions contain corrosion inhibitors, and for this reason can be as necessary in hot climates as in cold.

Cooling system maintenance

To ensure that the cooling system remains in a serviceable condition, certain periodic maintenance tasks should be carried out at regular intervals.

Air-cooled systems

Although the system on an air-cooled engine requires very little in the way of maintenance, the areas that need routine attention include the following.

1. On air-cooled engines without cowlings, the cooling fins should be regularly cleaned to remove any build-up of deposits on the fins, and surface corrosion.
2. On multi-cylinder air-cooled engines that have a belt-driven cooling fan, the tension of the fanbelt should be checked and adjusted if necessary.

Water-cooled systems

This type of cooling system requires a higher degree of maintenance. In particular, the following areas need to be regularly inspected:

1. Check that the coolant level in the radiator or expansion tank is between the minimum and maximum levels.
2. Test the strength of the coolant inhibitor, and top up if necessary.
3. Check the condition and security of the flexible hoses: for example, tightness of the hose clips, and signs of cracking or rubbing on the hoses.
4. Check that the radiator matrix is not punctured or blocked, or showing signs of leakage.
5. Check the opening pressure of the filler cap, and pressure-test the entire cooling system for leaks using a pressure tester.
6. Check and if necessary adjust the tension of the fanbelt.
7. Check the operation of the thermostat, temperature sender unit and cooling fan by warming up the engine to its normal operating temperature. Observe that the overheating light does not come on or, if a temperature gauge is fitted, that it registers in the halfway position.
8. Over a period of time, the tubes inside the radiator can become blocked up with sediment. To remove this it is necessary to carry out a procedure called **back flushing**. To back-flush a radiator, it needs to be removed from the vehicle and then turned so that the filler or inlet is at the bottom. Pressurised water is then forced through the radiator's outlet pipe to dislodge the sediment inside the tubes.
9. The corrosion inhibitor in the cooling system gradually becomes used up. For this reason it is important to renew the coolant and the inhibitor at regular intervals – usually every one or two years.

Heading and ventilation

To ensure that the temperature inside the vehicle is comfortable for all the occupants, all vehicles are equipped with a combined heating and ventilation system.

The interior heater consists of a small heater radiator (similar to a normal engine radiator) and an electrically driven fan. The radiator is supplied with hot coolant from the engine side of the cooling system, and the fan blows air through it to heat the passenger compartment. A set of combined heater and ventilation controls on the dashboard enables the driver to vary both the temperature and the amount of air supplied to the ventilation vents (Figure 15.22). On some models, the air intake for the interior ventilation system is fitted with a fine filter to remove any particles of dust or pollen.

Air conditioning

An efficient, modern air conditioning system can maintain a constant air temperature inside a vehicle (when the engine is running) in hot or cold weather conditions. It incorporates both a heating and refrigeration unit.

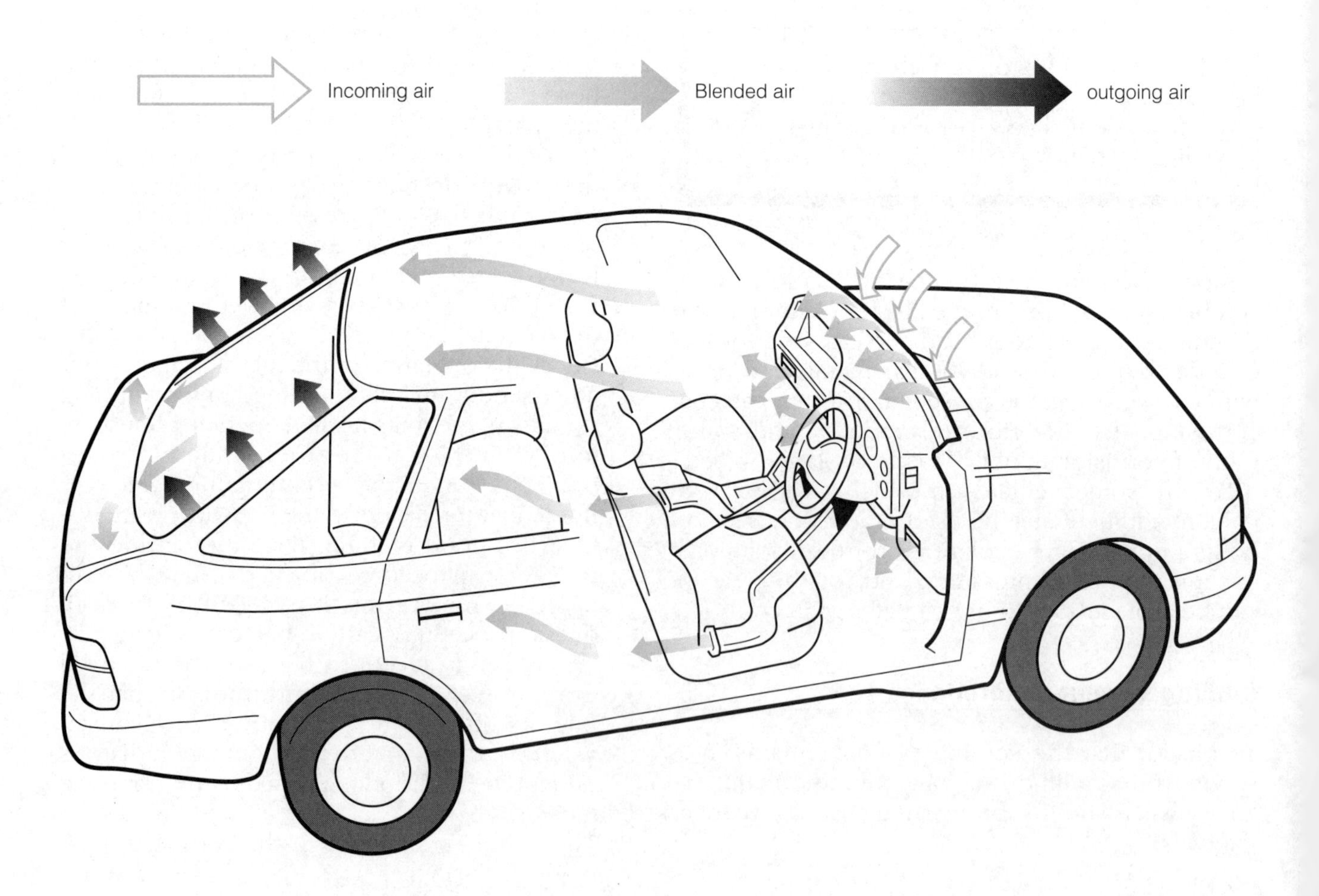

Figure 15.22 Heating and ventilation system.

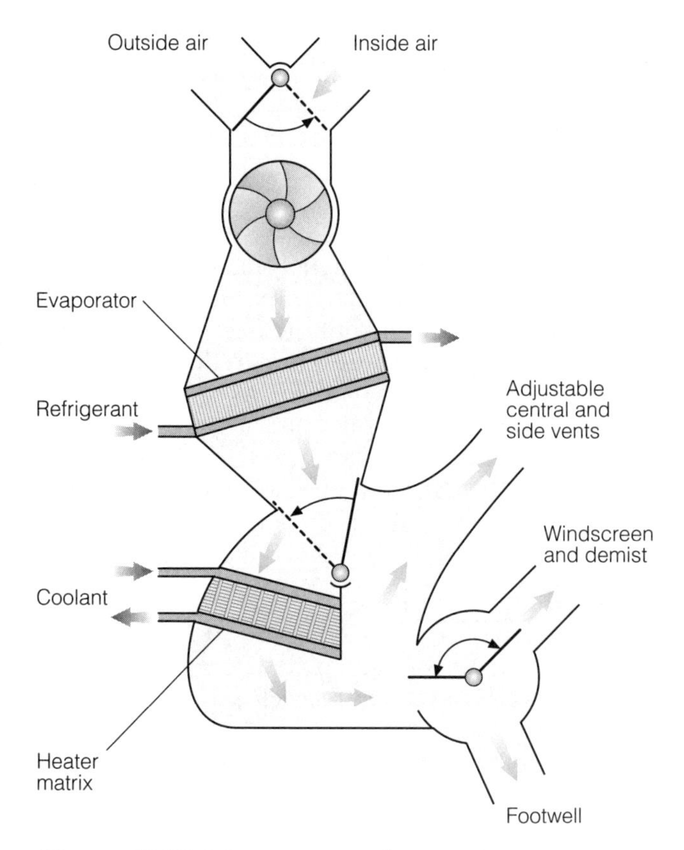

Figure 15.23 Climate control system.

The correct term for a unit that does this automatically is a **climate** or **environmental control system**. Basically, such a system incorporates an air conditioning evaporator, which cools the vehicle's air inside the heater unit (Figure 15.23). Automatic control is achieved from sensors in the passenger compartment.

Basic refrigeration circuit

Refrigerant flows around a circuit, which has a condenser to cool the liquid and an evaporator to absorb the heat from the passenger compartment (Figure 15.24).

Study the diagram, and note in particular how the compressed gas changes state from a vapour to a liquid in the condenser and from a liquid to a vapour in the evaporator. Figure 15.25 shows two possible layouts for the system.

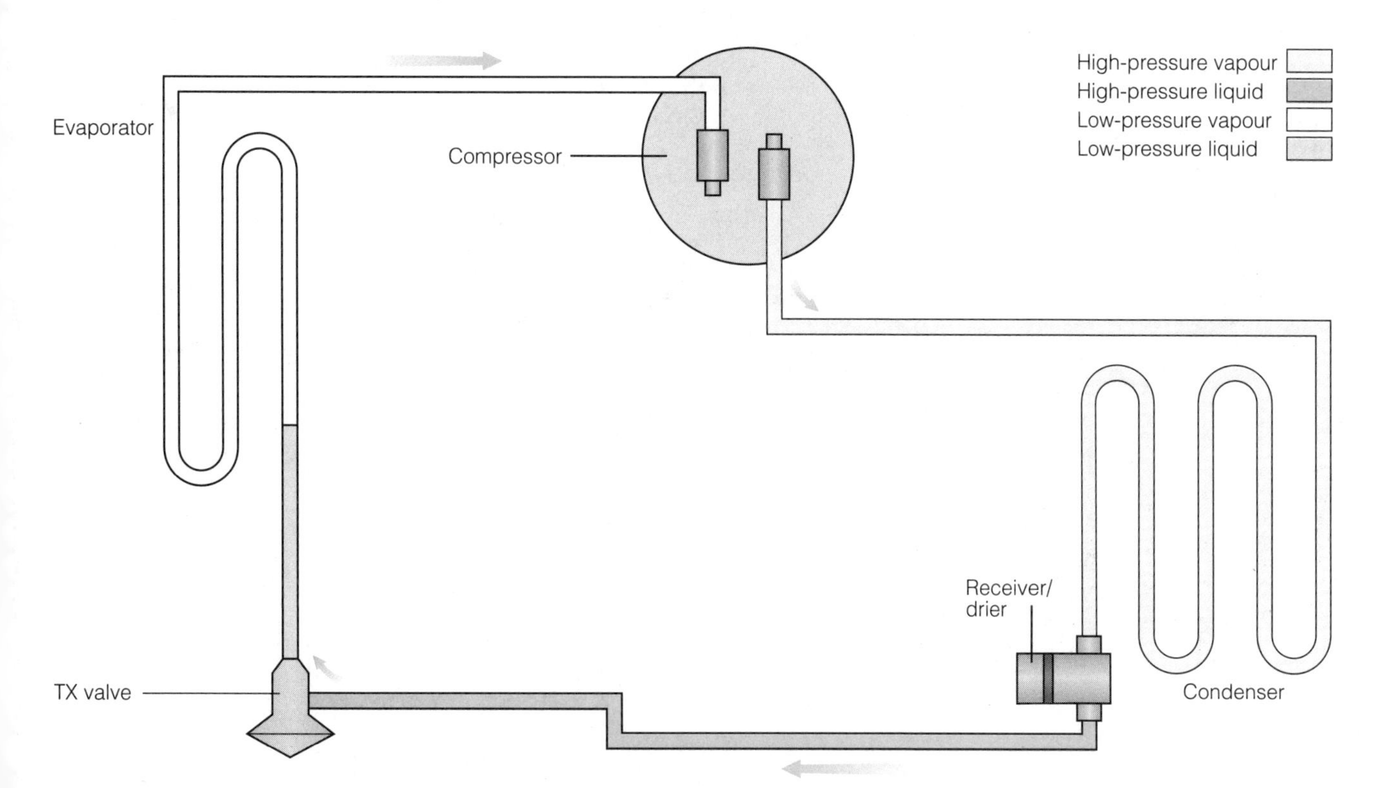

Figure 15.24 Basic refrigeration circuit.

Basic operation

The air conditioning system operates on a vapour compression and refrigeration cycle. The purpose of the system is to remove heat from the passenger compartment and transfer it to the air outside the vehicle. The heat is absorbed by the refrigerant when it passes through the evaporator and is released by the refrigerant as it passes through the condenser.

The compressor, which is driven from the engine's crankshaft pulley, is operated by a magnetic clutch. The compressor raises the pressure, and therefore also the temperature, of the vaporised refrigerant. It is fed to the condenser, which acts like a radiator, at the front of the vehicle. As the hot, high-pressure vapour is fed through the tubes of the condenser it is cooled, and condenses into a high-pressure liquid. This liquid refrigerant then travels to the receiver/drier, where it is temporarily stored and filtered, and moisture is absorbed by desiccant or silica gel crystals.

The refrigerant continues to the expansion valve, from where it passes through a small orifice, which restricts its flow into the evaporator. The small orifice, in combination with the depression created by the compressor, results in a reduction of the pressure in the evaporator. As refrigerant is metered into this low pressure, it boils or vaporises, and in so doing draws heat from the evaporator. The air for the vehicle interior is blown over the cold evaporator and is cooled.

Types of refrigerant

Since 1993 a refrigerant called R134a has been used, but older systems use R12, a CFC (**c**hloro-

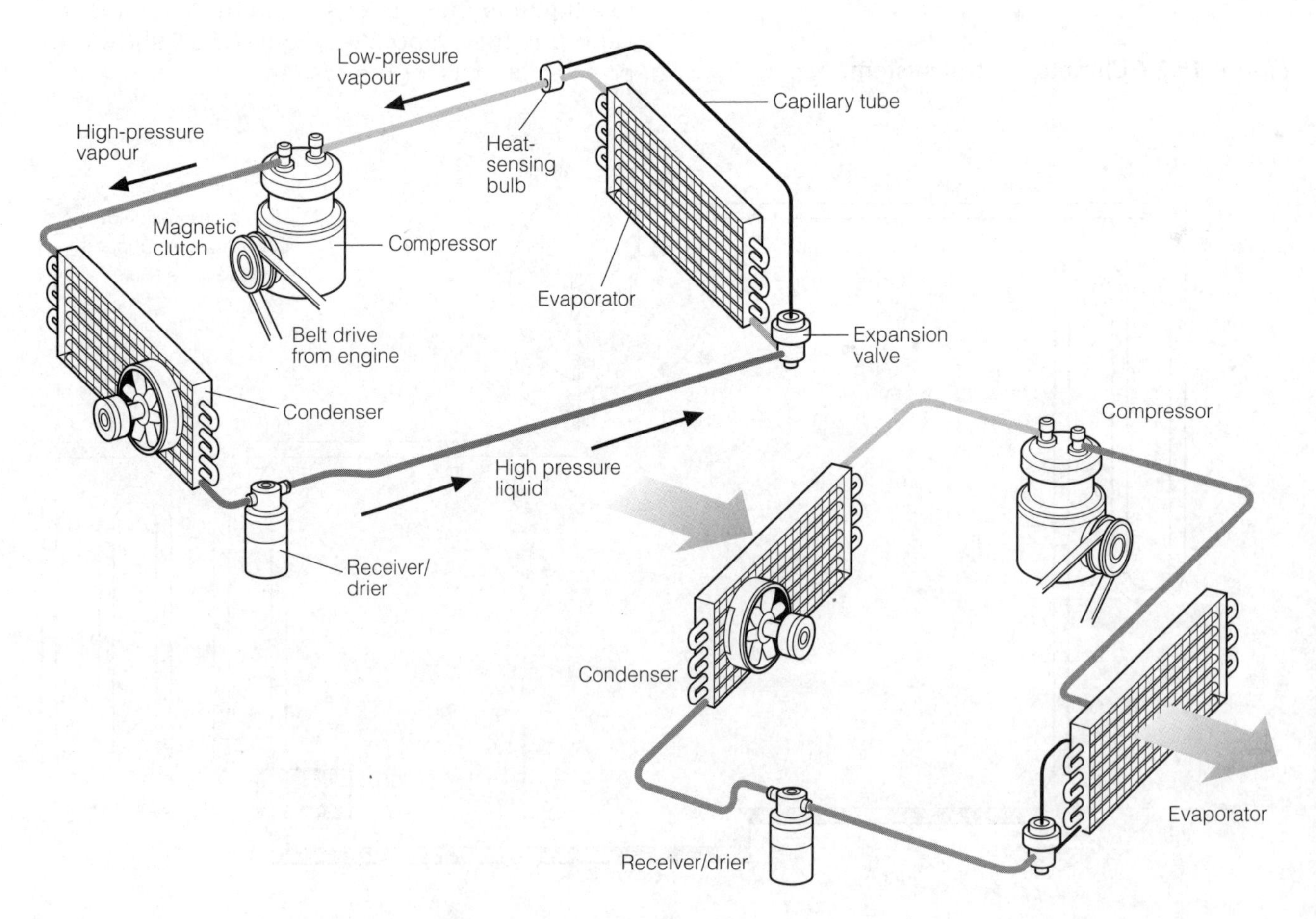

Figure 15.25 Air conditioning systems.

fluoro**c**arbon) gas. This gas has been identified as the primary cause of damage to the Earth's ozone layer, and for this reason it has been withdrawn from use in all new systems.

R134a is an HFC (**h**ydro**fl**uoro**c**arbon) gas. This gas, although less damaging than R12, causes environmental damage by contributing to the **greenhouse effect** if it is released to atmosphere.

Refrigerants are stored in pressurised containers, and must not be mixed when recharging after repair.

At atmospheric pressure, refrigerant boils at –30 °C: that is, it changes from a liquid to a vapour. When in the system it is under great pressure, and is very dangerous if released in an uncontrolled manner.

Repairs should be carried out by a professionally trained mechanic or refrigeration engineer. Manufacturer's instructions should be read and understood before working on any part of an air conditioning system.

Remember:

- If refrigerant comes into contact with the skin or the eyes it will freeze them. This could result in frost bite or even blindness.
- As refrigerant is heavier than air, it must never be discharged over a pit; if someone is working there, they could be suffocated.
- A refrigerant in contact with a naked flame will create a poisonous gas. In certain circumstances this can form an explosive mixture with air. Smoking is very dangerous in the presence of refrigerant, particularly if the vapour is inhaled through a lighted cigarette.
- Never allow stored pressurised refrigerant containers to heat above 50 °C, as an explosion could occur.
- The vehicle's air conditioning system must be de-pressurised: if any welding, brazing or soldering is carried out in the vicinity of the system; if the vehicle is to be oven dried at a temperature exceeding 70 °C; or if any part adjacent to the system is exposed to infrared heaters.

CHECK YOUR UNDERSTANDING

- One of the functions of a cooling system is to ensure that the engine temperature is kept within controllable limits; a cooling system can also provide heat for the vehicle's interior.
- A cooling system relies upon three scientific principles for its operation: conduction, convection and radiation.
- On an air-cooled engine, a set of cooling fins must be cast into both the engine block and the cylinder head. If the engine is cowled, an engine-driven fan will also be fitted.
- To prevent the formation of corrosive acids inside the cooling system, vehicle manufacturers recommend that a cooling system inhibitor be added to the water.
- At regular intervals the cooling system should be inspected for signs of damage, and designated maintenance activities should be carried out.

REVISION EXERCISES AND QUESTIONS

1. State the *three* main functions of a cooling system.
2. Name the scientific terms used to describe how heat is transferred through solids, liquids, gases and a vacuum.
3. Why do some of the cooling fins on the cylinder of an air-cooled engine have a larger surface area?
4. Name *three* technical advantages that a liquid-cooled system has over an equivalent air-cooled system.
5. Why is a thermostat fitted to a pressurised cooling system?
6. Name *two* types of radiator matrix used on motor vehicles.
7. What does the term a *semi-sealed cooling system* refer to?
8. State the purpose of a corrosion inhibitor.
9. Name the *two* components in an air conditioning system that are responsible for conducting heat away from the interior of a vehicle, and the function that each performs.
10. What happens to the refrigerant that enables it to absorb heat?
11. In what way is a pit or a naked flame dangerous if refrigerant escapes in the workshop?

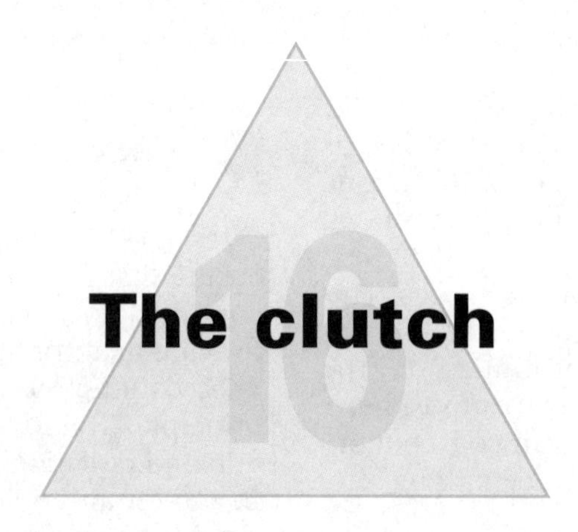

The clutch

Introduction

The purpose of the clutch is to:

- permit a smooth and gradual engagement of the drive (so that the vehicle can gradually move away from rest);
- assist gear changing;
- provide a temporary neutral.

The internal combustion engine, unlike a reciprocating steam engine, is not able to work from rest; it must be running to provide power. It must also be turning over at a good fast idle speed before it develops enough torque to move a vehicle. The clutch permits a gradual and smooth engagement of torque from the running engine to the stationary transmission and driving wheels.

When engaged, the clutch must transmit the maximum engine torque without slipping. To permit smooth and easy gear changes, there must be no turning effort on the gearbox input shaft when the clutch is disengaged.

There are many types of clutch available for use on vehicles. All vehicle clutches of the gradual engagement type that transmit the power from the engine to the driving wheels do so by friction, so they are called **friction clutches**.

The dry plate clutch

This is the most common type of friction clutch; it is used almost universally in light vehicles and in many commercial vehicles.

The driven members of the clutch are the **flywheel** and the **pressure plate**. The pressure plate is contained within a cover, which is attached to the flywheel by bolts, and revolves with it as a unit. The pressure plate is driven at all times by a number of projections, which engage in slots in the cover. Clamped between the flywheel and the pressure plate is the **driven plate**.

There are two methods of applying pressure to clamp the driven plate: by a series (six or more) of coil springs, or by a single diaphragm spring. Both are located between the cover and the pressure plate, and press the plate towards the flywheel face. This action grips the friction-lined driven plate between the flywheel and the pressure plate.

The input shaft to the gearbox is splined so that the driven plate (also known as the **clutch disc**, **centre plate** or **friction plate**) can slide backwards and forwards on the splines slightly, and can drive the gearbox input shaft. The input shaft is supported by bearings in the flywheel or crankshaft and the gearbox.

Coil spring clutch

Figure 16.1 shows a simplified version of the clutch. When it is engaged (Figure 16.1a), the springs located between the pressure plate and the clutch cover force the pressure plate towards the flywheel, and the driven plate is clamped between the two surfaces. Provided there is sufficient spring pressure, rotation of the engine will also turn the driven plate and the input shaft to the gearbox.

When the driver disengages the clutch by pressing the clutch pedal downwards, the pedal linkage moves a release bearing (Figure 16.1b).

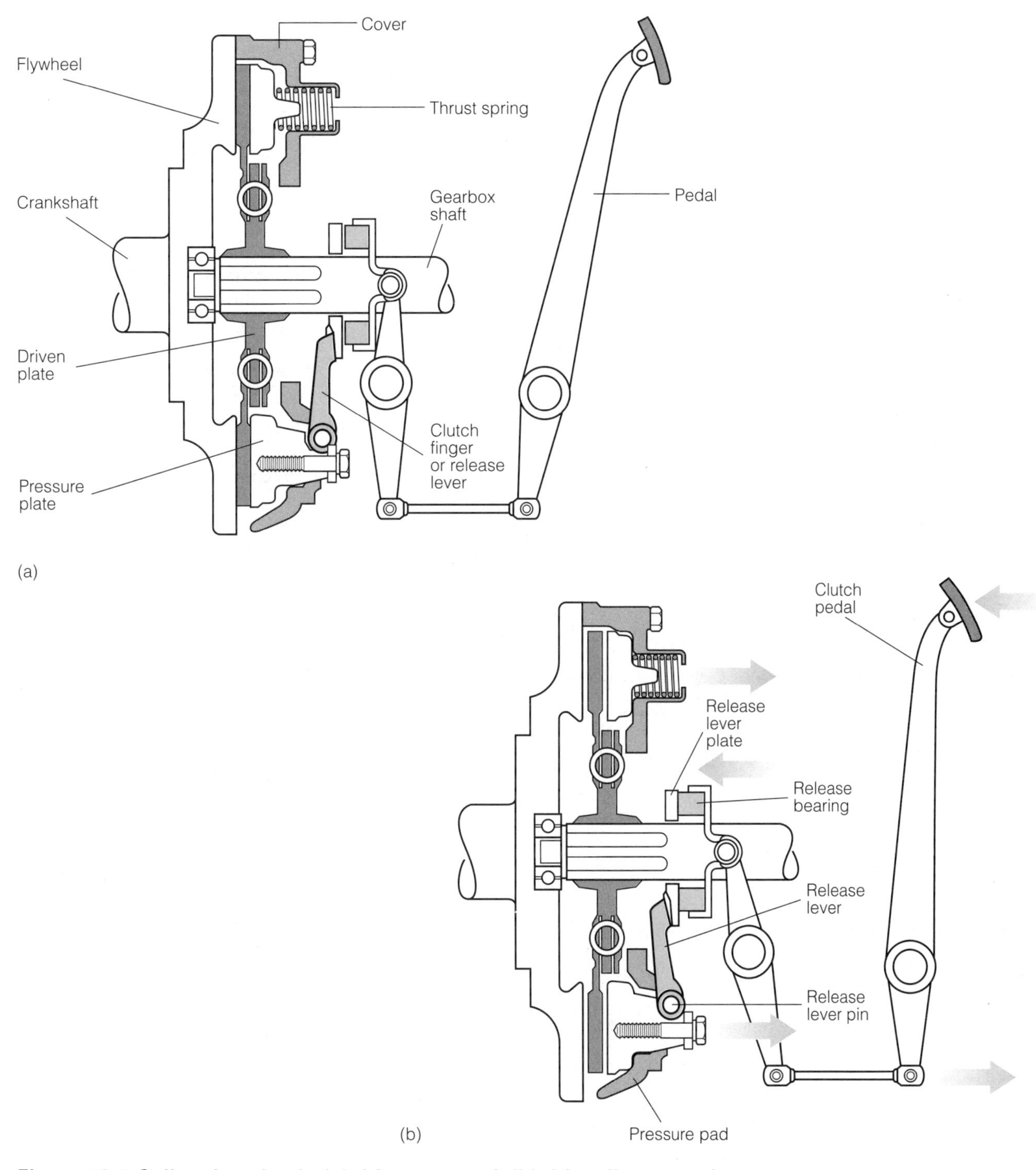

Figure 16.1 Coil spring clutch: (a) drive engaged; (b) drive disengaged.

This pushes on the levers (or fingers), which are pivoted in the clutch cover, and they pull the pressure plate away from the flywheel. As the driven plate is no longer clamped, it is free to slide slightly along the input shaft splines and out of contact with the flywheel and pressure plate. As a result, engine torque is not transmitted to the gearbox.

Note that a certain amount of slip will occur before the clutch is either fully engaged or disengaged. This is particularly important when pulling away, as it allows smooth take-up of the drive.

Cover assemblies

The cover assembly incorporates the pressure plate, and the complete unit is often called the **pressure plate assembly** or simply the **pressure plate**. Although coil spring cover assemblies were commonly used on light vehicles in the past, they are used only on heavy vehicles today (Figure 16.2). Note that the actual movements inside the clutch are very slight.

> As clutches rotate at engine speed, balance is very important: for this reason the cover plate assembly is positively located to the flywheel by dowels.

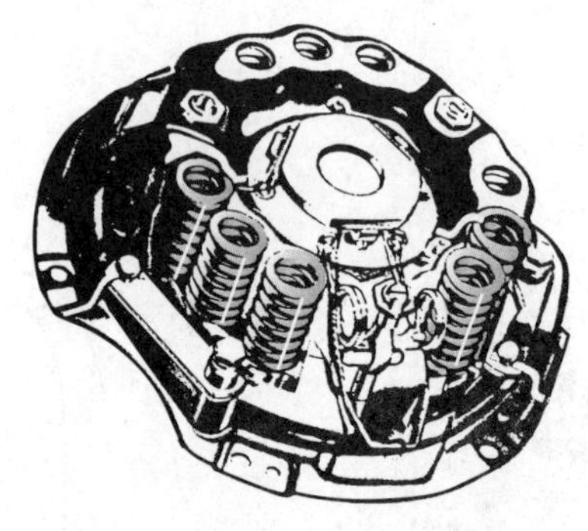

Figure 16.2 Typical heavy-duty coil spring cover assembly.

Coil spring clutch covers have the following **disadvantages**:

1. As the friction plate wears, the pressure plate moves nearer to the flywheel when it is engaged. The springs extend further, and this has the effect of reducing the clamping pressure slightly.
2. At high engine speeds, centrifugal force tends to bend the centre of the springs outwards. This effect also weakens the clamping pressure.
3. Compared with other designs this type of pressure plate is heavy, and has many moving parts.

However, it has the **advantage** that it is possible to overhaul it if it becomes faulty.

Diaphragm spring pressure plate

Clamping pressure is provided by a one-piece diaphragm spring made from tempered steel (Figure 16.3). It looks like a large, slightly conical washer, slotted from the centre to produce fingers. These fingers act as fulcrum levers. The outer end of the slots are formed into holes to prevent cracking as the fingers flex.

Operation

> The action of the diaphragm spring is similar to the movement of the dished end of a tin can. If the end is forced through the 'flat' position, it flips inwards to form a dish curved the other way.

When the clutch pedal is depressed, the release or thrust bearing is moved towards the flywheel, and presses on the inner ends of the diaphragm fingers (Figure 16.4). The diaphragm then pivots

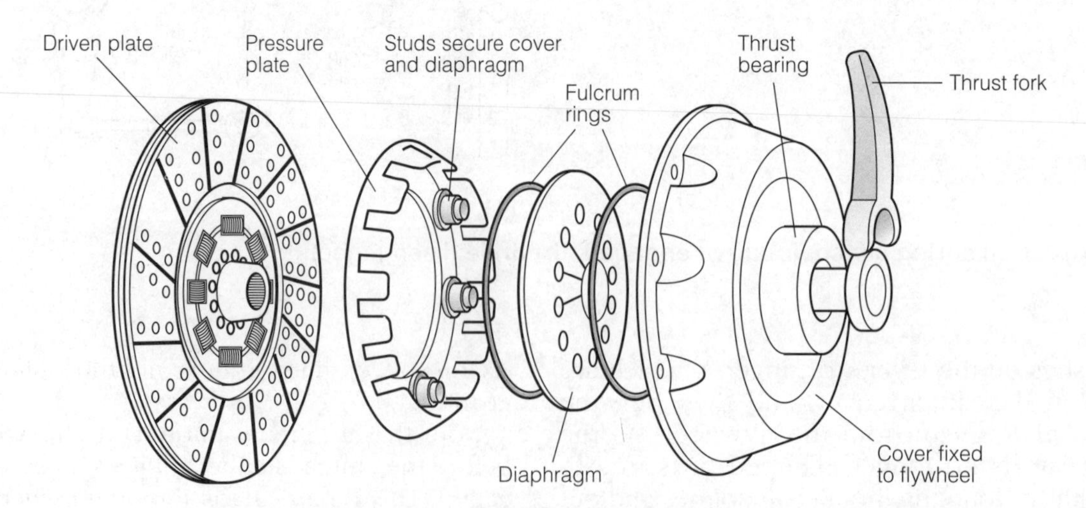

Figure 16.3 Exploded view of diaphragm-type clutch, showing diaphragm spring pressure plate.

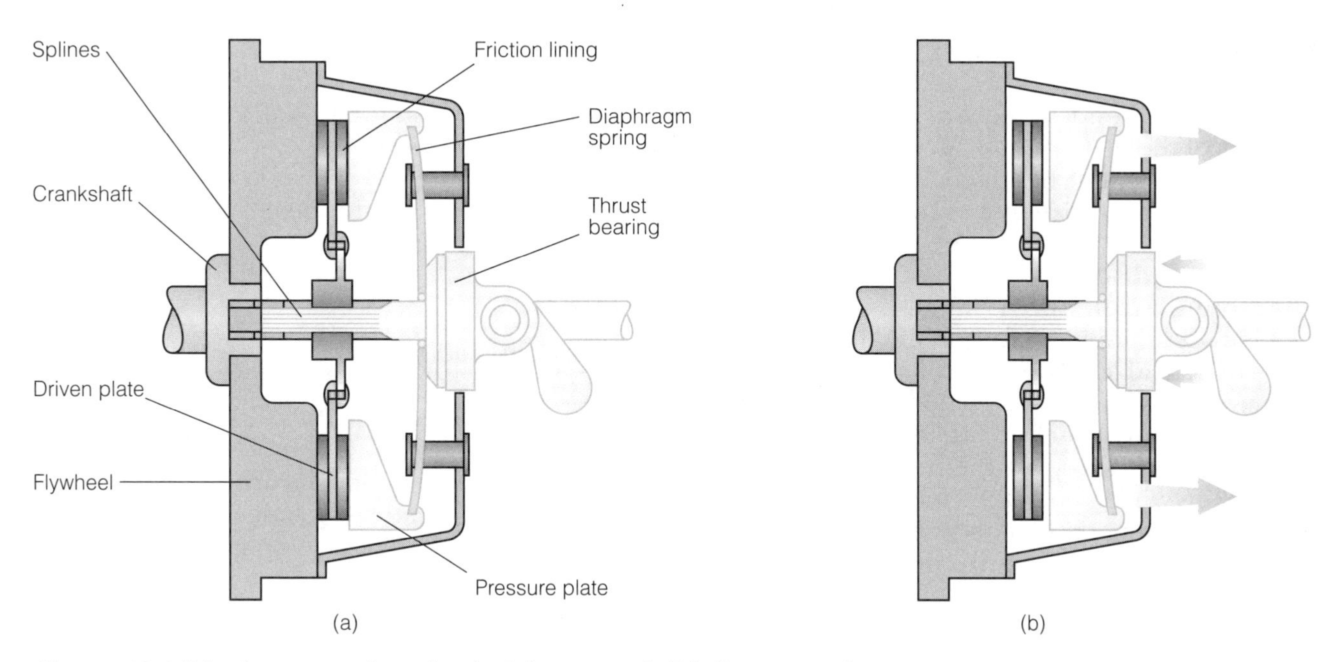

Figure 16.4 Diaphragm spring clutch: (a) engaged; (b) disengaged.

or flexes on the inner fulcrum ring, and its outer end flips away from the flywheel, releasing the pressure. With the clamping pressure removed, the pressure plate is pulled back and the clutch is disengaged.

Unlike the coil spring type, in which the clamping pressure of the springs reduces as the driven plate wears, the diaphragm spring moves back from its flattened position as wear takes place and clamping pressure is increased. Compared with the coil spring, the diaphragm spring offers the following **advantages**:

1. It is compact and can therefore be fitted in a smaller space.
2. It has fewer moving parts to wear or fail.
3. Less effort is needed to disengage the clutch.
4. Clamping pressure increases slightly as the driven plate wears.
5. It is not affected by centrifugal force, and can be used on high-speed engines.

It has the **disadvantage** that it is non-repairable.

Withdrawal mechanism

As the clutch cover assembly is revolving with the engine, a thrust bearing of some form is used to push against the fingers when the driver depresses the clutch pedal. The bearing may be a sealed ball unit or a hard graphite ring. The former is usually prepacked with lubricant, and the latter is self-lubricating. A release lever, pivoted in the bell housing, transmits the movement of the operating mechanism to the bearing.

Driven plate

This component may variously be described as the driven plate, friction plate, centre plate or clutch plate, and is installed between the flywheel and pressure plate.

Modern driven plates are cleverly designed, and they typically consist of three main components (Figure 16.5):

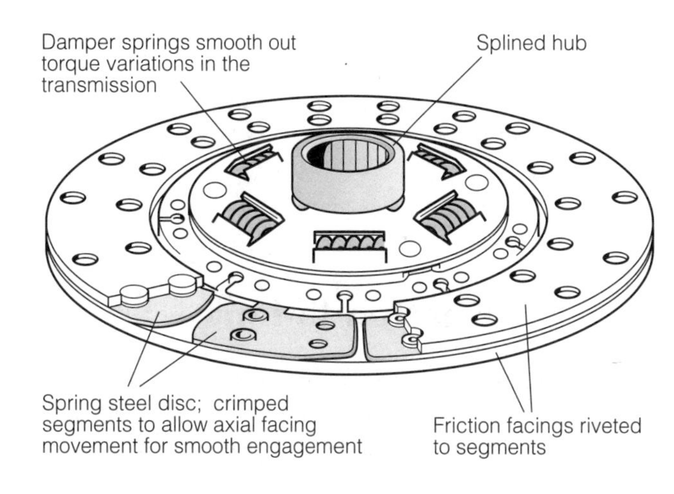

Figure 16.5 Typical spring-centre friction plate.

1. a spring steel plate, which is normally split into segments;
2. riveted or bonded friction material on both sides of the plate;
3. a splined central hub, which slides upon and drives the gearbox input shaft.

Spring steel disc

The spring steel disc is slightly crimped, to provide a cushioning effect as the drive is taken up. This **axial cushioning** takes place as the pressure plate clamps the friction linings between itself and the flywheel. In addition, the crimping acts like a spring to push the friction lining away from the flywheel when the clutch is disengaged, thereby reducing drag. It also allows air between the friction plates to assist cooling. See Figure 16.6 for an enlarged view of a different type of spring steel disc; it does the same job.

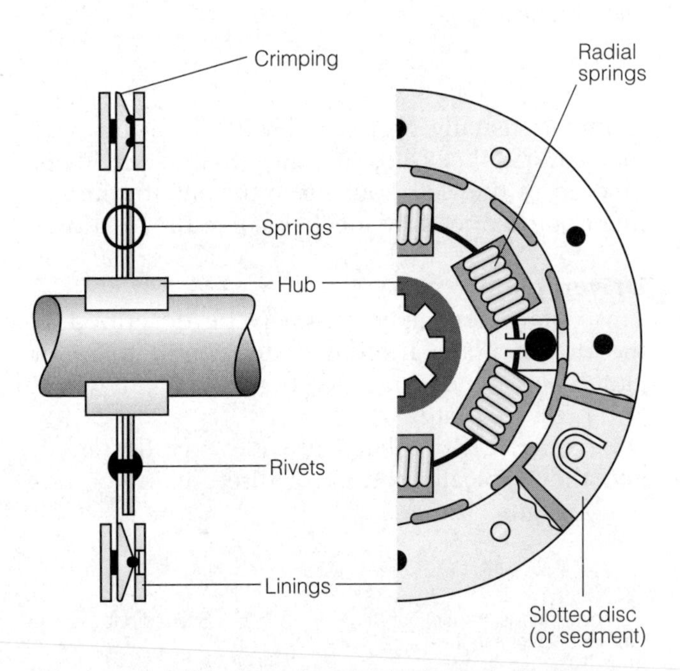

Figure 16.6 **Friction plate with slotted disc type axial springing.**

Friction linings

Every time the clutch is engaged to pull away from rest, slip occurs between the faces. The friction generates a tremendous amount of heat. To cope with this, the friction lining must have the following properties:

1. stable frictional qualities over a wide range of operating conditions;
2. the ability to withstand high compressive and centrifugal loads;
3. good shear strength;
4. compatibility with the metals of the flywheel and pressure plate;
5. high resistance to wear.

Asbestos-based linings

Asbestos has been commonly used as a friction material. It is normally woven or moulded, with threads of brass or zinc incorporated into the asbestos to aid heat dissipation. The material is compressed and bonded to form the friction face (or lining).

Asbestos linings have the following **advantages**:

1. high friction properties;
2. good resistance to fade;
3. high resistance to wear;
4. some resistance to oil contamination.

> Asbestos has one major **disadvantage**. If particles of material or the dust from wear are inhaled, life-threatening illness may result.

Alternative materials

In many countries the use of asbestos has been phased out. A common alternative is material developed from nylon polymers. Compared with asbestos, it has the following properties:

1. It has better rates of wear.
2. It is lighter in weight, which reduces the inertia of the driven plate. This means that the driven plate stops spinning sooner and also spins more quickly, reducing drag and allowing quicker gear changes.
3. It has higher tensile strength.
4. It has greater resistance to high temperature.

Another alternative material is based on a mixture of ceramic and copper, and is popular in heavy vehicle clutches. Instead of a lining in the shape of a ring, the ceramic material is formed into segments, which are mounted around the driven plate (Figure 16.7).

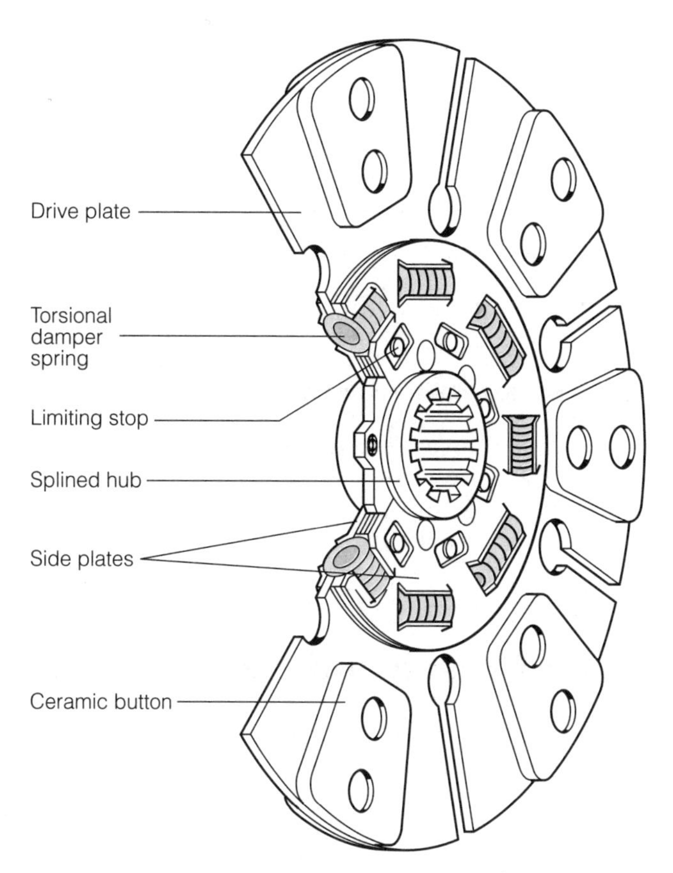

Figure 16.7 Clutch driven plate with ceramic facings.

Its **advantages** are:

1. a very low inertia, allowing quicker gear changes;
2. high frictional qualities, increasing torque capacity;
3. high temperature resistance, which reduces the tendency to fade;
4. better cooling, because air can circulate between the separate faces;
5. greater resistance to wear.
6. resistance to oil and grease.

> Despite some resistance to oil or grease contamination, clutch components – and particularly the friction surfaces – must be kept quite clean during handling and assembly.

Driven plate hub

Although some plates are attached rigidly to the hub, they are often separate parts. The drive between the hub and the plate is transmitted by a series of radial springs (Figures 16.5–16.7). The springs take the torsional shock and act as a damper when engaging the drive. More importantly, they absorb engine crankshaft torsional vibration, which is set up by the cylinder firing pulses. In a solid-drive clutch this vibration causes gear teeth chatter in the gearbox. The main advantage of a spring-centre driven plate is less noise and wear on the transmission components.

The multi-plate clutch

Multi-plate clutches employ a number of metal and friction discs, and are used on engines that produce a high torque output, such as those of heavy goods vehicles (Figure 16.8). The use of several discs has the advantage of reducing the operating pressure and the overall diameter. This also makes them suitable for use where space is restricted, typically on motorcycles. The clutch disengages in exactly the same way as the single-plate clutch.

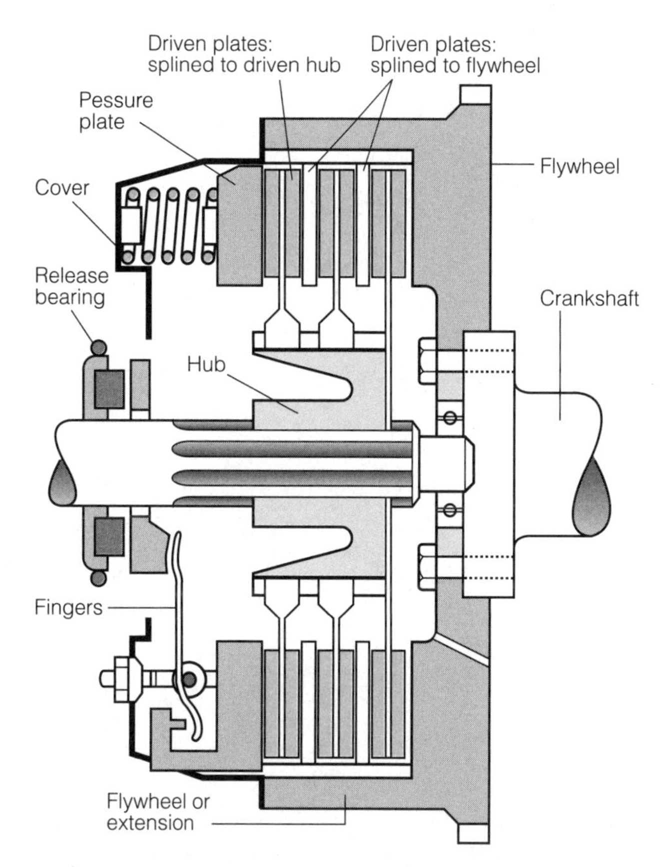

Figure 16.8 Multi-plate clutch.

Clutch operating mechanisms

Hydraulic

On modern cars, the clutch may often be operated hydraulically. Apart from a smoother operation, hydraulic operation allows for movement of the engine on its flexible mountings (Figure 16.9).

> The clutch pedal operates a master cylinder, similar to that used in a hydraulic braking system. When the pedal is depressed, fluid is displaced from the master cylinder and operates the slave cylinder, which is attached to the clutch operating mechanism.

When the clutch is released, the returning clutch thrust bearing pushes the slave piston back up the slave cylinder to its rest position.

Maintenance of this type of operating system is mainly concerned with topping up the hydraulic fluid to the correct level, and ensuring that the running clearances are retained. Frequently the adjustment is automatic.

Mechanical

> Most mechanically operated clutches use a flexible cable linked between the clutch pedal and the operating mechanism (Figure 16.10).

The cable has a fixed outer casing in which an inner cable is free to slide. Because of wear in the system some form of adjustment, which may be manual or automatic, is essential.

Fault finding and maintenance

As the friction lining of the driven plate wears away, the release levers move closer to the thrust bearing. If the clearance was allowed to disappear

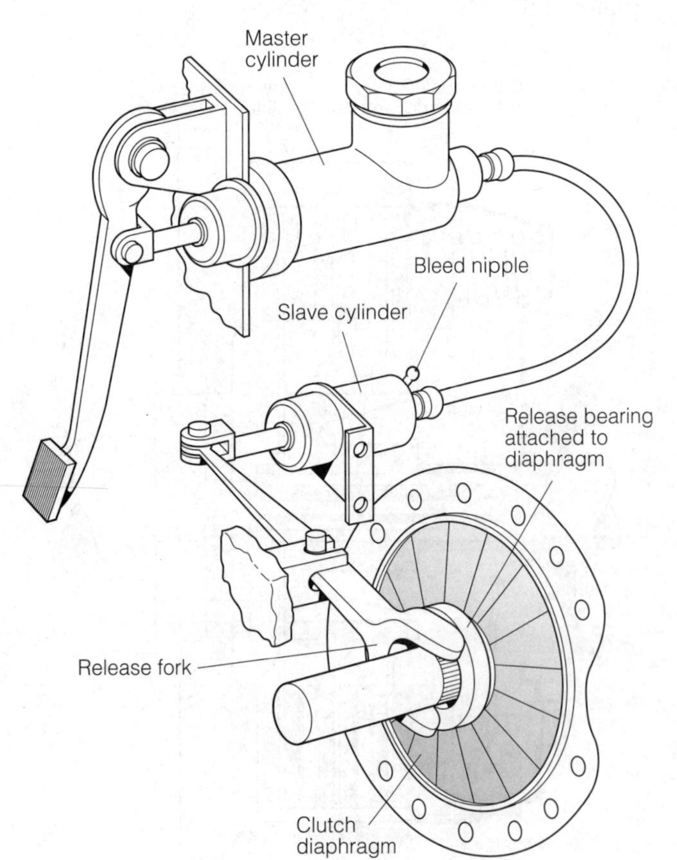

Figure 16.9 Hydraulic clutch-operating mechanism.

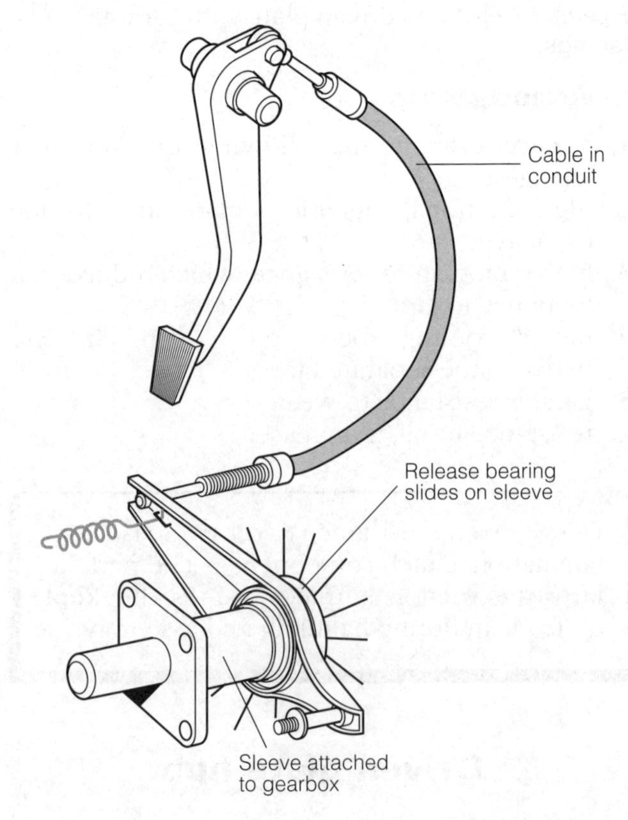

Figure 16.10 Mechanical cable clutch-operating mechanism.

altogether the clutch would be prevented from engaging fully, and the clutch could start to slip. This would cause heat and rapid wear and, as a result, the clutch could not transmit all the engine power output.

To prevent this happening there should always be a certain amount of free play in the clutch operating mechanism, usually between 10 mm and 30 mm measured at the pedal. Although many modern vehicles have automatic adjustment, some mechanisms have a facility for initial adjustment. Clutch repair or replacement should always involve setting up the mechanism correctly.

Clutch slip

Clutch slip occurs when the clutch cannot transmit the engine torque to the gearbox.

It may be caused by any of the following:

1. insufficient free play;
2. oil or grease on the friction linings;
3. worn linings;
4. weak clutch pressure plate spring or springs.

Clutch drag

Clutch drag occurs when the clutch will not fully disengage the drive. It causes difficulty in engaging gear or in gear changing.

It may be caused by:

1. excessive free play at the pedal;
2. defective thrust bearing;
3. driven plate seized on the gearbox input shaft splines;
4. gearbox input shaft spigot bearing seizure;
5. driven plate cracked or buckled;
6. oil or grease on the driven plate.

Clutch judder

This is vibration or judder, produced as the clutch is engaged.

It may be caused by:

1. cracked or distorted pressure plate;
2. loose or badly worn linings;
3. misalignment of the gearbox, caused by a loose or distorted clutch housing;
4. engine or gearbox mountings broken or sloppy;
5. partly seized or stiff operating mechanism;
6. oil or grease on the linings.

Clutch rattle

This usually results from something loose or broken inside or around the clutch.

It may be caused by:

1. pedal return spring missing or broken;
2. excessively worn release mechanism;
3. finger spring (anti-rattle spring) weak or broken;
4. driven plate springs loose or rivets slack;
5. release bearing loose in its holder.

Very rapid wear

Apart from mechanical defects, incorrect driving methods may cause clutch trouble. The usual causes are holding the vehicle (from running backwards down a slope) with the clutch, and resting the foot on the clutch pedal. These will cause heat build-up and excessive wear due to the slipping of the driven plate lining and the constant pressure on the thrust bearing.

CHECK YOUR UNDERSTANDING

- The clutch is a coupling (normally of the friction type) through which the drive from the engine to the gearbox is transmitted.
- It allows gradual take-up of the drive from the engine to the stationary transmission and driving wheels.
- It provides a means of temporarily disconnecting the drive from the engine to the gearbox.
- It assists in gear changing.
- There are two main types: coil spring and diaphragm spring.
- When moving away from rest the spinning pressure plate and flywheel gradually come

together, clamping the stationary driven plate between them. Slipping will take place between the driven plate, and the pressure plate and flywheel, until full clamping pressure is achieved, at which point the clutch pedal has been fully released. It is the slipping action that gives the gradual take-up of the drive.

REVISION EXERCISES AND QUESTIONS

1. Why must a driver be able to easily disconnect the engine from the gearbox?
2. Why is special friction material required on the clutch plate?
3. What is meant by the term *clutch slip*? List the possible causes.
4. Some means of adjustment, either manual or automatic, must be provided in the clutch operating mechanism. Why?
5. List the *four* principal components of a clutch.
6. List *three* possible causes of clutch judder.

Fluid flywheels and torque converters

Introduction

Torque converters are an essential part of modern automatic transmission systems. However, to help you understand how they work it is best to first learn about the fluid flywheel. This is why a component that you may never see is dealt with first in this chapter.

The fluid flywheel

The purpose of the fluid flywheel, also known as a **fluid coupling**, is to act as an automatic clutch between the engine and the gearbox. It is used instead of a dry plate clutch with automatic or semi-automatic gearboxes. When the engine is at idle speed, there is insufficient torque transmitted to enable the vehicle to move, but as the speed of the engine is increased, the fluid flywheel gradually transmits sufficient engine torque to move the vehicle.

The two main components of a fluid flywheel are the **impeller**, which is driven by the engine, and the **turbine**, which transmits the engine's torque to the gearbox (Figure 17.1). Both the impeller and the turbine have a number of vanes or partitions built into them. When the fluid flywheel unit is assembled together, the vanes on both the impeller and the turbine are facing each other. To ensure that the vanes do not touch when rotating, a small running clearance is provided. The fluid flywheel is partially filled, to the filler plug level, with engine oil, and it is this that transmits the torque from the engine-driven impeller to the turbine on the gearbox shaft (Figures 17.2 and 17.3).

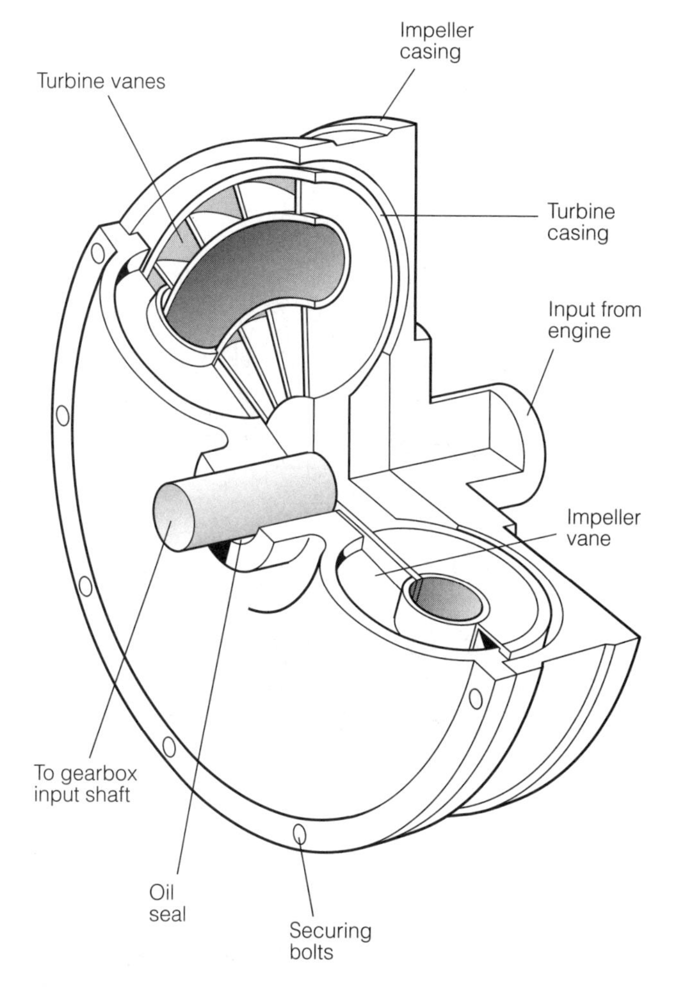

Figure 17.1 The fluid flywheel.

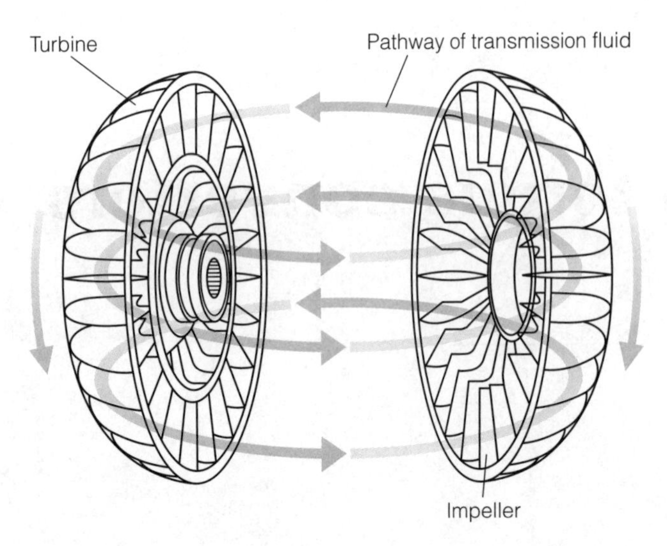

Figure 17.2 Operating principle of the fluid flywheel.

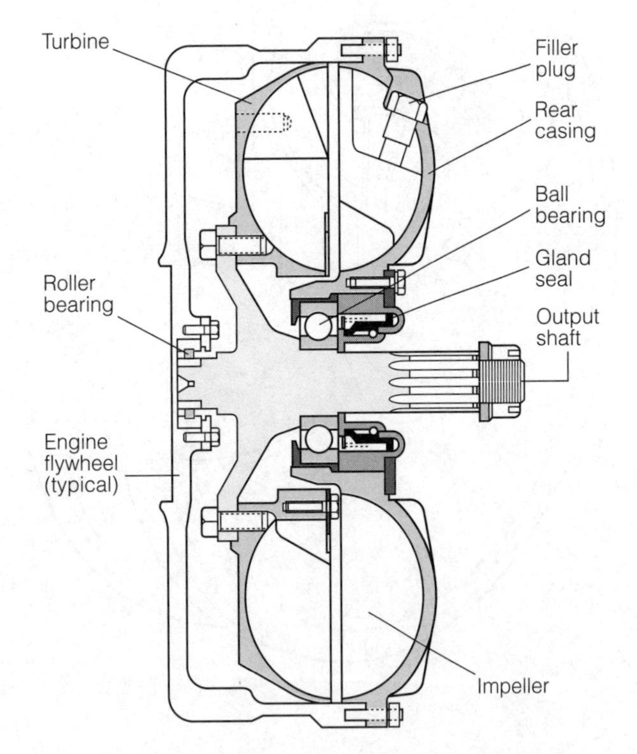

Figure 17.3 Cross-section of the fluid flywheel.

Operation: idling speed

When the engine is idling, the impeller, which is part of the casing and is bolted to the engine flywheel, revolves. This causes the oil in the impeller vanes to be flung outwards by centrifugal force into the turbine, which is connected to the gearbox input shaft. At idling speed, the centrifugal force exerted on the fluid is insufficient to drive the turbine and its attached gearbox shaft, and move the vehicle. The handbrake should always be kept on, however, when the vehicle is stationary.

Operation: pulling away and driving

When the accelerator pedal is depressed, the increasing engine and impeller speed also increase the centrifugal force acting upon the oil. The oil flows to the outer edge of the impeller and passes across onto the turbine blades with sufficient force to move the turbine, rotate the input shaft, and propel the vehicle. The oil is constantly recirculated between the impeller and the turbine. Eventually, the speed difference or slip between the two units is almost zero, but the turbine always revolves a little slower than the impeller.

Advantages and disadvantages of the fluid flywheel

Some of the main **advantages** of a fluid flywheel are as follows:

1. The engine's torque is transmitted progressively to the gearbox. This results in a much smoother and more comfortable ride, which is particularly important for passenger-carrying vehicles.
2. The unit has a relatively long service life and requires little in the way of routine maintenance. It is necessary only to keep the oil level topped up, and to check for leaks.
3. The smoothness of operation tends to damp out any torsional vibrations created by the engine.
4. No clutch pedal is needed.

The main **disadvantages** of a fluid flywheel are as follows:

1. The drive cannot be disconnected when the engine is running to allow gear changes to be made, which means that the gearbox must be automatic or of the pre-selector type.
2. The turbine slip and oil drag when driving result in a small loss of the power that is being transmitted to the roadwheels. This causes an overall increase in fuel consumption.

Torque converters

For vehicles fitted with a fully automatic transmission system, a modified fluid flywheel known as a **torque converter** is used (Figure 17.4). The purpose of a torque converter is to multiply the amount of torque produced by the engine as the vehicle accelerates from rest to the speed required and to transmit the drive to the gearbox. Under certain conditions a torque converter can double the amount of engine torque being transmitted to the gearbox.

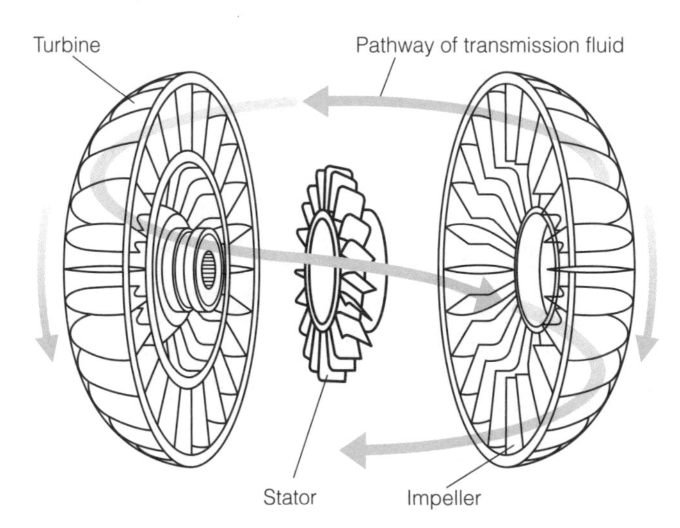

Figure 17.4 Operating principle of the torque converter.

Although the construction is similar to that of a fluid flywheel, a torque converter has a third, bladed unit called a **stator**, which is mounted on a **freewheel**, a type of one-way clutch. This is located between the impeller and the turbine. The impeller, turbine and stator blades are all curved to make the direction of fluid flow more efficient, and to allow the turbine to absorb the power of the circulating fluid, which causes the torque to increase.

Principal features of operation

As the unit rotates, centrifugal force causes the fluid to circulate from the impeller to the turbine. The purpose of the stator is to re-direct the flow of transmission fluid from the turbine so that it strikes the vanes of the impeller at a more effective angle. This increases the force of the fluid as it re-enters the turbine. It is this action that increases the amount of torque.

The movement of the stator is controlled by a special one-way clutch mechanism, which locks it to the gearbox casing at low engine speeds (Figure 17.5). During acceleration, when the turbine speed rises to that of the impeller, the stator is no longer needed, and fluid begins to hit the back of the stator blades. The stator, which was being held firmly against the gearbox casing by the one-way clutch, is now free to move, and turns at the same speed as the turbine. Since the

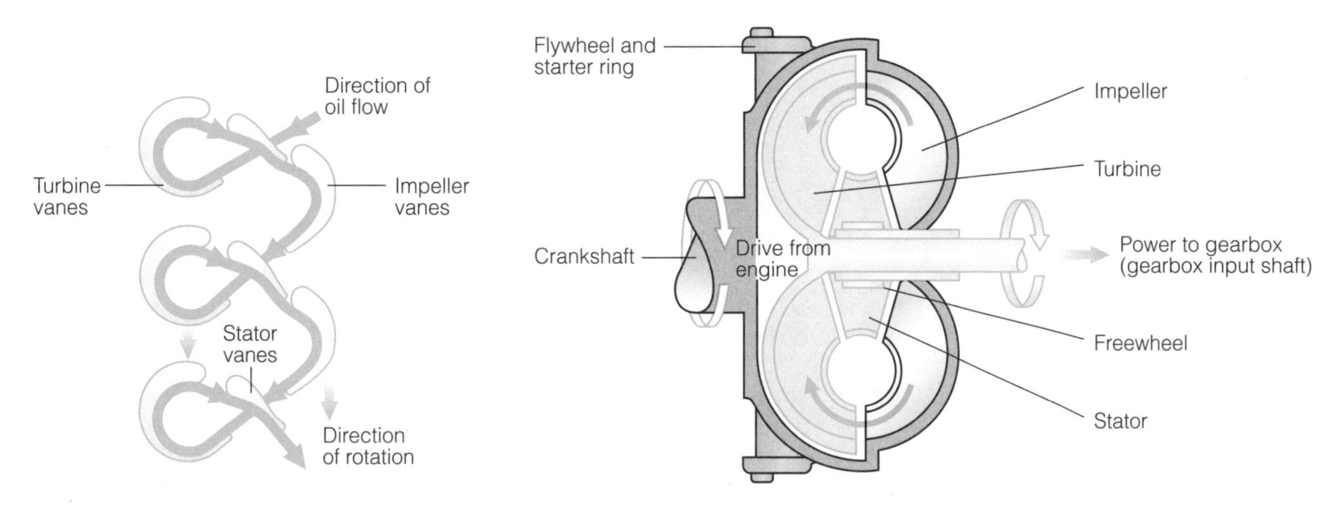

Figure 17.5 Torque converter: cross-section.

stator is now 'freewheeling', the torque converter is operating exactly like a fluid flywheel.

The torque converter uses specially formulated **automatic transmission fluid (ATF)**, pumped to it from the automatic transmission.

Advantages and disadvantages of the torque converter

The torque converter's main **advantage** is that it acts both as a smooth-acting clutch and as a gearbox. The 'gearbox' gives a limited but infinitely variable gear ratio from about 2.5 : 1 to 1 : 1, when both the turbine and the output shaft are rotating at virtually engine speed. Effectively, this means that the automatic gearbox can use fewer gears than a manual gearbox for the same type of vehicle.

The **disadvantage** is that, as with the fluid flywheel, some turbine slip still occurs, and there is a slight power loss.

CHECK YOUR UNDERSTANDING

- For vehicles fitted with semi-automatic gearboxes, a fluid flywheel is used. The fluid flywheel acts as an automatic clutch between the engine and gearbox.
- The main components of a fluid flywheel are the impeller and the turbine. By allowing fluid that is under centrifugal force to flow between the impeller and turbine, it provides the vehicle with a fluid drive system.
- A vehicle that is fitted with an automatic gearbox utilises a modified fluid flywheel called a torque converter.
- The main feature of a torque converter is the use of a stator, which is located between the impeller and the turbine. The purpose of the stator is to redirect the fluid enabling it to take a more efficient pathway. The operation of the stator is controlled by a special one-way clutch called a freewheel.
- The efficiency of both units relies on the correct type of transmission oil or fluid being used.

REVISION EXERCISES AND QUESTIONS

1 What is the main purpose of a fluid flywheel?
2 Name the *two* main components of a fluid flywheel.
3 What type of oil is used in fluid flywheels and torque converters?
4 What is the maximum amount of torque multiplication that a torque converter can produce?
5 In a torque converter, what is the purpose of the stator?

The gearbox

Introduction

In the early days of motoring, engines often ran at a fixed rpm. In order to vary the road speed of the vehicle, and to enable it to climb hills, the wheels were driven through several sets of gears. This is why, for example, we refer to four- or five-speed gearboxes.

The function of the gearbox is to:

- enable the torque being transmitted from the engine to the driving wheels to be varied to suit load and speed requirements;
- provide a means of reversing;
- provide a permanent neutral position.

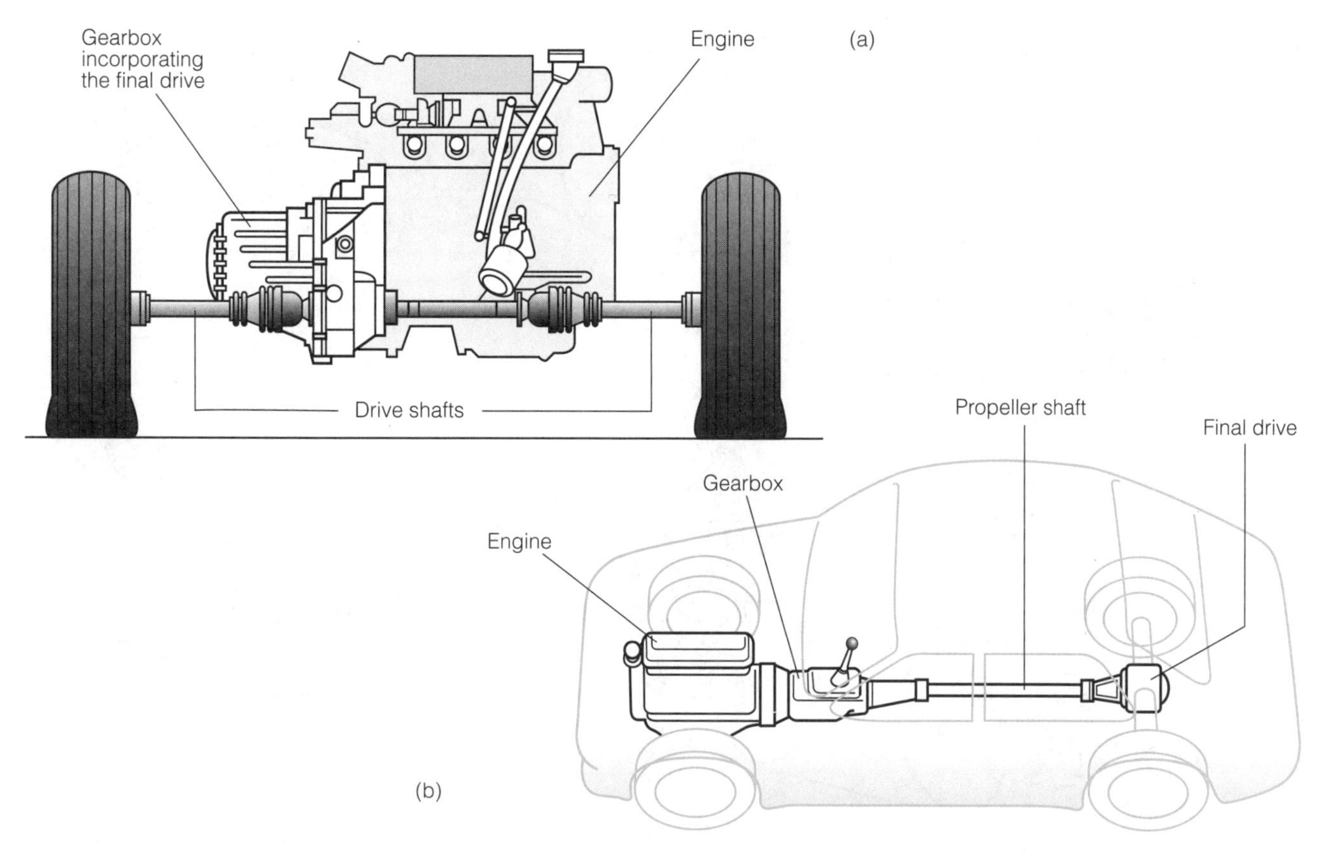

Figure 18.1 Gearbox location: (a) transverse layout (front engine, front-wheel drive); (b) conventional layout (front engine, rear-wheel drive).

The gearbox is normally fitted adjacent to the engine, with the flywheel and clutch between them. This provides a logical flow for the engine's torque to be transmitted to the final drive and then on to the driving wheels. Two of the most common layouts are shown in Figure 18.1.

Some vehicles use combined gearboxes and final drives. The British Mini is an example of this type of combined 'transmission' unit.

Principles of gearing

Put simply, the principle of gearing is a type of leverage, where a small input force is able to move a much larger force.

The basic principles can perhaps be best explained by looking at the gear system fitted to a pedal cycle. When several gears are fitted to a bicycle they enable you, the rider (the 'engine'), to make the most efficient use of the torque available (your pedalling effort). This is done by selecting a suitable gear ratio that matches the prevailing road conditions (Figure 18.2).

When climbing a gradient, you select a low gear ratio. Although the speed of the bicycle reduces, you find it easier to pedal because of the torque multiplication by the selected gear. In contrast, when descending a gradient the cycle's speed increases. By selecting a high gear ratio, you are able to pedal without much effort and turn the pedals at a comfortable rate.

Types of gear teeth

To allow each of the gearwheels to transmit the available torque, they are machined with teeth of

Figure 18.2 Basic principles of gearing.

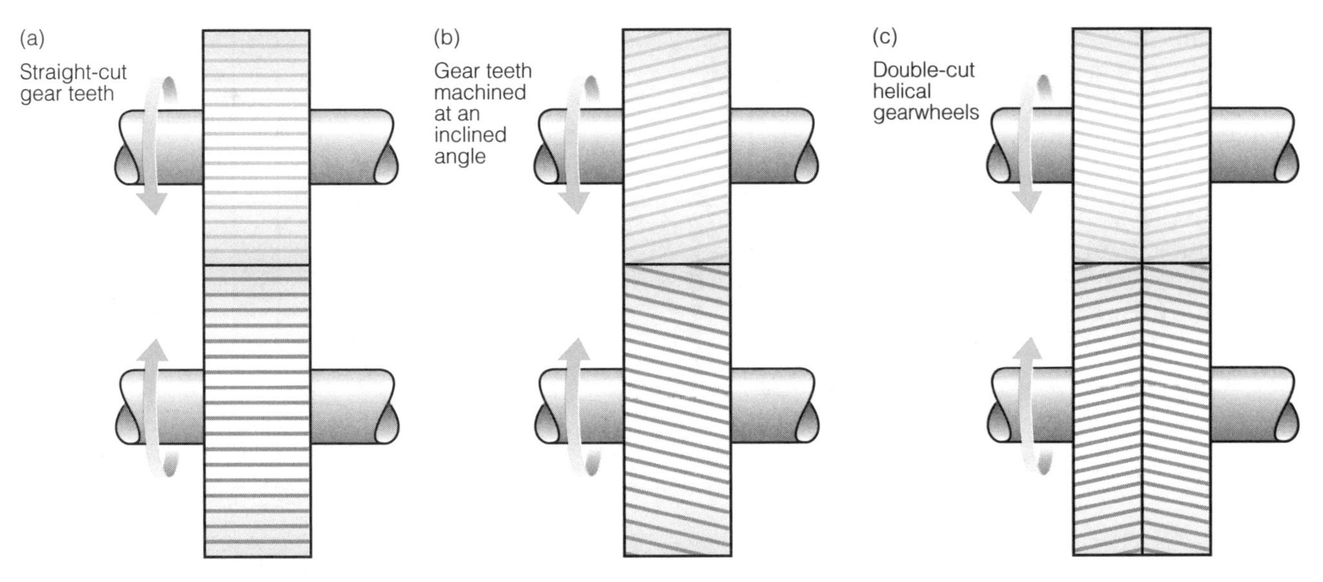

Figure 18.3 Types of gear teeth: (a) spur; (b) helical; (c) double helical.

a shape that enables them to **mesh** with one another and rotate.

Three of the most common shapes for gear teeth are:

1. spur;
2. helical;
3. double helical.

Spur

These teeth are straight cut across the gear, and are noisy in operation (Figure 18.3a).

Helical

The teeth are machined at an inclined angle (Figure 18.3b). The longer teeth are quieter in operation, and enable a higher torque loading to be transmitted.

Double helical

This gear is machined with a double row of helical cut gear teeth, and is therefore expensive to manufacture (Figure 18.3c). Its main advantages are that the opposed tooth shape minimises sideways thrust, and that it can transmit more torque.

Gear ratios

> A gear ratio is a measure of the relationship between two or more gearwheels that are in meshed contact with each other.

Gear ratio = *output/input*

where *output* is the number of teeth on the driven gearwheel, and *input* is the number of teeth on the driving gearwheel.

This is easier to remember as

$$\text{Gear ratio} = \frac{\textit{driven}}{\textit{driver}}$$

For example, in Figure 18.4 two gearwheels are meshed in contact with each other. Gearwheel A (the driver) has 15 teeth and gearwheel B (the driven gear) has 30 teeth.

$$\text{Gear ratio} = \frac{\textit{driven}}{\textit{driver}} = \frac{30}{15} = \frac{2}{1} = 2:1$$

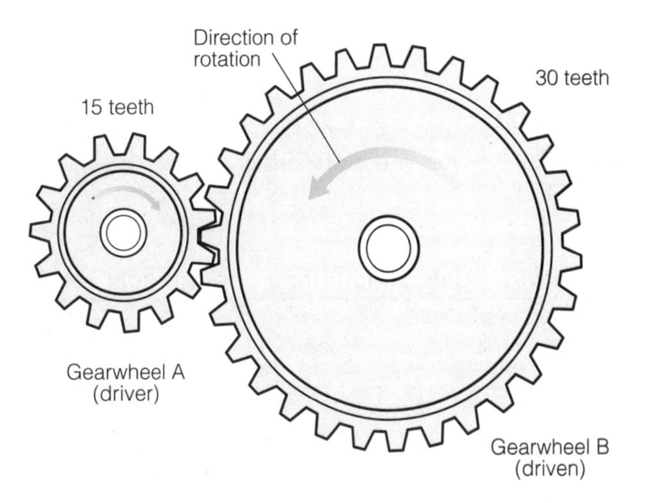

Figure 18.4 Gear ratio = 2 : 1 (see text).

This means that for every two complete revolutions of the driver gearwheel (A), the driven gearwheel (B) will rotate only once, but the torque is doubled.

To provide a vehicle with a suitable set of gear ratios, manufacturers use gearboxes that contain several sets of gears. These are called **compound gears**, and form the operating basis of all modern gearboxes.

To calculate a compound gear ratio, we use the formula

$$\text{Gear ratio} = \frac{output_1}{input_1} \times \frac{output_2}{input_2}$$

where $output_1$ is the first driven gear, $input_1$ is the first driving gear, $output_2$ is the second driven gear, and $input_2$ is the second driving gear.

Put more simply:

$$\text{Gear ratio} = \frac{driven}{driver} \times \frac{driven}{driver}$$

For example, the compound gear train shown in Figure 18.5 has two sets of gearwheels meshed in contact with each other.

$$\text{Gear ratio} = \frac{driven_B}{driven_A} \times \frac{driven_D}{driven_C} = \frac{30}{10} \times \frac{25}{15} = 3.75 : 1$$

Calculate the compound ratios listed in Table 18.1, and put your answers in the spaces provided.

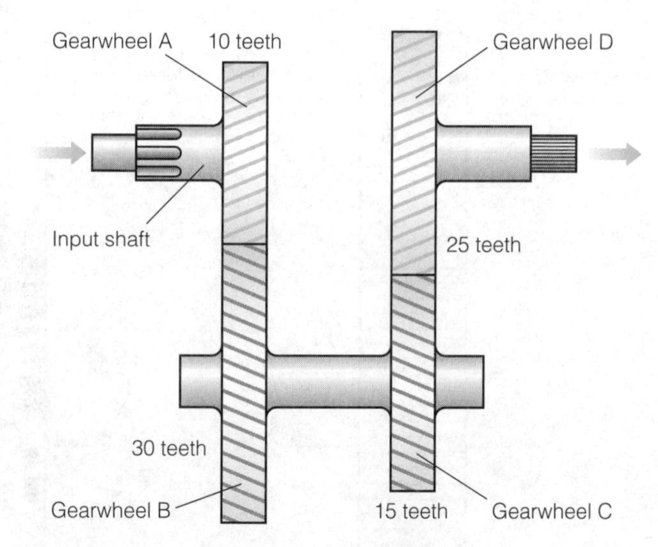

Figure 18.5 Compound gear train. Gear ratio = 3.75 : 1.

Manual gearboxes

There are two main types of gearbox, manual and automatic, the latter often being called **automatic transmission**. Manual gearboxes depend totally on the driver to select and change gear. Automatic gearboxes can change gear according to engine load, road speed, driver's demand and, in the latest computer-controlled units, according to the style of driving.

There are three types of manual gearbox:

1. sliding mesh;
2. constant mesh.
3. synchromesh.

Sliding-mesh gearbox

This is the simplest of the three types of manual gearbox.

Table 18.1 Calculation of compound gear ratios

Number of teeth on the input driver	Number of teeth on the input driven	Number of teeth on the output driver	Number of teeth on the output driven	The overall gear ratio is:
15	45	20	40	
24	36	15	45	
20	30	10	40	
5	40	15	30	
16	38	18	36	

The name derives from the sliding action of the mainshaft gearwheels, which are moved into or out of mesh with the appropriate layshaft gearwheels. Because of this sliding action, spur gears are used. This type of gearbox is also sometimes referred to as a **crash gearbox**, because the gear teeth may crash into each other if their speeds are not evenly matched when a gear change is attempted. Also, because of the use of spur-cut gearwheels, the gearbox is rather noisy in operation. It is little used today, but is easy to understand.

The main components of the sliding-mesh gearbox are shown in Figure 18.6.

Operation

Engine torque is transmitted through the clutch centre plate, which is splined to the primary or input shaft. The constant-mesh gears transfer the torque to the layshaft. To transmit the torque from the layshaft to one of the mainshaft gears, the driver must use the gear lever to select the appropriate gear. The drive path for each gear is shown in Figure 18.7. To obtain reverse gear, a **reverse**

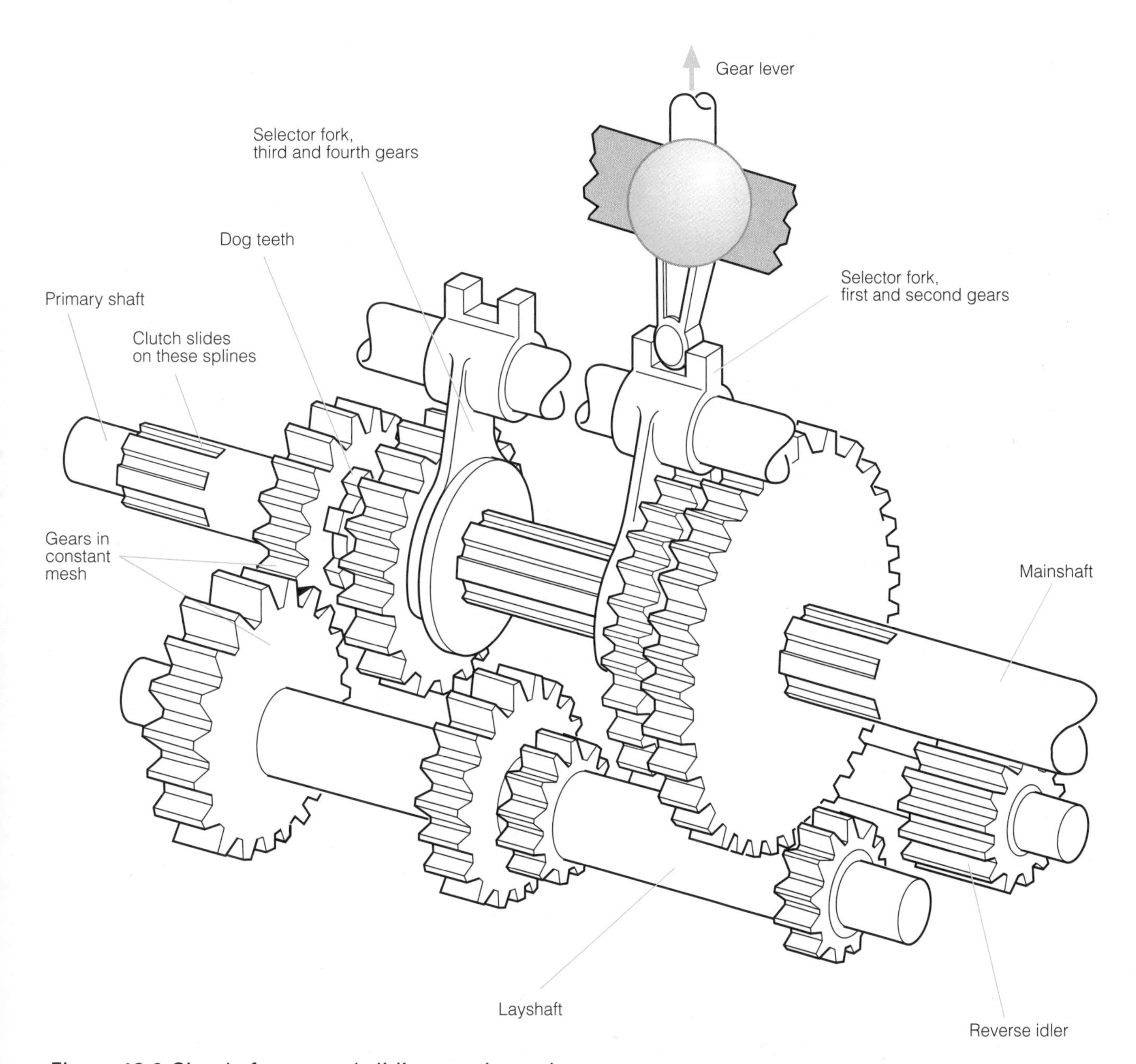

Figure 18.6 Simple four-speed sliding-mesh gearbox.

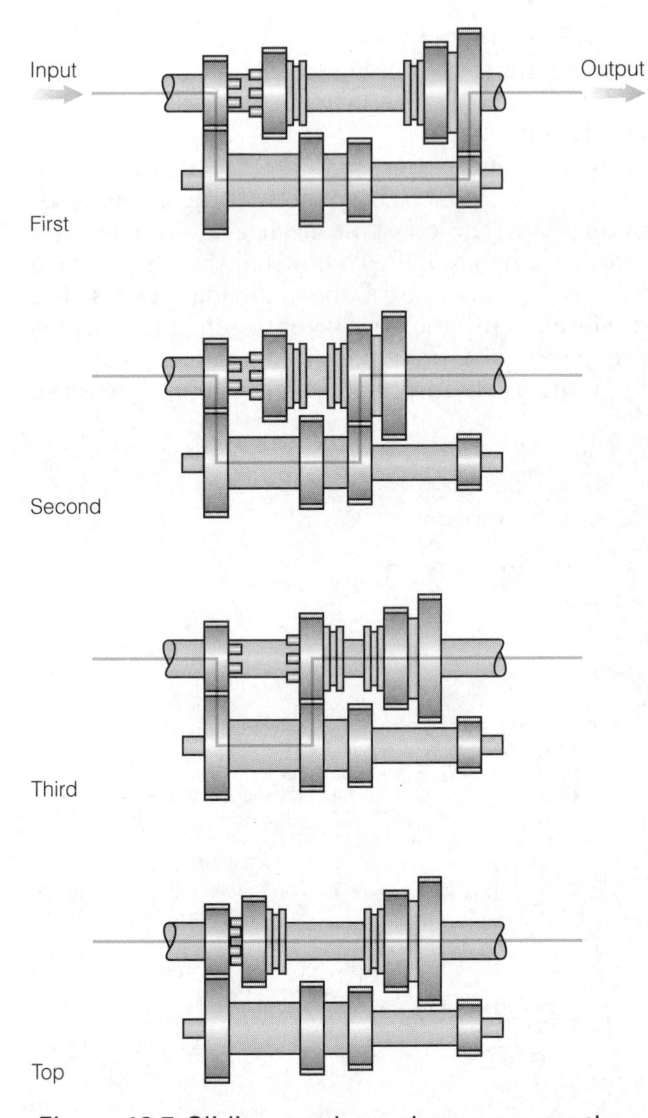

Figure 18.7 Sliding-mesh gearbox: power paths.

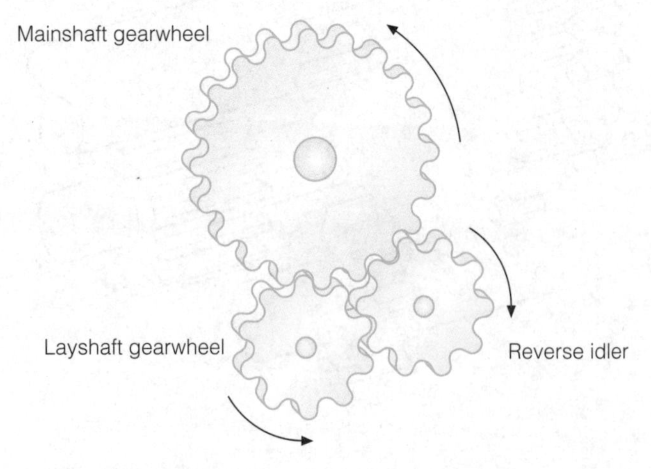

Figure 18.8 Sectioned view showing operation of a reverse idler.

idler gear is used to reverse the rotation of the mainshaft gear (Figure 18.8).

Constant-mesh gearboxes

In this design, the gearwheels are in constant mesh with each other (Figure 18.9). The mainshaft gears are mounted on bearings that allow them to rotate independently of the mainshaft. All the gears have helical teeth to help give both smooth and quiet operation, with the exception of reverse.

To lock any gear to the mainshaft, a **dog clutch** is used. This consists of a small sliding collar with teeth on each end. Similar teeth are also machined onto each of the mainshaft gearwheels. When the teeth on the dog clutch engage with those on the gearwheel, that gear is mechanically locked to the mainshaft.

Operation in neutral

When the gear lever is in neutral position, the two dog clutches (2) and (5) are not in contact with any of the gearwheels, and cannot transmit torque to the mainshaft (Figure 18.9).

Operation in first gear

The dog clutch (5) is moved along the mainshaft by the **selector fork** until it engages with the first gear (6), locking it to the mainshaft. The drive path along which the torque is transmitted is similar to that shown in Figure 18.7 (first gear).

Operation in second, third and fourth gears

The dog clutch (5) is moved until it engages with the second gear (4). To engage third gear, the gear lever returns the first/second dog clutch to the neutral position before moving dog clutch (2) into mesh with the third gear (3) in a similar way.

In fourth or top gear the dog clutch (2) engages with the dog teeth of the primary gear (1) and locks the primary and mainshafts together. The drive path is now straight through, giving a 1 : 1 ratio.

Operation in reverse gear

To obtain reverse gear a set of spur gearwheels is often used, which include an additional reverse idler gear to reverse the rotation of the mainshaft

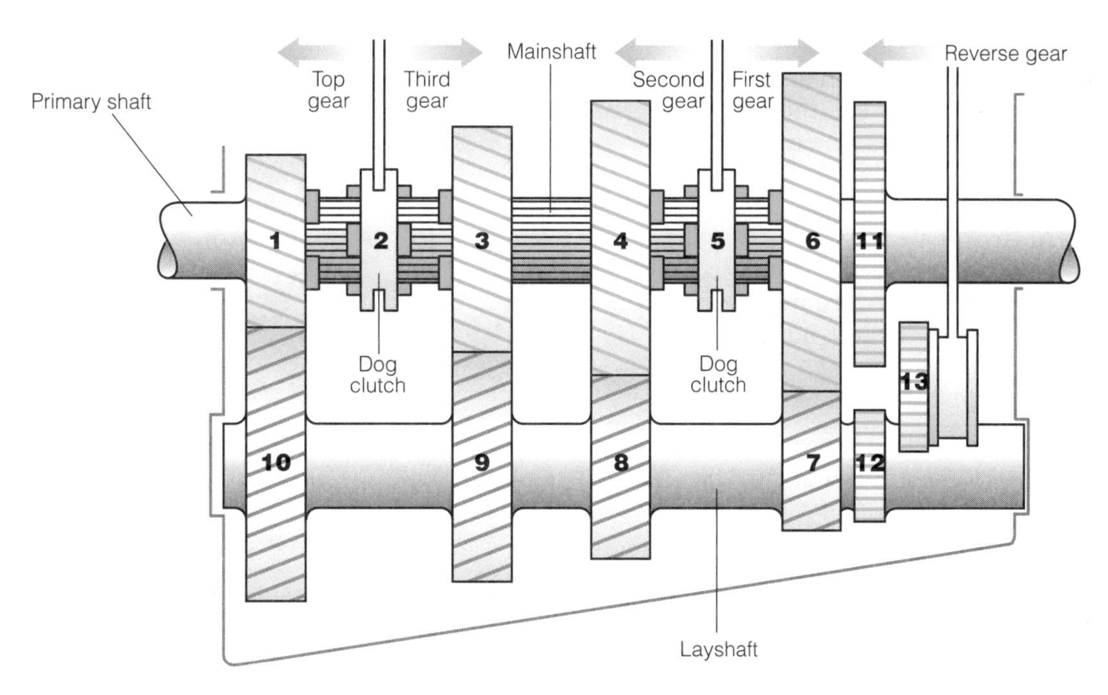

Figure 18.9 Constant-mesh gearbox.

(Figure 18.9). When the reverse idler gear (13) is moved into meshed contact with the reverse gears located on both the mainshaft (11) and layshaft (12), the direction of rotation is reversed (Figure 18.8).

Synchromesh gearboxes

The demand for quiet and easy gear changing has brought about the widespread use of the fully synchromesh gearbox. It is similar in many respects to the earlier constant-mesh gearbox, but the dog clutch is replaced by a device called a **synchromesh hub**. The synchromesh hub is designed to synchronise (equalise or make the same) the speeds of the selected mainshaft gearwheel and the mainshaft.

Constant-load synchromesh hub

This is the most basic form of synchromesh. It consists of a hub and an outer sleeve (Figure 18.10). The hub is splined onto the gearbox mainshaft, and the outer sleeve is splined to the hub. To ensure that the sleeve remains in the neutral position, a set of spring-loaded balls called **detents** are fitted to the hub; they locate in indentations in the sleeve.

During the first part of gear engagement, the selector fork moves the complete synchromesh hub towards the selected gearwheel (Figure 18.10). The first contact is made by the internal cone of the hub and the external cone of the gearwheel. The friction between them matches (or synchronises) the speed of the hub and the free-moving gear in a few moments. Further movement of the gear lever overcomes the

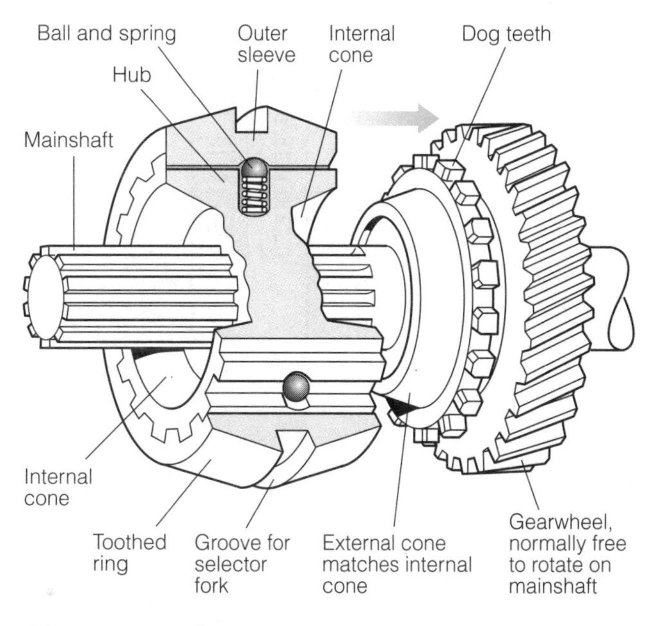

Figure 18.10 Constant-load synchromesh hub.

detents and slides the sleeve on its splines towards the gearwheel. The splines on the sleeve slide over the dog teeth on the gearwheel, locking it to the shaft: the gear is **engaged**.

Baulk ring synchromesh

An improved version of the constant load synchromesh hub, which incorporates a pair of phosphor bronze collars called **baulk rings**, is shown in Figure 18.11.

The **advantages** of baulk ring syncromesh are:

1. more precise matching of gearwheel speeds, which reduces wear and tear on gearbox components;
2. prevention of engagement of gearwheels until their speeds are fully synchronised;
3. smoother gear changing throughout the gearbox range without the need to double-declutch.

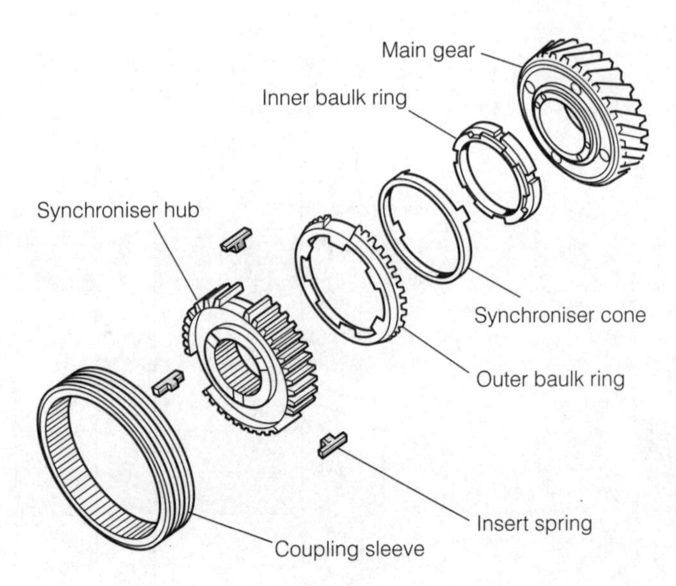

Figure 18.11 Double baulk ring synchromesh hub unit.

Five-speed gearboxes

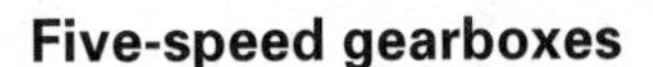

The fourth or top gear on a four-speed gearbox provides a 1 : 1 ratio between the primary shaft and the mainshaft by locking the two shafts together. Fuel economy and the service life of components during prolonged high-speed motoring can both be improved by providing a fifth gear, an **overdrive** ratio, in which the mainshaft rotates at a higher speed than the primary shaft.

> Typically, all the ratios of a five-speed gearbox are obtained by locking a gearwheel to the mainshaft (Figure 18.12). This also allows the fourth gear ratio to be reduced slightly to improve vehicle performance.

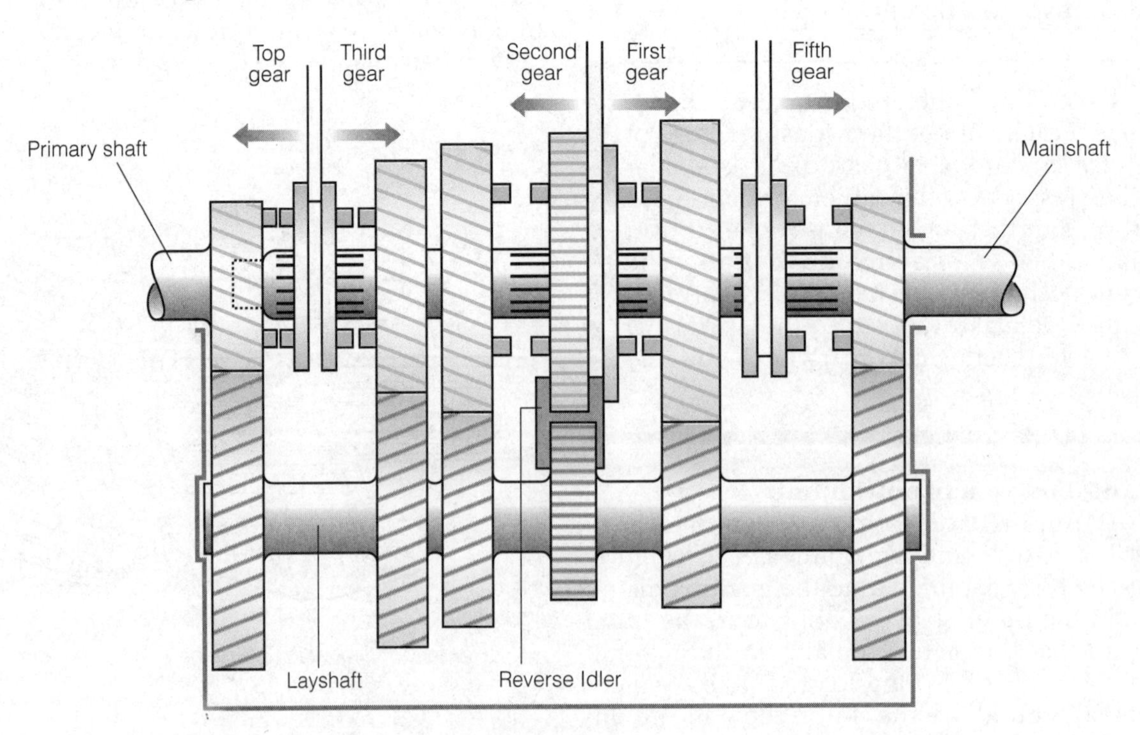

Figure 18.12 Diagrammatic view of a five-speed gearbox.

A summary comparison of typical gear ratios between a four- and five-speed gearbox is shown in Table 18.2.

Front-wheel-drive gearboxes

For vehicles with a front engine and front-wheel drive a modified gearbox is required. Its most obvious feature is that it has much more bulk than a conventional gearbox. This is because the gearbox incorporates the final drive and differential unit (Figure 18.13). Such a layout is shown diagrammatically in Figure 18.14.

Table 18.2 Typical gear ratios for four- and five-speed gearboxes

Gear	Four-speed gearbox	Five-speed gearbox
First	3.58	3.78
Second	2.04	2.06
Third	1.35	1.35
Fourth	1	0.97
Fifth	–	0.77
Reverse	3.60	3.60

Gear selectors and interlocking mechanisms

To allow the driver to select the most suitable gear ratio, manual gearboxes are fitted with a gear

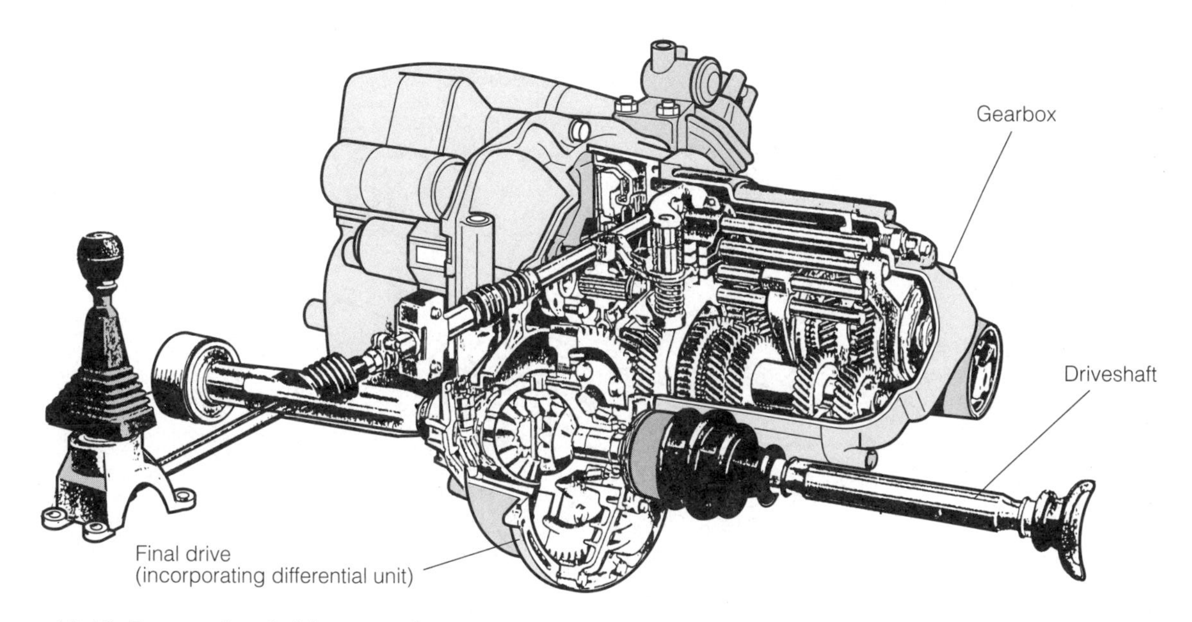

Figure 18.13 Front-wheel-drive gearbox.

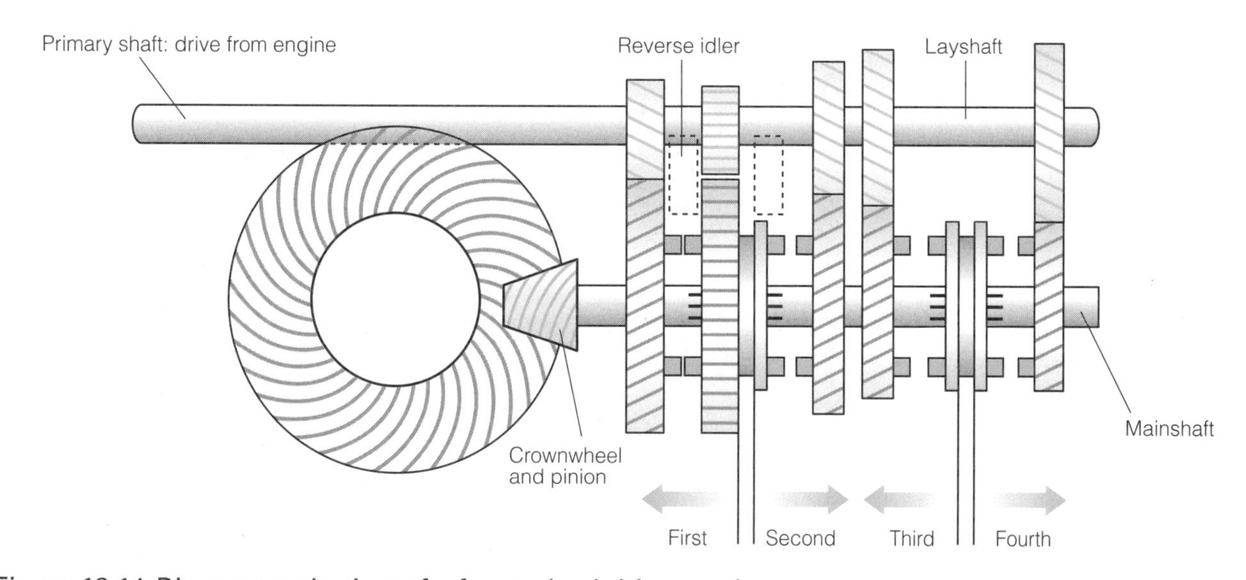

Figure 18.14 Diagrammatic view of a front-wheel-drive gearbox.

lever and selector mechanism. The main components of such a selector mechanism are shown in Figure 18.15. When the driver uses the gear lever to select a particular gear, the movement is transmitted along the appropriate selector rail to the gearwheel. Selector-locking or gear-locating devices hold a gear engaged when it has been selected (Figure 18.16a).

To ensure that only one gear can be selected at a time, an **interlocking mechanism** is incorporated into the gearbox selectors. A selection of interlocking mechanisms are shown in Figure 18.16b.

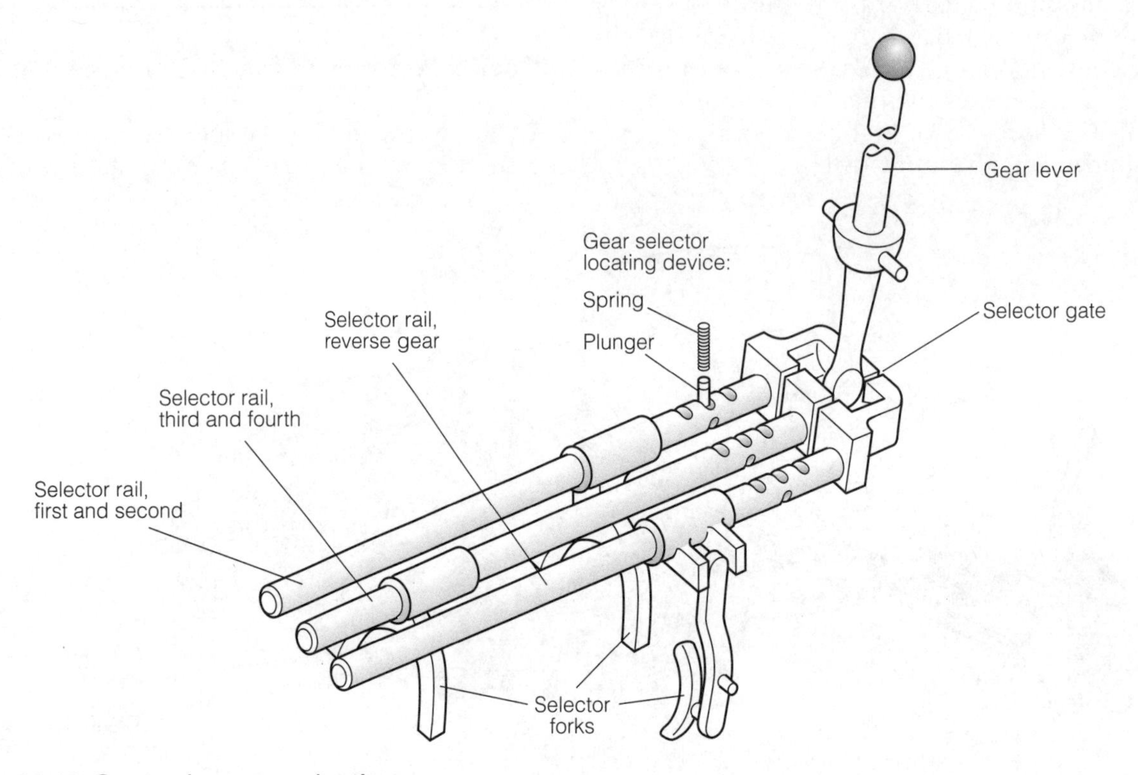

Figure 18.15 Gear selector mechanism.

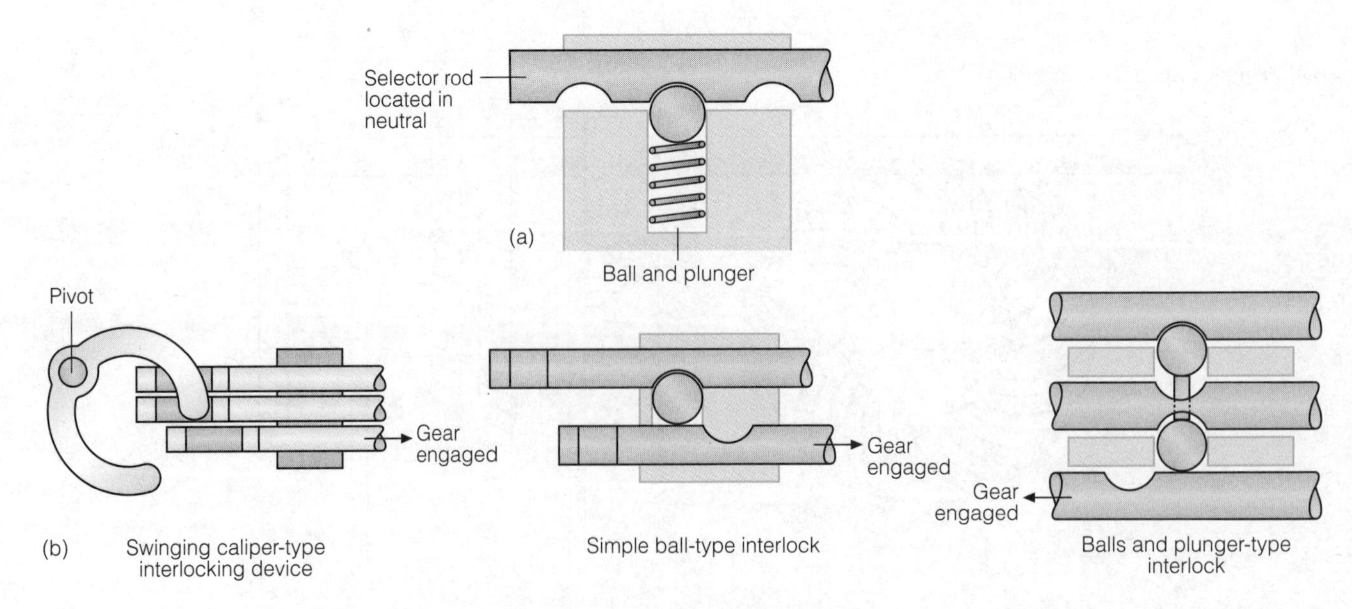

Figure 18.16 (a) Gear/selector locating device; (b) gear interlocks.

Gearbox lubrication and bearings

> Efficient gearbox operation depends upon adequate support and lubrication for all the internal components.

Some of the features built into gearboxes (Figure 18.17) are as follows:

1. There is a means of checking oil level, and sometimes draining and replacement.
2. Splash feed is the method of lubrication frequently used, although some gearboxes do employ a pump.
3. To prevent the possible loss of lubricant, shafts that protrude from the gearbox are fitted with an oil seal. Often this is an O-ring seal, although many primary shafts use an oil scroll and slinger ring or washer.
4. Some form of breather or vent is essential to prevent pressure build-up in the gearbox when it becomes hot.

Four-wheel-drive transmission layouts

Specially modified transmission systems are required for vehicles designed for off-road four-wheel-drive operation (Figure 18.18). A final drive and differential unit is fitted to both front and rear axles.

The gearbox is fitted with an auxiliary unit called the **transfer box**. Its main function is to enable the driver to select either two- or four-wheel drive. To do this a second gear lever is fitted, which enables a splined sleeve to connect

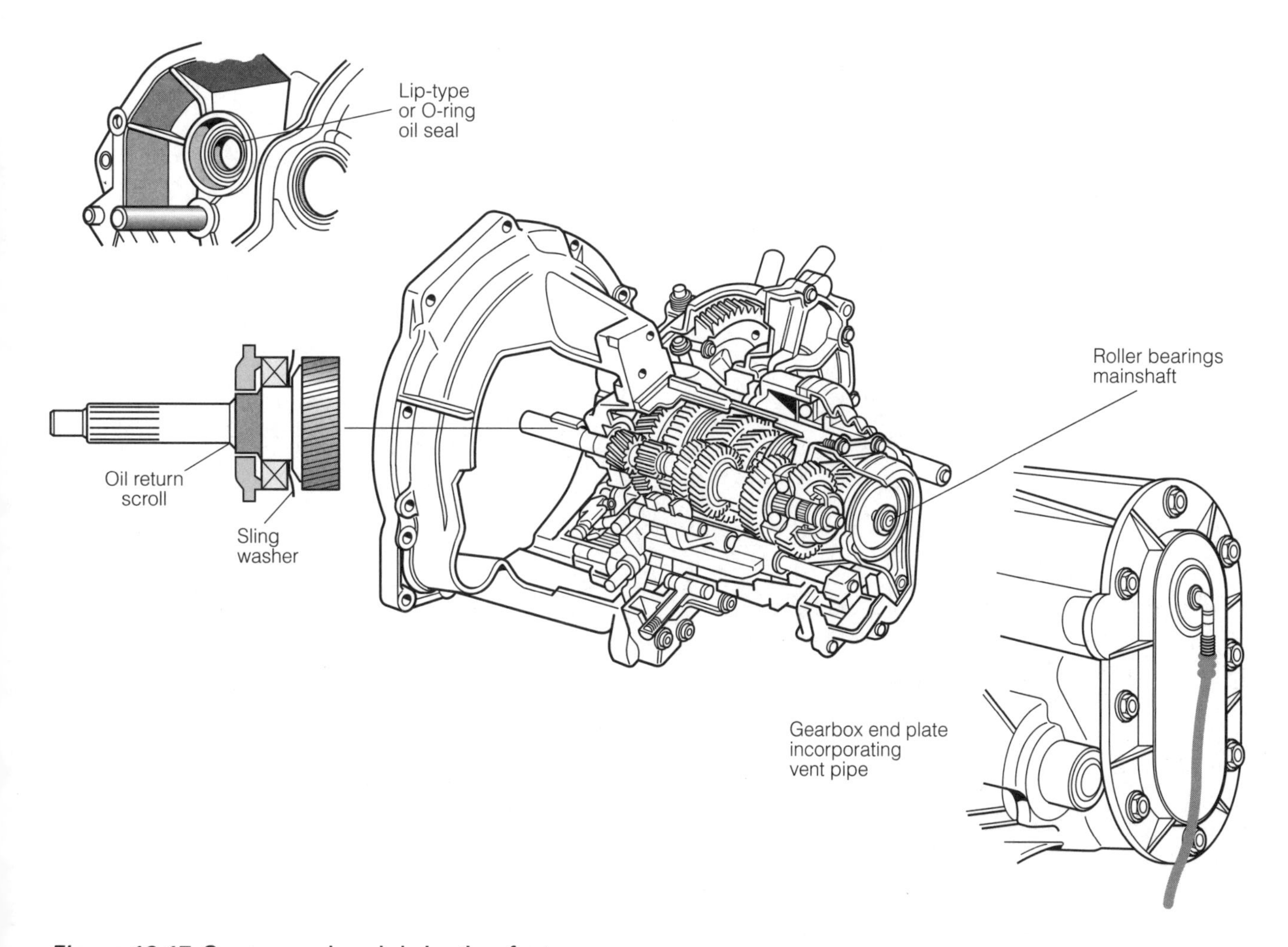

Figure 18.17 Some gearbox lubrication features.

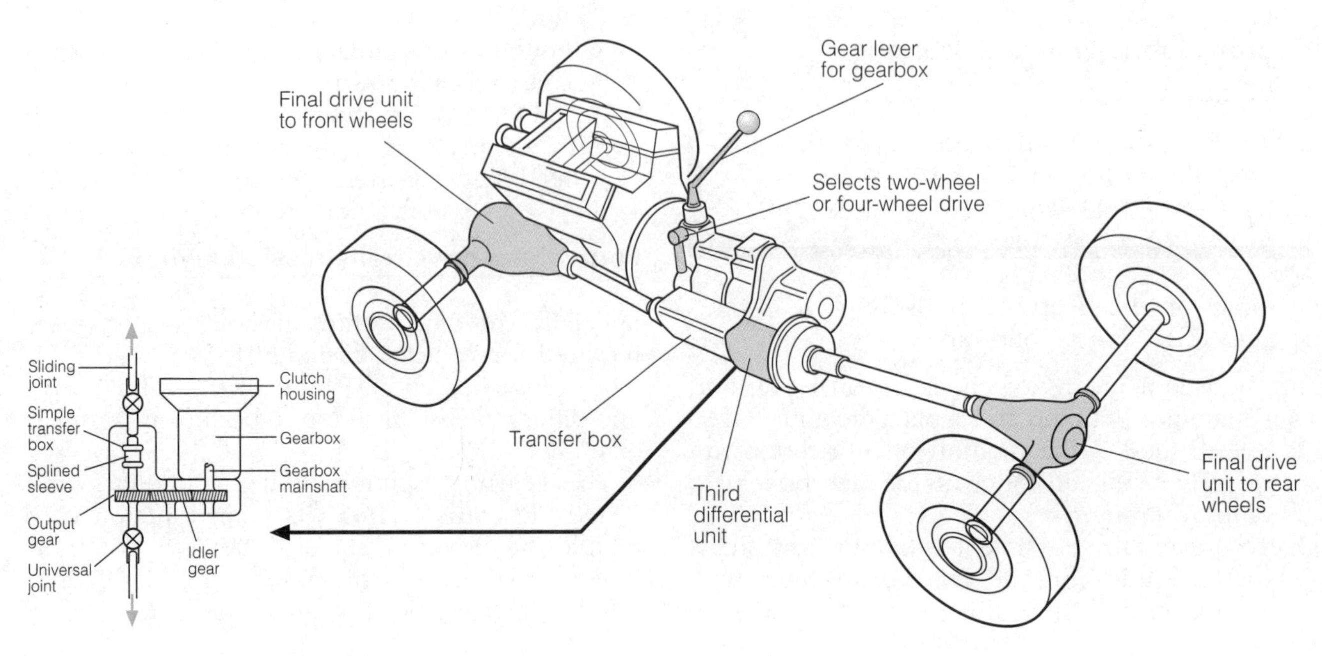

Figure 18.18 Four-wheel drive.

or disconnect the drive to the front axle (Figure 18.18).

Where permanent or semi-permanent four-wheel drive is employed, the main gearbox typically carries out the function of the transfer box in providing the drive connections to both final drive units.

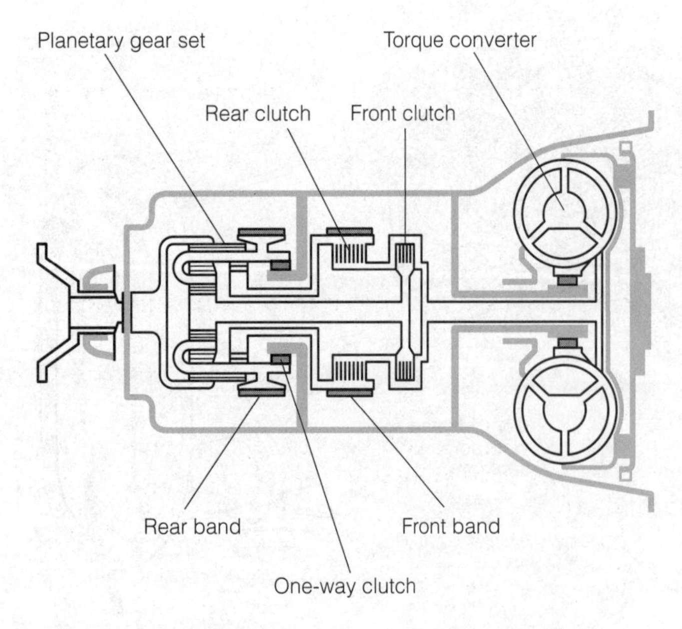

Figure 18.19 Simplified layout of an automatic transmission unit.

Automatic transmission

Automatic transmissions or automatic gearboxes not only take much of the effort out of driving, but also mean that the driver does not need to be skilled in gear changing. Another benefit of automatic transmissions is the reduced wear and tear on the entire drive line from the engine to the roadwheels. This is largely because a properly designed system used sensibly will take up the drive smoothly, and will usually be in the correct gear for the conditions. A simplified layout of an automatic transmission unit is shown in Figure 18.19.

The main essentials of most automatic transmissions are:

- a torque converter, which replaces the clutch and gives a limited, but progressively variable, range of ratios (see Chapter 17);
- a set of **epicyclic gears** (these have the great advantage of being permanently in mesh and, by means of special brake bands or clutches, can be engaged smoothly and quietly);
- various control sensors.

The control sensors take account of such things as engine load, road speed and driver demand to determine which gear is suitable and when to change up or down. The most modern units are computer-controlled, and by using **fuzzy logic** can make precise decisions. Actuation of gear brake bands or clutches is generally by oil pressure generated by a pump within the transmission.

Epicyclic or planetary gears

Epicyclic gears can be arranged in several different ways; a very simple layout is shown in Figure 18.20. According to how the various gears are held stationary or allowed to move, a variety of outputs can be obtained. These outputs are not always through the centre shaft as with a conventional gear train.

For example, if the **annulus** is held stationary and the **sun gear** is being rotated, the **planet gears** will also rotate. The rotating planet gears will run around the inside of the annulus, taking the planet carrier with them. However, the planet carrier will rotate at a slower speed than the sun gear, but with a greater torque. It provides the same effect as a conventional reduction gear.

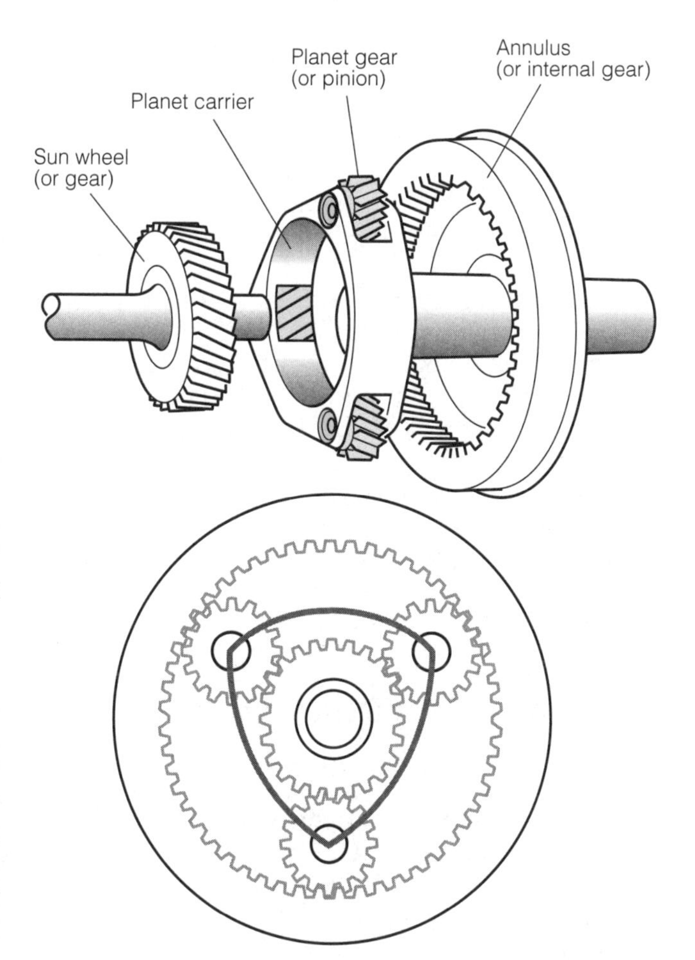

Figure 18.20 A simple planetary or epicyclic gear train.

Alternatively, if the sun gear is held stationary and the planet carrier is driven, the planets will revolve around the sun gear, moving the annulus at high speed: in other words, an **overdrive**.

The same epicyclic train can also provide reverse. The planet carrier is held stationary and the sun gear is rotated. The planets now rotate on their pivots in the stationary planet carrier, causing the annulus to rotate in the reverse direction to the sun gear, but at a reduced speed.

In practice, automatic transmission units consist of several epicyclic gear trains. Their internal construction is quite complicated, and they must be serviced only by trained personnel.

Maintenance tip

When checking the oil level or changing the oil of an automatic transmission, absolute cleanliness is essential. Just one tiny speck of dust or fluff entering the unit can cause serious problems.

Overdrives

An overdrive is a gear ratio in which the speed of the output is greater than that of the input. This principle is put to good use on motor vehicles to reduce engine wear and fuel consumption.

Almost all early cars had four-speed gearboxes with a straight-through or 1 : 1 drive in fourth gear. Nearly all modern cars have five-speed gearboxes, with fifth gear being an overdrive ratio. Similarly, most modern automatic transmission units have their epicyclic gearing so arranged that their top gear, usually fourth, is an overdrive.

There are, however, some vehicles still in use that fit a four-speed manual gearbox, but with a separate overdrive unit fitted behind, or in an

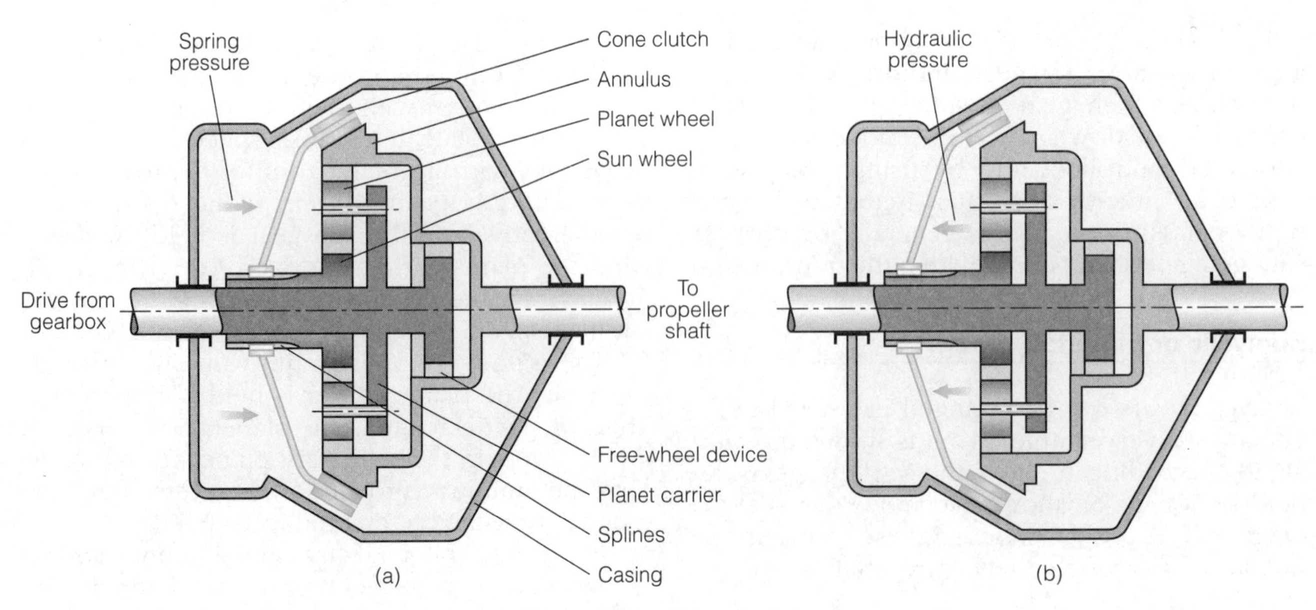

Figure 18.21 Laycock overdrive unit: (a) direct drive; (b) overdrive engaged.

extension to, the gearbox. Such separate units normally use an epicyclic gear train to provide the overdrive ratio. A simplified drawing of the popular Laycock type can be seen in Figure 18.21.

Operation: direct drive

Spring pressure forces the cone clutch mounted on the sun wheel firmly against the annulus. In such a position the input shaft and the output shafts both rotate at the same speed (Figure 18.21a).

Operation: overdrive

When the overdrive is selected, hydraulic pressure forces the cone clutch against the casing, which prevents the sun wheel from rotating. The planet carrier and planet gears rotate around the stationary sun wheel, which drives the annulus and output shaft at a higher rotational speed (Figure 18.21b).

Transmission maintenance

As with all vehicle systems, the transmission requires some routine maintenance to ensure reliability. Some of the common checks that should be carried out include the following:

1. The gearbox selector linkages, and particularly the remote type, should be checked for signs of wear and for security, and should be lubricated.
2. The gearbox may need to be drained of oil and refilled with new, using the recommended type and grade at suitable intervals. In this connection never mix synthetic oils with conventional types.
3. The gearbox casing should be inspected for signs of damage or oil leakage from the various oil seals.
4. The gearbox mountings and securing bolts should be checked for security and signs of deterioration.
5. Automatic transmission vehicles should be checked for correct operation of the inhibitor switch. This prevents the engine being started with 'drive' or a gear selected.

CHECK YOUR UNDERSTANDING

- One purpose of a gearbox is to provide the vehicle with a means of matching the engine's torque to the operational needs of the vehicle.
- The three types of manual gearbox that can be fitted to motor vehicles are the sliding mesh, constant mesh and synchromesh.
- A gearwheel will have one of three types of gear teeth: spur, helical or double helical.

- A gear ratio is simply an expression of the relationship between two gearwheels that are meshed together. Where two sets of gearwheels are connected with each other this is called a compound gear ratio.
- To ensure that only one gear can be selected at a time, the gear selectors are fitted with an interlocking mechanism.
- For vehicles that have four-wheel drive capability, an additional gearbox called a transfer box is often fitted. One of its purposes is to connect the front and rear propeller shafts to the main gearbox.
- Vehicles that require the gearbox to drive additional equipment are fitted with a power take-off unit.
- For automatic transmission the conventional friction-driven clutch is replaced by a torque converter to provide a constantly variable set of gear ratios. Automatic gearboxes use epicyclic gears.
- An overdrive unit allows a vehicle to cruise economically by providing a higher gear ratio than that available by a straight-through drive.

REVISION EXERCISES AND QUESTIONS

1 State the *three* functional requirements of a gearbox.
2 What are the main advantages of helical gearwheel teeth?
3 What is the formula for working out a compound gear ratio?
4 Name *two* types of manual gearbox that can be fitted to a motor vehicle, but excluding the synchromesh gearbox.
5 Name *two* types of synchromesh hub that can be fitted to a synchromesh gearbox.
6 Which design feature of a gear selector mechanism is provided to prevent engagement of more than one gear at a time?
7 Give *one* of the functions of a transfer box when fitted to a four-wheel drive transmission system.
8 Name the *three* main components of an epicyclic gear train.
9 List *four* routine maintenance operations required by a manual gearbox.

Propeller shafts, universal joints and driveshafts

Introduction

The components of a vehicle's drive train – the gearbox, final drive and driving wheels – are sometimes widely spaced. They must be connected together to transmit the engine torque. The axles and wheels – particularly those with independent suspension – will be moving away from their static positions under the influence of road irregularities and other effects.

The drive train components are linked together with driveshafts, which have couplings, generally at each end, to allow the movement to take place and yet transmit the driving torque continuously.

Propeller shafts

The purpose of a **propeller shaft** is to transmit the torque from the gearbox to the final drive unit.

In general, propeller shafts are fitted to vehicles that have a **conventional in-line** layout (Figure 19.1). In this layout the engine and gearbox are in line with the longitudinal axis of the vehicle, and generally at the front, with the final drive located at the rear. The propeller shaft is commonly of tubular steel construction. Solid shafts are sometimes used, but this is rare.

Tubular shafts have a number of **advantages** over the solid versions:

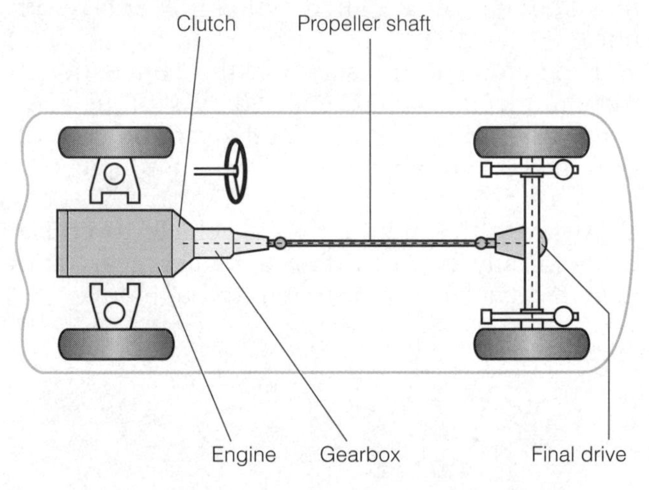

Figure 19.1 Conventional 'in-line' vehicle layout. The dotted line represents the torque's path from the engine to the rear driving wheels.

1. A tubular propeller shaft weighs less than a solid shaft; this helps to improve fuel economy.
2. A tubular shaft is less likely than a solid shaft to go out of balance when subject to centrifugal forces, because it has a smaller mass.
3. A tubular shaft is considerably stronger than the equivalent solid propeller shaft of similar mass, and is much less likely to bend or whip when spinning at speed.

Universal joints

A **universal joint** is a component fitted to a propeller shaft that allows it to transmit the available torque through varying but limited angles of drive.

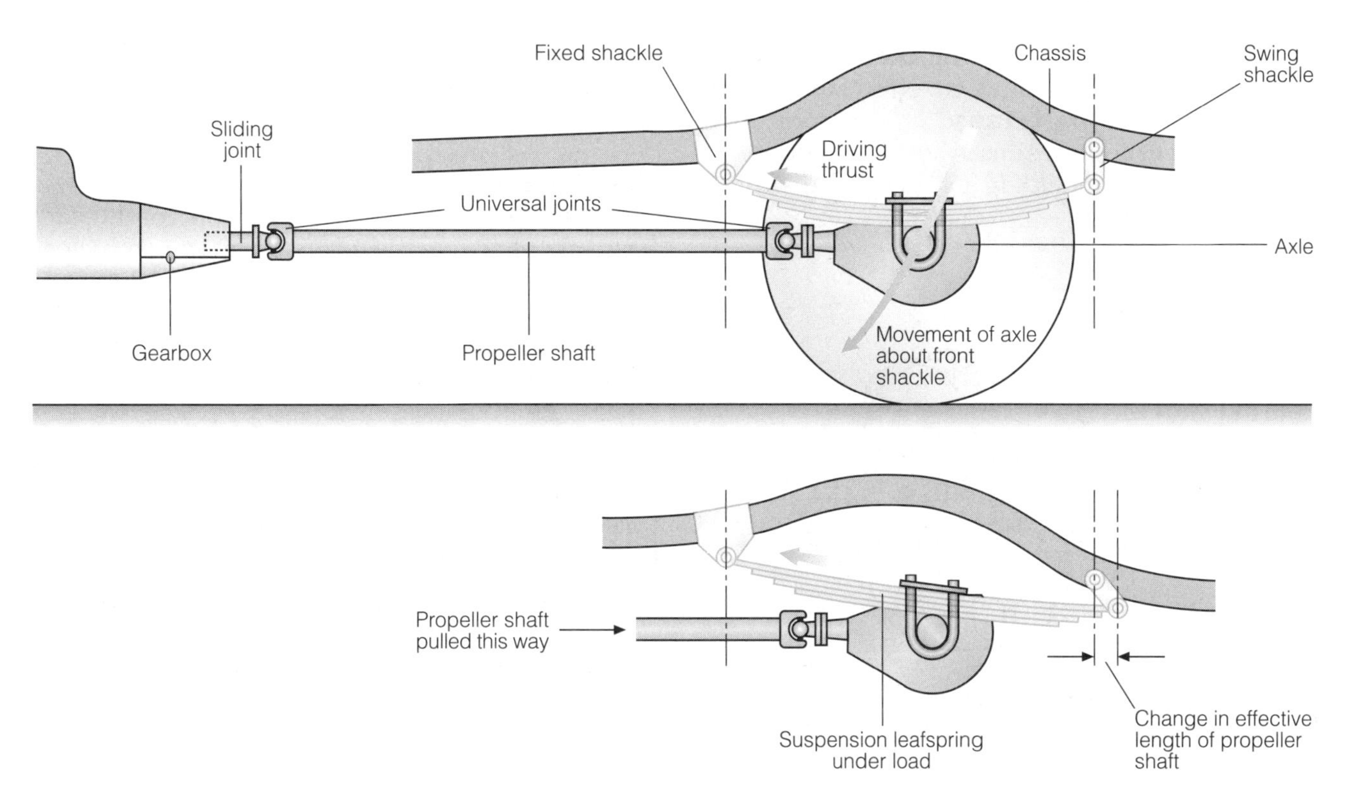

Figure 19.2 Universal joints fitted to each end of the propeller shaft. This transmission layout is known as the Hotchkiss drive.

To link two independent units, such as the gearbox and final drive, a universal joint must be fitted to each end of the propeller shaft (Figure 19.2). The universal joints enable the propeller shaft to rotate smoothly and to transmit the engine's torque, even though the axis of the engine and gearbox, propeller shaft and final drive does not form a straight line. The sliding joint allows for minor variations in length.

Layrub and metalastic couplings

The **layrub coupling** consists of a metal disc, which has a number of equally spaced moulded rubber blocks bonded into it. Each of the rubber blocks has steel inserts through which a bolt passes. These secure the two halves of the propeller shaft (Figure 19.3). Although these rubber blocks are under constant compressive strain, they do allow for shaft misalignment of up to 15°.

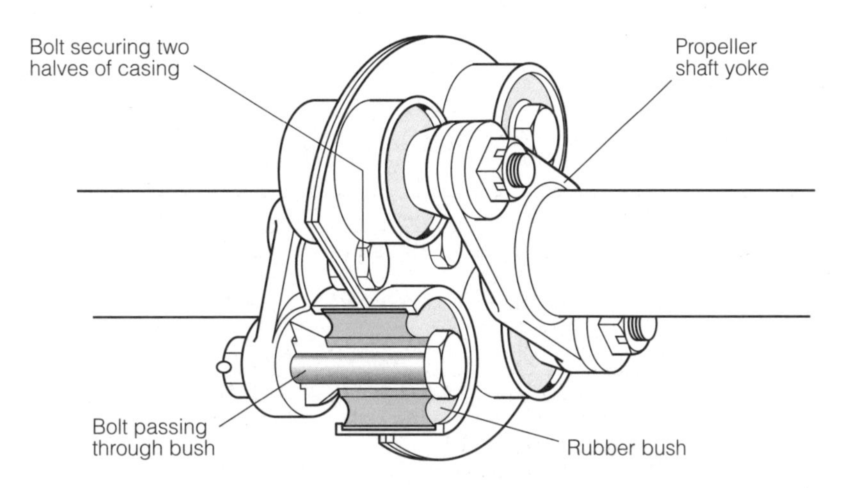

Figure 19.3 Layrub coupling.

An alternative design is the **metalastic coupling**. This is sometimes referred to as the **doughnut coupling** because of its appearance (Figure 19.4). It shares many of the features of the layrub type, including its metal and rubber construction.

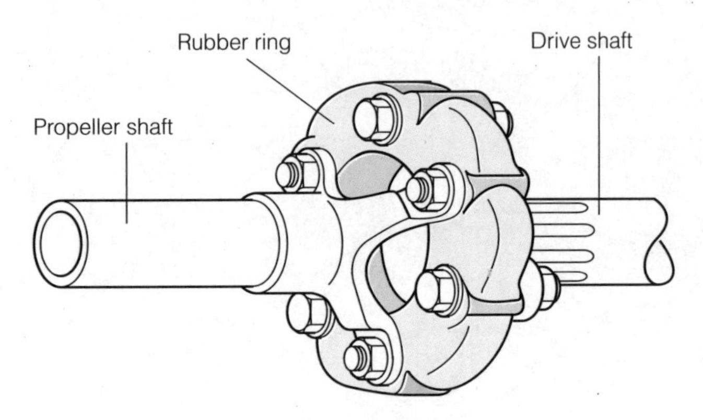

Figure 19.4 Metalastic coupling.

A **disadvantage** of both couplings is that they must be kept free from oil, which could cause the coupling to fail during operation.

Hooke's universal joint

Apart from the wheel itself, this is one of the earliest inventions to be used on motor vehicles, having been patented by Robert Hooke in 1664. This type of universal joint is commonly fitted to motor vehicles, particularly those with a front engine and rear final drive layout.

> A Hooke's joint consists of two forked ends, commonly called **yokes**. The yokes are fitted onto a component called a **spider**, which is shaped in the form of a cross (Figure 19.5).

When assembled onto the spider, the yokes are at right angles to each other. To reduce the

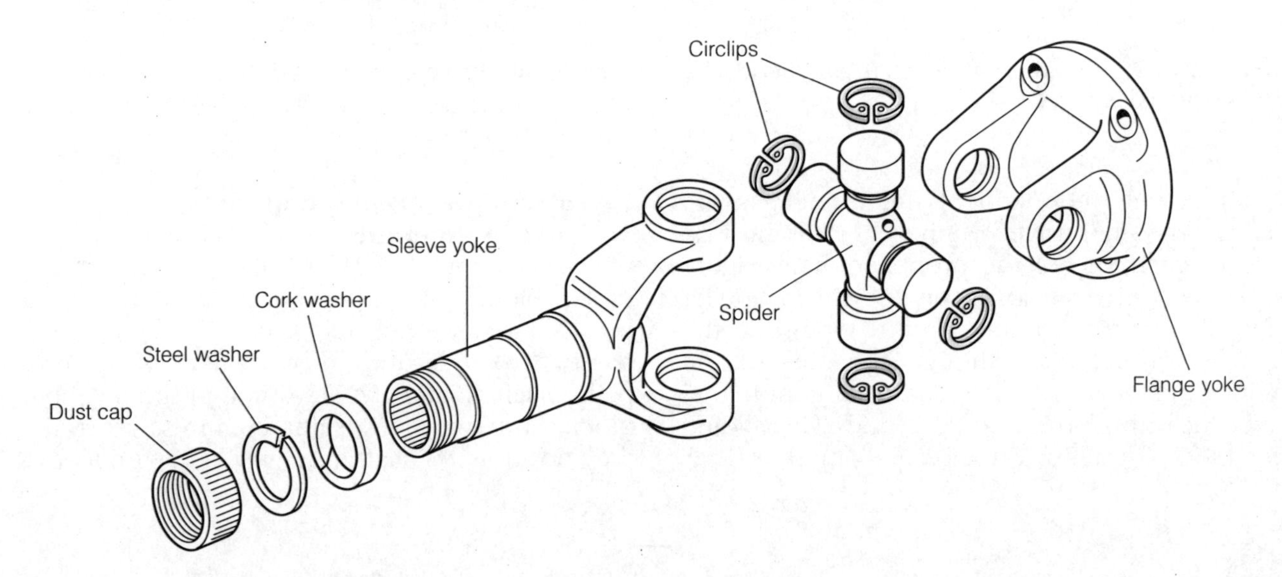

Figure 19.5 Hooke's universal joint.

Table 19.1 Universal joints

Type of universal joint	Advantages	Disadvantages
Layrub coupling	• Can transmit torque through angles of up to 15° • The rubber helps to absorb any vibrations • No lubrication is required	• Rubber deteriorates and breaks up with age • The joint can transmit only a limited amount of torque
Hooke's joint	• Relatively compact design • Can transmit torque through angles of up to 20° • Accurate position of shafts makes it suitable for high-speed operation	• More expensive than rubber universal joint types • Requires accurate alignment • Requires some periodic maintenance

internal friction on each of the universal joints, the yokes are fitted with a set of needle roller bearings housed in hardened steel cups. These cups are normally held in place by steel circlips. To prevent dirt and moisture from getting into the bearings, each leg of the spider is prepacked with grease, and fitted with a rubber seal.

One of the advantages of a Hooke's joint is that it can transmit the available torque through a greater degree of angular displacement, up to 20°, than other designs. In general this angular displacement is kept as small as possible to minimise the possible speed variations acting upon the propeller shaft.

It is important that the two Hooke's joints fitted to a propeller shaft are accurately aligned with each other, to avoid transmission vibration. This is because an angled Hooke's joint speeds up and slows down twice in every 360° of shaft rotation. To compensate to some degree, the second joint on the shaft must be installed so that its fast and slow periods cancel out those of the first joint. A comparative summary of each universal joint type is shown in Table 19.1.

Sliding joints

Movement of the rear axle of a vehicle will affect any components attached to it, including the propeller shaft. As the suspension flexes, the axle pivots around the fixed shackle, and the effective length of the propeller shaft varies (Figure 19.2). This variation in length is made possible by a **sliding joint**, which is fitted to the gearbox end of the shaft.

Divided propeller shafts

Long-wheelbase vehicles (those in which the distance between the axles is considerable) often have a propeller shaft in two sections (Figure 19.6). These are used because a long single shaft would tend to 'whip' when rotating at speed. To provide extra support for the long drive line a **centre bearing** is fitted, which supports the shaft and dampens out slight torsional vibrations.

It consists of a rubber collar contained within a steel casing, which is mounted on the vehicle's chassis. The centre bearing normally uses self-aligning bearings, which allow for slight misalignment of the shaft caused by the gearbox moving on its mountings. In most other respects the divided propeller shaft shares many of the constructional features of the conventional single shaft.

Propeller shaft balancing

A propeller shaft must be accurately balanced if it is to give smooth, trouble-free operation. Balancing is necessary to avoid creating whip or any excessive rotational vibrations, which could damage components of the transmission system. To balance a propeller shaft when it is made at the factory, small balancing weights are welded at specific points on the tubular part of the shaft.

Hotchkiss drive

This is a combined suspension and transmission layout in which the rear axle and final drive is located on the chassis by a pair of leafsprings. The forward end of each leafspring is held by a **fixed shackle**, whilst the rearmost end of each leafspring is mounted on a **swinging shackle** (Figure 19.2). Such a design layout enables the rear axle to twist with changes in drive conditions – backwards under acceleration conditions and forwards during braking.

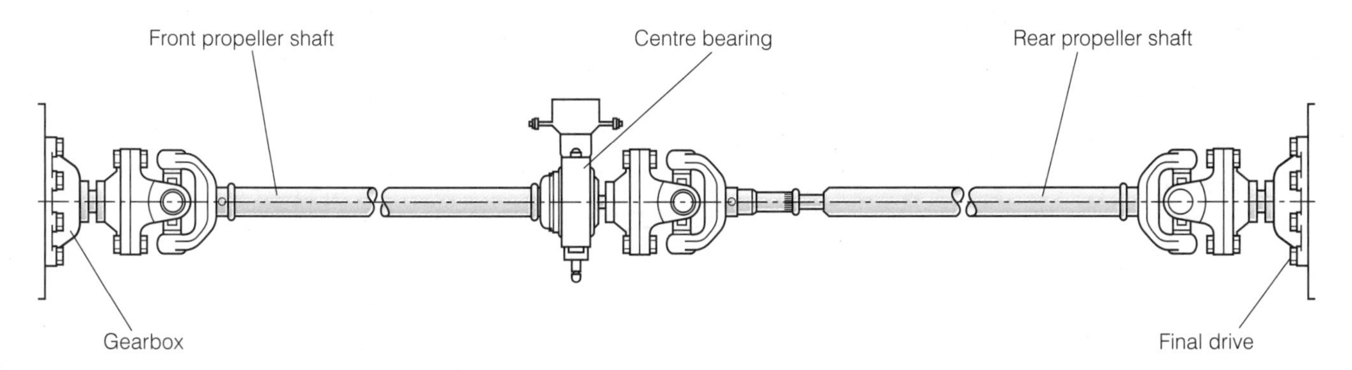

Figure 19.6 Two-section propeller shaft.

Torque tube drive

With this type of drive system, a torque tube or extension housing is located on the forward end of the final drive (Figure 19.7). The torque tube limits the fore and aft movement of the rear axle, and relieves the leafsprings of some of the driving and braking thrust by means of a support secured to the chassis by a rubber bush.

Driveshafts

A vehicle equipped with rear-wheel drive and independent suspension has **drive-shafts** to enable driving torque to be transmitted through varying angles to each driving wheel (Figure 19.8).

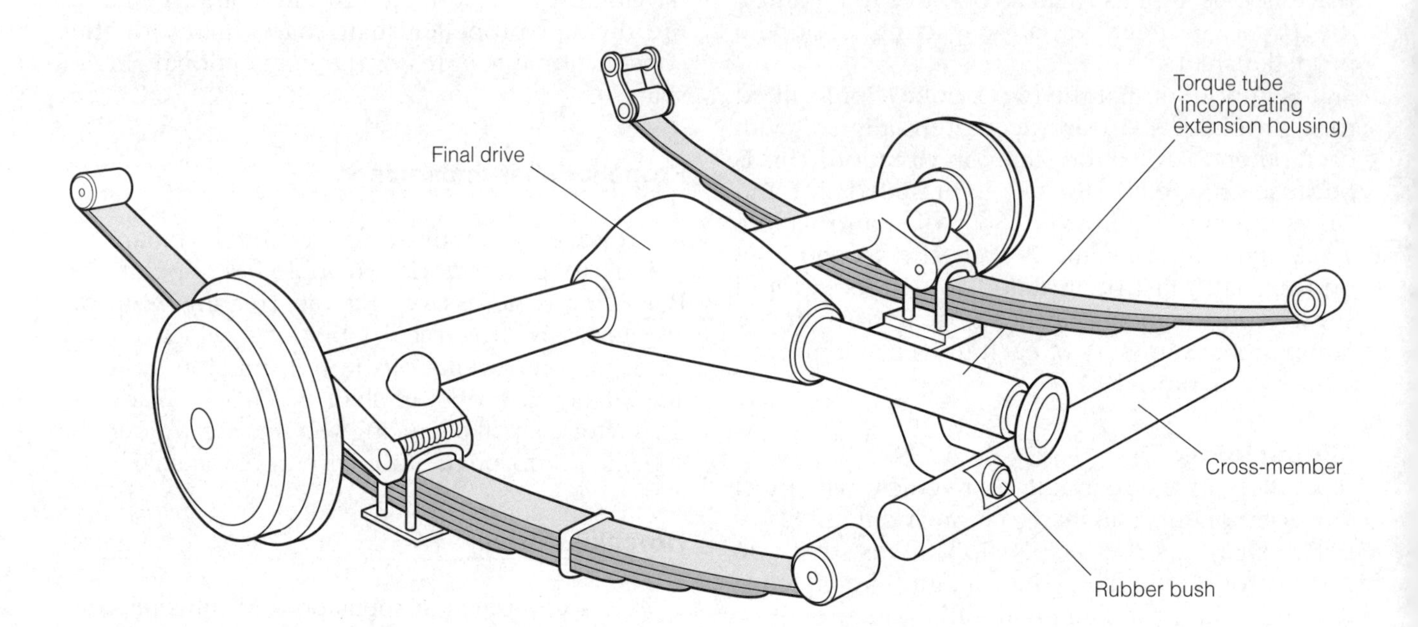

Figure 19.7 Torque tube drive.

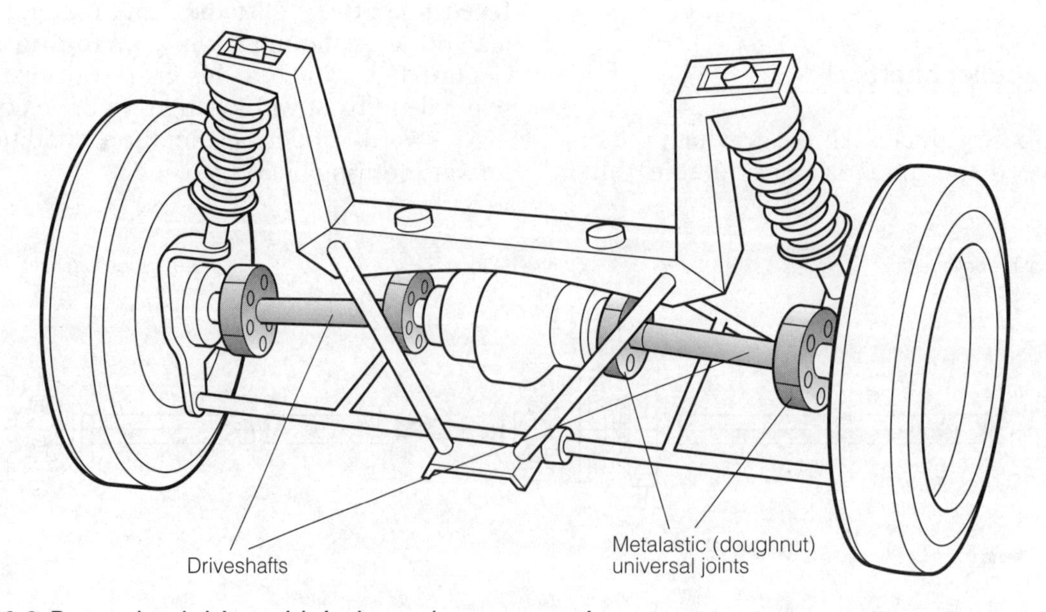

Figure 19.8 Rear-wheel drive with independent suspension.

These shafts are normally solid in construction, and commonly use Hooke's universal joints or, alternatively, rubber trunnion couplings (Figure 19.9).

Constant velocity joints

Front-wheel drive vehicles of either **transverse** or **in-line** layout use similar shafts but with **constant velocity (CV) joints**.

Hooke's joints are unsuitable with front-wheel drive because they are limited to an angle of 20°, giving a poor steering lock, and the speed variations would give rise to some steering 'twitching' during cornering.

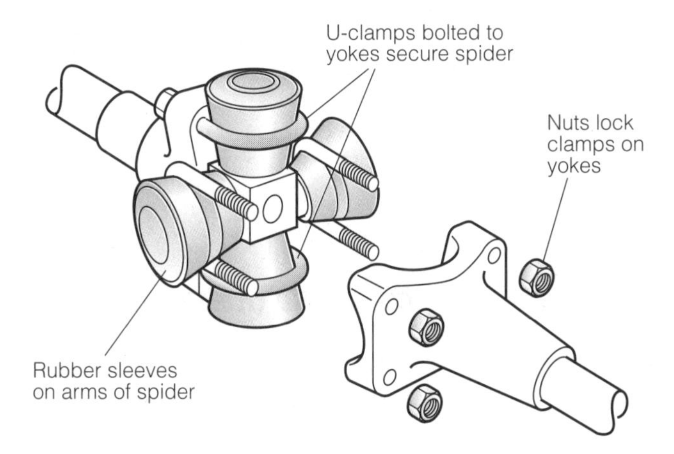

Figure 19.9 Rubber trunnion universal coupling.

In contrast, a CV joint can transmit the available torque through varying angles without any noticeable difference in the speeds of the two shafts. This results in the vehicle's having an acceptable steering lock, but without the vibration associated with other designs of coupling.

The Birfield joint is one of the most popular CV joints fitted to front-wheel-drive vehicles. It consists of a specially designed ball and socket to which both the driveshaft and the output shaft are fitted (Figure 19.10).

The part of the output shaft that forms the socket of the joint is machined with six curved grooves, which align with the axis of the shaft. The ball of the joint is splined onto the end of the driveshaft. This ball is also machined with six curved grooves, within which six smaller steel balls move. These six balls are located between the grooves of both the joint's ball and socket, and are held in place by a steel ring cage. This allows the joint both to move with the suspension, and to transmit power to the steered wheels through an angle of up to 44°. Whatever the angular deflection though which the joint has to transmit drive the velocities of the driveshaft and output shaft are the same: hence the name.

To ensure trouble-free service the joint is prepacked with a special grease designed for CV joints, and a protective gaiter is fitted to prevent dirt or water from getting in.

The Tripot CV joint is a variation on this design. Instead of a spherical ball it uses a splined spider hub onto which three hemispherical rollers are mounted via a set of needle roller bearings

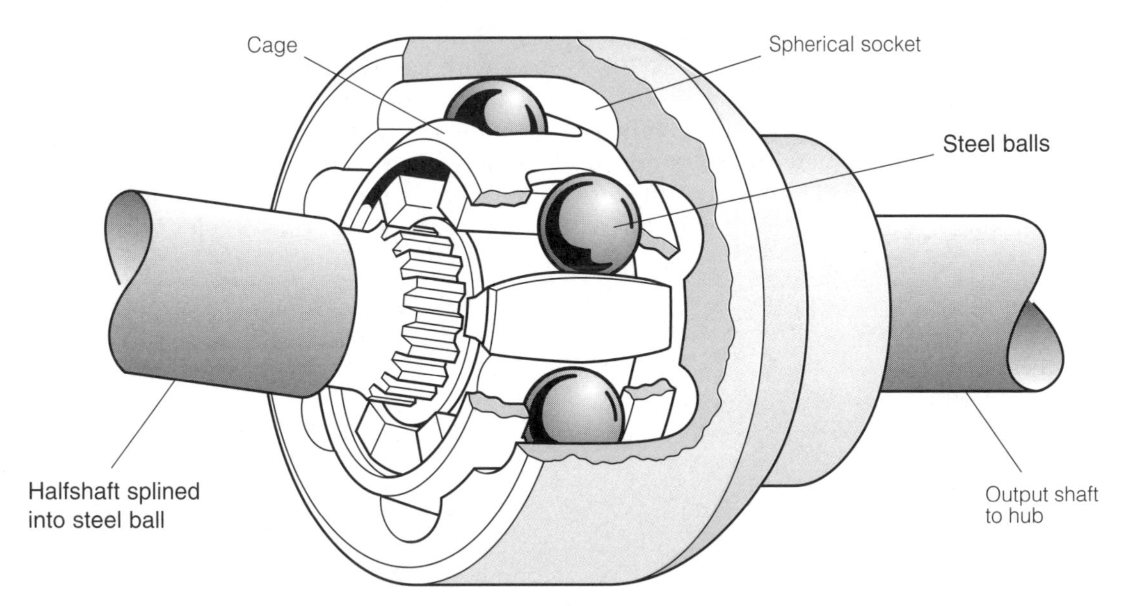

Figure 19.10 Constant velocity joint (Birfield type).

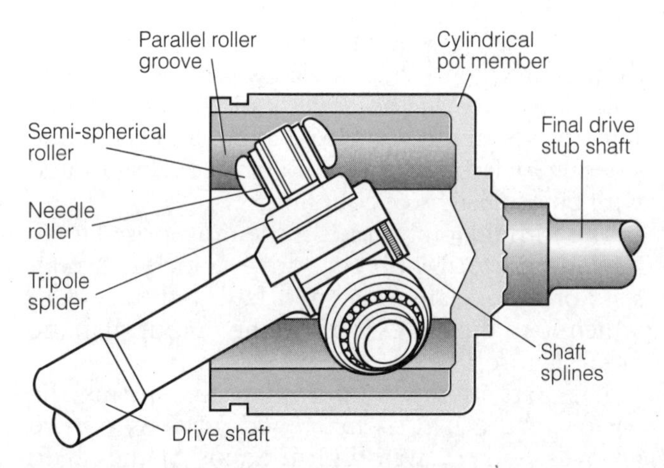

Figure 19.11 Tripot constant velocity joint.

(Figure 19.11). The rollers align with a matching set of parallel roller grooves machined onto the socket of the output shaft. Movement of the rollers within their guides allows the drive from the gearbox to be transmitted through varying angles of both suspension and steering movement.

> An important routine requirement for any vehicle equipped with CV joints is that the protective gaiter surrounding each joint must be carefully checked for tears or splitting. This must be done frequently if the vehicle drives over rough terrain or through low, tough undergrowth. If a gaiter becomes damaged, lubricant will be lost, dirt and water will enter, and the joint will fail very quickly.

To check the operation of a CV joint the vehicle must be driven fairly slowly with the steering wheel being turned from full right- to full left-hand lock alternately. A defective joint will start to knock as it tries to transmit the torque through varying angles of drive.

CHECK YOUR UNDERSTANDING

- Vehicles with front engines and rear-wheel drive use a tubular propeller shaft to connect the gearbox to the final drive.
- Propeller shafts are carefully balanced to ensure that they do not vibrate when rotating at speed.
- On a vehicle having the Hotchkiss drive layout, the propeller shaft is fitted with a pair of universal joints and a sliding joint to allow for relative movement between the gearbox and the final drive.
- Long drive lines usually have two propeller shafts with a centre bearing.
- Short, solid driveshafts are used to transmit engine torque to the driving wheels of vehicles with independent suspension.
- Front-wheel drive vehicles need constant velocity joints for smooth torque transmission.

REVISION EXERCISES AND QUESTIONS

1. State the *three* main reasons why a tubular rather than a solid propeller shaft is fitted to a vehicle.
2. How does a shaft manufacturer counteract out of balance forces?
3. Why must Hooke's joints be properly aligned with each other?
4. State *two* reasons why Hooke's joints are unsuitable for front-wheel driveshafts.
5. How is a constant velocity joint checked?
6. What is the important routine check that must be carried out on vehicles with CV joints?

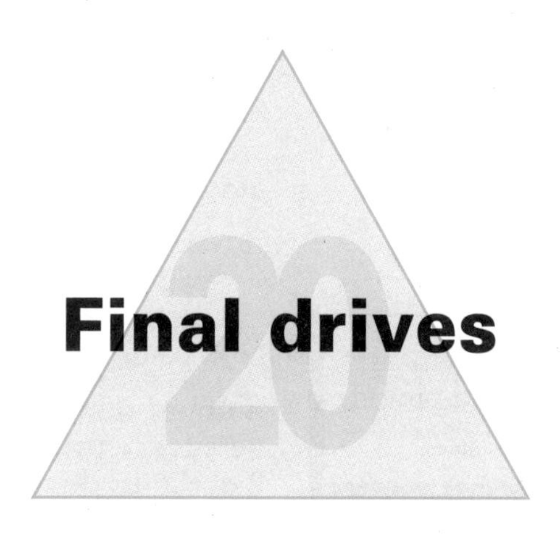

Final drives

Introduction

The final drive is that part of the transmission system that provides a final reduction gear and an even distribution of the engine's torque to the roadwheels.

The position and type of final drive varies according to the vehicle's layout. With a transverse engine the final drive is driven directly from the gearbox output shaft, and is known as **reduction gearing** (Figure 20.1a). When an in-line engine layout is employed, a **crown wheel and pinion** is used. Some heavy vehicles are equipped with **worm and wheel drive** (Figure 20.1b).

The purpose of the final drive is to:

1. provide permanent reduction gearing to increase the torque available;
2. where an in-line engine is employed, to turn the drive through 90° (Figure 20.2).

For most light vehicles, a final drive gear ratio of approximately 4 : 1 is common, while for heavier vehicles the reduction may be as high as 20 : 1. The actual gear reduction is calculated by dividing the number of teeth on the crown wheel or larger driven (follower) gear by the number of teeth on the pinion or small drive gear. That is:

$$\text{Gear ratio} = \frac{\text{Number of teeth on crown wheel (driven or follower)}}{\text{Number of teeth on pinion (driver)}}$$

More simply:

$$\text{Gear ratio} = \frac{\text{follower}}{\text{driver}}$$

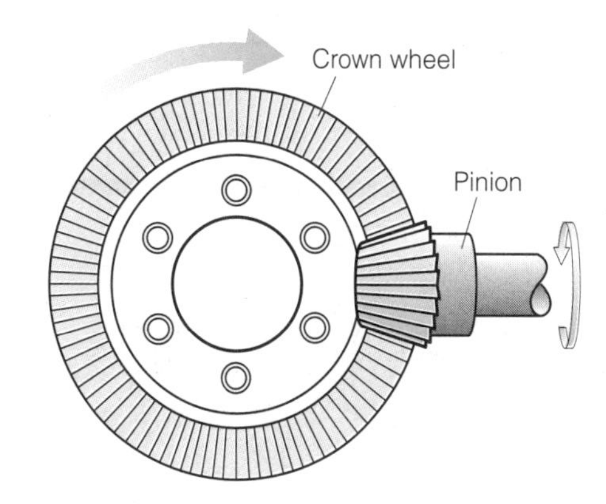

Figure 20.2 Crown wheel and pinion.

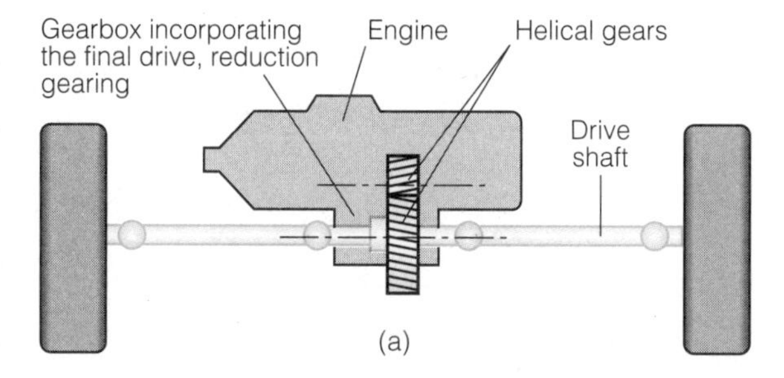

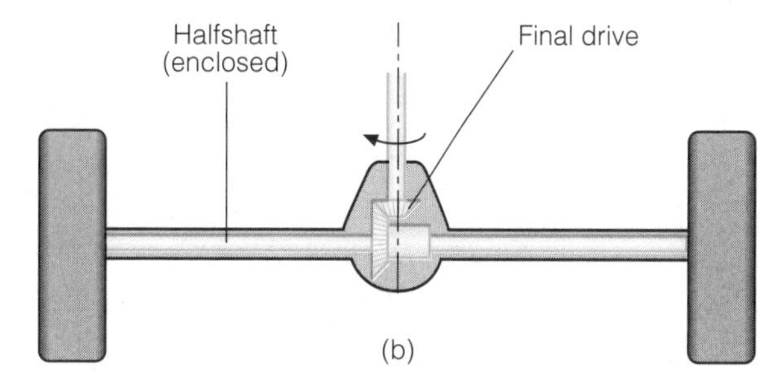

Figure 20.1 Final drive and differential location: (a) front-wheel-drive layout (transverse engine); (b) rear-mounted live axle (conventional) incorporating crown wheel and pinion.

Types of final drive

Straight bevel final drive

In this design, straight-cut bevel teeth are machined onto both the cone-shaped pinion and the crown wheel (Figure 20.3).

The gear teeth are specially hardened and tempered to withstand the torsional stresses and shock loadings that may be imposed when transmitting the engine's torque. There are several **disadvantages** with this type of drive:

1. The axes of the pinion and the crown wheel must coincide, which requires a high floor level or deep propeller shaft tunnel.
2. With straight-cut gears the drive is noisy.
3. Only one pair of gear teeth are in contact at any one time, which limits the amount of torque that the final drive can transmit.

Because of these limitations, straight-cut teeth are no longer used on final drives.

Spiral bevel final drive

Spiral bevel drives have the teeth machined at an inclined angle (Figure 20.4).

The use of spiral bevel gears has technical **advantages**:

1. More than one pair of gear teeth are meshing with each other at any one time. This enables the gears to take a higher loading
2. The drive is quieter in operation.

In most other respects, there is little external difference between the spiral bevel and the straight bevel final drives.

Hypoid final drive

This is the type of bevel drive most likely to be found on current vehicles. One of its main features is that the centreline axis of the pinion is **offset** relative to the centreline axis of the crown wheel (Figure 20.5). An offset of one-fifth of the crown wheel diameter is common.

Because of this offset, as the crown wheel and pinion rotate, the gear teeth are subjected to a high-pressure sliding and rolling action. To deal with this operating condition a special type of extreme pressure (EP) lubricating oil must be used. Additives such as chlorine and sulphur prevent the gear teeth from 'scuffing', as well as providing adequate lubrication at all likely temperatures.

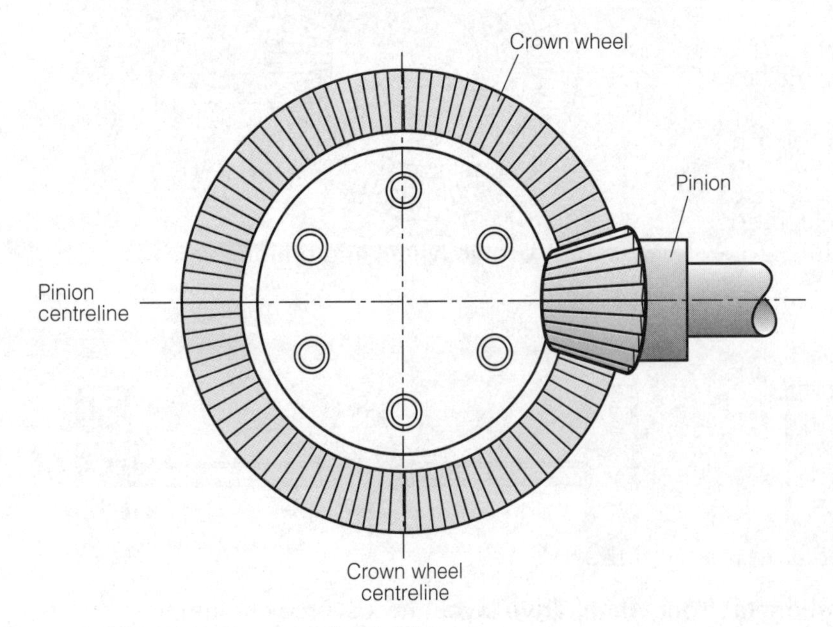

Figure 20.3 Straight final drive.

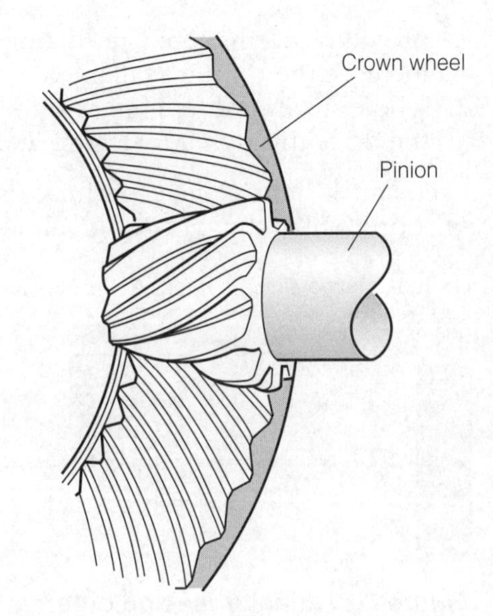

Figure 20.4 Spiral bevel final drive.

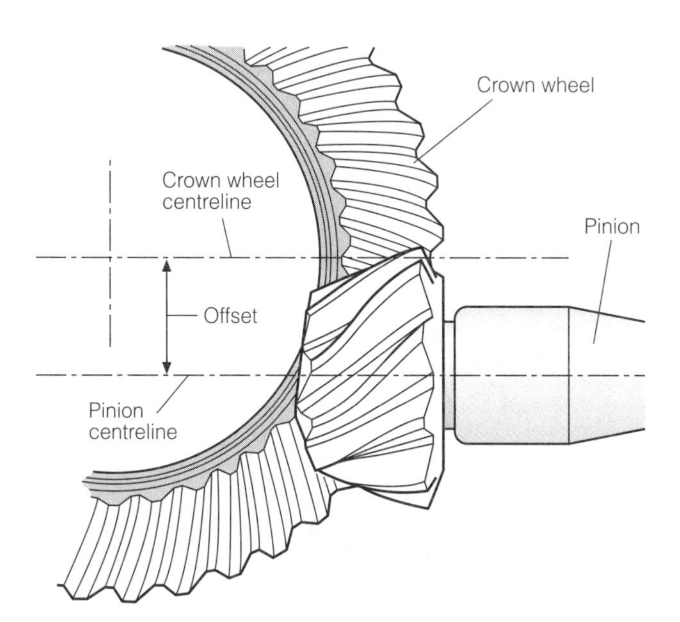

Figure 20.5 Hypoid final drive.

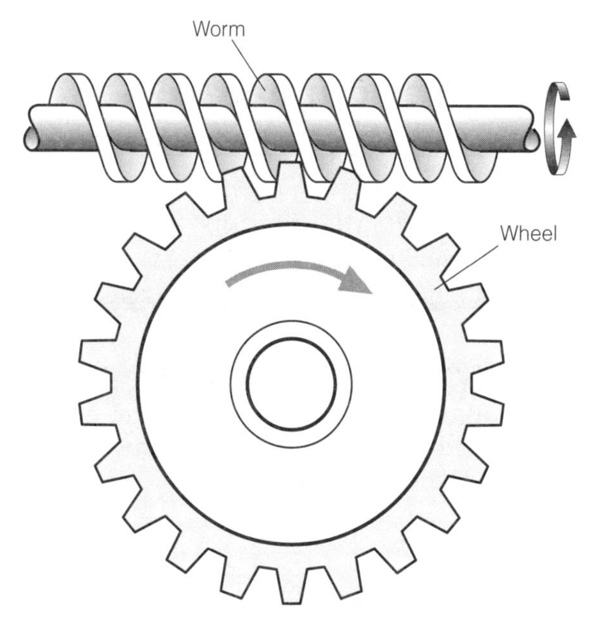

Figure 20.6 Worm and wheel final drive.

The pinion is one-third larger and stronger than the spiral bevel type, and failure due to breakage is rare.

Worm and wheel final drive

This drive consists of a spiral-shaped worm and a toothed wheel (Figure 20.6).

The wheel is made from phosphor bronze, and the worm is normally made from case-hardened steel. The worm can be placed either above or below the wheel to give, respectively, a higher ground clearance or a lower floor line. Although this final drive provides a large gear reduction in a relatively small, confined space, the materials used in its construction are expensive. This restricts its use to heavy goods vehicles and buses.

Double reduction final drive

Specialist vehicles such as earthmoving equipment and very heavy commercial vehicles, which require an extremely low gear, employ a **double reduction final drive** (Figure 20.7). The first stage of gear reduction is achieved by means of the crown wheel and pinion. The second stage is by helical reduction gears, which reduce the speed and increase the torque again.

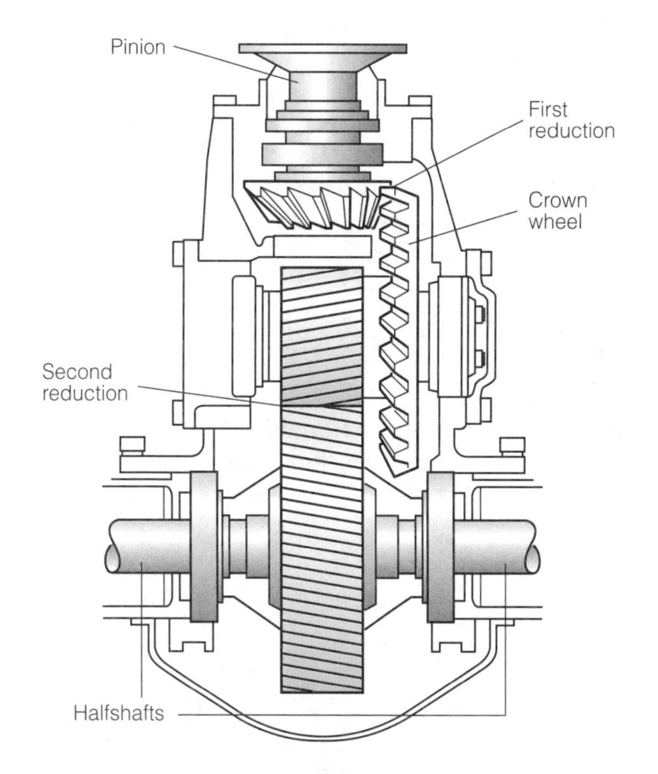

Figure 20.7 Double reduction final drive.

Helical gear final drive

The popularity of transverse, front-wheel drive vehicles means that a pair of helical gears is now one of the most common types of final drive, as shown in Figure 20.1a. It employs two helical-cut gears mounted in substantial bearings.

The differential

> The differential is a device that enables two driveshafts to be driven at different speeds, but with equal torque.

Commonly it is located in the final drive itself. A centre differential may also be used to equalise the drive and prevent 'wind-up' of the transmission of four-wheel drive vehicles.

Construction

The final drive differential is mounted inside a housing secured to the crown wheel. Inside the housing are two pairs of meshed, bevel gearwheels. The **planet gears** are located inside the differential housing by a cross-pin. In contrast, the **sun gears** are also inside the housing, but they are splined to the **halfshafts** or **output drive flanges**. Halfshafts are used to drive the roadwheels in one-piece axle casings, and output drive flanges locate the driveshafts used with independent suspension.

Operation of final drive differential

Straight ahead
When the gears are engaged, the engine rotates the crown wheel, together with the differential housing (Figure 20.8). If both roadwheels have equal rolling resistance, neither sun wheel can turn more easily than the other. This prevents the planet wheels from rotating: the whole assembly rotates together, and the differential is inoperative.

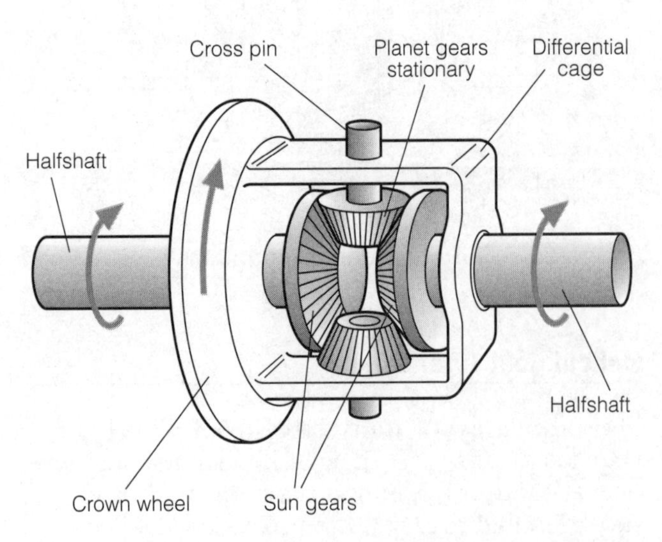

Figure 20.8 Differential operation: straight ahead.

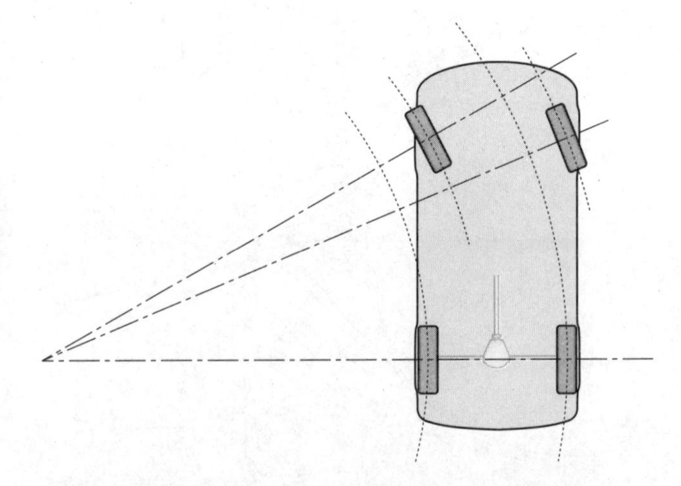

Figure 20.9 When rounding a bend, the outer wheels travel a greater distance than the inner wheels.

Cornering

> When a vehicle negotiates a bend or corner the distances travelled by the inner and outer driving roadwheels (that is, the circumferences of the turning circles) will be different (Figure 20.9).

As a result, the rolling resistance and the speed of each wheel are different: the inner roadwheel has high resistance, and the outer roadwheel must speed up. Consequently, the differential housing, driven by the engine, begins to wind itself around the inner sun wheel (Figure 20.10). The planet wheels are made to rotate and, in so doing, they also turn the outer sun wheel at a faster speed. In this way the engine torque is equally divided between the roadwheels all the time they are gripping the road.

It follows that if one roadwheel loses all adhesion, that wheel can spin, and all drive to the other will be lost. In some circumstances, such as with off-road vehicles or in slippery driving conditions, a differential can be undesirable. To overcome such problems vehicles may be fitted with **differential locks**.

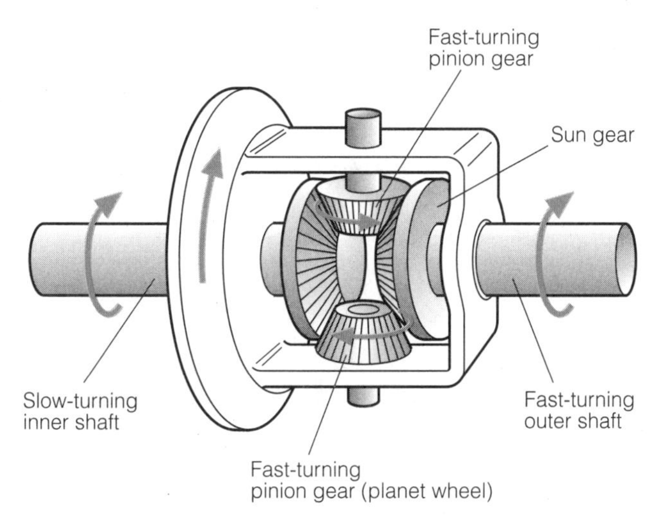

Figure 20.10 Differential operation: cornering.

Differential lock

> A differential lock is a mechanical device that, when fitted to a differential, prevents the driving wheels from rotating at different speeds.

One of the most common types of differential lock consists of a sliding dog clutch, which is moved by an electrically operated solenoid unit or by compressed air. When engaged, the sliding dog clutch meshes with a similar set of dog teeth machined onto the differential cage (Figure 20.11). This prevents the planet gears from driving the sun gears at different speeds. It is important to remember that a differential lock must not be selected for normal road use, as this can cause serious damage to the final drive and differential.

Third differentials

Four-wheel drive transmission systems give much improved driveability, because all four wheels are used to drive the vehicle. Using four-wheel drive for normal road use can result in **transmission wind-up**, which is caused when the front and rear final drives have slight speed variations between them. Over a period of time the resulting variations can cause some transmission components to fail, particularly halfshafts. To overcome this problem a third differential, which works on the same principle as the front and rear units, is installed between the axles to allow for differences in their speed. It is commonly fitted inside the transfer box.

Limited-slip differentials

High-performance vehicles such as rally cars have engines that have a high torque output coupled with low vehicle weight, and this can cause the driving wheels to spin uncontrollably while attempting to transmit torque. To prevent this, such vehicles are often fitted with limited-slip

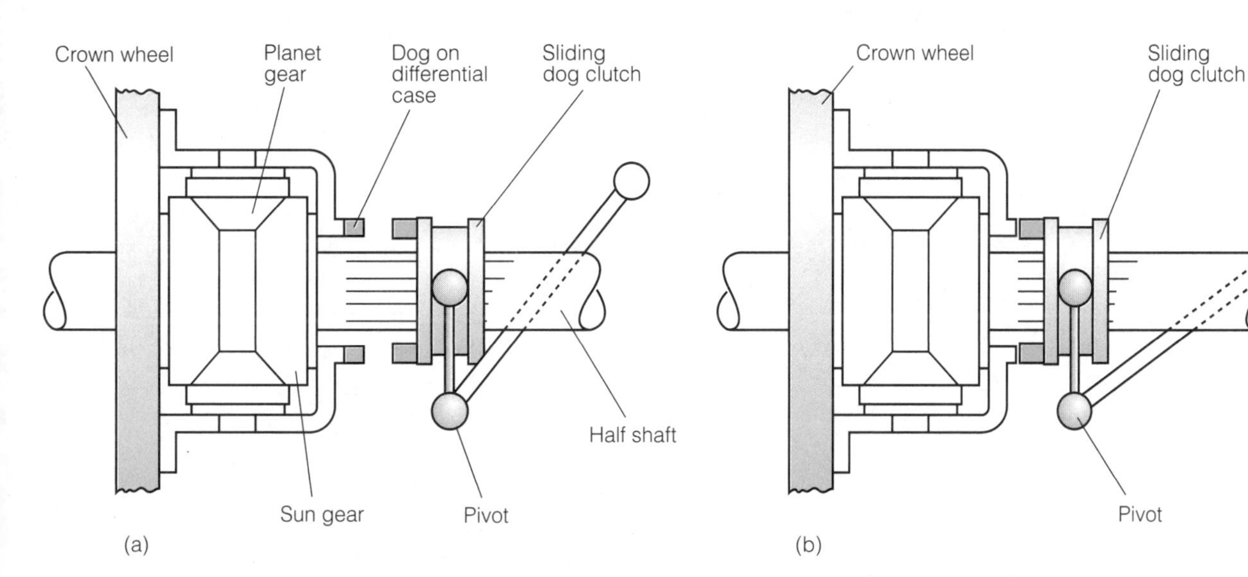

Figure 20.11 Differential lock: (a) disengaged; (b) engaged.

differentials, which are available in a number of designs. One of them is the **limited-slip viscous coupling**.

Viscous coupling limited-slip differential

The **viscous coupling** is a fluid shear unit used as a centre differential, or as part of a final drive unit.

The multiple plates inside the unit are alternately attached to the outer casing for the input and to the centre hub for the output (Figure 20.12a). The space between the closely fitted plates is filled with silicon fluid. When there is limited variation between the speed of the input and output shafts, the silicon fluid remains viscous. If the speed of the two components begins to change too much, the fluid effectively solidifies, and the plates are locked together. When the torque difference returns to an acceptable level, the silicon becomes fluid again and there is limited slip.

When used to limit the slip of a conventional differential the viscous coupling is incorporated into the final drive unit (Figure 20.12b). In this version the input is from one of the sun wheels, and the output is to one roadwheel. Normal cornering speed variations within the differential are acceptable; there is limited slip. As soon as one wheel starts to spin, the coupling locks up.

Lubrication and maintenance

To ensure that the final drive and differential remain in serviceable condition, the level of the gear oil in drive units should be checked and topped up with the correct grade of oil at periodic intervals, as directed and specified in the vehicle manufacturer's service information. Most modern rear-axle final drives are filled with oil for life, and do not need draining.

To prevent the build-up of excessive pressure in the axle casing, most drive units have a vent to atmosphere. Where this is fitted, check that the airway is clear, to prevent pressurisation and oil

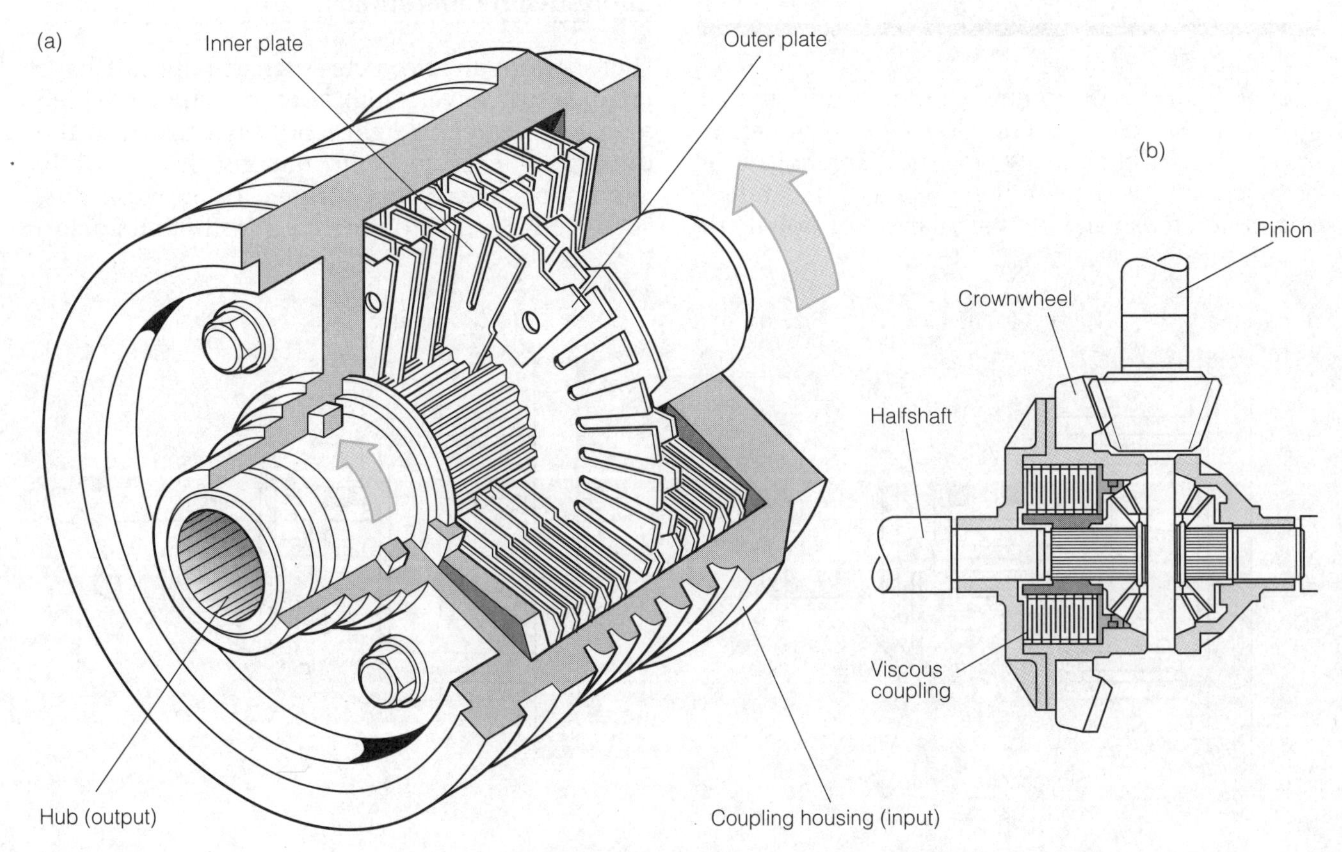

Figure 20.12 (a) Viscous coupling limited-slip differential. (b) Shaft-to-cage viscous coupling.

leaks. Non-moving components of a drive unit or rear axle are fitted together with gaskets, and **lip-type oil seals** for the rotating parts, such as the pinion. Defective oil seals must be replaced before serious damage results from loss of lubricant.

Halfshafts and hubs

Halfshafts

> The purpose of a halfshaft is to allow the torque from the final drive to be transmitted to each of the driving roadwheels.

One end of the halfshaft is machined with a set of splines to engage with the sun wheel, and the other provides a location for the brake drum or disc and wheel.

The halfshaft must be able both to support the weight of the vehicle and to withstand the forces associated with driving and braking. To resist the torsional stresses imposed upon the shaft it is made from carbon steel, to which chromium and nickel are added to give additional resistance to stress fatigue. The three most common types of hub arrangement are:

1. semi-floating;
2. three-quarter floating;
3. fully floating.

Semi-floating axle

> This is the simplest of the three hub arrangements. In this design the halfshaft is supported in the axle casing by a single set of ball bearings, the bearing being held in place by a retainer plate (Figure 20.13).

The bearing is prepacked with grease, and is also lubricated by a spray mist from the final drive. To prevent the lubricant from contaminating the brake linings, an oil seal is fitted between the bearing and the retainer plate. Because of the large stresses imposed upon the halfshaft, it is suitable for light vehicles only.

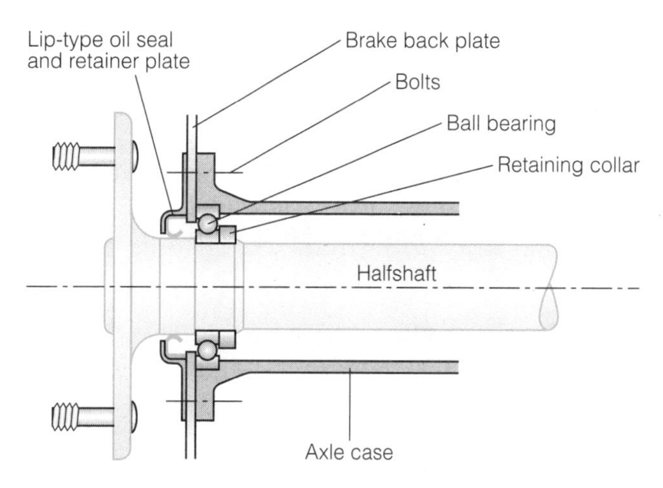

Figure 20.13 Semi-floating hub.

Three-quarter floating axle

> This is a stronger design, which is commonly fitted to light and medium-weight cars and goods vehicles.

In the three-quarter floating axle only part of the weight is carried by the halfshaft: consequently the single-row ball bearing is positioned between the axle casing and the hub. It is held in place by means of a locknut, which presses it against a shoulder machined into the casing (Figure 20.14).

To prevent the locknut from loosening, it is fitted with a locking washer. As in the semi-floating axle, the bearing is prepacked with grease, and is also lubricated by oil mist spray

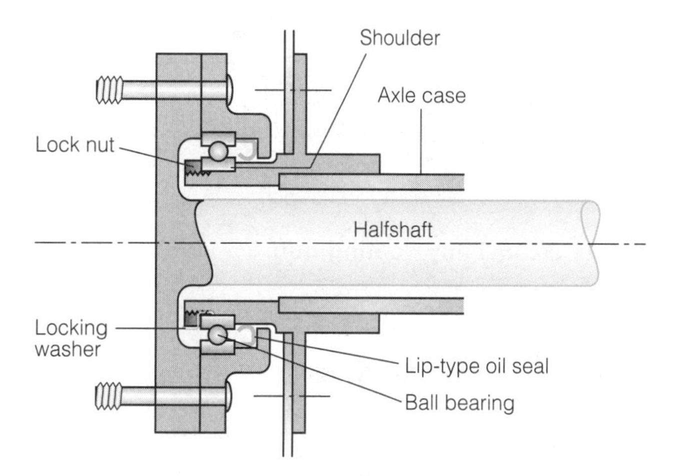

Figure 20.14 Three-quarters floating hub.

from the final drive. To minimise the possibility of contamination of the brake shoe linings a lip-type oil seal is fitted. As the axle is of more robust construction, and the weight of the vehicle is supported by the axle casing, the halfshaft is required to withstand mainly the torsional forces associated with driving and braking. Most other stresses are absorbed by the axle casing.

Fully floating axle

> This is the strongest of the three axles. It is always used on heavy goods vehicles and buses. In this axle design all the driving, braking, and cornering forces, as well as the actual vehicle weight, are placed on the axle casing. The halfshaft is required only to transmit the torque from the final drive to the driving wheel.

There are two sets of taper roller bearings positioned between the axle casing and the hub (Figure 20.15). The bearings are retained by means of a locked but adjustable nut, with which the bearings are **preloaded** or tensioned to remove any free play.

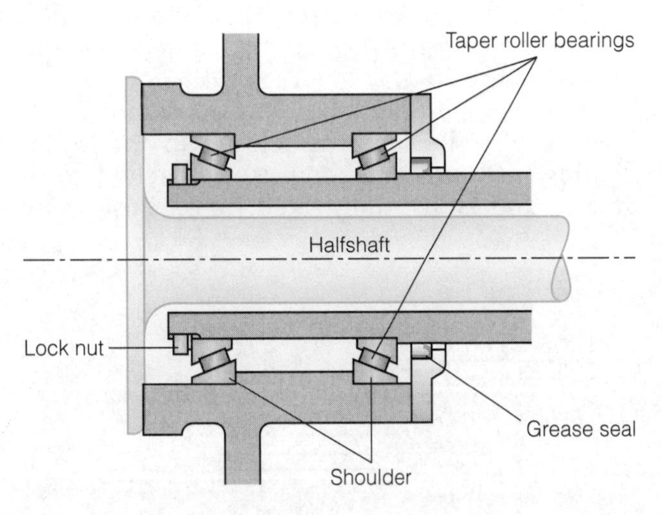

Figure 20.15 Fully floating hub.

Front wheel hub designs

The construction of the stub axle, which must swivel to allow the vehicle to be steered, depends on whether it is a driving or non-driving hub.

Non-driving hub

A typical hub and brake disc assembly, mounted at the lower end of a Macpherson strut (see Chapter 22), is shown in Figure 20.16. The hub is mounted on adjustable taper roller bearings. Lubrication is by high melting-point grease (HMP), which is retained by a lip-type oil seal and a dust cap.

There are two important points to note:

1. Roller bearings in this environment must have running clearance to avoid seizure.
2. The bearings must be packed with HMP grease before assembly, with perhaps a little smeared inside the hub. Neither the dust cap nor the space between the bearings should be filled with lubricant, as this will escape and contaminate the roadwheel and brake.

Follow the vehicle manufacturer's adjustment sequence if it is known. In general, taper roller bearing adjustment from the dismantled state starts by making sure that the bearings are fully seated. This is done by clamping up the adjusting nut while turning the wheel. Continue with the sequence for routine adjustment by slackening the adjusting nut until there is a little free play. Take up the nut carefully until the point of no free play can just be detected by rocking the wheel. Then

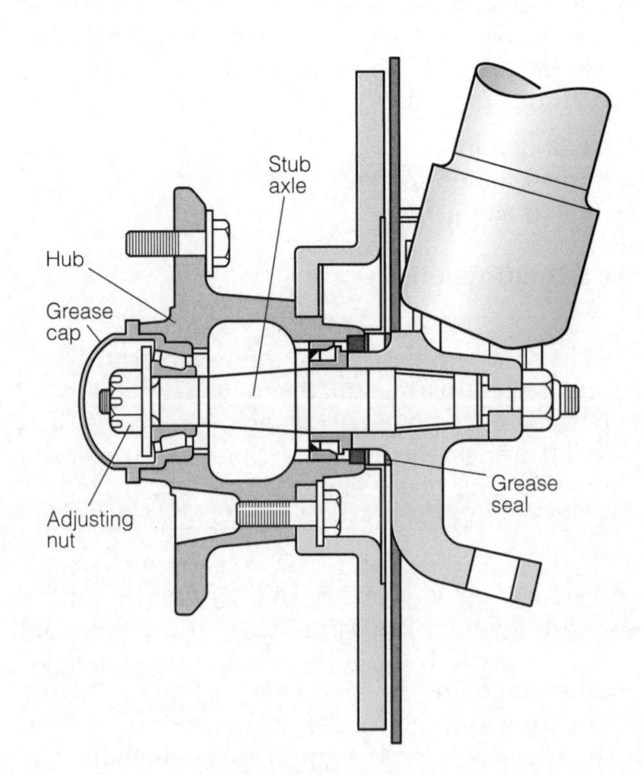

Figure 20.16 Front hub: taper roller type.

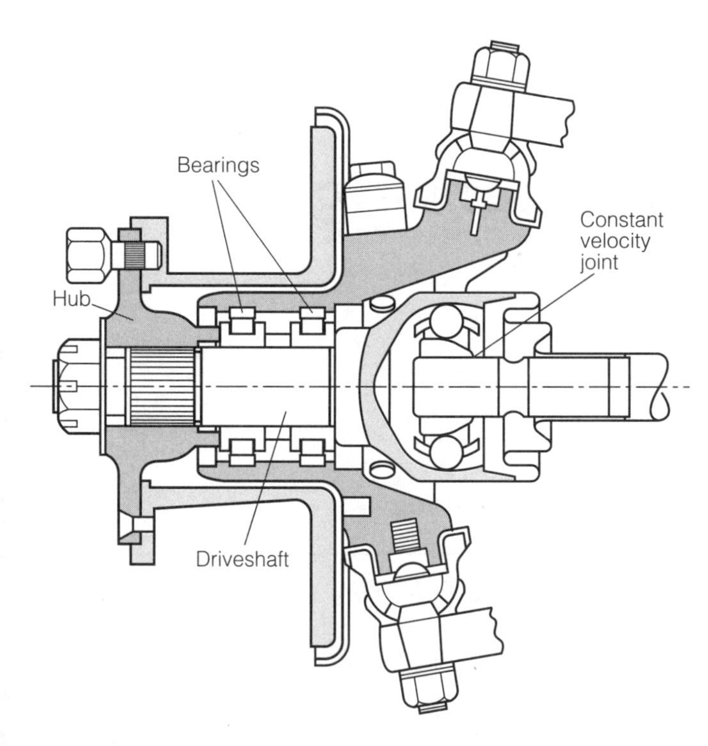

Figure 20.17 Front hub: front-wheel drive.

back off the nut one flat, check that there is a trace of free play, and lock the nut in place.

Driving hub

The stub axle on a driving hub must rotate inside the stub axle housing (Figure 20.17). One end of the stub axle forms the outer end of the **constant velocity (CV) joint**, while the other supports the wheel hub and brake disc. The hub shown uses separate roller races, which are tightened to a specified torque, and lip-type oil seals. Other designs employ one-piece bearings.

CHECK YOUR UNDERSTANDING

- The purpose of the final drive is to provide a permanent gear reduction, as well as turn the drive through an angle of 90° where necessary. There are various types, which include helical gears, straight bevel, spiral bevel, and hypoid.
- Hypoid final drives have the pinion offset from the centre-line axis of the crown wheel. A special extreme pressure (EP) gear oil must be used to prevent premature wear of the gear teeth.
- The purpose of the differential is to allow the driving wheels to be driven at different speeds but with equal torque when cornering. The differential consists of a set of sun and planet gears, which are mounted inside the differential housing.
- Specialised vehicles sometimes need to use a differential lock when being driven on soft ground.
- Vehicles with permanent four-wheel drive need a third differential between the front and rear drive units. The third differential prevents transmission wind-up from developing. A viscous coupling may also be used for this purpose.
- Limited-slip differentials are used on some high-performance vehicles to limit the slip of any one driven wheel.
- The three types of rear axle hub arrangement are semi-floating, three-quarter floating and fully floating.

REVISION EXERCISES AND QUESTIONS

1. Give *two* reasons for using a final drive in a vehicle transmission system.
2. Briefly state the main feature that distinguishes a spiral bevel from a hypoid final drive.
3. What is the main reason for fitting a differential?
4. What is the purpose of a differential lock?
5. What is the purpose of a third differential, and where can it be found on the vehicle?
6. State *two* uses for a viscous coupling.
7. Which type of rear axle hub arrangement is used for heavy goods vehicles?

Front axle and steering

Introduction

The purpose of a steering system is to control the direction in which a vehicle travels.

A number of requirements must be met if it is to do this satisfactorily:

1. The effort needed to operate the steering should be as small as possible.
2. The steering should be responsive at all times.
3. There should be feedback without too much sensitivity.
4. The steering system should promote true rolling motion.

Steering layouts

Swinging beam steering

In this layout, the front axle is mounted onto the vehicle by means of a central turntable, which allows the whole axle to pivot (Figure 21.1). As each of the steered wheels is at right angles to the centre of the turn, the vehicle can follow a curved pathway. This gives **true rolling motion**, in which the wheels have minimal rolling resistance. Although the swinging beam design has the advantage of simplicity, its use on motor vehicles is mainly limited to drawbar trailers and other specialist applications.

Fixed-beam steering

In fixed-beam steering the front axle is unable to turn. Instead, the wheels are mounted on pivoting stub axles, mounted on each end of the axle beam (Figure 21.2).

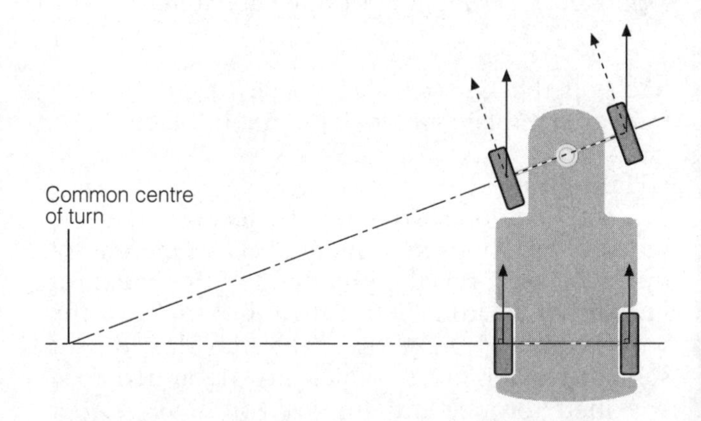

Figure 21.1 Swinging-beam steering system.

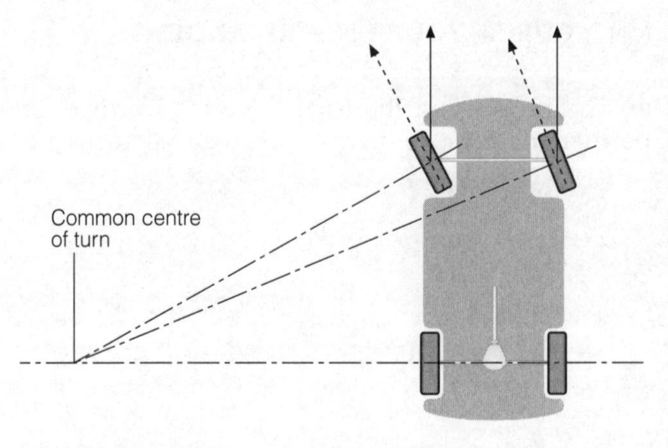

Figure 21.2 Fixed-beam steering system.

Although designed at a time when all horse-drawn carriages had axle beams, the method is still the basis of all steering. Vehicles with independent suspension have their stub axles mounted in the same relative positions.

To ensure that tyre wear is kept to a minimum, the steering geometry must provide true rolling motion. This is obtained by making the wheels share a common centre of turn, using a layout known as the **Ackermann principle**, after its inventor Rudolf Ackermann (Figure 21.2).

Ackermann steering principle

To ensure that the front steered wheels rotate around a common centre, the inner and outer roadwheels must be moved by different amounts (Figure 21.2). This is achieved by setting the steering arms at an angle, so that their projected centrelines meet on or near the centre of the rear axle (Figure 21.3).

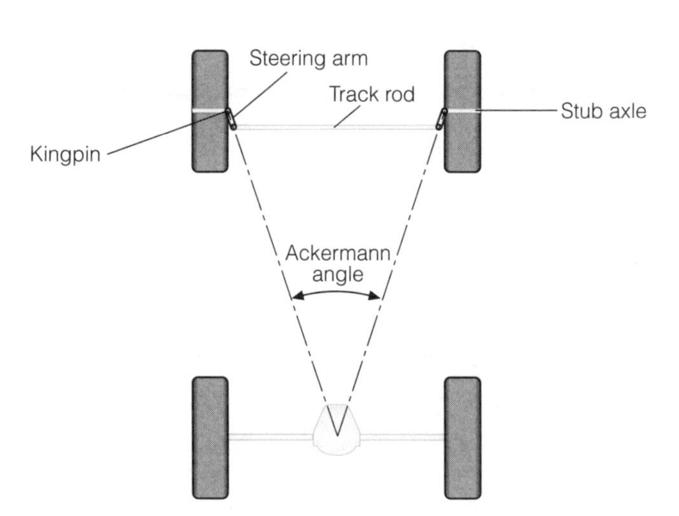

Figure 21.3 Ackermann steering principle.

When the steering wheel is turned, the inner steering arm will move the inner roadwheel through a greater angle than the outer. The difference between them is called **toe out on turn**, which can be remembered by the acronym **TOOT**, and is normally between 2° and 3° (Figure 21.4).

Wheel alignment

To ensure that true rolling motion occurs in the straight ahead position, the steered wheels must be set to run parallel as they rotate.

Front-wheel drive vehicles normally require **toe out**, because the wheels pull inwards to a parallel position under power (Figure 21.5a). Conversely, rear-wheel drive vehicles commonly use a **toe in** setting, because the wheels pull back when the vehicle moves forwards (Figure 21.5b).

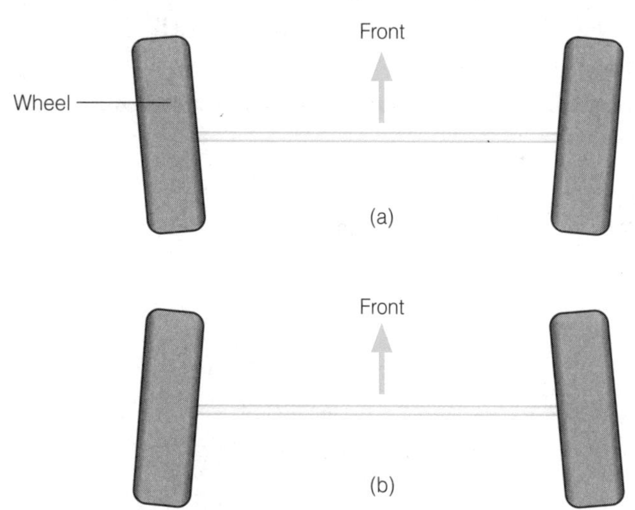

Figure 21.5 Wheel alignment: (a) toe out; (b) toe in.

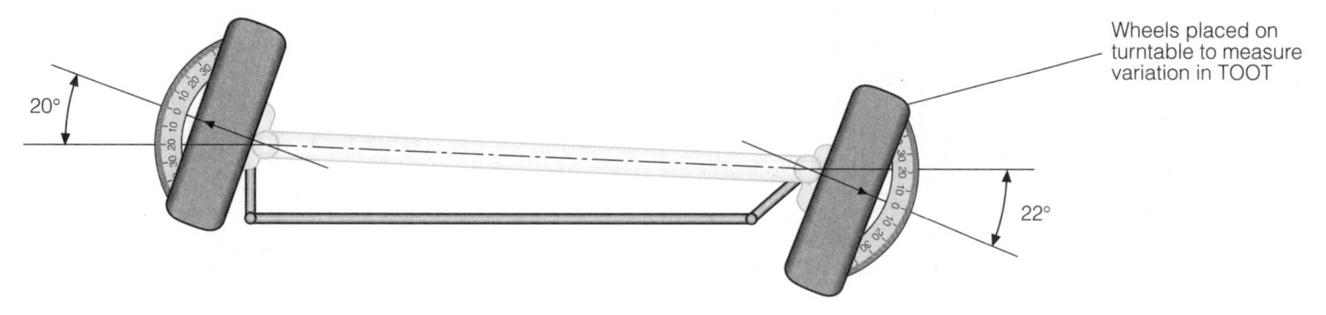

Figure 21.4 Toe out on turn (TOOT).

Steering angles

The steering geometry of a vehicle is purposely designed with certain steering angles, and these have an important effect on how the vehicle steers and handles. The three angles are:

- caster angle;
- camber angle;
- kingpin inclination (KPI).

Caster angle

One of the characteristics of a steering system is that the steered wheels should be able to self-centre. To ensure that this occurs, the vehicle's steering geometry incorporates **caster angle**.

Caster angle is created when the axis of the roadwheel trails behind the axis of the swivel hub, producing **caster trail** (Figure 21.6).

The principle of caster angle is used in many applications. One example is the bicycle (Figure 21.7). On a motor vehicle, positive caster angle is obtained by tilting the kingpin, or the centreline of the swivel joints, back from the vertical plane in relation to the normal direction of travel.

Camber angle

The roadwheel is mounted onto the stub axle so that its axis is laterally inclined outwards for positive camber by anything up to 2° (Figure 21.8). For negative camber the wheel is inclined inwards from the vertical.

The purpose of **camber angle** is to enable the steered wheels to swivel more easily, giving light and easy steering.

Kingpin inclination

KPI is the angle at which the centreline of the kingpin or the axis of the steering swivels leans inwards from the vertical (Figure 21.8).

Kingpin inclination (KPI) helps the steering to self-centre, and reduces stresses on the steering components.

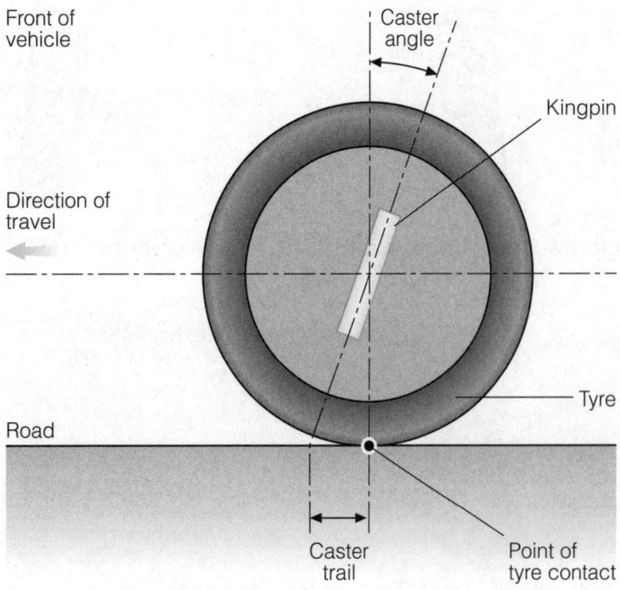

Figure 21.6 Caster angle.

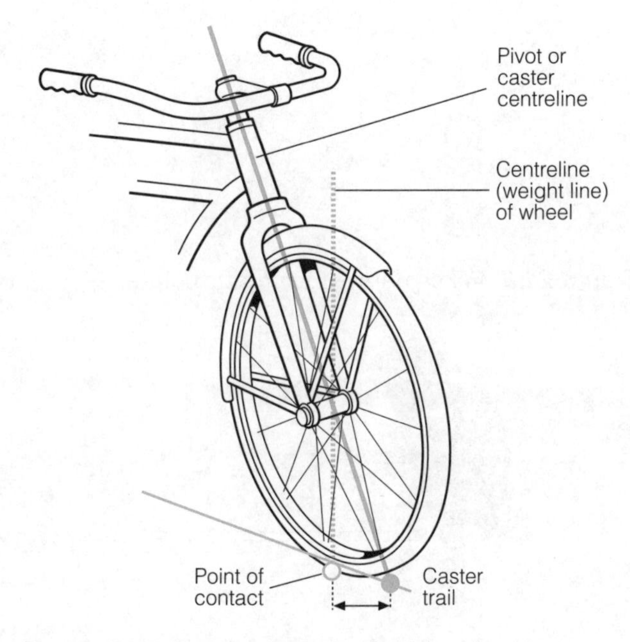

Figure 21.7 Caster angle in the bicycle.

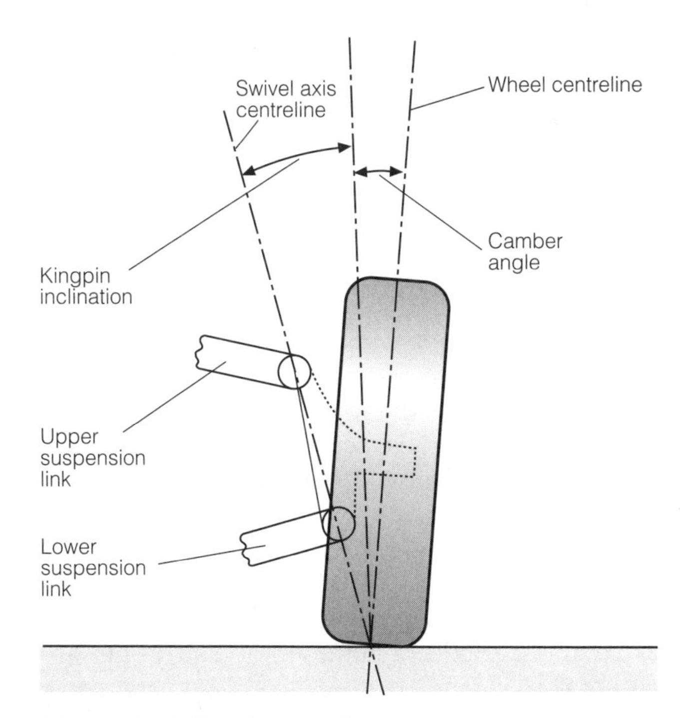

Figure 21.8 Camber angle.

The inclination of the swivel joints on independent suspensions is more correctly called **steering-axis inclination** (SAI).

Centre-point steering

To reduce steering effort, especially on large commercial vehicles, the steering geometry can be arranged to give **centre-point steering**. In this layout the axes of the roadwheel and of the swivel axis (or king pin) intersect where the tyre touches the road (Figure 21.9a).

Negative offset steering

In this layout, the axis of the roadwheel and the swivel axis intersect slightly above ground level (Figure 21.9b). It has been found that this arrangement improves stability and reduces the pull on the steering wheel if there is a tyre blow-out or the front brakes become unbalanced. It is now widely used on cars.

It is sometimes called **negative scrub** or **roll radius**.

Positive offset steering

In this layout the axis of the roadwheel and the steering axis meet below ground level (Figure 21.9c). It gives plenty of 'feel' to the steering, but can make it heavy.

Steering gear

The purpose of steering gear is to enable the driver to alter the vehicle's steered direction with a minimum of effort.

Three of the most common types in use are:

1. worm and peg;
2. recirculating ball;
3. rack and pinion.

However, regardless of the type, all steering gear should possess the following characteristics. It

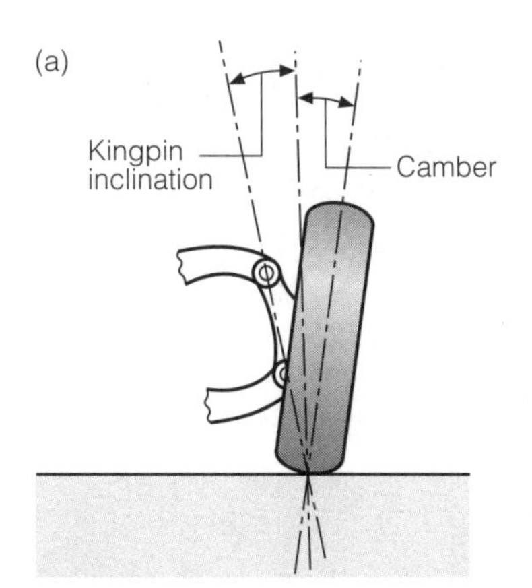

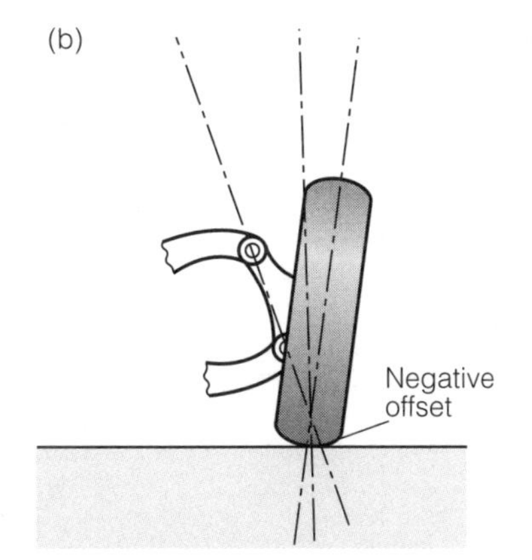

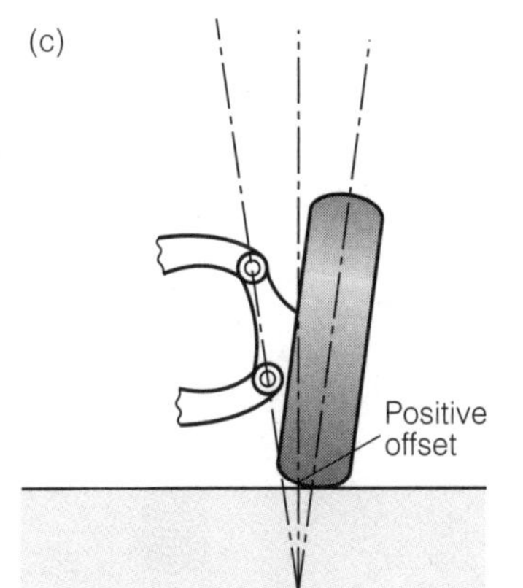

Figure 21.9 Steering geometries: (a) centre-point steering; (b) negative offset; (c) positive offset.

should normally have some degree of **reversibility**, the term used to describe the feedback of road conditions to the driver and felt at the steering wheel, but should also prevent excessive road shocks being transmitted to the steering wheel. It should ensure that the amount of **backlash** (the free play at the steering wheel) is kept to a minimum.

Worm and peg steering

With this type of steering mechanism the lower part of the steering column shaft is machined with a worm-type screw thread, which meshes with a peg protruding from the arm of the cross-shaft (Figure 21.10). When the steering wheel is rotated, the worm moves the peg along, and the arm and cross shaft turn. This movement is transferred to a steering drop arm and linkages to move the roadwheels.

Recirculating ball steering

On the lower part of the steering column shaft is a worm, and surrounding it is a sliding nut (Figure 21.11). Instead of threads, the nut and worm are linked together by a continuous row of ball bearings to give a reduced-friction drive. A transfer tube links the ends of the 'thread' to provide the recirculating movement of the ball bearings. When the steering wheel is turned, the rotating worm moves the nut up or down the shaft, and the sector shaft pivots. This movement is transmitted to the roadwheels by a drop arm and linkage.

Rack and pinion steering

Rack and pinion steering gear is fitted to many modern vehicles (Figure 21.12). The steering wheel turns the pinion on the end of the steering shaft, which slides the toothed rack to and fro in the housing. Tie rods, sealed by gaiters, link the rack to the wheel assemblies.

Steering ball joints

To transmit the movement of the steering gearbox to each stub axle, a number of ball joints are required.

The purpose of a ball joint is to link together two components but at the same time allow both angular and rotational movement between them. It consists of a spherical socket in which the ball end of a pin is held under spring compression (Figure 21.13). Most ball joints are not adjustable, which means that they must be replaced once free play reaches unacceptable levels.

Note that many suspension ball joints are of similar construction.

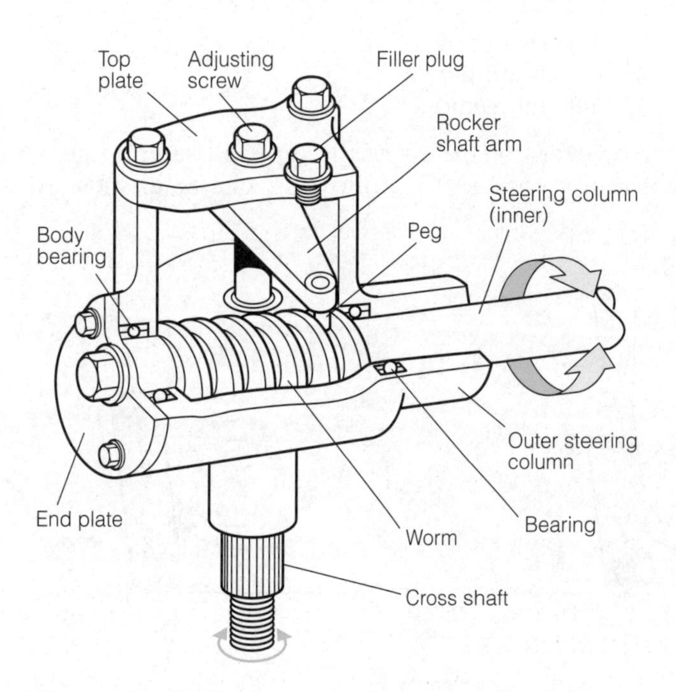

Figure 21.10 Worm and peg steering box.

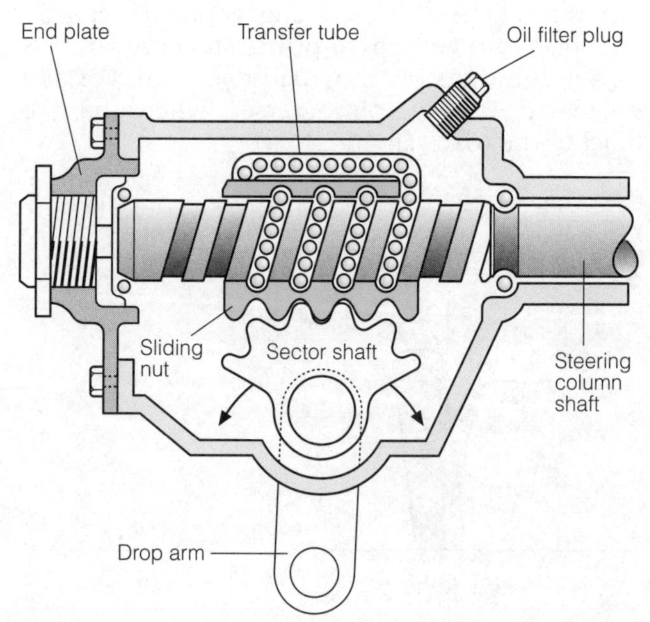

Figure 21.11 Recirculating ball steering box.

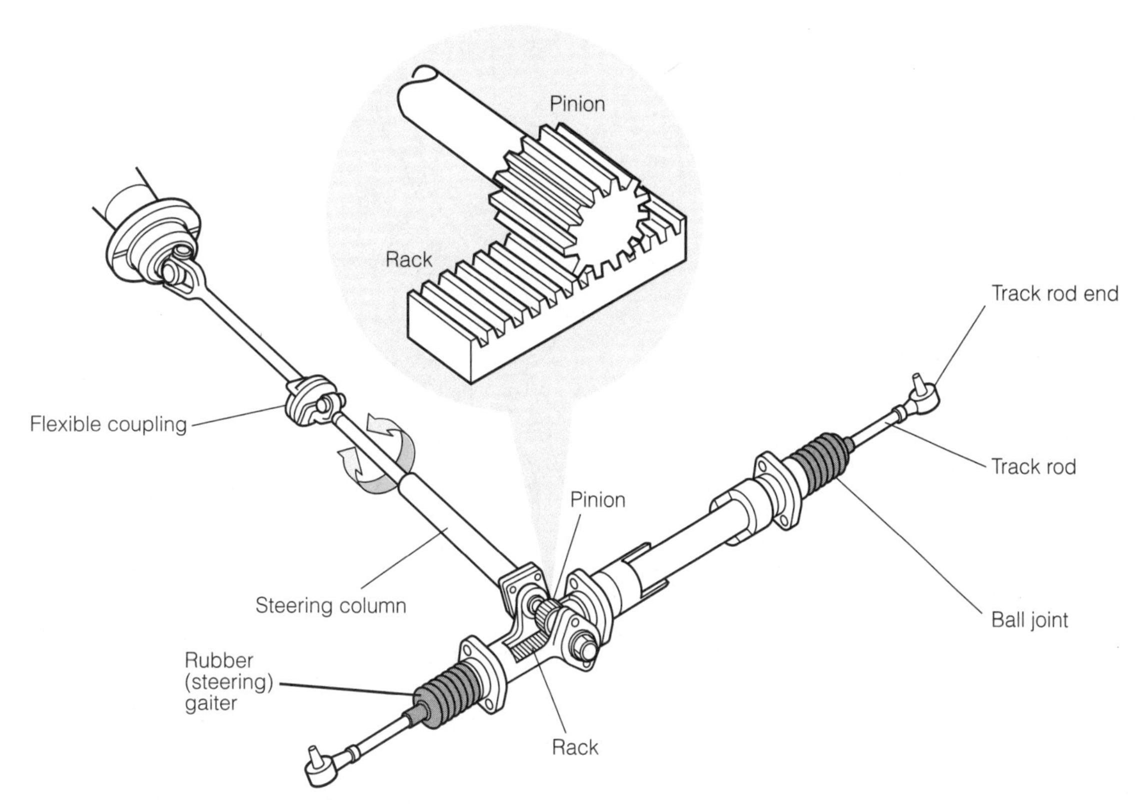

Figure 21.12 Rack and pinion steering mechanism.

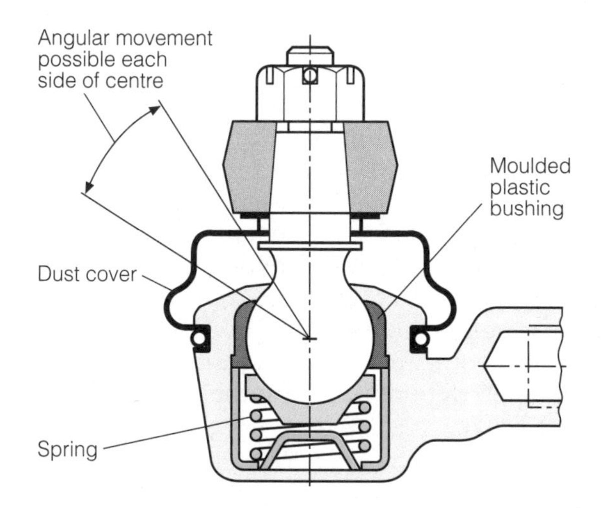

Figure 21.13 Non-adjustable ball joint.

Power-assisted steering

To make steering as easy as possible many vehicles are now fitted with power-assisted steering (PAS).

Three of the most common types are:

1. integral;
2. external ram (in-line cylinder);
3. semi-integral.

Regardless of which type is fitted, all systems must comply with the following functional requirements:

1. The system should reduce the amount of driver effort needed to turn the steering wheel.
2. The system should be **fail safe**. This enables the driver to steer the vehicle safely if a fault develops in the power assistance.
3. The system should preferably be speed sensitive; it must give maximum assistance at low speed but reduce it as the vehicle speed rises.

Integral PAS system

This type of steering mechanism consists of a conventional rack and pinion steering mechanism that has been modified to provide power assistance (Figure 21.14). The fluid reservoir holds the hydraulic oil, which both lubricates the system and enables it to function. It is connected to the

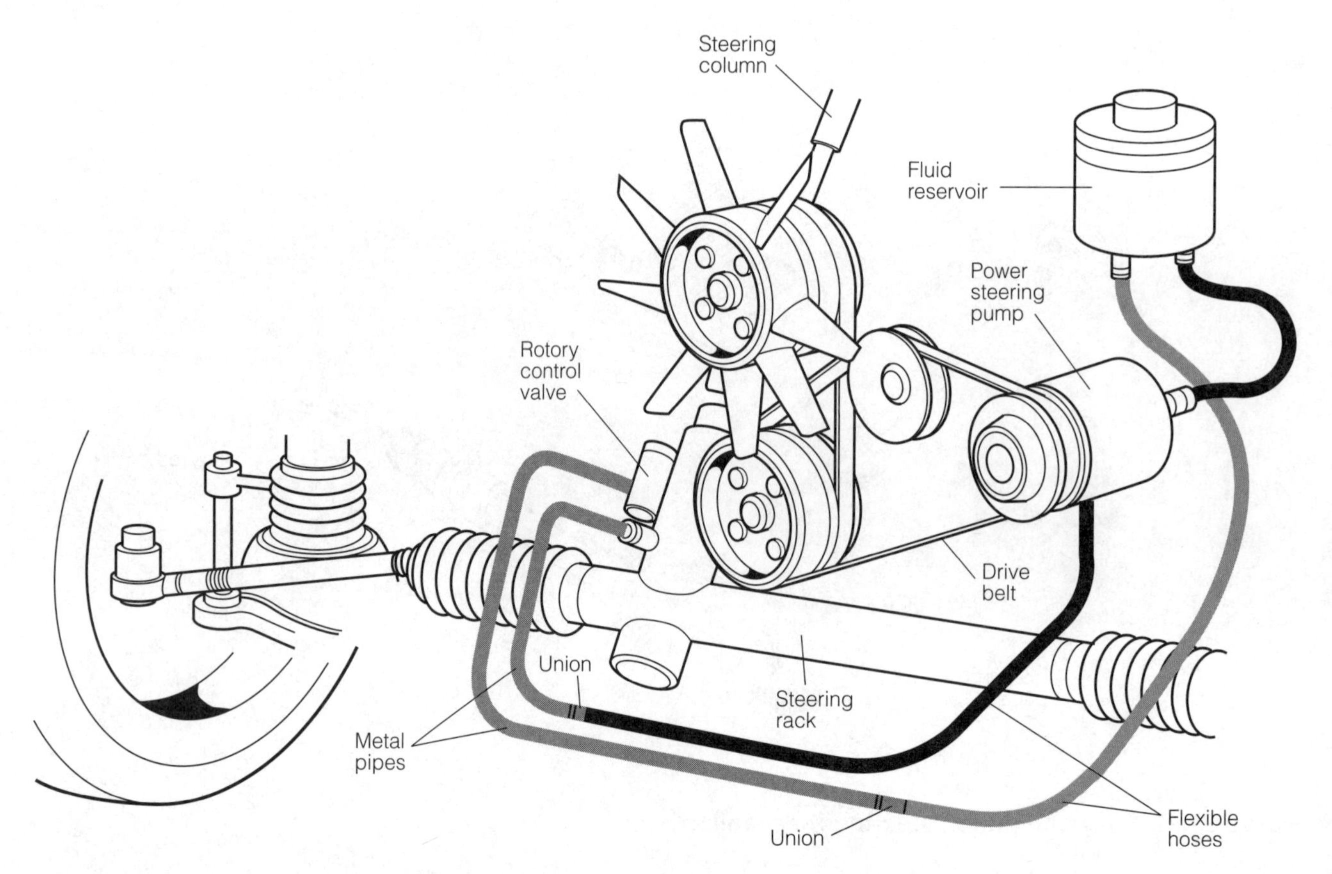

Figure 21.14 Layout of an integral power steering system.

engine-driven power steering pump by flexible hoses. The oil is pressurised and fed to the steering rack through the rotary control valve. This valve, often called the **spool valve**, consists of a number of inlet ports of varying size to control the amount of pressurised fluid entering the rack and its destination.

Operation

When the steering wheel is turned, the inner shaft rotates the rotary control valve. This movement causes one side of the inlet ports to close while the remaining inlet ports are opened. Pressurised hydraulic fluid is then forced into the steering rack through the open inlet ports, and pushes against a piston on the steering rack. A return pipe built into the rotary control valve allows the hydraulic fluid to return to the fluid reservoir.

External ram

The external ram type of PAS tends to be fitted to larger commercial vehicles because of their need for a large amount of power assistance. The main feature of this system is the use of an externally mounted in-line, double-acting power cylinder, located between the chassis and the steering drop arm (Figure 21.15). Movement of the steering wheel allows pressurised hydraulic fluid to enter the in-line power cylinder through a control valve mounted internally. The pressurised fluid provides both an expanding and a contracting movement, depending upon the operation of the control valve.

Semi-integral PAS

The semi-integral PAS system shares many of the constructional features of both the integral and external ram PAS systems (Figure 21.16). The control valve is mounted inside the steering gearbox as in the integral PAS system, but hydraulic assistance is exerted by an external in-line power cylinder, as in the external ram PAS system. This system is an alternative fitting on heavy commercial vehicles.

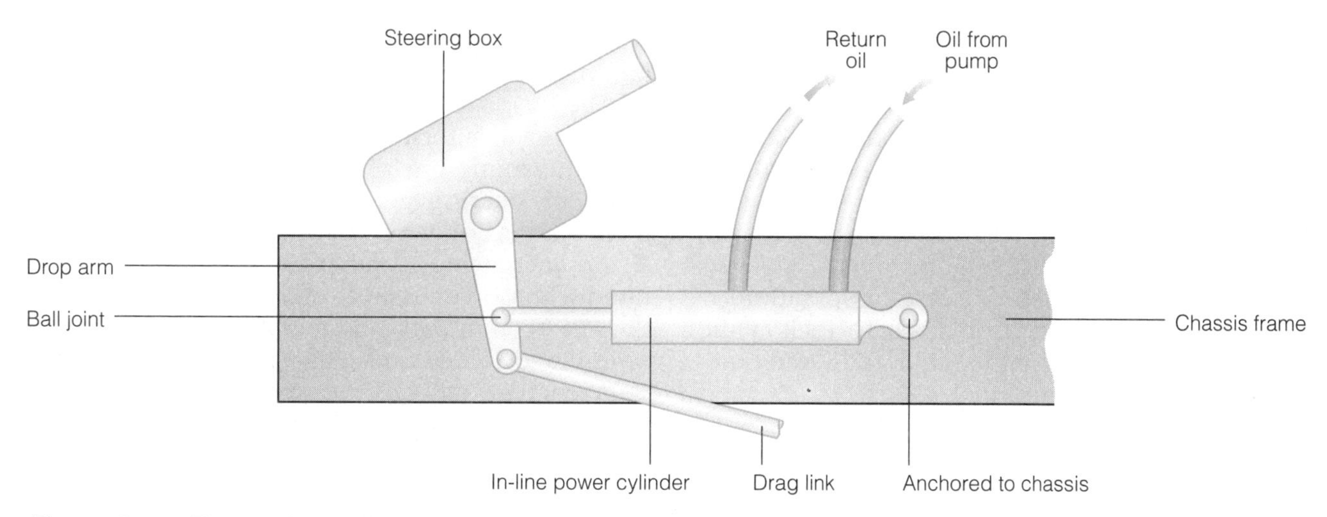

Figure 21.15 External ram (in-line power cylinder) power-assisted steering.

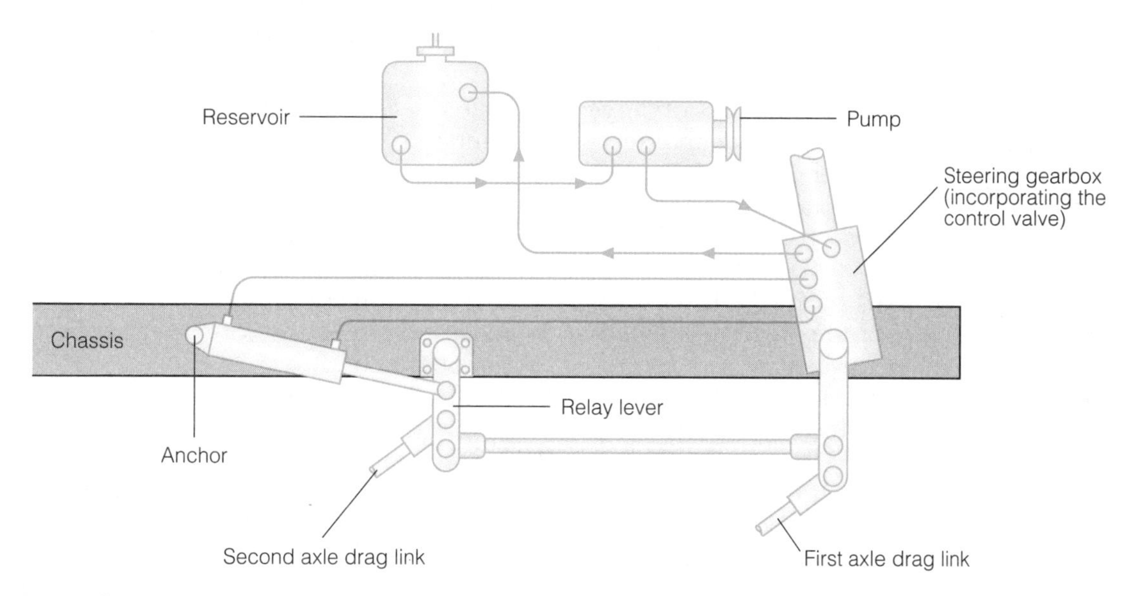

Figure 21.16 Semi-integral power-assisted steering.

Steering gear maintenance

The maintenance that should be carried out at regular intervals includes the following:

1. Check that the vehicle's wheel alignment complies with the manufacturer's recommendations.
2. Check the amount of free play in the steering column.
3. Check the security of the steering box or steering rack mounting points.
4. Check the steering box or rack and pinion gaiters for signs of oil leakage or damage.
5. Check the ball joints and swivel joints for excessive free play or damaged dust covers.
6. Check the steering drop arm for cracks or damage.
7. Check the operation of the steering gear for smoothness.

To ensure that a PAS system remains in a safe and serviceable condition, some extra routine maintenance activities should be carried out. These include the following:

1. Check the system for signs of fluid leakage and security of the external pipework.

2. Check the external ram anchor points for security and tightness (semi-integral and external ram types only).
3. Check the fluid level in the reservoir, and change the power steering fluid at the recommended service intervals.
4. Check for fraying, wear and tension of the pump's drive belt.
5. Check the PAS system for ease of operation by turning the steering from lock to lock while the vehicle is stationary and, at the same time, listening for any abnormal noises.

CHECK YOUR UNDERSTANDING

- One of the functions of a steering mechanism is to enable the driver to change the vehicle's steered direction. An important feature of any steering system is that it should promote an effect called true rolling motion, especially when the vehicle turns corners. To obtain true rolling motion all the wheels must rotate around a common centre of turn.
- The term 'toe out on turn', or TOOT, is used to describe the characteristic of the steering linkage in which the inner wheel on a turn is made to adopt a greater angle than the outer wheel.
- On front-wheel-drive vehicles the steered roadwheels are generally set to toe out, while for rear-wheel drive vehicles the setting is toe in.
- To ensure that the steering is both light and easy to operate, the steering geometry is designed with three angles: caster angle, camber angle, and kingpin inclination or KPI.
- The purpose of a steering gearbox is to enable the driver to alter the vehicle's steered direction with the minimum of effort. The most popular types of steering gearbox are: worm and peg, recirculating ball, and rack and pinion.
- An increasing number of vehicles are now fitted with power-assisted steering (PAS). Three of the most common types are: integral, external ram or in-line cylinder, and semi-integral.
- At regular intervals the various components of the steering system should be routinely examined for signs of defects, or adjusted as required by the manufacturer's service recommendations.

REVISION EXERCISES AND QUESTIONS

1. State the *three* functional requirements that all steering systems must be capable of meeting.
2. Describe how true rolling motion can be obtained when cornering.
3. Define the Ackermann steering principle.
4. Which types of vehicle generally have their wheel alignment set to toe out?
5. What is the purpose of caster angle, and how is it obtained?
6. Briefly describe what is meant by *negative roll radius*.
7. Briefly state the *three* characteristics that all steering gearboxes should promote.
8. Name *three* types of power-assisted steering gearbox.

22 Suspension systems

Introduction

The basic purpose of a suspension system is to isolate the vehicle's body from uneven road surfaces. This ensures that both the passengers and goods being carried benefit from the smoothest possible ride (Figure 22.1).

The main functional requirements of a suspension system are:

1. to ensure that the roadwheels remain in contact with the road surface;
2. to ensure that the front and rear axles are correctly located;
3. to support the sprung weight of the vehicle (that is, everything supported by the suspension springs).

Suspension systems with springs are normally fitted with **dampers** (often wrongly called shock absorbers) to damp out spring oscillation (that is, to reduce unwanted bounce of the springs).

Suspensions may be divided into two types: **independent** and **non-independent**.

Axle suspension systems (non-independent)

This is a simple and relatively inexpensive type of suspension design. It is fitted to vehicles that have beam axles, and for light vehicles is usually combined with leafsprings (Figure 22.2).

One of its main **advantages** is its simplicity and relatively low manufacturing costs. A **disadvantage** is that when one of the roadwheels rises or falls because of an uneven surface, the movement is transmitted across the whole axle and causes the vehicle to tilt (Figure 22.3).

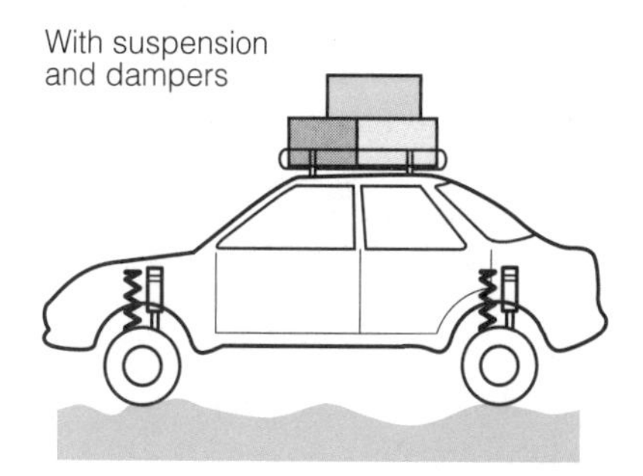

Figure 22.1 The role of the suspension system.

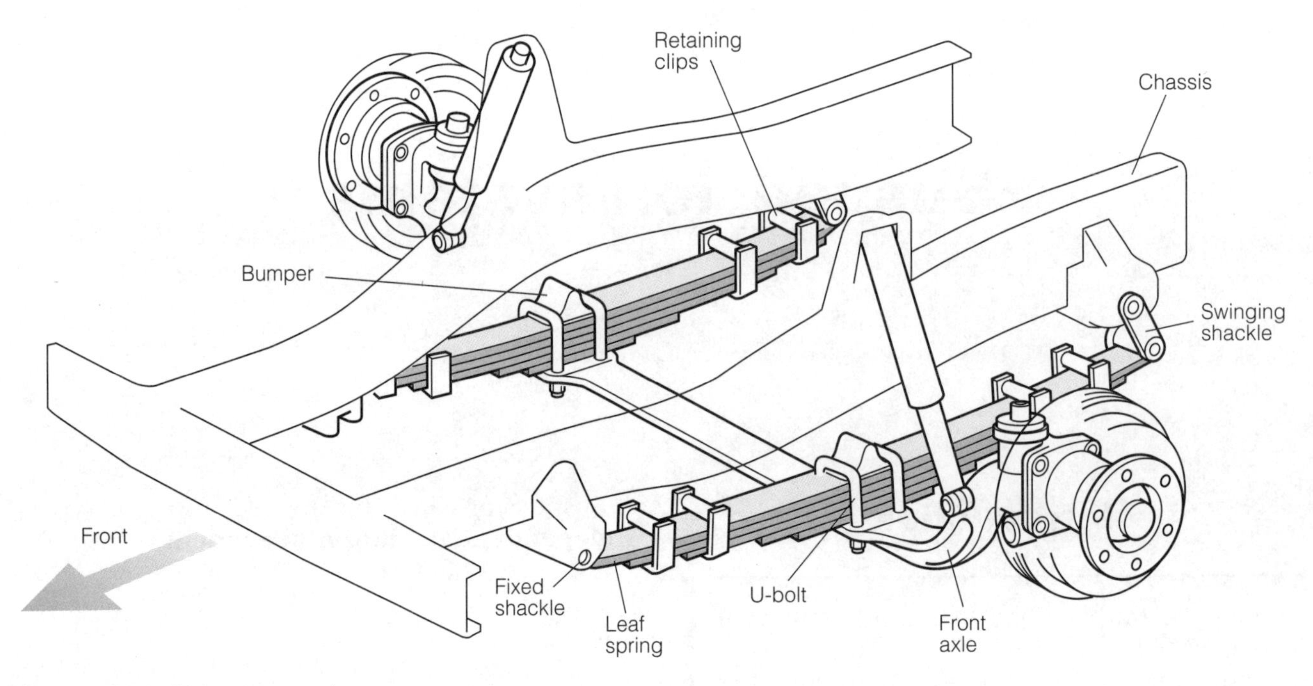

Figure 22.2 Axle suspension system.

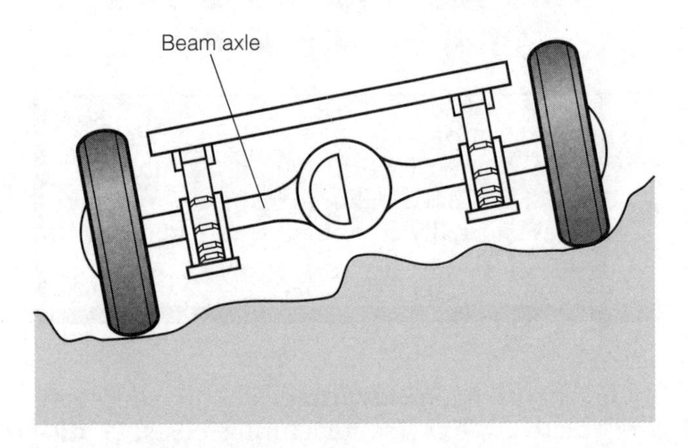

Figure 22.3 Rigid axle suspension.

Leafspring suspension

This consists of a pair of **semi-elliptic leaf-springs**, which are fitted between the vehicle's chassis and its axle. The term *elliptic* refers to the slight curvature of the suspension spring (Figure 22.4). The spring is bolted to the axle by a pair of U bolts. The individual leaves of the spring are held together by retaining clips to prevent excessive flexing. Each end of the spring is shaped with a location eye to hold a bush and shackle pin for connection to the chassis.

It is normal practice for the front spring eye to have a single **fixed shackle**, while at the rear the

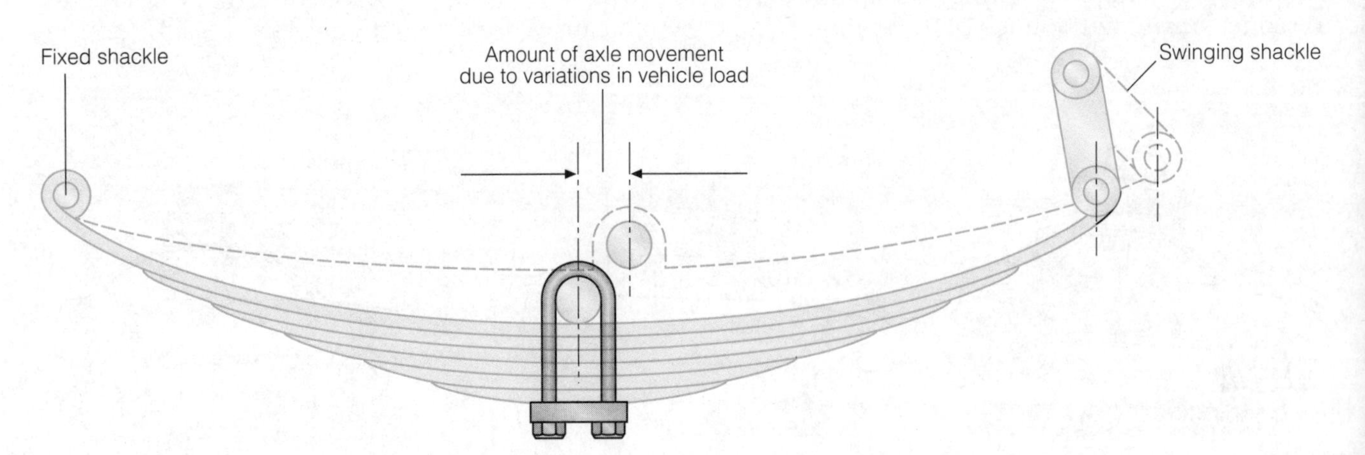

Figure 22.4 Leafspring suspension.

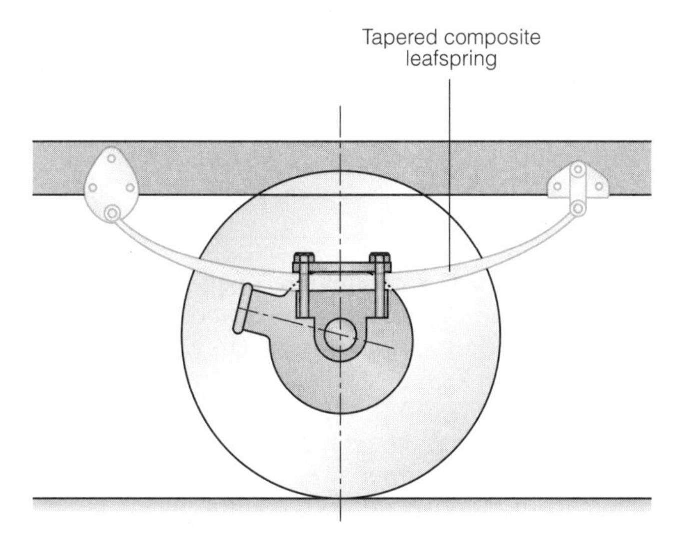

Figure 22.5 Composite leafspring.

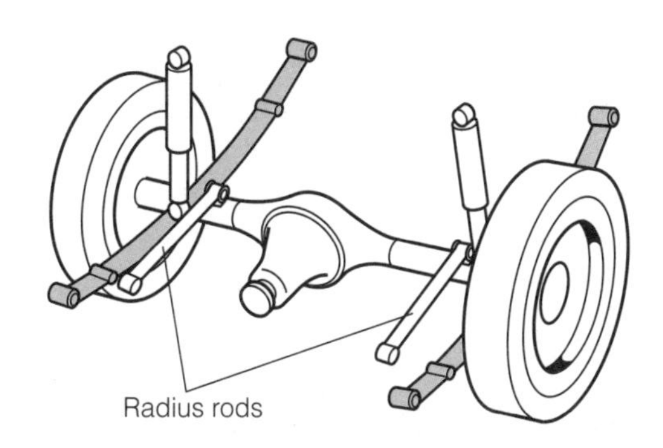

Figure 22.6 Leafspring suspension with radius arms.

eye is linked to the chassis with a **swinging shackle** (Figure 22.4). The swinging shackle allows the leafspring to increase its overall length as the spring flexes.

Composite leafsprings

To reduce any unnecessary weight, composite leafsprings are increasingly being used. This type of spring is made from lightweight materials such as carbon fibre, glass fibre and kevlar. The spring is a one-piece construction, thickest in its centre section and tapered at either end (Figure 22.5). It is tough and long lasting, and needs virtually no maintenance.

Springs for rear axles

On a driving rear axle fitted with a leafspring suspension, the action of the final drive unit attempts to twist the axle backwards during acceleration, and forwards on the over-run or on braking. To counter this fore-and-aft movement, some manufacturers fit **radius arms** (Figure 22.6).

An alternative method of supporting a live rear axle is by using coil springs. The springs allow up-and-down movement but cannot prevent the axle from twisting when accelerating and braking, or from moving sideways when cornering. Such an axle is located using radius arms to prevent twisting and a **panhard rod** to prevent sideways movement (Figure 22.7).

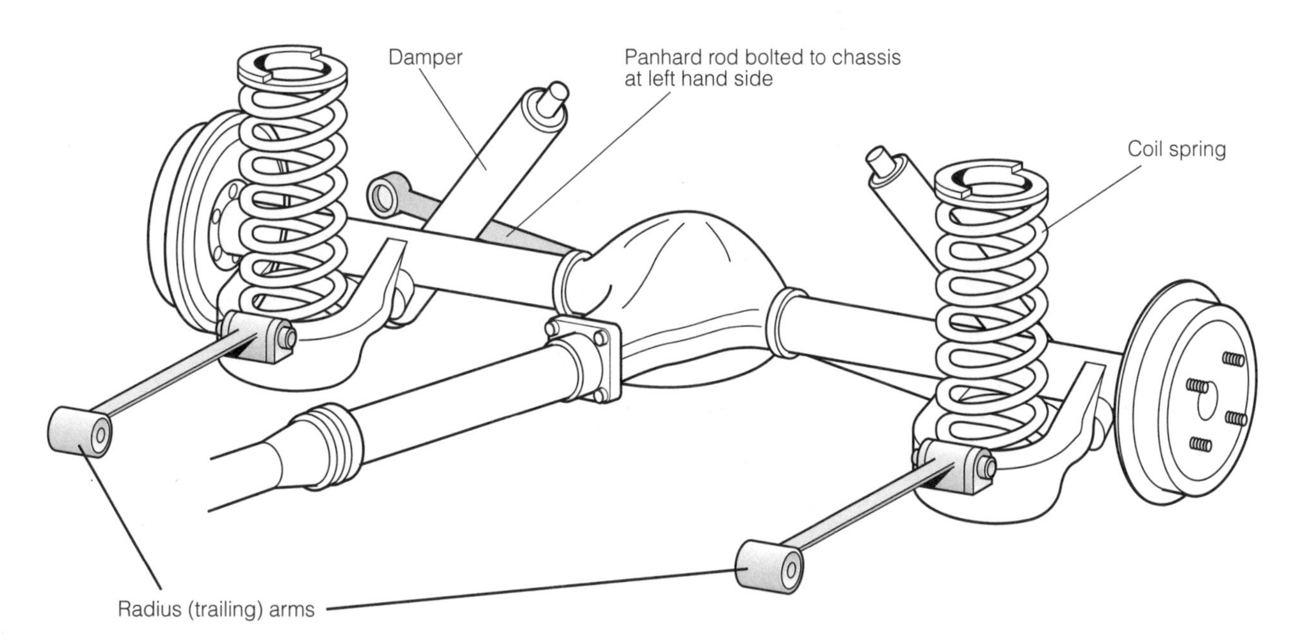

Figure 22.7 Coil spring suspension.

Independent suspension systems

Independent suspension allows wheel movement that has little or no effect on the other wheels or the body. This ensures that the vehicle remains at a more even and constant ride height (Figure 22.8).

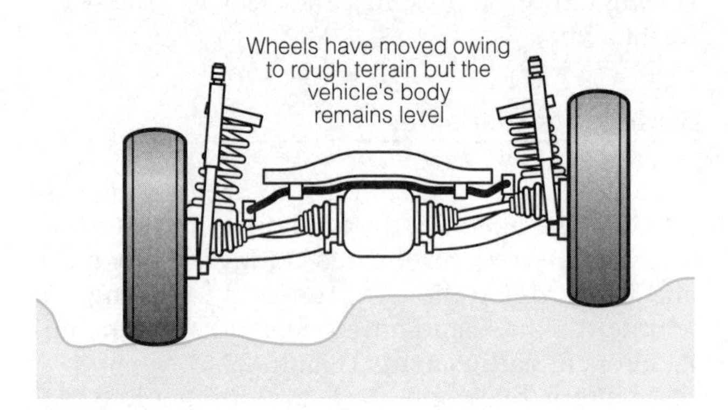

Figure 22.8 Typical independent suspension system.

Although there are many types of independent suspension, two of the most popular are **double transverse link** and the **Macpherson strut**.

Double transverse link

In this suspension design, two vee-shaped links are used. The links are often called **wishbones** because of their appearance. They are located onto the front suspension cross-member by pivot pins, which allow both the upper and lower links to move with roadwheel movement. A coil spring and telescopic damper are also fitted. The stub axle carrier is mounted between the two links by a pair of swivel joints. These joints enable the roadwheels to turn when cornering (Figure 22.9).

To ensure that the lower link remains correctly located under all operating conditions, a **tie rod** is fitted. Note that in most layouts the links are of unequal length, the upper normally being shorter than the lower. This minimises possible tyre wear due to changes in the vehicle **track**, which is the distance between wheels on the same axle (Figure 22.10).

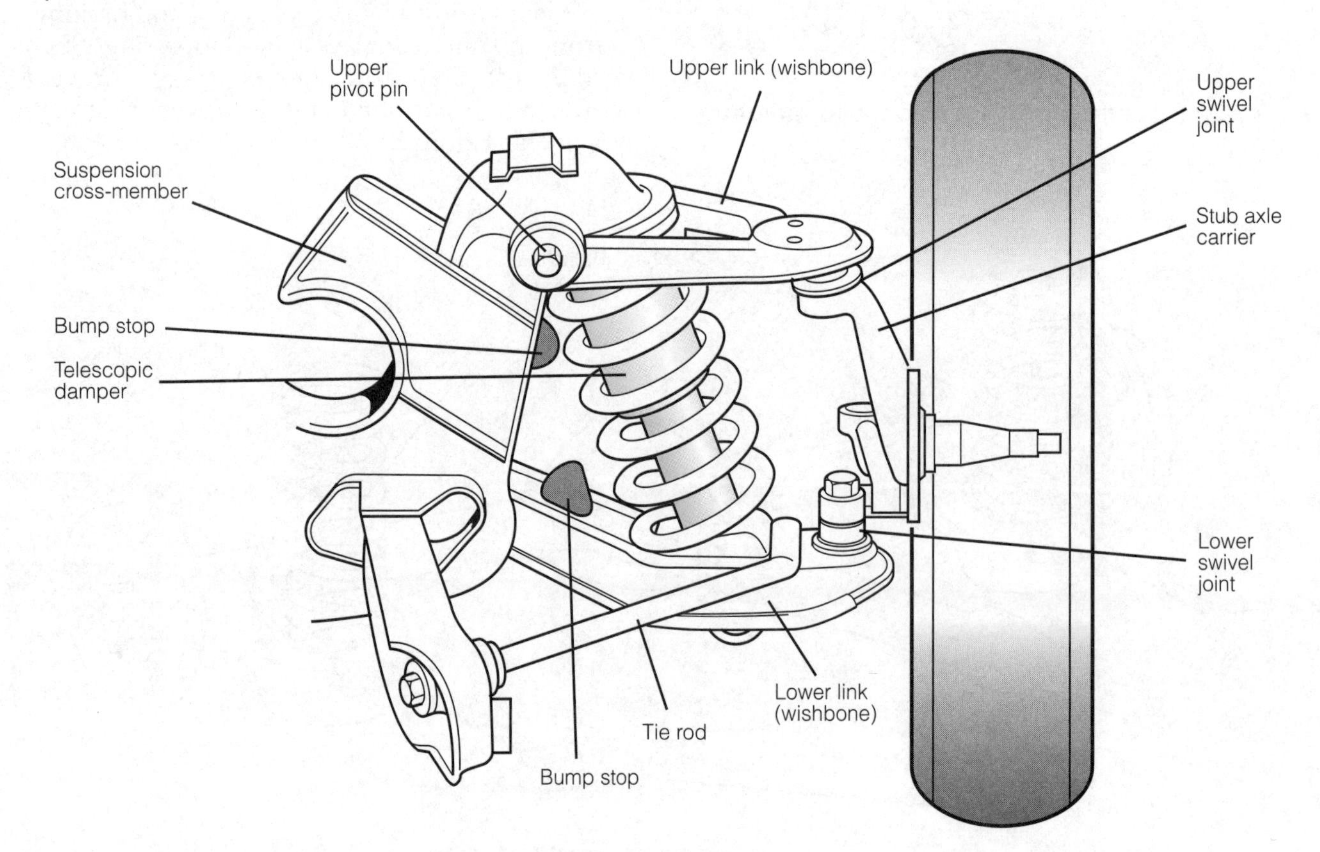

Figure 22.9 Double transverse link suspension.

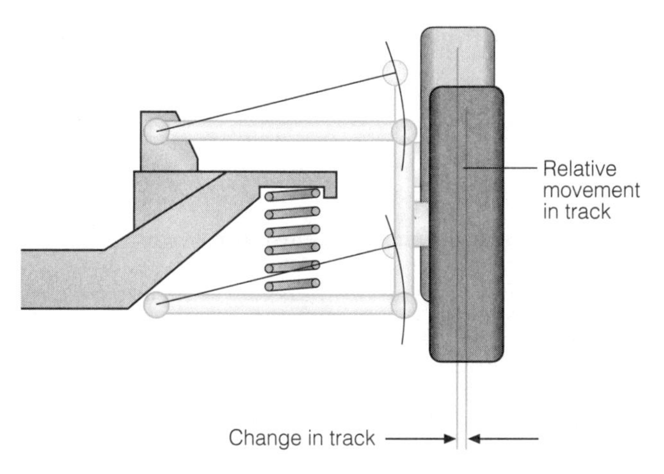

Figure 22.10 Problems caused by having the two transverse (wishbone) links the same length.

Macpherson strut

This suspension design consists of a single transverse link, which is connected to the chassis by locating pins. A single swivel joint is used to locate the base of the telescopic strut to the transverse link (Figure 22.11). The upper part of the strut, which incorporates both a telescopic damper and a coil spring, is attached to a strengthened section of the vehicle's inner wing panel.

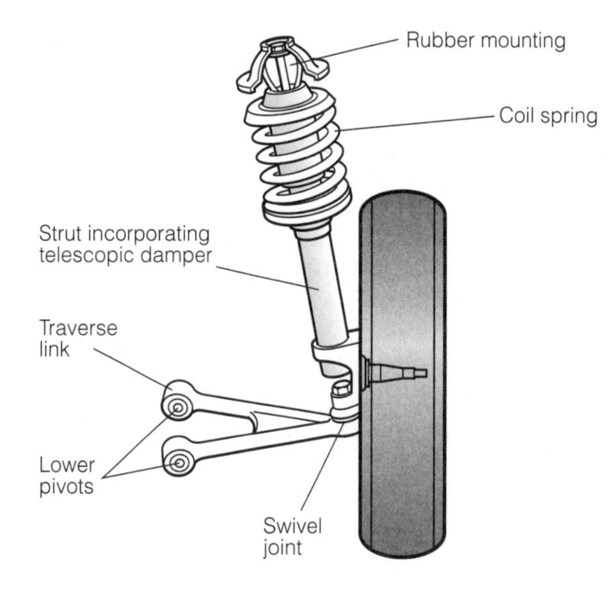

Figure 22.11 Macpherson strut.

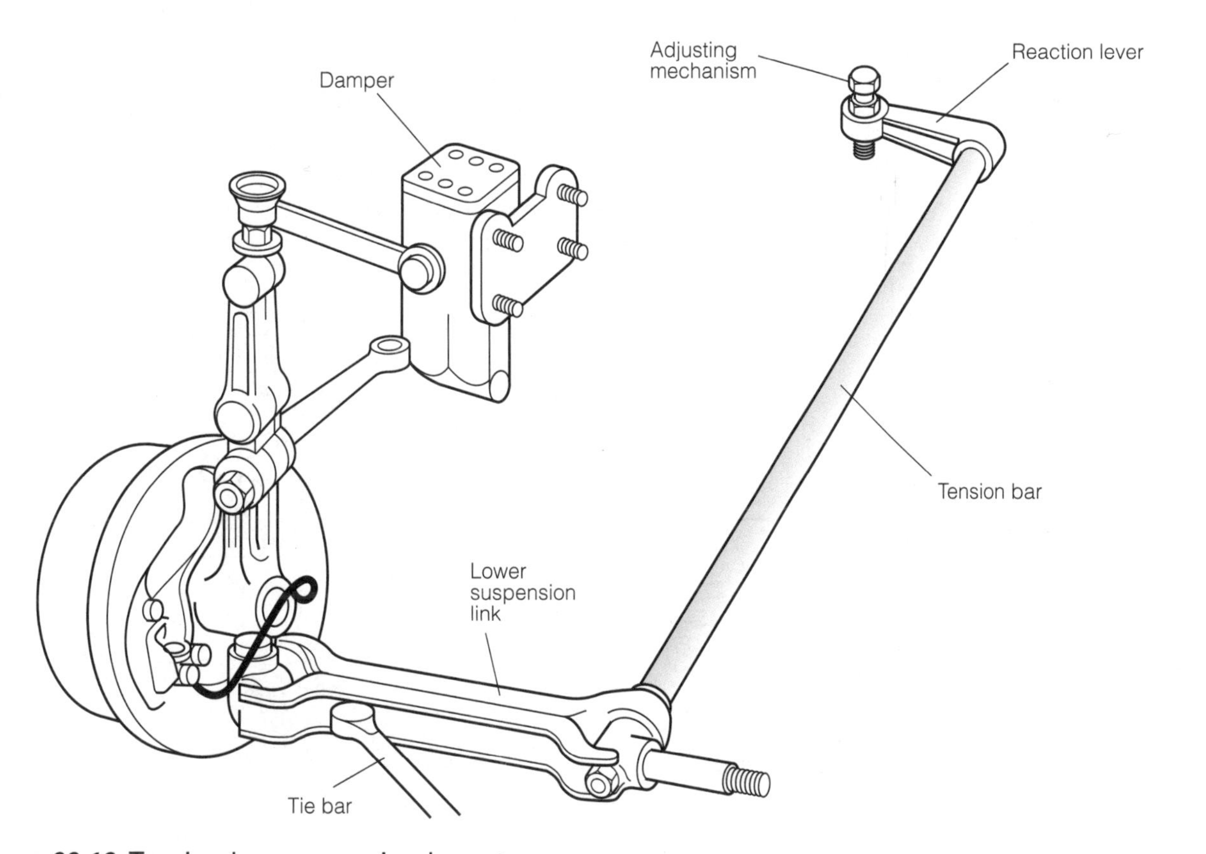

Figure 22.12 Torsion bar suspension layout.

Torsion bar suspension

As an alternative to coil springs, **torsion bars** can be used (Figure 22.12). A torsion bar is made from a high-grade steel that has the required elasticity. This allows it to be twisted and yet return to its original shape.

One end of the torsion bar is splined into the suspension link, while the other is located onto the vehicle's chassis member. The amount of static twist imposed upon the bar can be varied by means of an adjuster, or by altering the splined location.

When the roadwheel is deflected by an uneven road surface, the suspension link twists the torsion bar. The fixed opposite end creates an opposing force, which limits the amount of twist and hence suspension movement.

Note that torsion bars are made to be either right-hand or left-hand, and therefore should not be interchanged.

Rubber springs

Some vehicles are fitted with rubber suspension springs as an alternative to steel (Figure 22.13). Because of their flexible nature and low maintenance requirements, rubber suspension systems became popular on cars such as the British Mini.

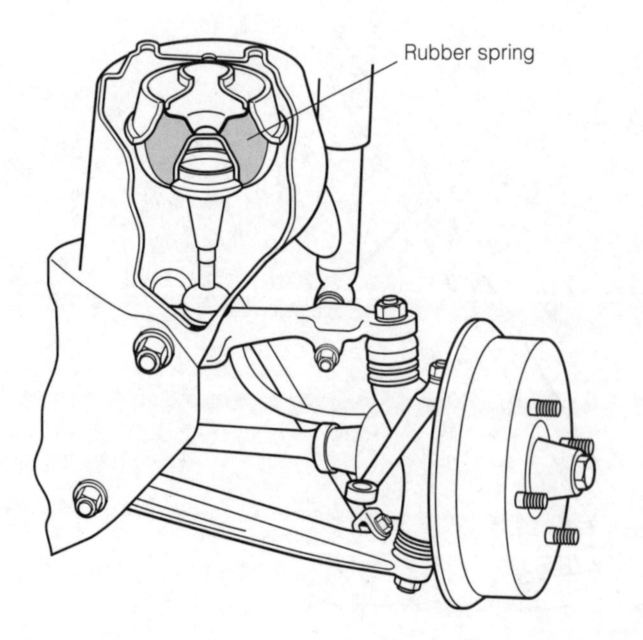

Figure 22.13 Independent front suspension using a rubber spring.

Independent suspension at the rear

For a higher level of ride quality, independent suspension is often fitted at the rear as well as at the front.

Front-wheel drive vehicles commonly use a simple trailing link design (Figure 22.14). It consists of a pair of trailing links, which can move independently of each other. The trailing links also provide a means of locating the roadwheels onto the vehicle.

A variation of this layout has the arms attached to a pivoting transverse flexible bar, called a **torsion beam**. Although the trailing links are then not fully independent in the true sense of the word, the torsion beam provides an anti-roll restraint that adds to the effectiveness of the suspension.

For rear-wheel-driven vehicles with independent rear suspension, a modified layout must be used (Figure 22.15). Some of the more important changes are as follows:

1. The final drive, incorporating the differential, is mounted to the vehicle's floorpan by means of a support member.
2. A pair of driveshafts are fitted.
3. Each driveshaft has a universal coupling at each end. These allow the engine's torque to be transmitted through the constantly varying angles adopted by the driveshafts as the wheels move up and down.

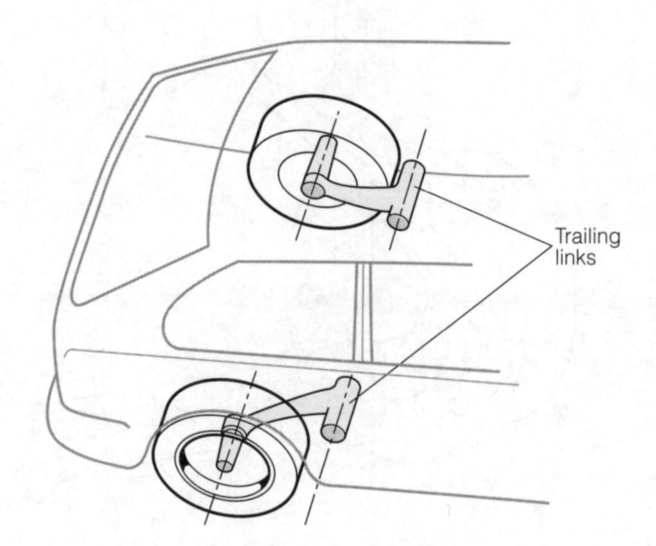

Figure 22.14 Trailing link suspension.

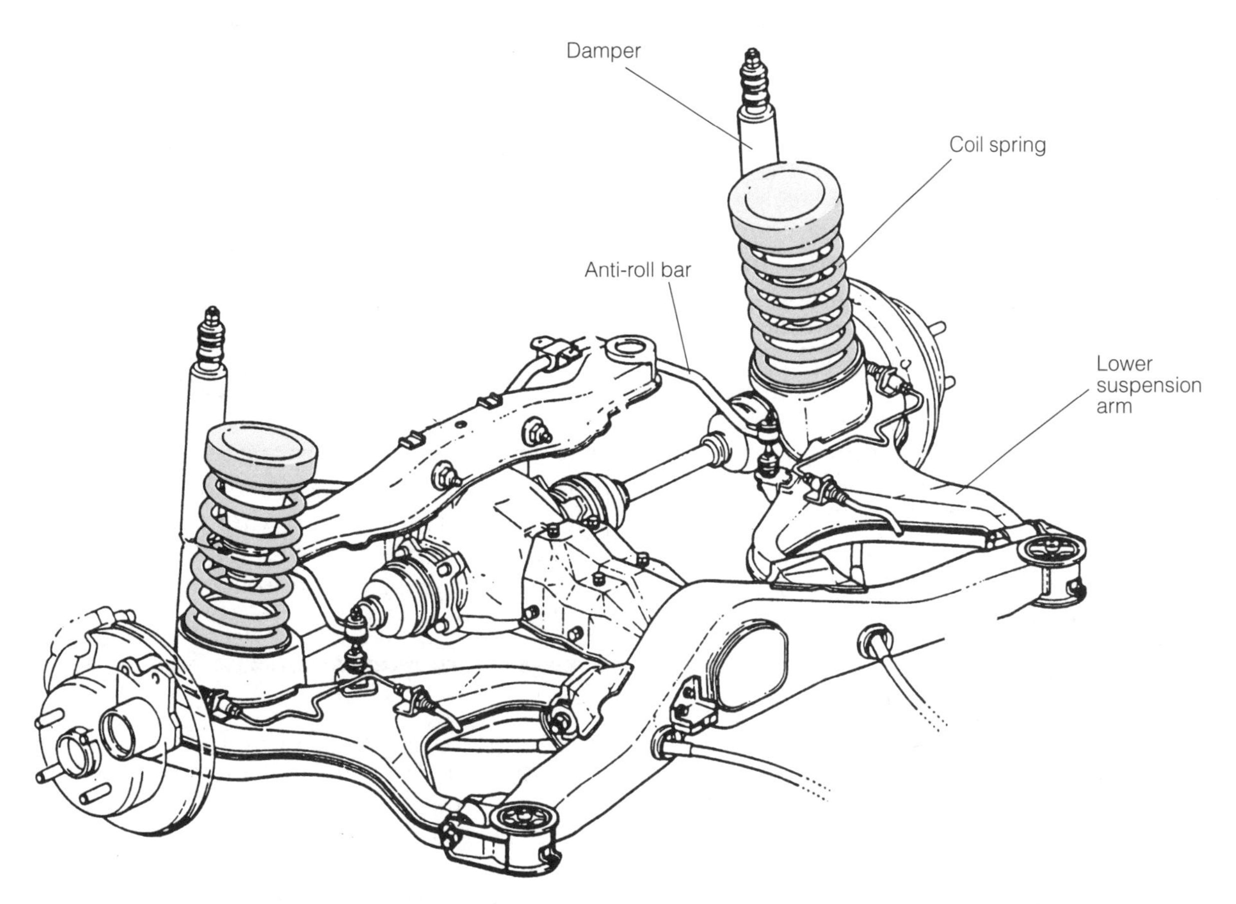

Figure 22.15 Independent rear suspension.

Semi-trailing links

This is another variation on the trailing link design. The semi-trailing links are attached to the chassis but are inclined outwards (Figure 22.16). This enables them to withstand the sideways forces that are present when cornering at almost any speed. In addition, the movement of the trailing links as the body rolls causes the inner wheel to steer slightly into the corner and so improve the vehicle's steering characteristics.

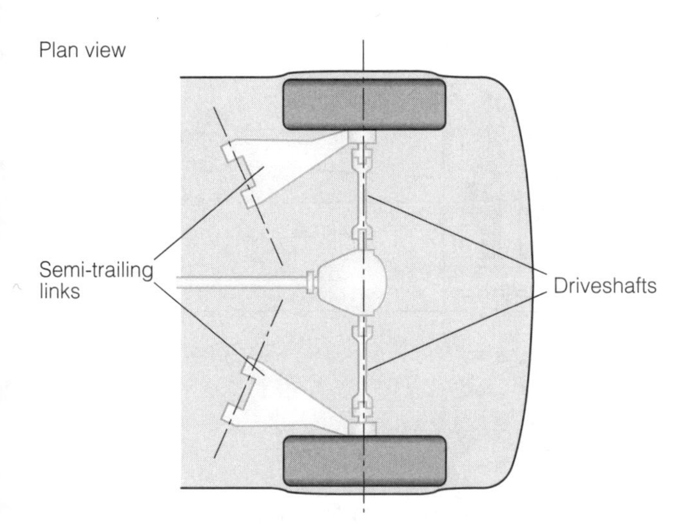

Figure 22.16 Semi-trailing link suspension.

Dampers (shock absorbers)

The purpose of a damper is to control the rate at which a suspension spring oscillates (bounces) after the roadwheel strikes an irregularity in the road surface. The damper offers a fluid resistance to the movement of the suspension spring and absorbs the stored energy. This ensures that the roadwheel does not bounce but remains in contact with the road surface.

Dampers are usually of the **telescopic** type.

Telescopic dampers

The telescopic damper consists of a steel cylinder that contains a piston attached to a connecting rod. The piston divides the cylinder into two chambers, the upper and lower; the space between the cylinder and the outer casing is the hydraulic fluid reservoir (Figure 22.17).

The cylinder is attached to the 'unsprung' suspension parts (the roadwheel and suspension arm or axle), while the piston and connecting rod are secured to the vehicle chassis or body.

Operation

The piston, fastened to its connecting rod, is held by the chassis or body. When the roadwheel is deflected upwards, the cylinder also moves and slides over the piston. At the same time, the hydraulic fluid located in the bottom chamber is forced through the **compression valve** into the upper chamber (Figure 22.17a). The resistance of the fluid to this flow limits or dampens the rate at which the spring can compress.

On rebound, when the spring pushes the roadwheel downwards to maintain contact with the road, the cylinder is pulled downwards over the piston. The fluid in the upper chamber is now returned into the lower chamber through the **rebound valve**. The amount of damping assistance that each telescopic damper provides is governed by the size of the drillings in the compression and rebound valves, and the viscosity of the hydraulic fluid used in the damper.

Although telescopic dampers are compact and require no maintenance, they must be replaced if found to be leaking or defective.

Anti-roll bars

As a vehicle turns a corner, side forces cause it to roll. If unchecked, this would make it difficult for the driver to retain control. To help control this reaction an anti-roll bar is fitted (Figure 22.18).

It is normally attached to the chassis, subframe or body by rubber bushes. Each end of the anti-roll bar forms a lever, which is attached to the lower suspension links. As the vehicle attempts to roll, the bar is subject to twisting forces, which act on the other suspension unit. This maintains a degree of stability and limits the roll.

Both front and rear suspension can incorporate anti-roll bars, although at the rear this function may be incorporated into a torsion beam.

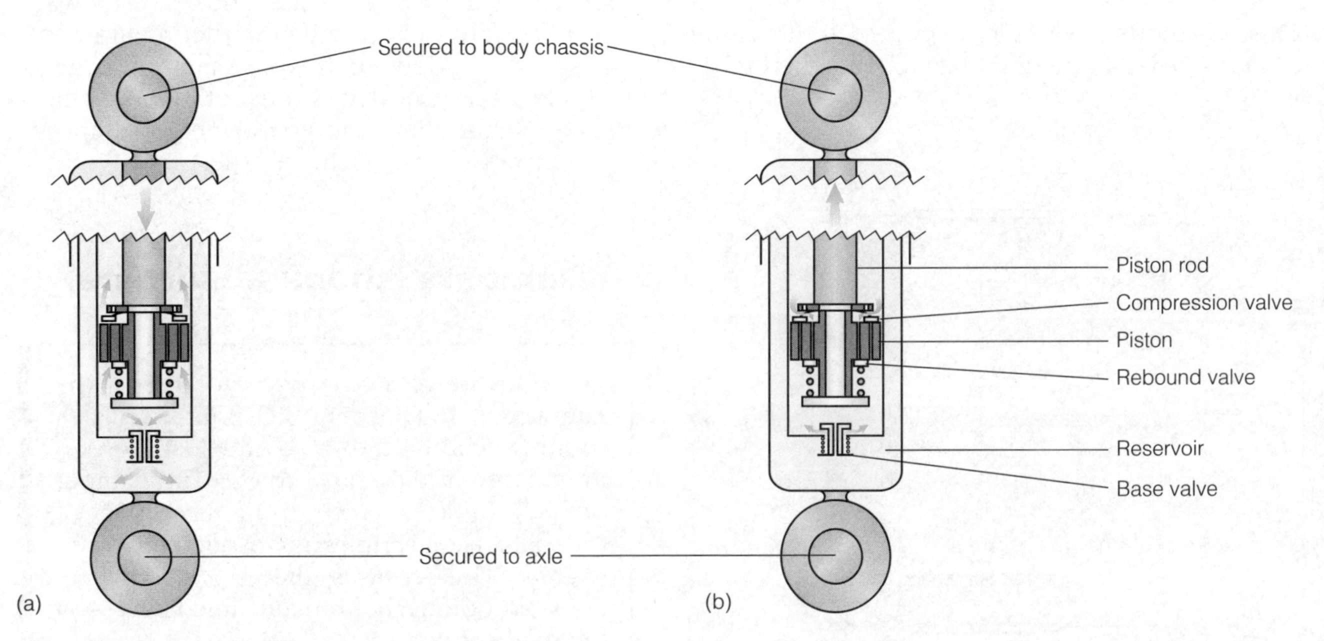

Figure 22.17 Telescopic damper. (a) Compression: piston rod moving down. (b) Rebound: piston rod moving up.

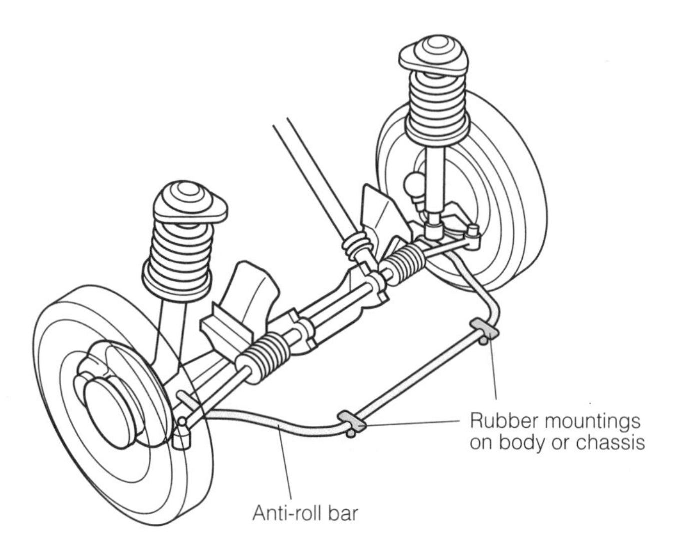

Figure 22.18 Anti-roll bar link.

Sprung and unsprung weight

An important design consideration for any suspension system is the sprung and unsprung weights. The term **sprung weight** refers to the overall weight that the suspension system must be capable of supporting. It includes all those components that are mounted 'above' the suspension springs: the chassis, body, power unit, transmission and associated components.

In contrast, the term **unsprung weight** refers to that group of components carried directly by the roadwheel that are not supported by the suspension springs. Whenever possible, vehicle manufacturers try to keep the unsprung weight as low as possible, as a vehicle with a low unsprung weight tends to have better riding qualities.

Linked suspension systems

The front and rear suspension are linked together on some vehicles to avoid the tendency to pitch backwards and forwards on uneven surfaces. The vehicle travels in a more level attitude, although at the expense of some up-and-down motion on the simpler variants, and has improved handling characteristics (Figure 22.19).

Three of the most common linked suspension systems are:

1. hydrolastic suspension;
2. hydrogas suspension;
3. hydropneumatic suspension.

Hydrolastic suspension

This system has a hydrolastic suspension unit at each roadwheel, and the front and rear units are linked together on each side (Figure 22.20). The system is inflated with a specially formulated fluid.

Figure 22.19 Principle of linked suspension. The body remains at a constant ride height.

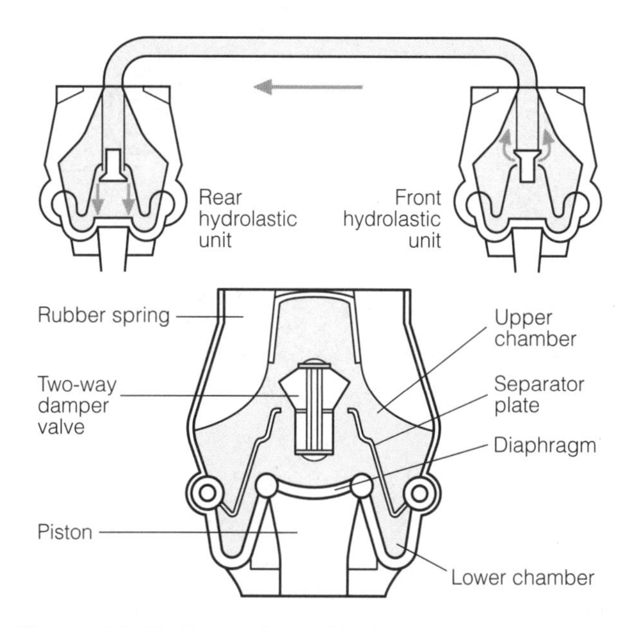

Figure 22.20 Operation of hydrolastic unit.

Operation

When the vehicle travels over an uneven surface, the operating piston attached to the upper suspension link causes the diaphragm located inside each unit to move.

On compression, the fluid in the lower chamber is forced into the upper chamber through the two-way damper valve. This valve acts as the system's damper or shock absorber. Any excess fluid is transferred along the interconnecting pipe to the other hydrolastic unit. It is this movement of fluid between the two interconnected hydrolastic units that ensures that the vehicle travels at a more constant ride height. When the roadwheel of the first unit returns to its normal position, the fluid transferred to the other suspension unit returns, and the suspension adopts its normal attitude.

Hydrogas suspension

The hydrogas units have an upper, sealed diaphragm sphere filled with high-pressure nitrogen gas and a lower chamber filled with hydrolastic fluid. The use of compressed nitrogen gas, which acts as the spring, ensures that the vehicle has excellent ride characteristics, comparable to the use of variable-rate springs.

Operation

Upward movement of the roadwheel moves the tapered piston in the same direction. Hydrolastic fluid is forced from the bottom chamber through the damper valve and into the upper chamber, which increases the pressure of the nitrogen gas. Excess fluid is transferred along the interconnecting pipe to the other unit (Figure 22.21).

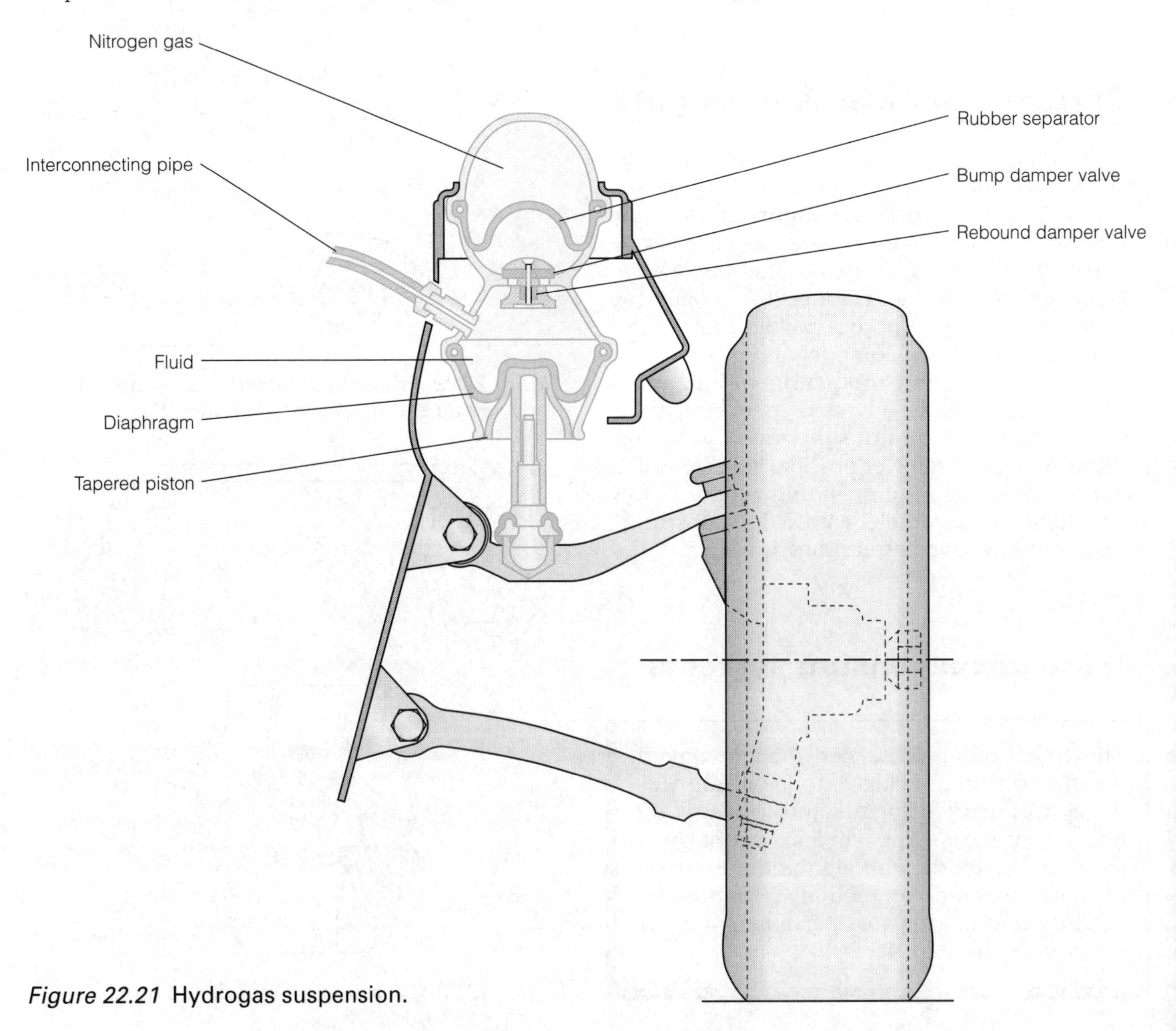

Figure 22.21 Hydrogas suspension.

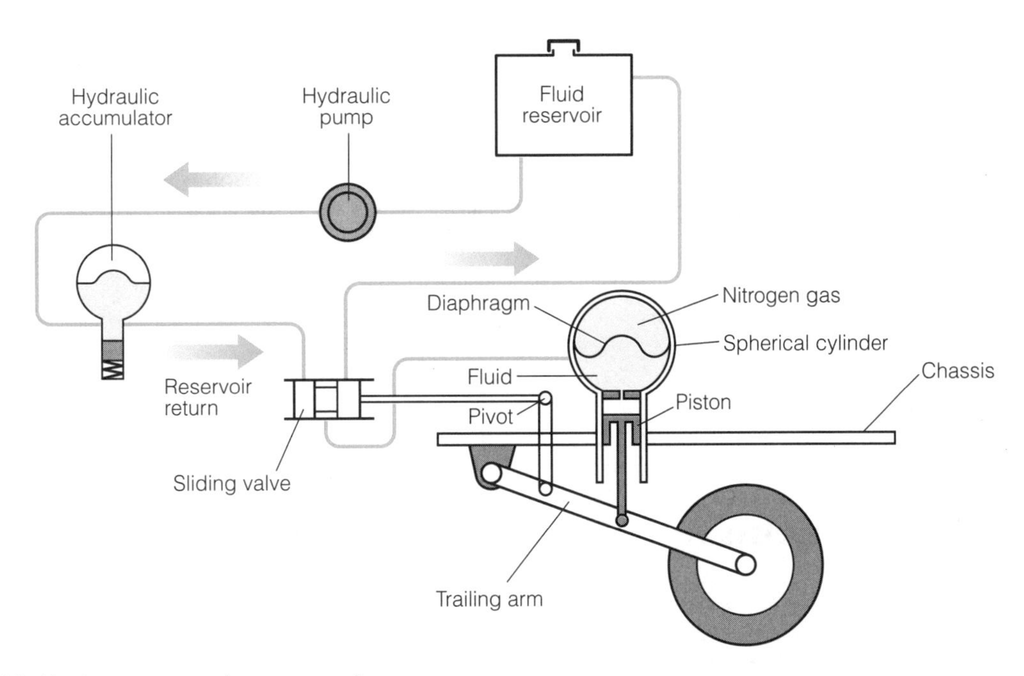

Figure 22.22 Hydropneumatic suspension.

Hydropneumatic suspension

In the hydropneumatic system a spherical container is fitted to each suspension unit, and contains a combination of fluid and nitrogen gas on either side of a diaphragm (Figure 22.22). All the spherical cylinders are linked to an engine-driven hydraulic pump, which inflates the system. The pump is controlled by a sliding valve, linked mechanically to the suspension.

Operation

Upward movement of the suspension moves the trailing arm closer to the body. The piston is forced upwards, and the link opens the sliding valve. This enables pressurised fluid to flow into the lower chamber of each sphere, which raises the suspension to its normal ride height. A feature of this design is that the vehicle's ground clearance remains constant regardless of the load being carried.

CHECK YOUR UNDERSTANDING

- The main types of suspension fitted to a vehicle can be classified as beam axles and independent suspension.
- Beam axles using leafsprings tend to give a poor ride but are robust.
- Independent suspension such as Macpherson strut and the transverse link types give a better quality of ride.
- A damper (or shock absorber) is used to control the natural oscillation of the spring during suspension movements.
- Anti-roll bars control the rolling movement of the vehicle body during cornering.

REVISION EXERCISES AND QUESTIONS

1. Name the *three* basic requirements of any suspension system.
2. What is the purpose of a swinging shackle as fitted to a leafspring suspension system?
3. Why are the upper and lower links on a double transverse link suspension often of different length?
4. On a torsion bar suspension system, how can the static twist on the torsion bar be adjusted?
5. What is the purpose of a damper?
6. What is meant by the terms *sprung* and *unsprung weight* ?
7. Name *three* types of linked suspension, and state their advantages.
8. From what material might a composite leafspring be made?

23 The braking system

Introduction

Vehicles use their engines as a means of converting energy into the work of moving the vehicle. When an object such as a vehicle moves, it is said to possess **kinetic energy**, the energy of movement. To stop a vehicle this energy must be given up or changed. If, for example, a car is moving and crashes into a solid object, it stops very rapidly. It has used up all its kinetic energy in damaging itself and the object it has run into.

> The function of the braking system is to bring a moving vehicle safely to rest. It does this by converting the kinetic energy to heat, which is then given up to the surrounding air as it flows past the brakes. The conversion of energy is achieved by friction, which is the resistance to movement of one object sliding over another. This is easily demonstrated by sliding one hand across the other: the harder you press, the more energy you use, which results in greater friction and higher temperature.

Vehicles have become progressively faster, and as a result more heat is generated by the brakes when bringing a vehicle rapidly to rest. This heat must be lost to the air quickly if the brakes are to remain effective.

There are two main types of brake: **drum brakes** and **disc brakes**.

The drum brake

Cam-operated internal expanding brake

This is one of the simplest types of brake (Figure 23.1). It was used on early cars, and may still be found on some commercial vehicles and motorcycles. When the brake pedal is depressed, it pulls the operating lever and the cam is rotated slightly. This forces the two brake shoes apart until they press against the inside of the drum. If the drum is revolving, friction between the friction material and the inside of the drum resists movement and converts it to heat, slowing the vehicle down. When the brake pedal is released the cam returns

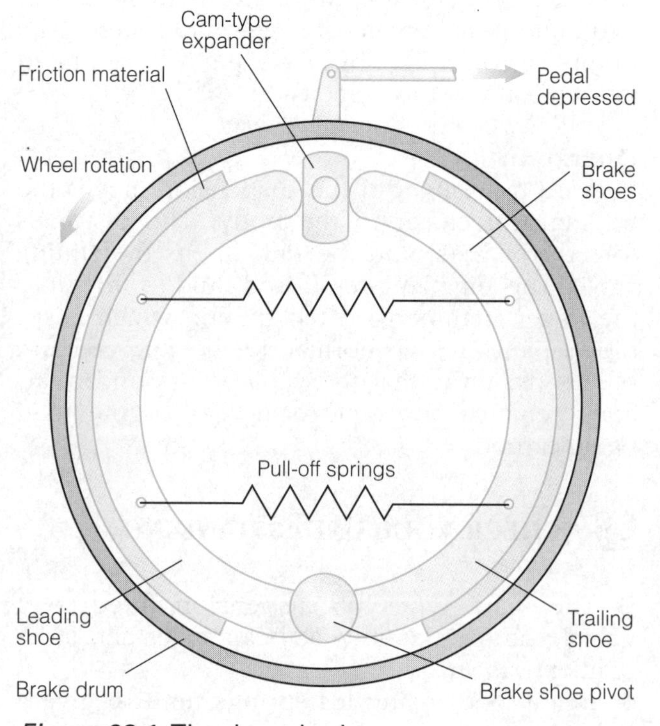

Figure 23.1 The drum brake.

to its original position, and the shoes are pulled away from the drum by the return springs.

Friction material

The material used for braking must have the following qualities:

1. good frictional properties;
2. wear resistance;
3. heat resistance.

Linings were once largely made of **asbestos**, but the health risks associated with this substance have brought about its replacement with synthetic materials.

Leading and trailing brake shoes

When the cam turns, one brake shoe is pushed out in the same direction as the drum rotation (Figure 23.1). This is known as the **leading shoe**. When the brake is applied, drum rotation helps to pull this shoe into harder contact with the drum and increases the driver's effort. This is known as **self-servo** action.

The other shoe is pushed against the direction of the revolving drum, and is called the **trailing shoe**. When the trailing shoe is pushed into contact with the drum the reverse is true: the drum rotation tries to push the shoe away. This results in less braking effort than that provided by the leading shoe.

Advantages and disadvantages

The **advantages** of the leading and trailing shoe arrangement are that:

1. it is relatively simple;
2. the same braking power is available in reverse as well as when going forwards.

Good braking power in reverse is an advantage for those vehicles that carry or pull heavy loads. One **disadvantage** where a vehicle is usually driving forwards is that the shoes wear unevenly because the leading shoes do more work. Some manufacturers have tried to overcome this by making the friction lining on the leading shoe thicker than that on the trailing shoe.

Twin leading brake shoes

In this layout both brake shoes are forced out in the direction of normal drum rotation (Figure 23.2). To achieve this, two expander units are used. Each shoe rests on a separate pivot, the other end being moved by its own expander.

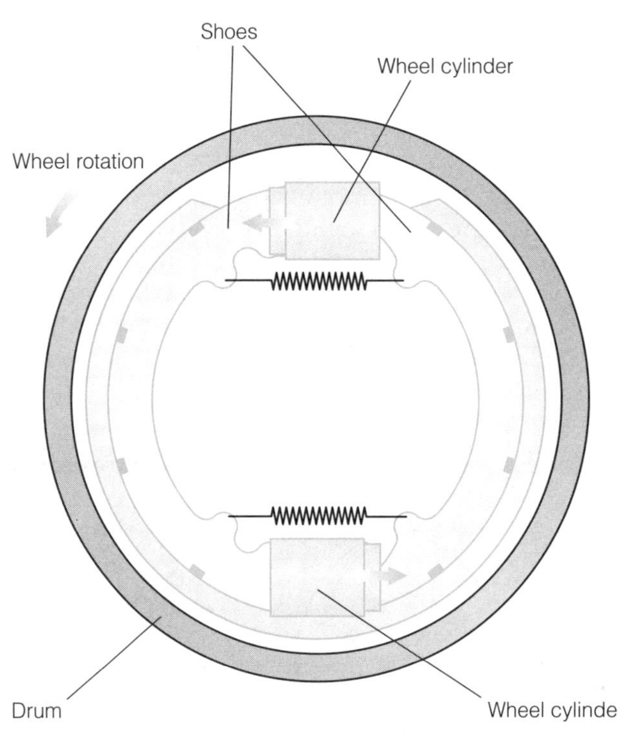

Figure 23.2 Twin leading shoe hydraulic brake.

Advantages

Both shoes now have the leading shoe self-servo effect, which gives a greater stopping force for a given size of brake drum. Compared with the leading and trailing shoe arrangement a more powerful braking effort is achieved for the same pedal pressure.

Disadvantages

The operating mechanism requires two expanders. When the vehicle is reversing, the two shoes become trailing shoes, which results in poor braking performance. Vehicles with twin leading brake shoes on the front often have leading and trailing shoes at the rear to provide some self-servo effect when the vehicle is reversed.

Disc brakes

Simple disc brake

Disc brakes have been used for many years on light vehicles, and are now sometimes seen on heavy vehicles too. Many vehicles have them at the front only, but they are being increasingly fitted on all four wheels.

> The disc brake employs the same principle as a calliper bicycle brake. Two pads (equivalent to the brake blocks) are forced onto a disc (the wheel) by pistons housed in cylinders in the calliper. The cycle brake clamps the brake blocks onto the wheel; the vehicle version clamps brake pads onto a disc (Figure 23.3).

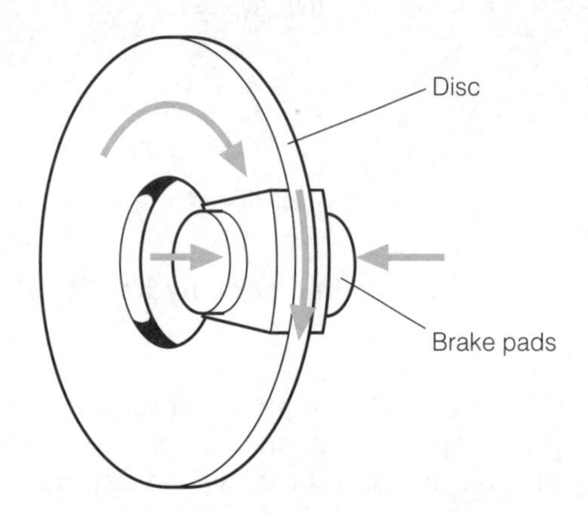

Figure 23.3 Disc brake.

Comparison of drum and disc brakes

The disc brake has two **disadvantages** over drum brakes:

1. Disc brakes are not as effective at slow speed.
2. The disc brake needs more pressure to work effectively.

However, the disc brake has many **advantages**:

1. The disc brake loses heat more effectively. Heat loss is dependent on the amount of air flowing around the brake assembly and the area of heated surface exposed to that air flow. The drum brake is generally enclosed and can lose heat only through the brake drum; much of a brake disc is exposed, and it can give up its heat very quickly off the surface. Resistance to **brake fade** (loss of braking effect due to overheating) is very high.
2. The disc brake has the same stopping power in forward or reverse.
3. Disc brakes have **progressive action**: the greater the effort applied to the pedal the more effective the brake will be.
4. Disc brakes are self-adjusting.
5. Disc brake pads can be easily checked for wear.
6. New brake pads are often very easy to fit.

The hydraulic system

The main hydraulic brake components

> A typical brake system includes a servo-operated dual-line master cylinder, which hydraulically operates front disc brakes and rear drum brakes (Figure 23.4). A pressure-limiting valve is fitted in the rear brake line. The handbrake operates through a mechanical linkage.

Hydraulic operation

A vehicle braking system must always operate quickly and reliably, and the resulting effect must be in proportion to the effort applied. Hydraulically operated brakes satisfy these requirements easily and most effectively.

> One of the major advantages of using fluid in a closed system of pipes is that the pressure exerted throughout the system is the same at any point. The effort to operate components is determined by the area to which the pressure is applied.

In the typical system (Figure 23.4), the pistons of the front disc brakes must apply more effort than those of the rear wheel cylinders. To achieve this the front brake pistons will be much larger in area than those at the rear.

> Fluid is not compressible; any effort applied at one place will be transmitted without loss of pressure or movement anywhere in the system.

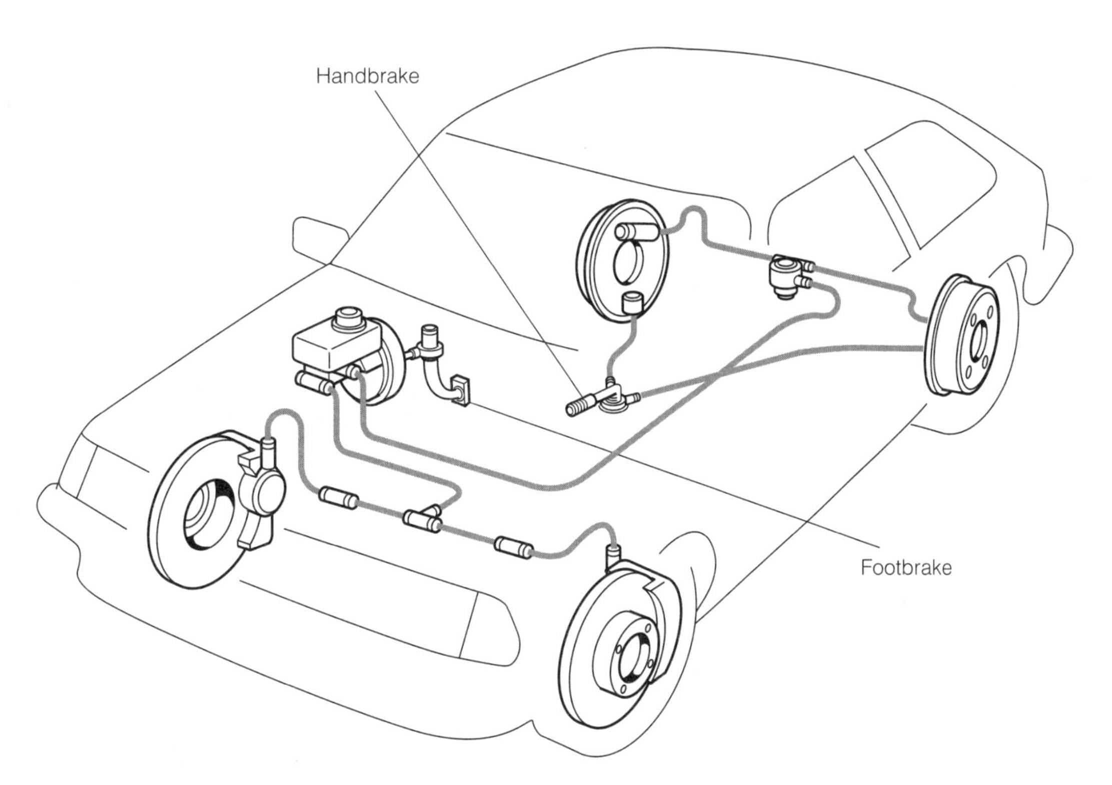

Figure 23.4 Typical layout of hydraulic brake system.

A basic drum brake system

The diagram shows a simple hydraulic braking system employing twin leading shoe drum brakes at the front and single leading shoe drum brakes at the rear (Figure 23.5).

The system can be said to consist of two elements: a **master cylinder**, which converts the driver's effort on the brake pedal into hydraulic pressure, and **wheel cylinders** that convert the hydraulic pressure into effort to move the brake shoes. The master cylinder and wheel cylinders are connected together by metal brake pipes and flexible hoses.

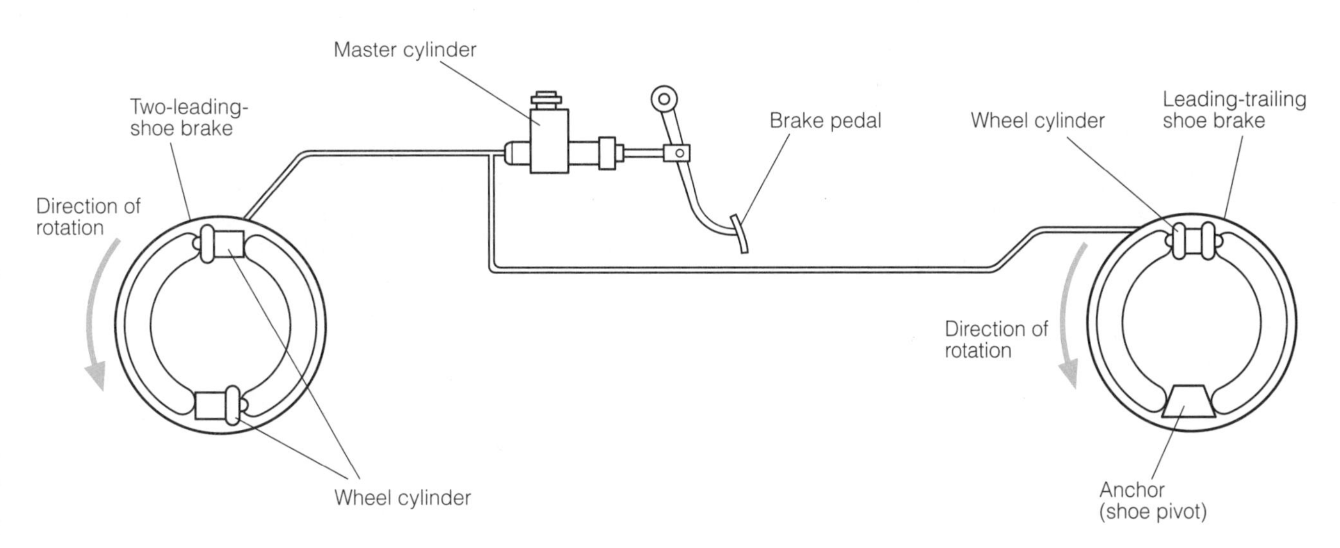

Figure 23.5 Basic drum brake system.

Operation

When at rest the brake shoes are held just clear of the brake drum by the adjusters, allowing the drum to rotate freely (Figure 23.6a).

When the brake pedal is depressed, the fluid in the system is pressurised. A small amount is forced out from the master cylinder into the system, where it increases the volume of fluid in the wheel cylinders, and moves the pistons outwards. The brake shoe linings are forced into contact with the brake drum and resist its rotation (Figure 23.6b).

Releasing the brake pedal allows the brake shoe return springs to pull the brake shoes clear of the drum, pushing the pistons back into the wheel cylinder. The excess fluid is forced back into the system and the master cylinder.

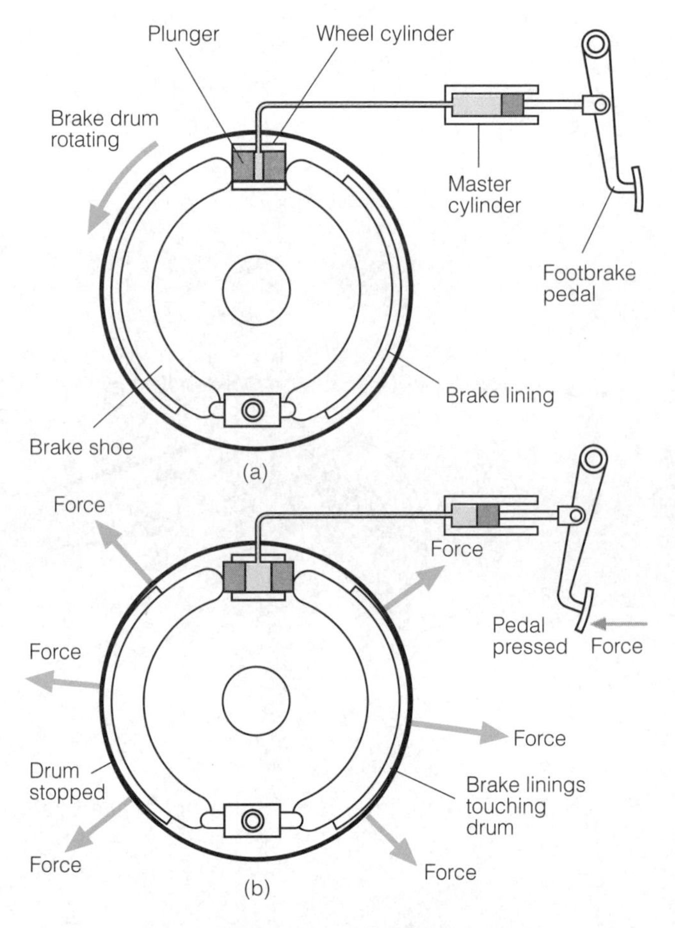

Figure 23.6 Operation of drum brake system: (a) at rest; (b) brake pedal pressed.

The master cylinder

Although there are detail differences between the many master cylinders in use, they all work on the same basic principles (Figure 23.7).

A typical master cylinder consists of a cast iron or aluminium alloy cylinder with an accurately machined and polished bore. A hole called a **port** connects the cylinder to a reservoir, which stores brake fluid. Another port links the master cylinder to the brake system and allows fluid pressure to act throughout the piping and wheel cylinders.

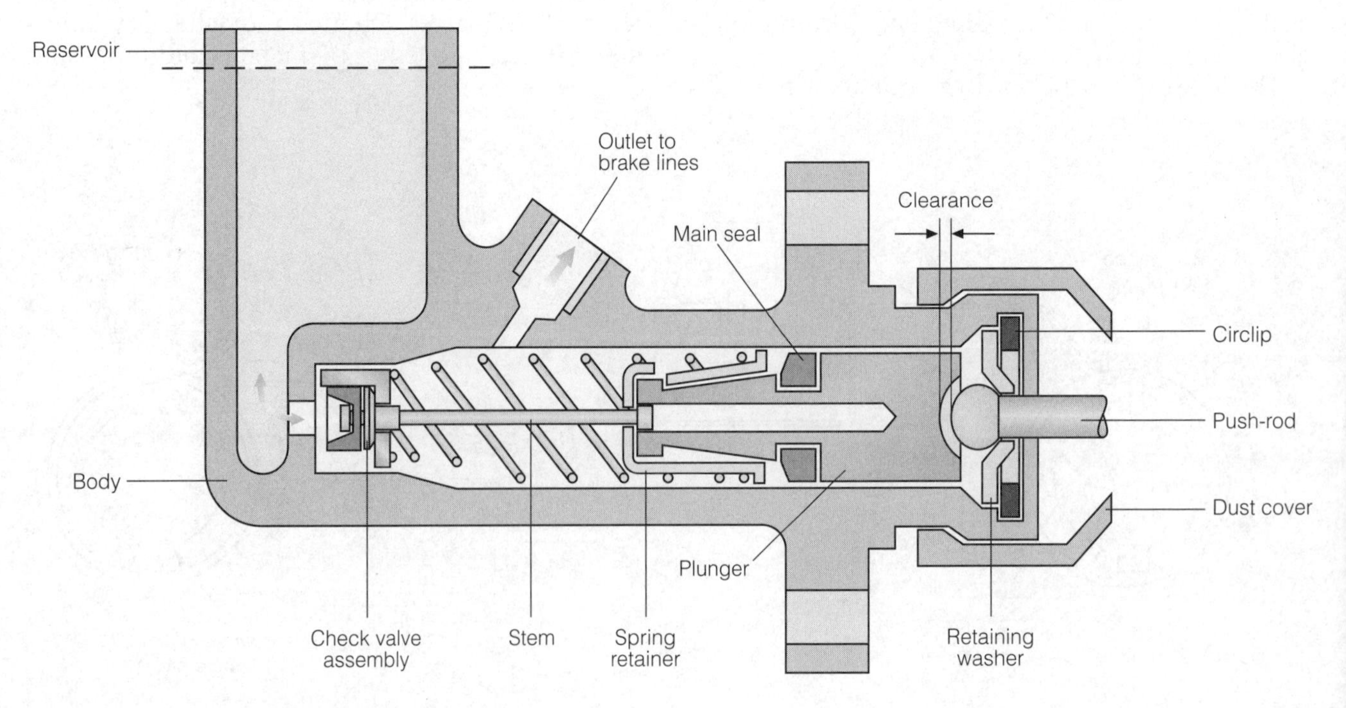

Figure 23.7 Master cylinder.

The cylinder contains a metal piston with rubber seals, a check valve to prevent fluid pushing back into the reservoir, and a return spring. At the open end of the cylinder is a pushrod, which transmits brake pedal movement to the piston.

Operation: brakes applied
When the brake pedal is depressed, the piston moves towards the end of the cylinder. The check valve closes the return to the reservoir, and fluid is forced into the system to apply the brakes. Further pressure on the brake pedal increases the force on the brake shoes and gives greater braking effort.

Operation: brakes released
Releasing the brake pedal allows all the return springs to function; the brake shoes are pulled off, returning the wheel cylinder pistons, and the master cylinder piston returns to its rest position. The fluid previously pushed into the system is returned to the master cylinder.

During this period the check valve opens, allowing fluid to flow between the system, the master cylinder and the reservoir. This allows for replenishing fluid loss or expansion of the fluid due to heat. Failure of the check valve to open could apply the brakes if the brake fluid expanded. For this reason there must always be a little clearance on the brake pedal pushrod.

Wheel cylinders

These are sometimes called **expanders** or **actuators**. It is the purpose of the wheel cylinder pistons to force the brake shoes into contact with the brake drum. There are detail differences, but all of them work on the same principle.

Construction
The wheel cylinder consists of a cylindrical casting made from cast iron or aluminium alloy. It is rigidly attached to the backplate, but is sometimes free to slide slightly to centralise its position.

There are two basic types: **single acting** and **double acting**. Internally both have a machined bore, but in a single-acting cylinder one end is blind and contains only one piston (Figure 23.8a). A double-acting cylinder is open at both ends and contains two pistons separated by a spring (Figure 23.8b). The pistons are free to move inside the cylinder.

Rubber cups or seals are fitted to each piston to prevent fluid from leaking out of the system. Correct fitting is essential to avoid brake failure.

Automatic brake adjustment

To compensate for brake lining wear, the brake shoes must be adjusted near to the drum from time to time. Some vehicles still use manual adjustment by spanner or screwdriver, but most modern vehicles with brake shoes now use automatic adjusters. One such is shown in Figure 23.9.

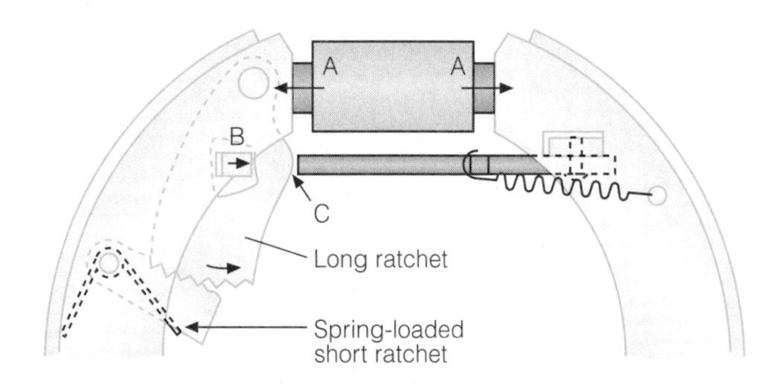

Figure 23.9 Automatic adjuster.

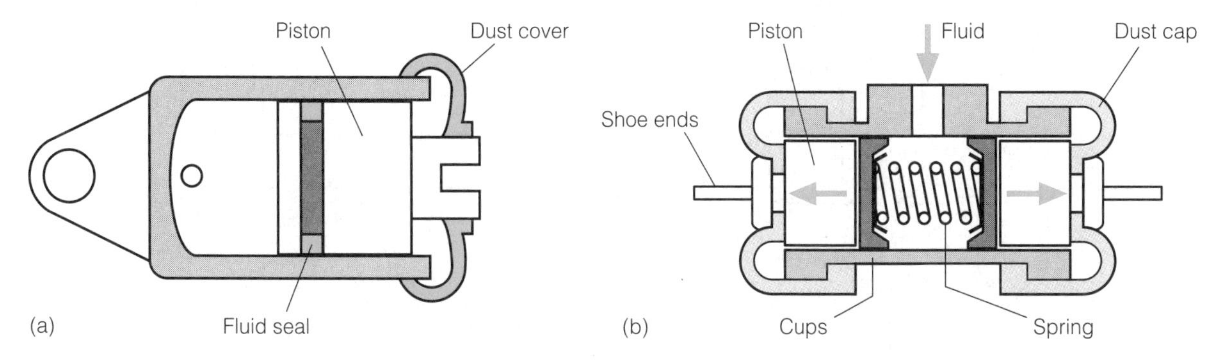

Figure 23.8 Wheel cylinders: (a) single acting; (b) double acting.

When the footbrake is applied, the shoes are pushed out (at A). If the travel is excessive, the strut pulls the long ratchet (at B) over the teeth on the short ratchet so that the strut holds the shoes further apart (at C) when the footbrake is released.

Disc brake and calliper

The disc is made from cast iron with a smooth machined braking surface, and is mounted to the revolving wheel hub. A U-shaped calliper is fitted over the disc, and is rigidly bolted to the axle or stub axle assembly (Figure 23.10). The calliper may contain one, two or even four pistons. The calliper is connected to the hydraulic system by a flexible hose, which allows for suspension movement.

The friction material of the brake pad is bonded to a steel backplate (Figure 23.11). The pads are located in the calliper with the friction material almost rubbing the disc. They are kept in place by retaining plates, pins or lock bolts.

The inner face of the brake disc is largely protected from road dirt and water by a splash shield; the outer face is protected by the wheel.

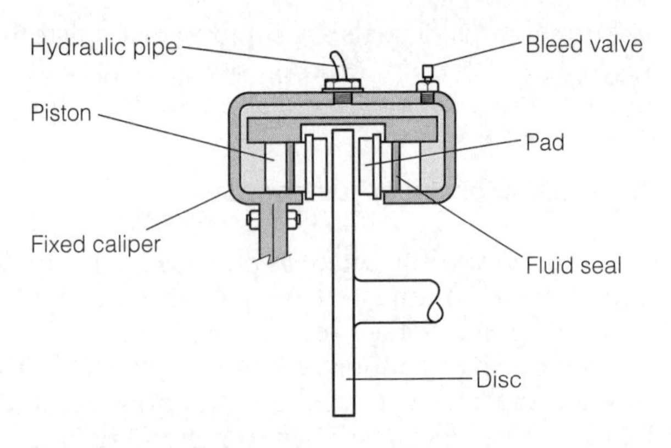

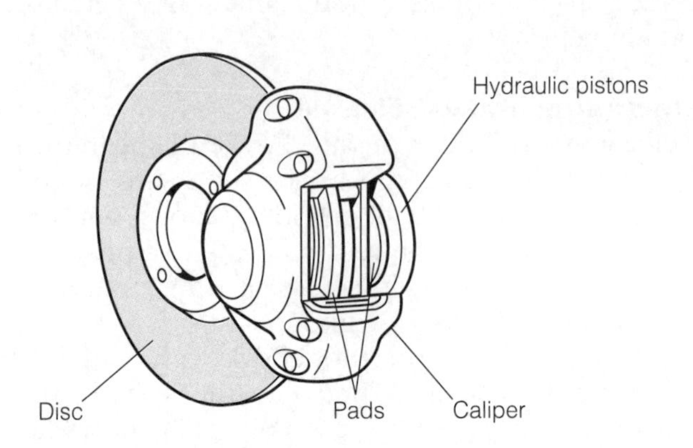

Figure 23.10 Disc brake and calliper.

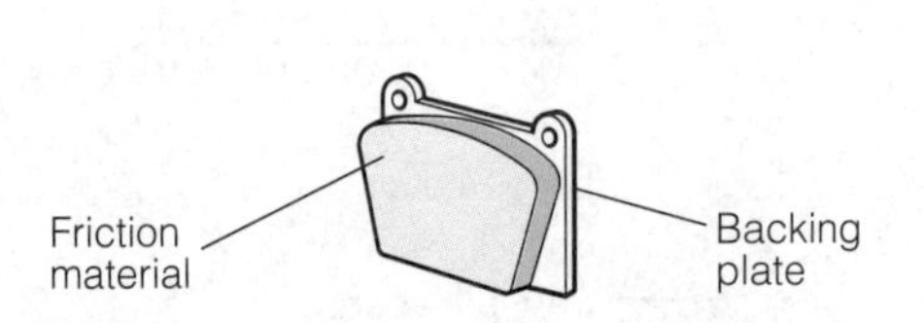

Figure 23.11 Disc brake friction pad.

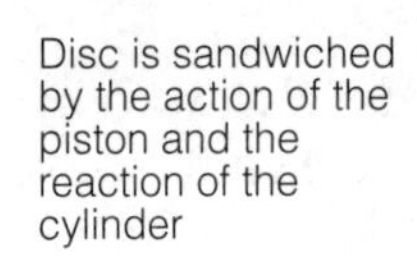

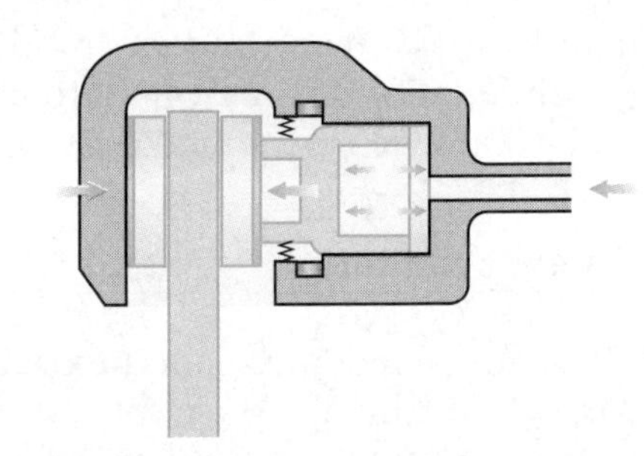

Figure 23.12 Disc brake operation.

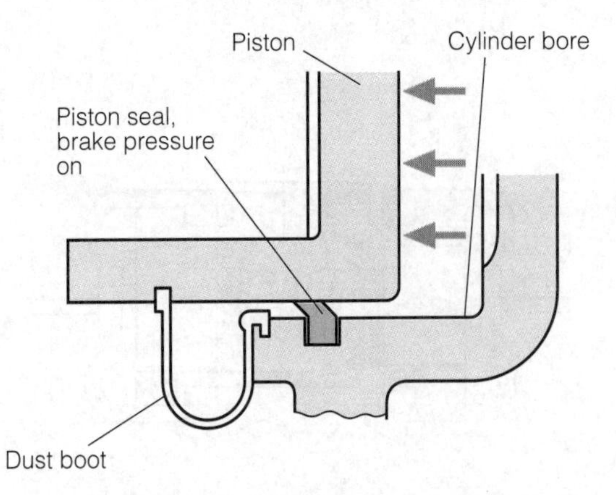

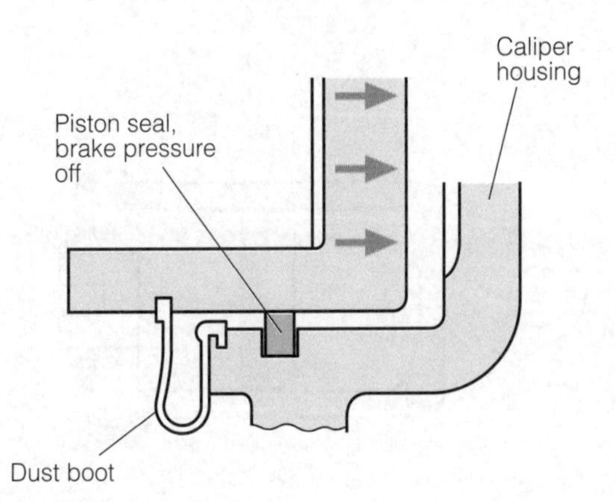

Figure 23.13 Operation of piston seal: (a) brake applied (on); (b) brake off.

Operation

Pressing the brake pedal displaces fluid into the brake system and moves the calliper pistons and the pads towards the disc. Greater pressure on the brake pedal increases the braking force.

When a single piston calliper is used, the calliper or cylinder housing is designed to slide in the stub axle carrier. When the brake fluid is pressurised the piston moves one way and the cylinder moves in the other direction (Figure 23.12).

When the brakes are released, the piston is returned to its original position by the piston seal (Figure 23.13). Applying the brakes causes the seal to distort. Releasing the brakes allows the seal to return to its original shape and, in so doing, retracts the piston.

As the pads wear, the piston is moved through the seal to take up a new position; the seal retracts the piston by only the small amount of running clearance. This means that disc brakes automatically adjust themselves.

Dual-circuit hydraulic braking system

One problem with hydraulic brakes is that a fractured pipe or leak anywhere in the system leads to a loss of fluid and complete brake failure. To overcome this disadvantage dual-circuit brake systems were developed.

These systems consist of a 'double' master cylinder, called a **tandem master cylinder**, and two sets of piping operating the wheel units (Figure 23.14). The systems may be split front and rear – so that each part of the master cylinder operates one axle – or divided diagonally. Half the system can still operate if there is a failure of one set of piping or a brake unit. Some manufacturers believe that if one system fails, better stability will be achieved if one front wheel is linked diagonally to the opposite rear wheel.

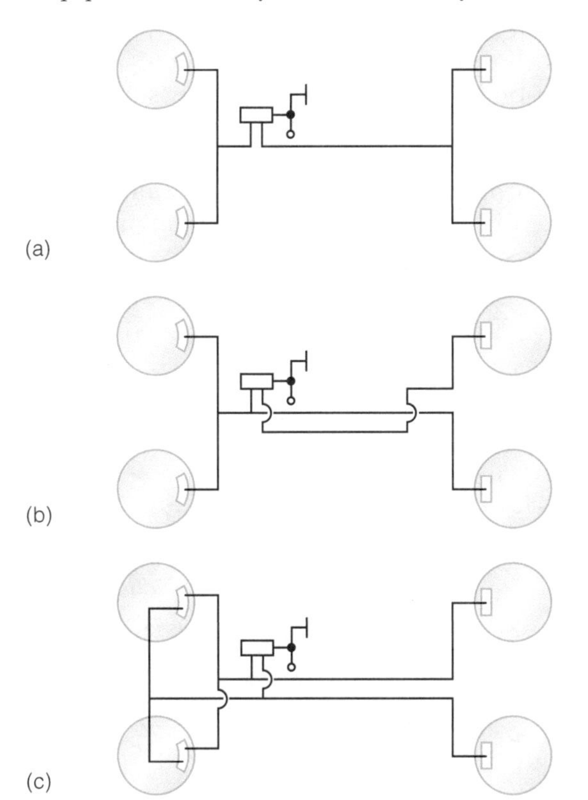

Figure 23.14 Divided-line brake circuits: (a) front – rear split; (b) X split; (c) L split.

The tandem master cylinder

The tandem master cylinder is basically two single master cylinders mounted end to end and operated by the same pushrod (Figure 23.15).

The cylinder contains two pistons, dividing it into two chambers. The first piston is operated by the brake pedal and a pushrod; the second piston is normally operated by the fluid pressure created by the first.

Operation

Two reservoirs, or one divided, supply fluid through ports to each half of the master cylinder as in a single unit. Separate reserves of brake fluid keep one system operating if the other drains away.

When the brake pedal is depressed, the fluid in chamber 1 becomes pressurised, and moves fluid into the first system. At the same time, this pressure also moves piston 2 and pressurises the fluid in chamber 2 and the other system *to the same*

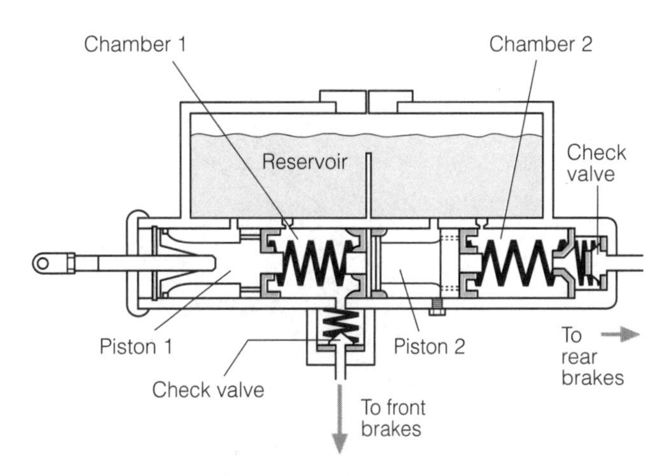

Figure 23.15 Tandem master cylinder.

pressure. Upon release of the brake pedal, return springs and seals return the wheel brake units to their rest positions, and fluid can return to the master cylinder and reservoirs. Inside the master cylinder, return springs for both pistons ensure that they return to their correct positions against the stops.

If failure occurs in system 1, no pressure will be built up when the pedal is depressed. There will be extra pedal travel until the bosses on piston 1 and piston 2 touch. Further movement of the brake pedal will pressurise system 2 in the normal way.

Failure of system 2 also results in extra pedal travel until piston 2 reaches the limit of its travel. From then on chamber 1 is pressurised by piston 1 in the usual way.

Brake pressure regulating valves

> Brake pressure must be regulated for two reasons: weight transference, and uneven weight distribution of the vehicle itself.

When the brakes of a vehicle are applied hard, as much as 70 per cent of its weight may be briefly transferred to the front wheels by inertia, in much the same way as when braking hard on a bicycle. In such circumstances, the rear wheels can readily skid, while the front wheels will not be using all the available friction effectively.

The widespread adoption of front-wheel drive means that many vehicles have a greater proportion of their total weight resting on the front wheels than was previously the case. With these vehicles, there can be very wide variations in the loading on the rear wheels.

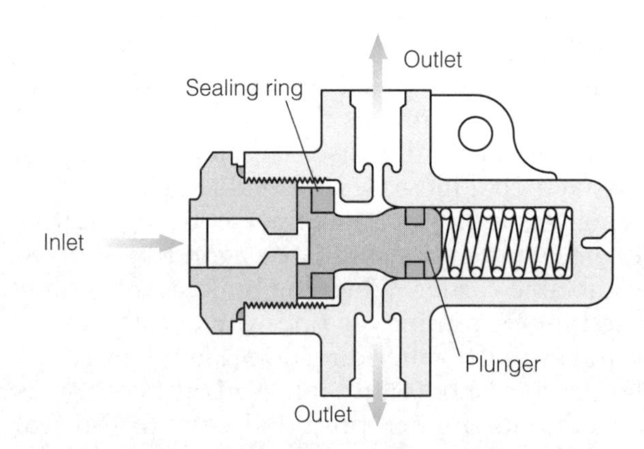

Figure 23.16 Pressure-regulating valve.

To achieve better distribution of braking effort, many vehicles employ pressure-regulating valves to vary the braking effort between the front and rear wheels (Figures 23.16 and 23.17).

Pressure-sensitive limiter

The pressure-sensitive limiter in Figure 23.16 limits the pressure of the brake fluid in the rear wheel brake lines. Fluid under pressure can flow through the valve until the fluid pressure overcomes the spring tension. At this point the plunger moves to compress the spring, and seals off the outlets to the rear brakes. Any further rise in pressure will be available only at the front brakes.

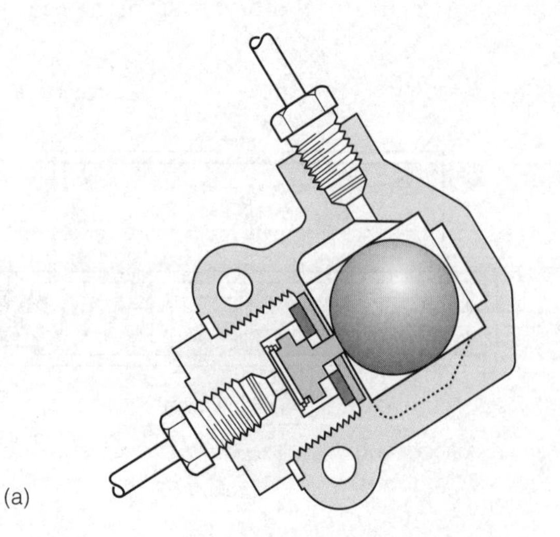

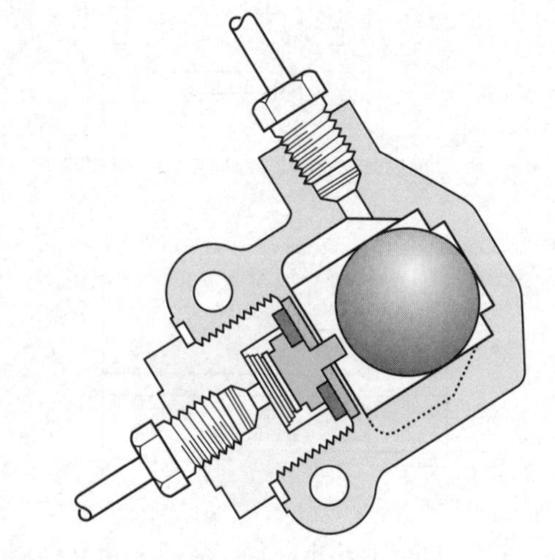

Figure 23.17 Inertia valve: (a) gentle braking; (b) hard braking.

Inertia-sensitive limiter

The inertia valve relies on the rate of deceleration of the vehicle to stop the flow of brake fluid to the rear brakes (Figure 23.17). During rapid deceleration (hard braking) the inertia created is sufficient to cause the ball to roll up the sloping cylinder (Figure 23.17b). When this occurs, the spring-loaded valve shuts off the flow of fluid to the rear brakes.

Load-sensitive regulators

Many vehicles now employ regulators linked to the rear suspension. The pressure at which the fluid pressure is cut off is determined by the positioning of a valve relative to the height of the body over the rear suspension: the greater the load, the lower will be the body, and the greater the pressure that can be used by the rear brakes before the wheels skid.

Brake pipes and hoses

There are two types: rigid metal pipes, in which there is no movement; and reinforced flexible hoses to connect the rigid pipes to components that move, such as the wheel brake units.

> Both forms of piping must be able to withstand the very high pressures that can occur during emergency braking. Up to three times body weight may briefly be applied, giving rise to system pressures well in excess of 10 000 kPa.

Brake fluid

Brake fluid is the 'lifeblood' of the braking system, and it must have several special qualities. Vehicles are used in widely varying temperatures, so it must have a very low freezing point and a very high boiling point. Throughout this range of temperatures the **viscosity** or thickness of the fluid must remain constant. It must not attack the rubber seals or corrode the metal components. However, brake fluid does have some drawbacks, as detailed below.

Brake fluid and safety

> Brake fluid is **hygroscopic**; it absorbs moisture from the atmosphere.

Water boils at 100 °C, while good-quality brake fluid boils at over 400 °C. The heat generated by braking, particularly hard braking in hot climates, may raise the wheel brake cylinder temperatures to over 200 °C.

Under these circumstances the water in the brake fluid will turn to steam. When this occurs the steam, being a vapour, compresses, and the brake pedal will push to the floor with little or no effect from the brakes. This is described as **vapour lock**.

So it is essential that:

1. brake fluid is stored in sealed containers until use;
2. fluid in the brake system is changed regularly.

> Brake fluid is also damaging to many types of paint.

Vehicles receiving attention to their brake systems must be suitably protected, and care must taken when handling the brake fluid.

> ▲ Brake fluid is poisonous in quite small quantities. Never bleed or pour brake fluid into discarded drink cartons or containers.

The colour of many brake fluids is not dissimilar to that of soft drinks. To avoid the possibility of accident it must be kept in the correct containers.

Mechanical actuating components

Parking brakes

> Parking brakes generally act on the rear wheel drum brake or rear disc assembly. Operation is normally entirely mechanical, and is usually applied by a hand lever working through cables or rods.

It is independent of the hydraulic part of the braking system, though it generally uses the same brake shoes or pads (Figure 23.18). The linkage is designed to multiply the force applied at the lever. This enables the driver to apply the handbrake with sufficient force to hold the vehicle on an incline.

Transmission handbrake

> This type is usually fitted to the transmission system at the rear of the gearbox.

It is typically found on some four-wheel drive vehicles, such as Land Rovers and the Mitsubishi Shogun. The advantage of the transmission brake is that the final drive multiplies the braking force and prevents the driveshafts from turning on all four wheels when in four-wheel drive.

Servo assistance

One problem that vehicle manufacturers have is that drivers are of differing strength; it is impossible to make an effective braking system that can be operated with ease by everybody. As a driver can exert only a limited amount of force on the brake pedal, a means of power assistance is

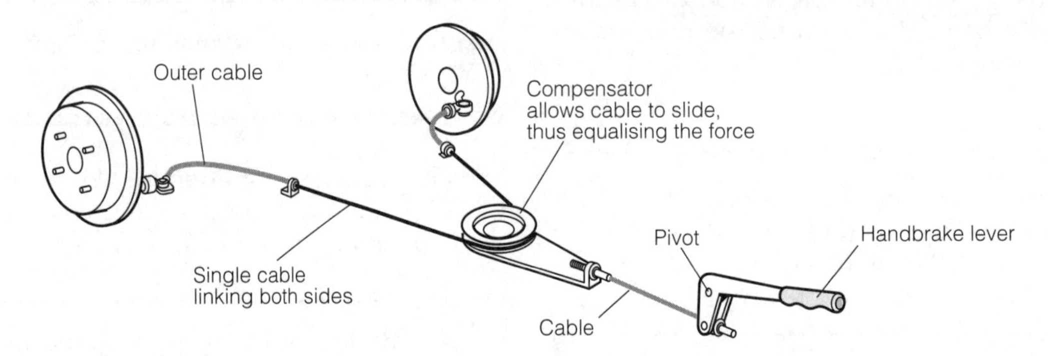

Figure 23.18 Parking brake.

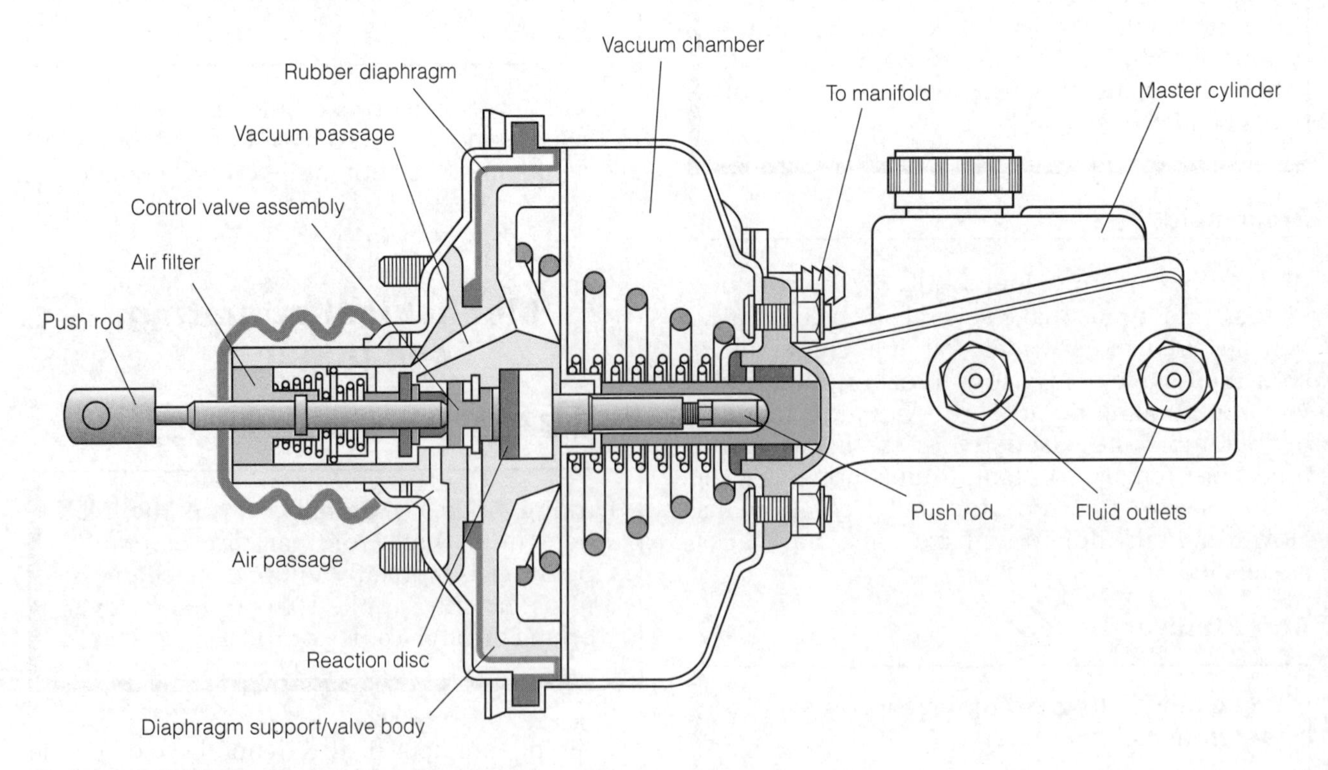

Figure 23.19 Direct-acting servo.

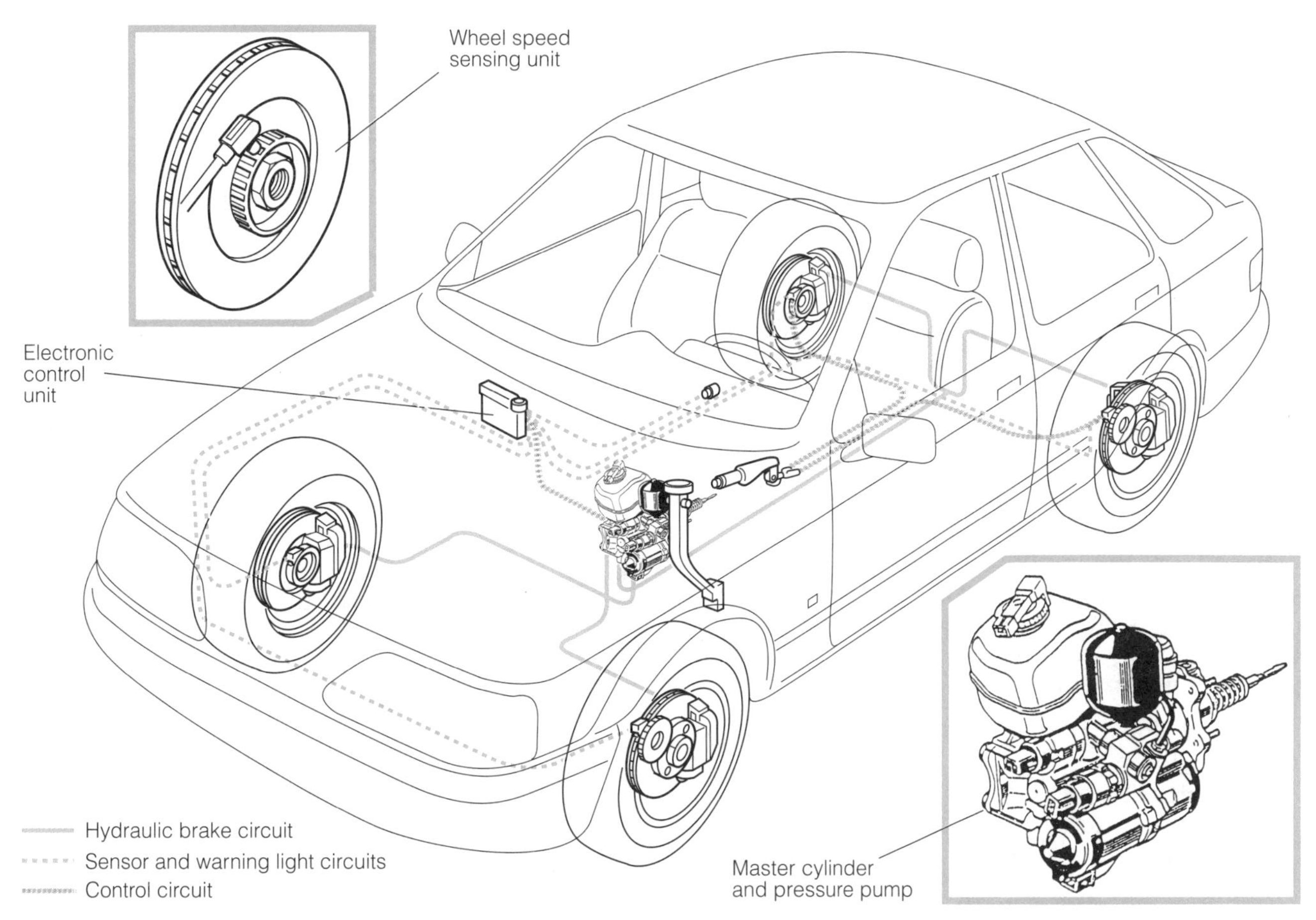

Figure 23.20 ABS braking system.

required that will enhance that effort. This is usually supplied by the servo.

The vacuum servo

The vacuum servo is mounted between the brake pedal and the master cylinder. A large diaphragm/ piston assembly is mounted in a circular housing, with the operating pushrod passing through the centre (Figure 23.19).

> The depression in the inlet manifold of petrol engines, or that produced by a vacuum pump on other engines, is used to evacuate air from one side of the diaphragm assembly in the circular housing. If, when assistance is needed, air at atmospheric pressure is allowed to press on the other side of the diaphragm assembly, a considerable force is available to act on the pushrod.

To prevent over-braking, the brake pedal pushrod operates a valve that controls the amount of atmospheric pressure permitted to enter the housing.

Anti-lock braking systems (ABS)

> Friction between the tyre and the road is essential for all aspects of vehicle control. The brakes may lock up and control of the vehicle may be lost by even the most careful driver under emergency braking, or when the road surface is slippery. Anti-lock brake systems (ABS) are fitted to many vehicles to overcome this danger (Figure 23.20).

Such devices maintain directional control, and decrease the stopping distance in slippery conditions. Designs vary, but a typical system is described below.

Components and operation

The heart of the system is an **electronic control unit** (ECU), which is provided with **inputs** of information, and gives **outputs** of instructions to the controls. The inputs consist of pulse-generated signals from sensors at each roadwheel. They indicate whether each wheel is revolving, and how fast it is turning. The ECU uses the sensor inputs to control the braking system through output to a hydraulic pump assembly.

Based on the input signals from the wheel sensors, the ABS system's ECU knows the speed of each wheel. When the brakes are applied, the wheels and the vehicle start to slow down. The ECU monitors the reducing pulses from each of the roadwheel sensors. If a wheel seems about to lock up, the ECU reduces the pressure at that wheel until the tyre grips again.

This sequence of sensing and adjusting is continuous, and is very fast. The process provides a rapid on–off operation of the brake very similar to the cadence braking routine practised by rally drivers. The wheels are maintained at the optimum braking point, which is just *before* they would lose their grip on the road surface.

Traction control systems (TCS)

It may seem strange to deal with traction control (the way the wheels grip the road surface during acceleration) under the heading of brakes. It is because ABS is also used to control the excessive speed of individual wheels that are about to lose their grip by spinning. In addition, the power being developed by the engine is also controlled. The system is of particular benefit during hard acceleration, or when cornering vigorously.

The traction control system (TCS) uses the ABS wheel sensors, the ECU and the hydraulic pump or modulator (Figure 23.21). In addition there is a throttle control intervention motor to reduce engine output.

Operation

When a wheel increases its speed relative to the others, the ECU applies the brake to slow it down and, if necessary, reduces the engine power output by partially closing the throttle. As with ABS the sensing is continuous, and the ECU will constantly strive to obtain the highest level of drive from each wheel, whenever it is demanded by the driver.

Commercial vehicle brakes

Air–hydraulic system

This system is sometimes used on light commercial vehicles, and is also known as the **air over**

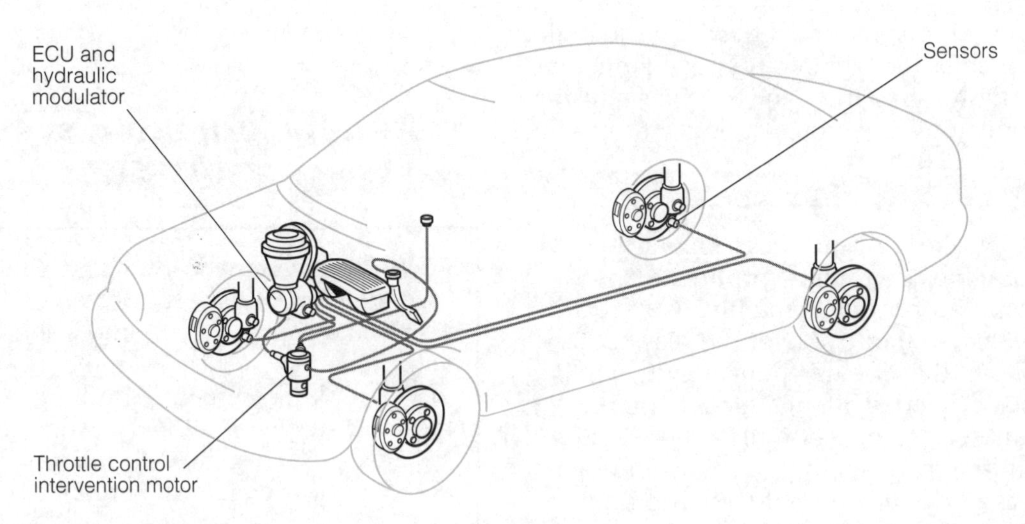

Figure 23.21 Traction control system.

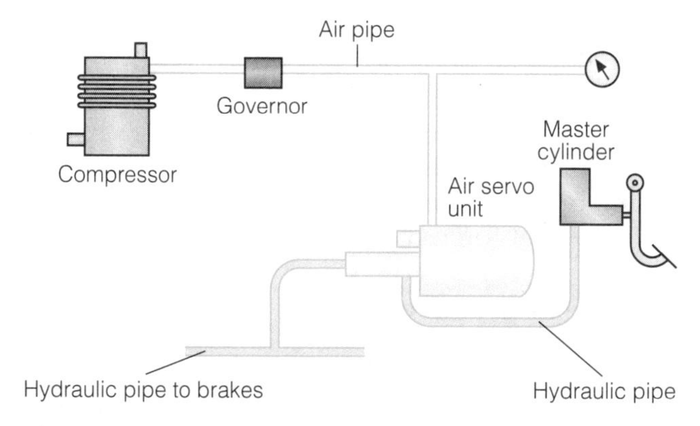

Figure 23.22 Air–hydraulic servo-assisted brake system.

hydraulic system (Figure 23.22). An engine-driven compressor controlled by a governor feeds air under pressure to a reservoir. This air is then used to assist the driver in operating the hydraulic brakes. It acts in a similar way to a vacuum servo unit, except that it uses pressurised air instead of atmospheric air pressure. The unit gives greater assistance than a vacuum servo for a given chamber size. The system provides the benefits of air brakes but at a much lower cost.

Air-operated brakes

Most heavy commercial vehicles now use air-operated brakes (Figure 23.23). In this system compressed air is used to actuate the brake mechanism. Air pressure is transmitted through pipes equally in all directions, in exactly the same way as fluid pressure in a hydraulic system. The actuation of each brake is similar to the simple cam brake shown earlier in the chapter.

The compressor

The compressor is a piston type driven by the engine or, in some cases, the gearbox. It supplies air under pressure to a reservoir for storage. A governor regulates the pressure in the reservoir, and when the operating pressure is exceeded, it is vented to atmosphere. The reservoir has to be strong enough to withstand pressures of around

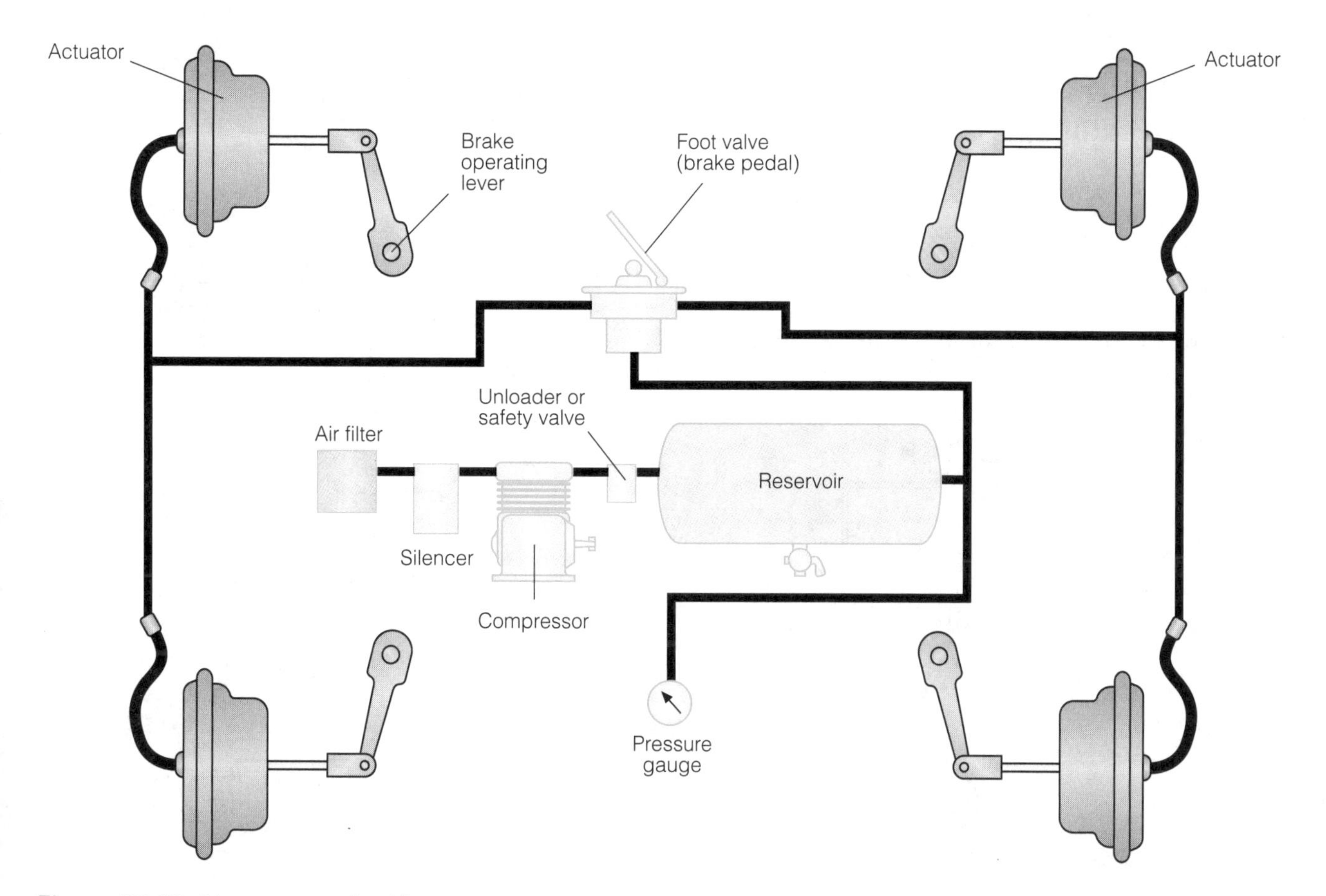

Figure 23.23 Air pressure braking system.

690 kPa (100 lbf/in^2). The brake control valve, which is operated by the driver's footpedal, allows the compressed air to travel from the reservoir to the diaphragm in the brake chamber at each wheel. The valve is designed to permit controlled application of the brakes.

The brake chambers are fitted with a movable diaphragm, which operates a rod connected to the brake shoe operating mechanism. The admission of air pressure to the diaphragm in the brake chamber moves the diaphragm and linkage to apply the brake. A quick-release valve is used to speed up the release of air pressure to the atmosphere once the brakes have been released. A relay valve speeds up the application and release of the rear brakes.

Increasing safety legislation has required manufacturers to provide more sophisticated air brake systems. The system described would fail if any air pipe fractured. More recent systems contain dual or triple brake lines.

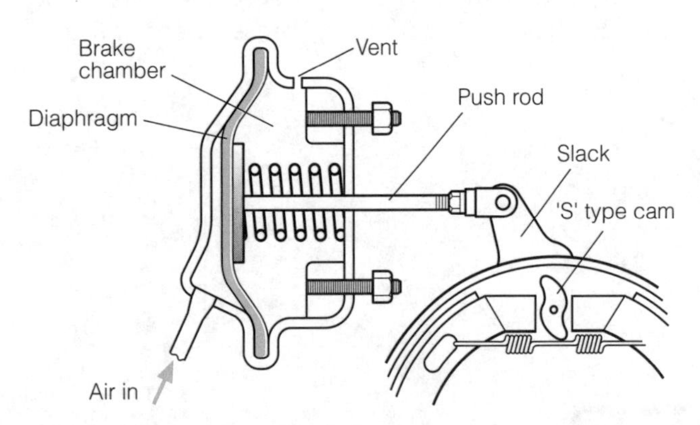

Figure 23.24 Single-diaphragm brake actuator.

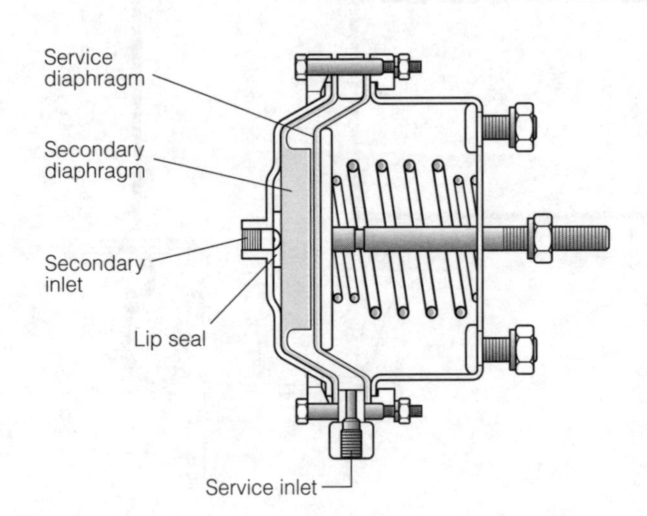

Figure 23.25 Double-diaphragm brake chamber.

Brake actuators

Although often called **brake chambers**, the brake actuators apply the brake. Those mounted on the axle operate a mechanical linkage to rotate a cam, or if mounted on the backplate, they move a wedge that forces the brake shoes apart.

Single-diaphragm actuator

A rubber diaphragm is clamped between the two halves of a steel chamber (Figure 23.24). Air under pressure acts on one side of the diaphragm. Attached to the other side are a steel pushplate and a pushrod, which operate the brake mechanism. When the brake is released, a spring forces the diaphragm to the off position. The force acting on the brake can be varied by altering the area of the diaphragm.

Double-diaphragm actuator

As the name implies, this unit contains two separ-

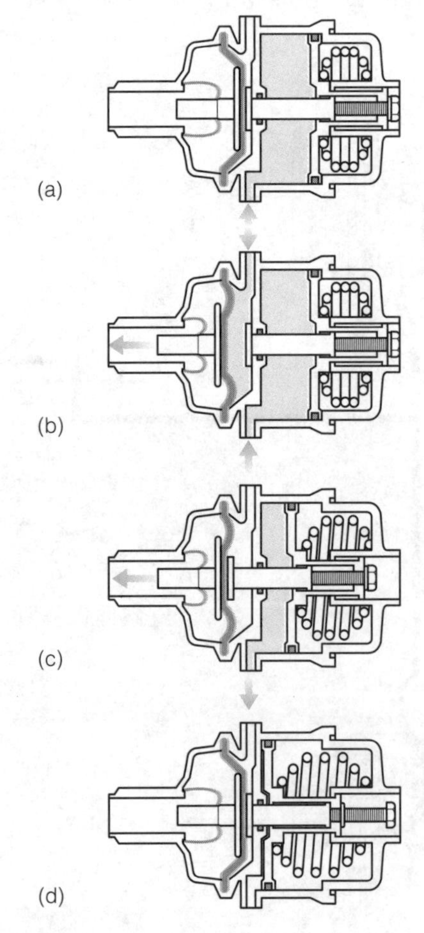

Figure 23.26 Operation of spring brake actuator (see text for explanation).

ate chambers and two diaphragms (Figure 23.25). Each diaphragm can be operated independently, for while one is activated by air from the service brake, the other is activated by the secondary or parking brake. Should one diaphragm fail the other will operate normally.

Spring brake actuators

The normal diaphragm chamber will not work if there is a total failure of the air supply. Spring actuators overcome this problem (Figure 23.26). They contain a spring, sufficiently powerful to apply the brakes, which is controlled by counter-balancing air pressure.

Under normal driving conditions air is supplied to the rear chamber, holding the spring in the off position (Figure 23.26a).

When braking, air pressure from the footbrake valve enters the front chamber and, acting on the diaphragm, applies the brake. The spring is still held off by air pressure in the rear chamber (Figure 23.26b).

Application of the secondary or parking brake releases air from the rear chamber (Figure 23.26c). The spring force can then apply the brake. When all the air has been exhausted, the brakes are held on by the spring.

If the engine is disabled, the vehicle cannot be moved without unscrewing a special release bolt fitted to the actuator (Figure 23.26d).

> Do not attempt to dismantle the spring actuators without specialist knowledge. An accidentally released spring may inflict fatal injuries.

Air supply

The split system

This is used mainly on rigid vehicles. The main system is divided into two separate circuits (Figure 23.27). A dual footvalve is used to supply and control air from two separate reservoirs to the front and rear brakes independently. A third reservoir operated by the handbrake supplies air to the rear brakes for parking purposes. This

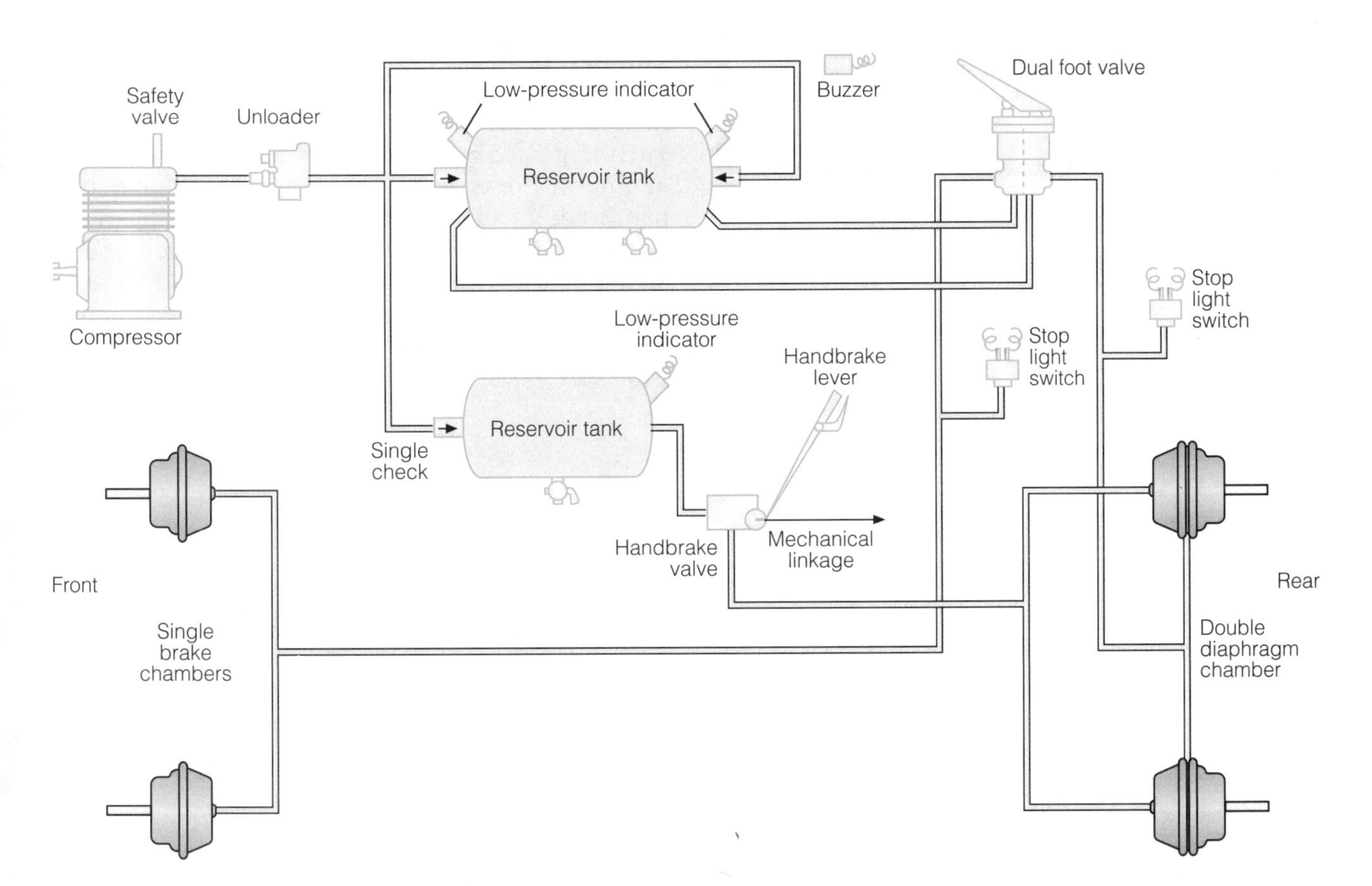

Figure 23.27 Split system fitted to a truck.

assists the mechanical linkage that applies the rear brakes, but the parking brake is held on by mechanical means after the air has been exhausted.

The triple-line system

The triple-line system is used on articulated vehicles or those pulling a trailer; the extra line is used to supply a reservoir fitted to the trailer. The three lines are: an emergency line, which supplies the trailer reservoir; a service line operated by the footvalve; and a second or auxiliary line.

When the driver operates the footvalve, air passes to a relay valve on the trailer. The air valve then releases air from the trailer reservoir to the trailer brakes. The second or auxiliary line is operated by a hand valve, and is used for parking or in an emergency.

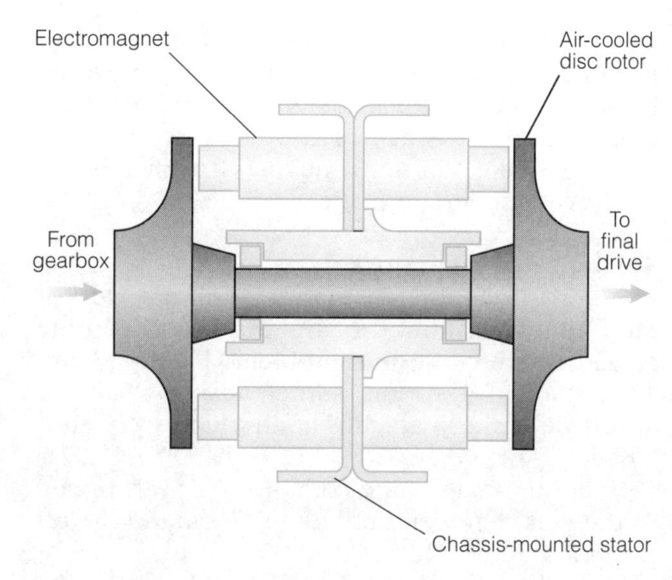

Figure 23.28 Electric eddy current retarder.

Retarders

> The main purpose of retarders is to limit the speed of the vehicle during long descents. In so doing they reduce the risk of brake fade and increase the service life of the brake shoes.

There are four main types:

1. electric (eddy current) retarder;
2. friction retarder;
3. hydraulic retarder;
4. exhaust brake.

The most popular are the electric retarder and the exhaust brake.

Electric retarder

The electric retarder is attached to the transmission, and makes use of eddy currents created by a magnetic field. It consists of a stator of coils attached to the gearbox, rotating disc rotors attached to the drive line, and a rheostat (a form of variable resistor) to vary the effect (Figure 23.28).

In normal driving the metal rotors spin freely. When the stator coils are energised, a magnetic field is produced. This creates eddy currents, which try to prevent the rotation of the rotors. They heat up from the conversion of energy, but this is easily released to the surrounding air. The braking effect depends on the current flow to the stator, and this is varied by the rheostat control.

Exhaust brake

Exhaust brakes were first introduced in about 1910. They make use of the braking power of the engine. A butterfly valve is placed in the exhaust manifold; it can restrict the flow of gases from the engine (Figure 23.29). In this way the engine is acting as a low-pressure compressor. Good seals are necessary on the exhaust system flanges because the pressure can build up to around 350 kPa (50 lbf/in^2).

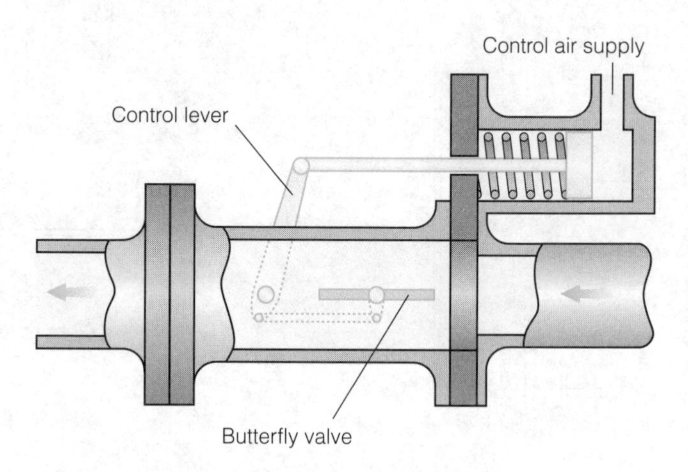

Figure 23.29 Exhaust brake.

The valve is moved by compressed air or by an electric solenoid. Fuel delivery is automatically stopped when the exhaust brake is activated.

Braking defects

Brake fade

Brake fade is reducing braking effect, even though the pedal is still firm and does not move further down.

It occurs in conditions of repeated hard braking, when the brake linings or pads heat to a point where they can be lubricated by resin released from the material. Lining materials vary, depending on their use. A **soft** lining is very good for slow-speed city driving, typical of taxis. High speed or hard use demands a **hard** lining, which is not so good at slow speeds but will delay the onset of brake fade.

Once brake fade has occurred it is quite likely that the braking surfaces of the discs and drums will be glazed. It is rarely possible to remove this completely without machining the braking surfaces. It may also be brought about by over-zealous 'drying out' of wet brakes, or by mechanics driving with the brakes held on 'to bed them in'!

Spongy pedal

Spongy pedal may be caused by two defects: air or vapour in the hydraulic system, and a 'ballooning' hose.

If the reinforcing in the walls of a hose fails, it will blow up like a balloon when the brakes are applied. This must be dealt with at once to avoid complete failure.

Air or vapour in the brake fluid can arise from two causes: air bubbles in the fluid, or water, which becomes steam vapour under the influence of heat. Fortunately, these causes are easy to diagnose. If the pedal is always spongy, it is air in the fluid and the brakes must be bled. Sponginess only after using the brakes hard so that they become hot is almost certainly water in the fluid, which must be changed without delay.

Spongy pedal can also be caused by a defective master cylinder rubber.

An excess of water in the fluid, coupled with high brake temperature, can result in total loss of braking during hard use.

Excessive pedal travel

Excessive pedal travel is almost always due to the brake linings and pads having too much clearance, or to one circuit of a dual circuit system's having failed.

Pedal travel resulting from excessive clearance can be caused by a number of faults, ranging from the need for adjustment to defective components, which will need to be replaced. A basic system will probably only need adjustment. Disc brakes may have sticking pistons, or sticking caliper frames where brakes are of single-cylinder design. Two other causes are automatic adjusters not working properly, and neglecting to slacken the handbrake adjustment before resetting the brakes.

A failed circuit of a dual-circuit system must be diagnosed and repaired without delay.

Brakes locking on

The light vehicle hydraulic system can keep the brakes applied if the fluid is unable to return to the master cylinder and reservoir.

This is usually due to failure of the piston to return to its stop. A sticking brake pedal or, more usually, insufficient clearance between the piston and the pushrod is the reason. Another cause can be a partially blocked flexible hose.

CHECK YOUR UNDERSTANDING

- The purpose of the braking system is to bring the vehicle quickly and safely to rest.

- The braking system converts kinetic energy to heat.
- The brakes on a vehicle are only as good as the friction between the tyres and the road.
- There are two main types of brake: drum brakes and disc brakes.
- On light vehicles the brakes are usually operated hydraulically.
- On heavy commercial vehicles the brakes are usually operated by compressed air.
- Hydraulic brakes can be power assisted by the use of a vacuum servo or air pressure.
- Auxiliary braking systems such as transmission retarders or exhaust brakes may be used on commercial vehicles.

PROJECTS

Brake adjustment

As the brake shoe friction lining wears it is necessary to adjust the brakes from time to time. Where brake drums are fitted to the front of a vehicle they will have a twin leading shoe arrangement. Twin leading shoes have two adjusters. Rear brakes usually have leading and trailing shoes, and have only one adjuster.

Procedure

1. Lift the vehicle until the wheel is clear of the ground.

> ▲ Ensure that the vehicle's weight is taken by axle stands or solid blocks if a vehicle hoist is not being used. If a two-post hoist is being used, ensure that the arms cannot move out from under the vehicle sill.

2. Using an appropriate tool, turn the adjuster clockwise until the brake shoes are hard against the brake drum. At this stage you will not be able to turn the wheel. Back off the adjuster until the wheel spins freely.
3. Repeat the procedure with the remaining wheels.
4. Adjust the handbrake after the footbrake. Always check that the wheels can rotate freely after adjustment has taken place.

Bleeding brakes

This should never be necessary as a routine requirement. However, if part of the system has been repaired and air has entered, the brakes must be bled.

Procedure

1. Adjust all the brakes correctly.
2. Make sure that the master cylinder reservoir is full. Maintain the fluid level throughout the procedure and, if necessary, get someone to help you.
3. Locate the bleed nipple that is farthest from the master cylinder.
4. Fit a piece of tubing to the wheel cylinder nipple, and place the other end in a container with a little fluid in it already.
5. Slacken the nipple and depress the brake pedal slowly. Allow the pedal to return freely.
6. Repeat the operation until there are no more air bubbles being pumped into the fluid in the container. Tighten the bleed nipple.
7. Make sure that the reservoir is full again, and repeat the operation on the other brakes, bleeding the next farthest from the master cylinder.
8. Remember to use only new, correct fluid from a sealed tin. Make sure that none is spilt on the paintwork.

REVISION EXERCISES AND QUESTIONS

1 What is the purpose of the braking system?
2 Why are vehicles fitted with twin leading shoes or disc brakes at the front, and leading and trailing shoes at the rear?
3 What is the main advantage of fitting a hydraulic braking system to a car compared with a mechanically operated system?
4 Name *four* required qualities of brake fluid.
5 What precautions should be taken when using brake fluid?
6 What symptom would the driver experience when pressing the brake pedal on a system that required adjustment?
7 What are the main advantages of a disc brake?
8 Why must air or water be kept out of a brake system?
9 List *three* factors that can affect a vehicle's braking efficiency.
10 Give *two* types of air brake chamber.
11 Name an auxiliary brake.

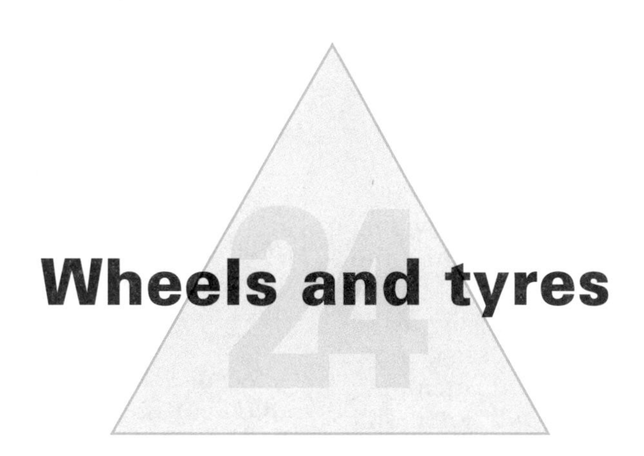

Wheels and tyres

Introduction

The pneumatic tyre serves two important purposes:

- It provides the vehicle with a frictional contact surface upon the road.
- It minimises the transmission to the vehicle of the shocks associated from travelling over rough road surfaces.

A tyre must be able to remain in contact with the road surface at any speed and under a variety of weather conditions, and it must have as little rolling resistance as possible, to aid fuel economy.

Functional requirements of a tyre

A tyre must be able to transmit all the available engine torque through a relatively small tyre **footprint** (the contact area) at all times. This same contact area must also handle directional control forces and braking.

Under the ideal condition of a dry surface, the maximum amount of tyre adhesion would be achieved by having a completely smooth tyre. Unfortunately, such a tyre would have little or no adhesion in the wet.

In order to give reasonable levels of road adhesion in both dry and wet conditions, together with a minimum level of rolling resistance, tyres for general use have a number of features, which include the method of construction and the type of tread pattern employed.

Tyre valves

A tyre valve allows inflation of the tyre with pressurised air, and permits its release when necessary.

It consists of two components: an outer sleeve located on the wheel rim, and a centre pin-type valve core (Figure 24.1). The valve is attached to the inner tube or, for tubeless tyres, sealed into the wheel rim. A dust cap provides a secondary air seal, and stops dust from getting in.

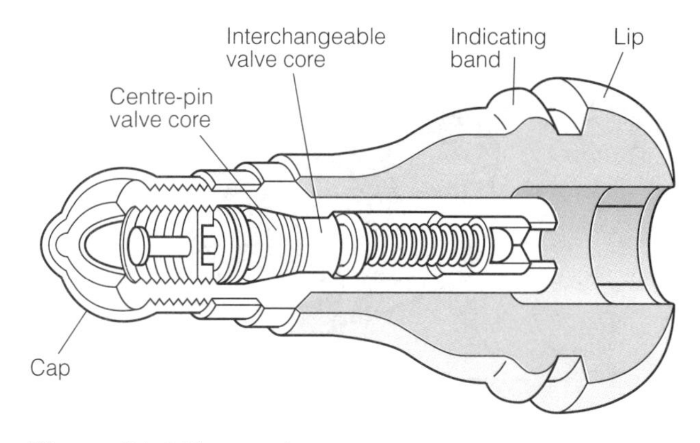

Figure 24.1 Tyre valve.

Types of tyre

Tubed and tubeless tyres

Motor vehicle tyres are supplied as either tubed or tubeless.

A **tubed** tyre has an inner tube fitted inside the tyre casing, as is common with pedal cycles. In contrast, a **tubeless** tyre does not have an inner tube, but relies on the bead of the tyre providing an air-tight seal when it is inflated against the wheel rim.

Both the wheel and the tyre are specially made for the tubeless mode. Most vehicles are now fitted with tubeless tyres as standard, including heavy commercial vehicles, although some still have tubed tyres.

Tyre construction

The basic 'framework' of a tyre is made from various layers of corded material called **plies** (Figure 24.2).

The plies are made from a combination of rayon, nylon and polyester, impregnated with rubber. The loads and forces that the tyre is able to withstand depend upon the number of plies and the way they are positioned.

Depending upon the method of construction, a tyre can be categorised as either a **cross-ply** or a **radial ply** tyre.

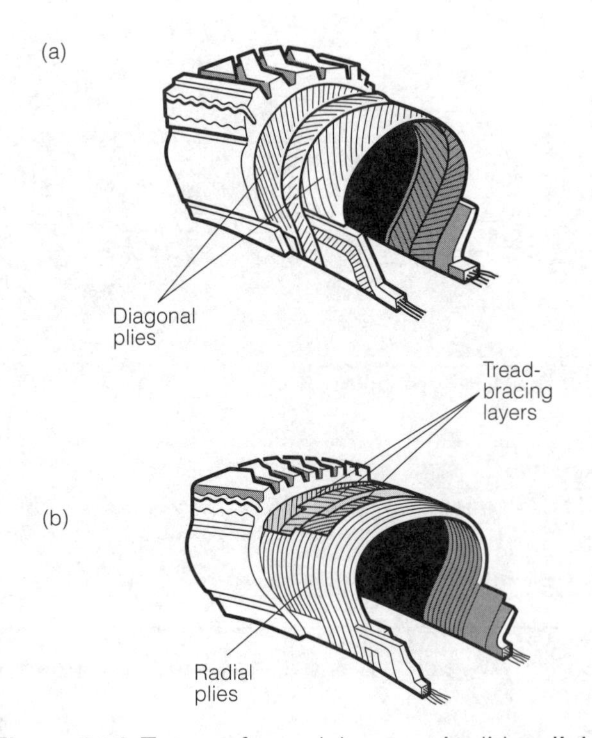

Figure 24.2 Types of tyre: (a) cross-ply; (b) radial.

Cross-ply tyres

In this design, each successive layer of ply material is laid at an angle of approximately 45° to the next (Figure 24.2a).

Because the plies can stretch while being pulled in different directions, this type of construction gives a relatively strong tyre, which has good load-carrying characteristics. However, it has some disadvantages. The sidewalls tend to be very stiff, which limits the tyre's ability to maintain full tread contact with the road surface, especially when cornering. Also, as the plies are laid in opposite directions, they can rub against each other, resulting in an effect called **ply shuffle**. This can cause heat to be generated, which could result in tyre failure.

Radial-ply tyres

In this design, the plies are laid radially across the tyre from bead to bead, with a belt of fabric or steel tread bracing layers positioned under the tread (Figure 24.2b).

One of the main advantages is that the sidewalls are much more flexible. This enables more of the tyre's tread pattern to remain in contact with the road surface, particularly when cornering (Figure 24.3). These tyres can grip the road better and last longer than cross-ply tyres. Steel-braced radials are now the most popular type of tyre for cars and commercial vehicles.

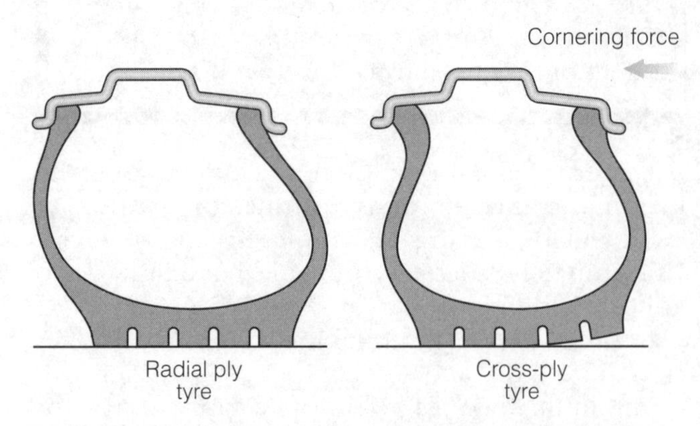

Figure 24.3 Comparison of radial and cross-ply tyres when cornering. The cross-ply tyre is starting to lose its grip.

Safety tyres

In an effort to improve vehicle safety, some tyre manufacturers have developed specific features in the design of their tyres.

When a tyre is punctured, the air-tight seal between the tyre bead and the wheel rim is lost. The tyre walls can then move into the centre (or **well section**) of the wheel rim, causing the vehicle to become very unstable, particularly at high speed. To prevent this from occurring, some special safety tyres have been developed.

Run-flat tyres

In one run-flat design, the tyre is prevented from being dislodged by a specially shaped wheel rim. With some military vehicles, the tyre walls are so thick and stiff that they can run without air for perhaps 80 km (50 miles).

Conti tyre system

As the tyre rapidly deflates, the central section of the wheel rim comes into contact with the crown section of the tyre. This allows the driver to steer the vehicle safely without any serious damage being caused to either the wheel rim or the tyre (Figure 24.4).

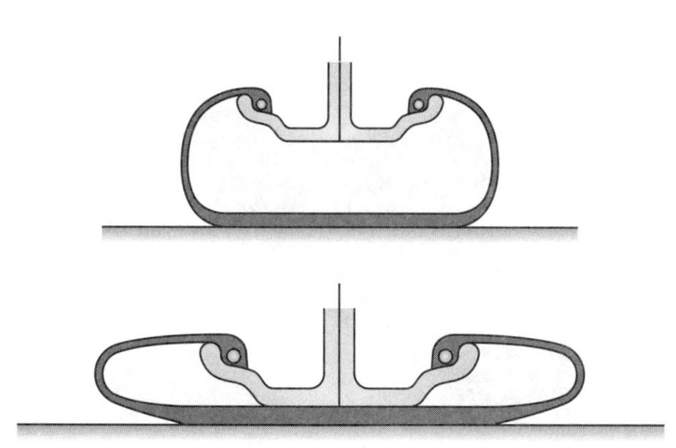

Figure 24.4 Run-flat tyre: Conti system.

TDX tyres

The TDX tyre wheel rim is shaped as shown in Figure 24.5. The tyre bead is specially shaped to fit into the wheel rim groove. If sudden deflation occurs, the bead toes are pressed firmly into the wheel rim grooves, so preventing tyre dislodgement and allowing a safe stop.

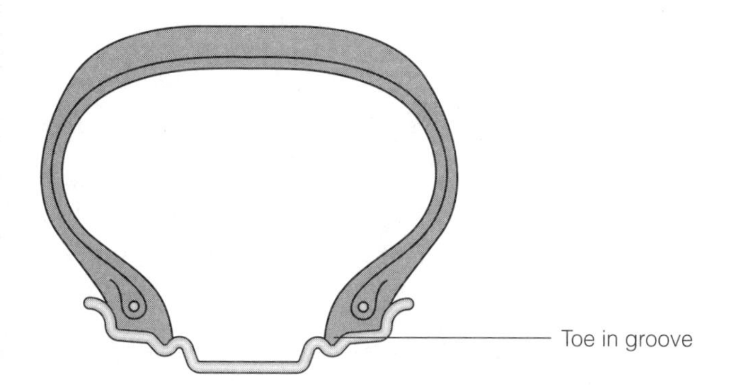

Figure 24.5 Run-flat tyre: TDX system.

Tyre sizes and markings

To ensure that all tyres have passed safety and constructional standards, they are marked with specific technical information on their sidewalls, some of it depending upon national requirements (Figure 24.6).

The information includes:

1. tyre type (cross-ply or radial);
2. ply rating;
3. cross-sectional width;
4. aspect or profile ratio;
5. tyre rim diameter;
6. speed rating;
7. load index rating.

Ply rating

> This indicates the number of plies that are used in the construction of the tyre.

The more plies that are used, the stronger the tyre will be. Thanks to improvements in tyre construction, the actual number of plies used has steadily reduced. For example, a tyre marked '6 ply / 4 ply' has the same load carrying capacity as a 6 ply tyre, but is constructed with only 4 plies. Because there is no common standard for the definition of ply rating, a more reliable indicator of a tyre's strength is the **load index**.

Cross-sectional width

Tyre width is the nominal width across the widest part of the tyre.

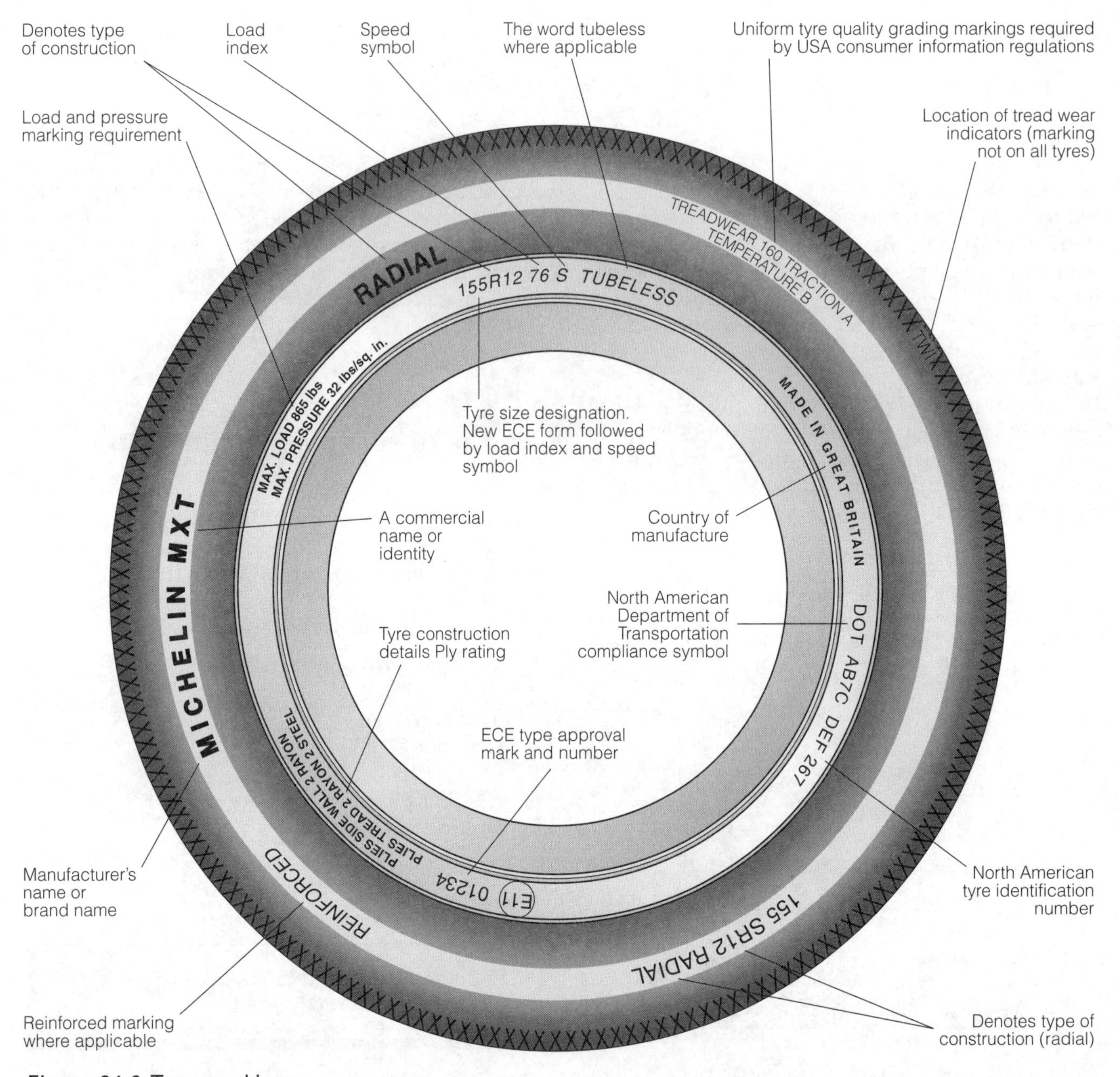

Figure 24.6 Tyre markings.

Aspect ratio

> This term describes the relationship between a tyre's cross-sectional width and its sectional height.

Early pneumatic tyres had aspect ratios of 100 per cent, which meant that the width of the tyre was approximately the same as its sectional height (Figure 24.7). Now that vehicles have become faster, many are fitted with tyres that have a low aspect ratio. This means that the tyre's sectional height is smaller than its cross-sectional width (Figure 24.7). Some of the advantages of using tyres with a low aspect ratio include the following:

1. More of the tyre is in contact with the road surface, which improves the vehicle's road-holding and steering characteristics.

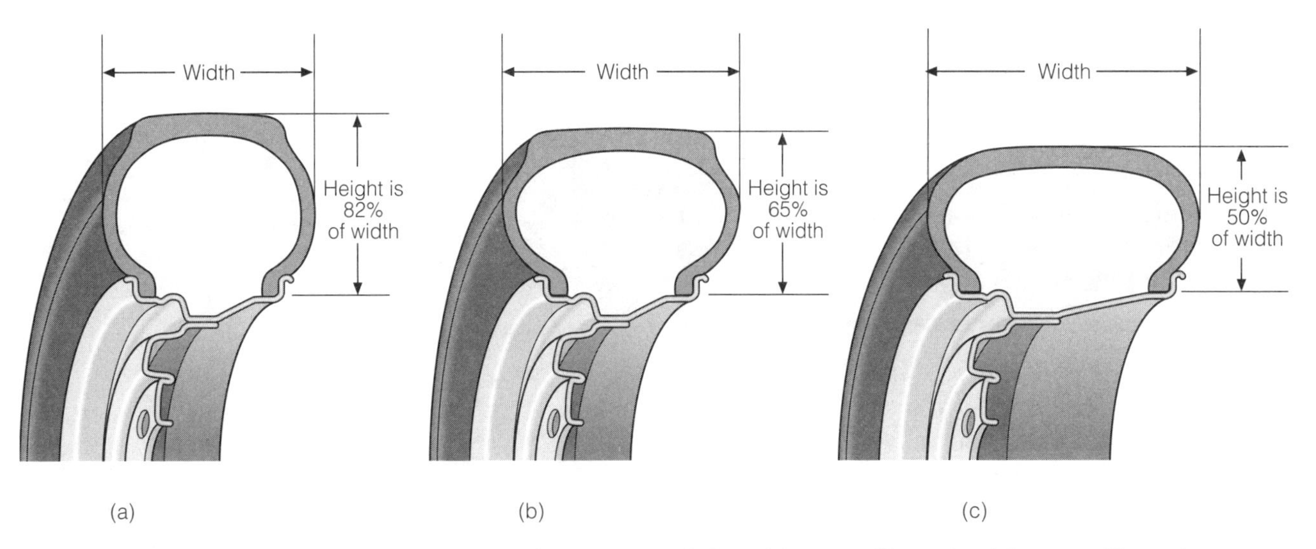

Figure 24.7 Tyre profiles: (a) standard profile ratio (radials); (b) 65 profile ratio; (c) 50 profile ratio.

2. Because of the tyre's smaller sectional height, the vehicle's centre of gravity is lower.

They do have the disadvantage of a more harsh ride as the sectional height is reduced.

Speed ratings

Tyre manufacturers now stamp each tyre with a speed code letter. This indicates the speed at which the tyre can safely be driven.

Table 24.1 shows a sample selection of speed rating codes. The letter H is out of alphabetical order because originally there were only three speed ring letters: S = slow, H = high speed, and V = very high speed.

Table 24.1 Tyre speed rating codes

Speed symbol	Speed (km/h)
L	120
M	130
N	140
P	150
Q	160
R	170
S	180
T	190
U	200
H	210
V	240

Load index

This is a number that indicates the carrying capacity of a tyre.

A sample load index chart is shown in Table 24.2. For example, a tyre with a load index code of 119 is capable of safely carrying a weight of 1360 kg under normal road conditions.

Table 24.2 Tyre load index

LI	kg	LI	kg	LI	kg
60	250	80	450	100	800
61	257	81	462	101	825
62	265	82	475	102	850
63	272	83	487	103	875
64	280	84	500	104	900
65	290	85	515	105	925
66	300	86	530	106	950
67	307	87	545	107	975
68	315	88	560	108	1000
69	325	89	580	109	1030
70	335	90	600	110	1060
71	345	91	615	111	1090
72	355	92	630	112	1120
73	365	93	650	113	1150
74	375	94	670	114	1180
75	387	95	690	115	1215
76	400	96	710	116	1250
77	412	97	730	117	1285
78	425	98	750	118	1320
79	437	99	775	119	1360

Wheel dimensions

Rim diameter and width

Rim diameter is a term used to describe the diameter of a wheel rim at the position where the tyre bead is seated (Figure 24.8).

Most wheel rims are of standard size, and are dimensioned in inches: for example, a tyre marked with '13' on its sidewall indicates that the wheel has a rim diameter of 13 in (330 mm). Exceptions to this rule are the TD and TR types of tyre, which are measured in millimetres.

Wheel width is the distance between the vertical faces of the wheel rim flanges, in inches.

A wheel rim marked '$4\frac{1}{2}$ J – 13' indicates that the wheel rim has a rim width of $4\frac{1}{2}$ in and a diameter of 13 in.

Notional flange height

To indicate the height of the flanges on a wheel rim, the rim is stamped with a code letter by the manufacturer. Typical letters include E, F, J and K.

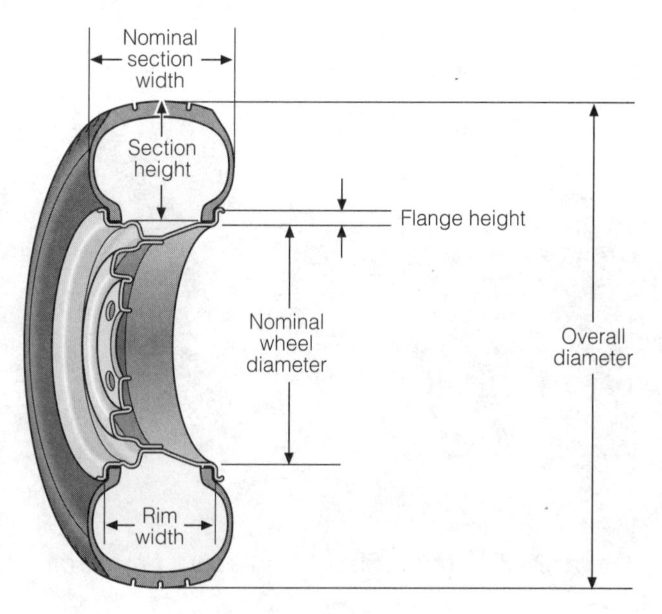

Figure 24.8 Some definitions.

Wheel offset

Some wheels are marked with the position of the wheel and tyre centreline relative to the wheel mounting flange. This is known as the **wheel offset** (Figure 24.9).

This is a critical dimension on vehicles with negative roll radius steering. When wheels are

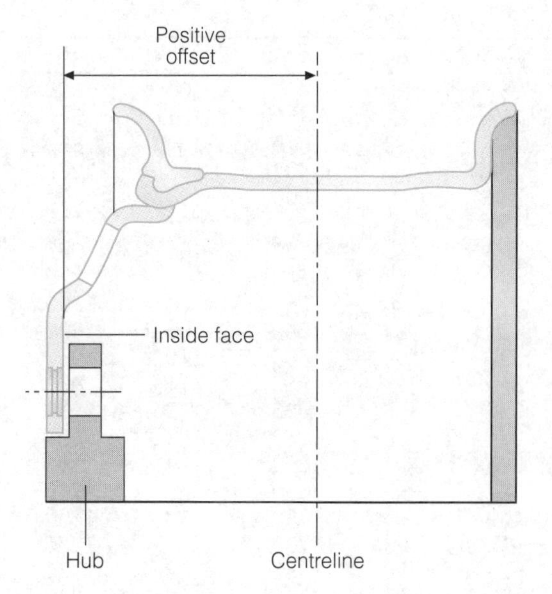

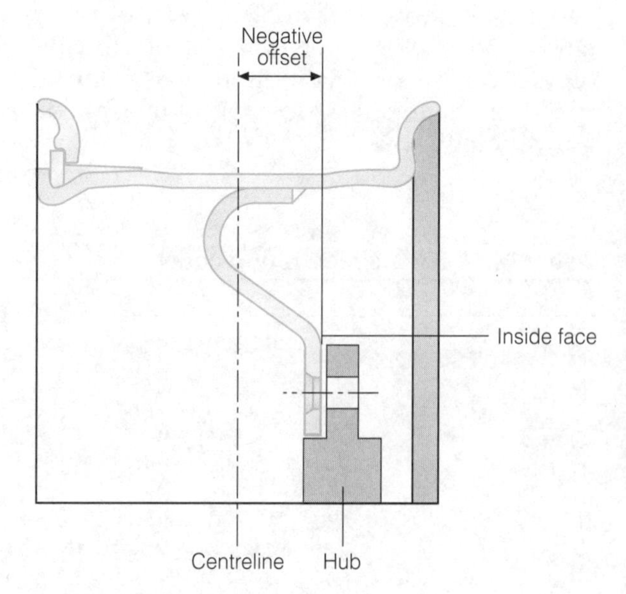

Figure 24.9 Wheel offset. (Wheels shown here are for commercial vehicles.)

replaced on such vehicles the new wheel must have the same offset figure if the self-stabilising nature of the steering is to be retained.

Note that steering offset and wheel offset are not the same thing, although they are related. See Chapter 21, page 191.

Tyre maintenance

To ensure that the tyres fitted to a vehicle are in a safe and usable condition, certain maintenance tasks should be carried out periodically.

Wheel rotation

This term refers to swapping the position of the tyres on the vehicle. Changing of tyre positions during servicing is often not now recommended.

Tyre inflation

Correct inflation is essential for optimum tyre performance. The tyre pressure should be checked regularly, *with the tyres at ambient temperature*, using an accurate tyre pressure gauge.

The actual pressure of each tyre should be compared with those specified by the vehicle or tyre maker *for the load that is carried*. There are three conditions: correct inflation, underinflation and overinflation.

Correct inflation

The tyre is correctly inflated to carry the load. This ensures that the tyre has the maximum amount of tread contact with the road surface (Figure 24.10a).

In this condition the sidewalls will also be properly supported, and will have full flexing movement without undue risk of damage.

Underinflation

The tyre pressure is lower than that recommended. This causes the sidewall of the tyre to bulge outwards, and results in poor contact between the tyre and the road surface (Figure 24.10b). Wear occurs at the outer edges of the tyre. Note that radial ply tyres may often appear to be underinflated, because of the flexible nature of their sidewalls. This is particularly true of tyres with a low aspect ratio.

Overinflation

Overinflation causes a reduction in contact between the tyre and the road surface, because the sidewalls tend to lift the outer edge of the tread pattern (Figure 24.10c). Wear occurs at the centre of the tyre tread. The major causes of overinflation are an inaccurate tyre pressure gauge, hot tyres, or incorrect reading by the operator.

Do not reduce tyre pressures when tyres become hot.

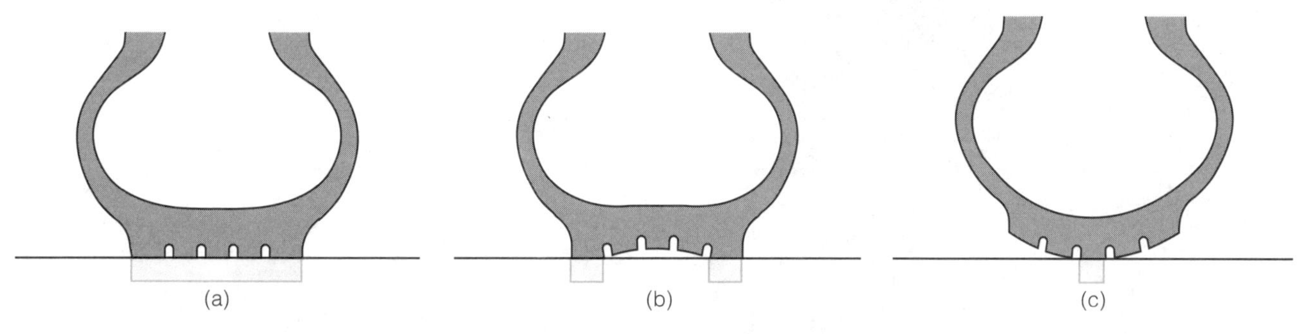

Figure 24.10 Tyre inflation. (a) Correctly inflated: tread flat across the width. (b) Underinflated: tread lifting in centre, throwing work on edges. (c) Overinflated: tread not fully flattened, work falling on centre only.

Wheel and tyre balancing

Over time a roadwheel and tyre assembly can become out of balance, caused by such things as wear and dirt becoming unevenly distributed around its axis. Uneven distribution of weight also applies when a new tyre is fitted to a wheel.

If uncorrected, the out-of-balance wheel can result in excessive vibrations of both the suspension and steering components.

The out-of-balance forces to which a wheel may be subject are **dynamic imbalance** and **static imbalance**.

Static imbalance

Static imbalance is caused by a heavy spot in the wheel assembly, which always comes to rest at the lowest point if the wheel is allowed to spin freely.

If uncorrected, this will cause the suspension to move up and down when the vehicle is travelling at speed.

Dynamic imbalance

Varying mass within the tyre and wheel assembly can both give rise to dynamic imbalance.

Figure 24.11 Wheel-balancing machine.

It is noticeable as a steering vibration or even wheel wobble at speeds, often between about 70 km/h (43 mph) and 90 km/h (56 mph).

Wheel balancing

Static imbalance is corrected by allowing the wheel and tyre assembly to spin freely, when the heavy spot will settle at the bottom. A counterbalancing weight is then attached to the opposite point.

Dynamic imbalance is corrected by spinning the wheel at speed to identify the precise point. Balance weights are then attached to the wheel rim to counterbalance the effect.

Modern wheel-balancing machines will perform all the checks and determine the position and size of the weights to be fitted (Figure 24.11).

Technical and legal requirements

Tyre tread patterns

All tyres, except those used for specialist applications such as racing cars and certain industrial vehicles, must have some form of tread pattern moulded into their outer circumference. The tread enables the tyre to grip the road surface in all conditions.

Off-road vehicles need a deep, chunky tread to enable them to cope with the difficult terrain likely to be encountered. However, such tyres are less suitable for road use.

Tyre manufacturers produce a very wide range of tread patterns for a variety of uses. A small selection is shown in Figure 24.12.

Tyre tread depth

A deep tread pattern is necessary if a tyre is to grip the road surface during wet conditions. Currently, European regulations require a minimum of 1.6 mm, forming a continuous band around the tyre equivalent to 75 per cent of the original tread area. To help identify the amount of tread remaining on the tyre, **treadwear indicators** are moulded into the tread pattern (Figure

Figure 24.12 Tread pattern designs.

24.13). The tread depth can, of course, be measured using a tyre tread depth gauge.

> Note that *any* wear of the tread will reduce the effective depth of the water-removing channels in the tread. The combination of high speed and a road surface awash with water may result in **aquaplaning**, a condition in which the tyres slide across the surface of the water and have no contact with the road surface.

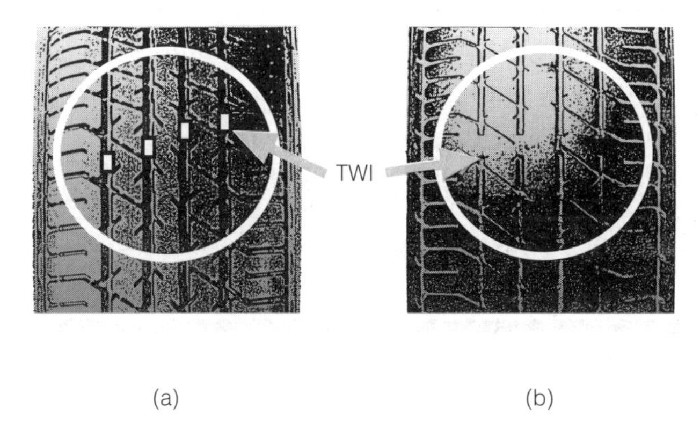

Figure 24.13 Treadwear indicators. (a) New tyre. (b) Worn tyre: this tyre is very close to, or has just become, illegal (in Europe).

Tyre combinations

Because of the different construction methods employed in making cross-ply and radial ply tyres, each type has different behaviour characteristics, especially when cornering.

> Tyre types should not be mixed on the same axle, or radials used at the front if cross-ply tyres are fitted at the rear. See your own country's regulations.

Tyre repairs

Repairs to tyres may be governed by local regulations. In Europe, for example, repairs are restricted in size and position on the tyre.

If a tyre is punctured it is important that the damage is repaired quickly. If permitted, permanent repair of simple punctures can be accomplished by using one of the following techniques:

1. hot vulcanising patch;
2. cold chemical cure patch;
3. plug and patch.

Regardless of the type used, it is important that the instructions supplied with the materials are closely followed. Remember: preparation is the key to effective tyre repair.

Wheels

Wheels serve a number of important purposes:

- They provide a location for the tyre.
- They enable accurate fitting to the vehicle and retention by the wheel nuts or bolts.
- They provide a location for the balancing weights.

The type of wheel used depends on a number of factors, such as cost, design considerations, and the use for which the vehicle is intended. Three types of wheel are commonly used on light vehicles:

1. pressed steel wheels;
2. alloy wheels;
3. wire spoked wheels.

Most wheels have similar constructional features. The middle of the wheel rim is recessed, and is called the **well base** (Figure 24.14). This well enables the removal and refitting of a tyre. The outer edge of the wheel rim is called the **rim flange**, and this is normally tapered. The taper ensures that, as the tyre is inflated, the tyre bead is forced into the taper, creating an air-tight seal. The rim shown is also humped, to prevent the tyre from readily dislodging if it is deflated.

Split or multi-part wheel rims

Heavier vehicles often have multi-part wheel rims. A spring-loaded flange or locking ring is used to hold the tyre in place (Figure 24.15). Special safety precautions must be observed when inflating wheels with such rims.

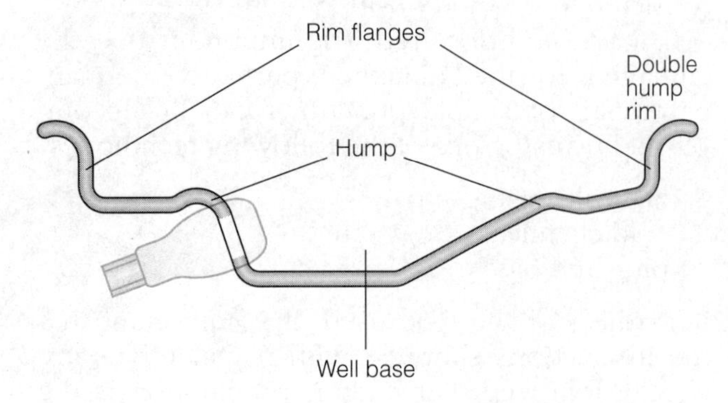

Figure 24.14 One-piece wheel rim construction.

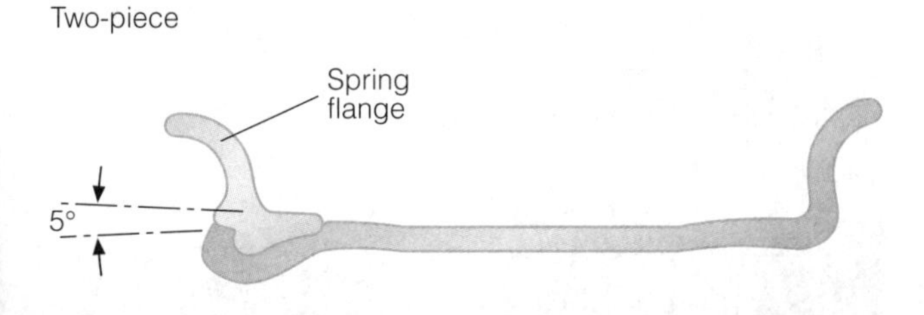

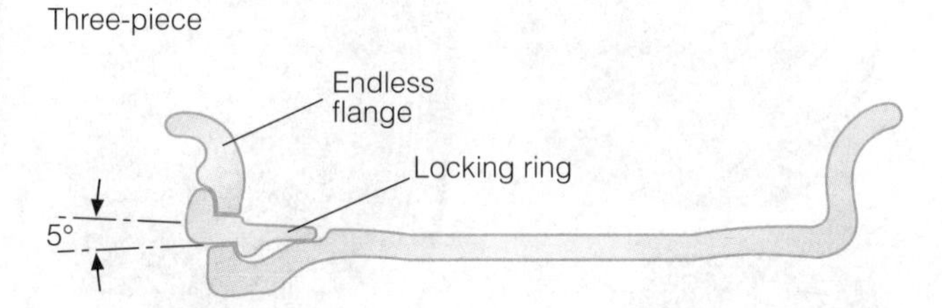

Figure 24.15 Multi-part wheel rim construction.

The spring flange or locking ring must be checked to ensure that it is properly located, and the tyre should be inflated inside a tyre cage. This prevents injury to the tyre fitter if the ring is not secure.

Divided wheels

Some specialist vehicles are equipped with **divided wheels**, incorporating a tubed tyre (Figure 24.16). The two halves of the wheel are held together by a set of clamping bolts and nuts. When a tyre change is required, the valve core

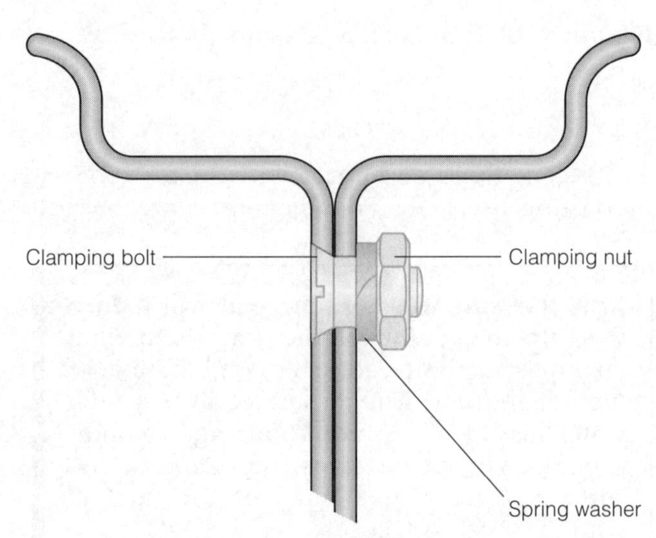

Figure 24.16 Divided wheel rim.

must be removed to release any trapped air, before the clamping nuts are released. The two halves of the wheel may then be prised apart to allow any repair or replacement to take place.

When reassembling the wheel, the clamping nuts must be tightened to the correct torque before the tyre is reinflated inside the tyre cage. It is helpful if the clamping nuts are painted in an appropriate warning colour.

> ▲ To remove an inflated wheel, only the wheel retaining nuts should be released. If some or all of the clamping nuts are released at the same time, the wheel could blow apart, with fatal consequences.

CHECK YOUR UNDERSTANDING

- The function of a tyre is to absorb some of the shock loads associated with travelling over rough roads. It also provides the vehicle with frictional contact with the road, essential for drive, directional guidance and braking.
- Tyres can be classified as either tubed or tubeless. They can also be classified by their method of construction, e.g. cross-ply or radial.
- Tyres are marked by the manufacturer with certain technical information on their sidewalls. This enables easy identification when checking for the correct tyre to be fitted to the vehicle.
- Aspect ratio is a measure of the tyre's cross-sectional width compared with its sectional height.
- At periodic intervals the tyres should be inspected for signs of cuts or bulges, and to check that their pressure is correct. To help identify the depth of tread remaining on a tyre, treadwear indicators are moulded into the tread.
- The wheel provides a location for the tyre, and the attachment point onto the vehicle. For light vehicles one-piece wheels are common; for some heavier vehicles multi-part wheels or rims are used.
- A tyre fitted to a multi-part wheel or rim must be inflated inside a safety cage.

REVISION EXERCISES AND QUESTIONS

1. State *two* reasons for fitting vehicles with pneumatic tyres.
2. Briefly state the main constructional features of a cross-ply and a radial ply tyre.
3. Name *five* items of information to be found on the sidewalls of a tyre.
4. Should the wheel positions of a vehicle be rotated periodically?
5. What does it mean when a wheel is stated to have *static imbalance*?
6. What does *dynamic balancing* of a wheel mean?
7. What are the *three* main methods of repairing a tyre?
8. What special safety precautions should be observed when inflating a tyre fitted to a multi-part wheel or split wheel?

25 Electrical equipment and wiring

Introduction

The aim of this chapter is to give basic electrical knowledge to a mechanic who is not specialising in electrical work.

The use of electrical and electronic equipment on modern vehicles is continually increasing. All mechanics will at some point need to diagnose problems, and service and repair electrical equipment just as they would any other component. The first part of this chapter explores the nature of electric current.

The problem with electricity is that we cannot see, hear or smell it. We can feel it, however. Although electricity can be immensely useful, it can also be very dangerous, and indeed has the capacity to kill. However, there is no possibility of anyone receiving an electric shock from most of the normal motor vehicle systems.

> The exception is the ignition; the high-tension part of the ignition circuit is capable of giving high-voltage shocks that in certain circumstances can be life threatening.
>
> Never wear a metal bracelet or watch strap when working on a vehicle. You may touch a live terminal and earth, causing a short-circuit. Electricity will discharge, so that the metal heats up. This can cause severe burns.

The flow of electricity is often likened to the flow of water. Figure 25.1 compares the battery to a pump, and the potential difference between two conductors (which is the difference in voltage from one end of a circuit to the other) to the potential head of water – its pressure.

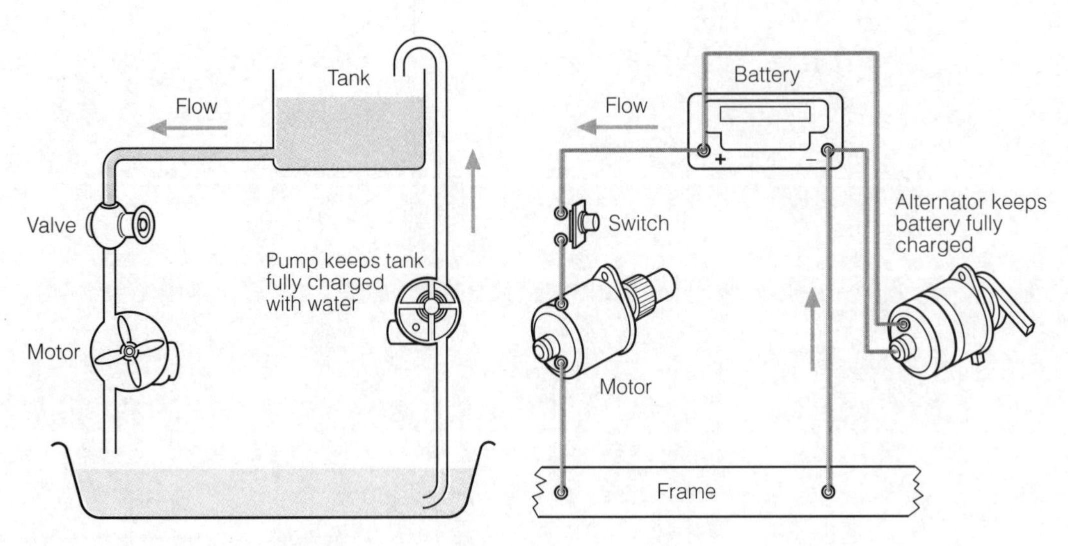

Figure 25.1 Flow of water and electricity.

When electricity flows through a conductor, like water in a pipe it flows from the higher to the lower potential. In much the same way that the pipes cause resistance to the flow of water, resistance to the flow of electricity is caused by the conductor through which it flows. This resistance varies with the material from which the conductor is made, and with the size of that conductor.

Electrical terms and effects

Terms

Conductor
This is the name given to any material through which electricity can easily flow. Good conductors, such as copper, allow the passage of electricity with little resistance.

Current
This is the flow of electrons through a conductor. It is measured in amperes (symbol A).

Electron flow
All materials consist of atoms, and atoms contain electrons. The movement of electrons in a material transports an electric current. Good conductors such as copper have many freely moving electrons.

Insulators
These are materials that have few free electrons, and do not readily pass current, so they are used as insulation in electrical systems. For example, plastic is often used as insulation around conductors to prevent them from contacting other conductors.

Potential difference (p.d.)
This is the voltage available to operate the component.

Electromotive force (e.m.f.)
This is the force (voltage) that causes electron flow. A battery or a working generator possesses an e.m.f.

Voltage drop
This is the small voltage required to push current around the circuit. Its value depends upon the resistance of the wiring. To measure voltage drop in a circuit:

Voltage drop = e.m.f. – p.d.

Resistance
This is a term used when an electrical circuit or component resists electric current flow. In some cases a resistance is created deliberately to make a component function, as with the filament in an electric lamp. The thin coil creates resistance, and heats up and produces light when a current is passed through it. In other cases resistance can be dangerous. For example, if a circuit is overloaded by forcing more current through it than the conductors can safely carry, they will heat up to such an extent that the insulation may melt and cause a fire.

Resistance is measured in ohms (symbol Ω).

The effects of electric current flow

Electricity is said to have three effects (Figure 25.2):

1. magnetic effect;
2. chemical effect;
3. heating effect.

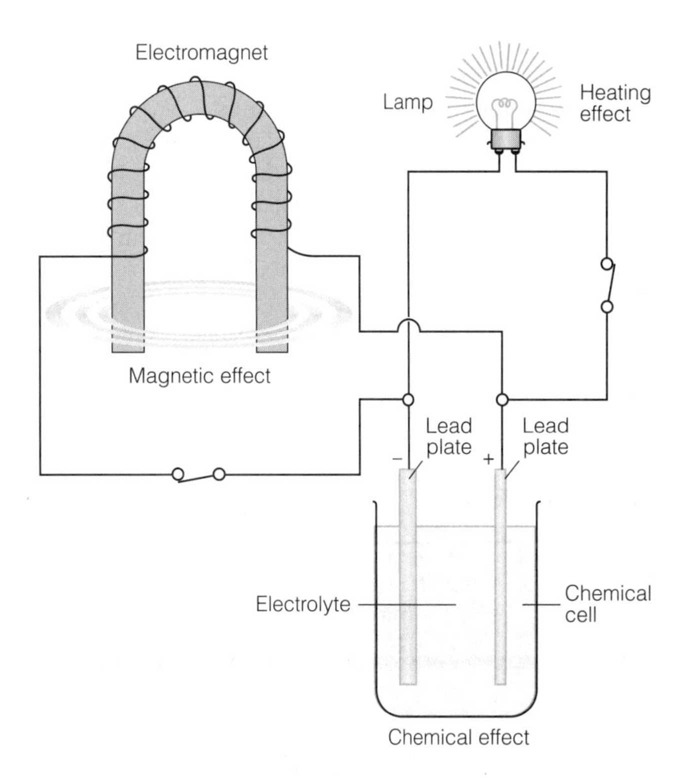

Figure 25.2 The three effects of electric current flow.

Magnetic effect

> The flow of current through a conductor causes a magnetic field around the conductor: the greater the current, the larger the magnetic field.

Considerable practical use is made of this effect, and vehicles rely upon it in many ways. It is the basis of operation of motors, generators, transformers and relays. The effect is also used to measure the current flowing through a circuit.

Chemical effect

> It is possible to pass an electric current through certain chemical solutions and cause chemical changes. These changes can then be reversed, and the chemical reaction can produce an electric current.

It is also possible for certain acids to cause current to flow when they are connected to a circuit.

Project
Connect two leads to an ammeter capable of measuring small current flows (milliamps). Attach these to two probes made of dissimilar materials: for example, one made of lead and the other of carbon or copper. Force the probes into each side of a lemon or orange. The chemical reaction should produce a measurable current (Figure 25.3).

The chemical effect of an electric current makes possible batteries, and such activities as electroplating.

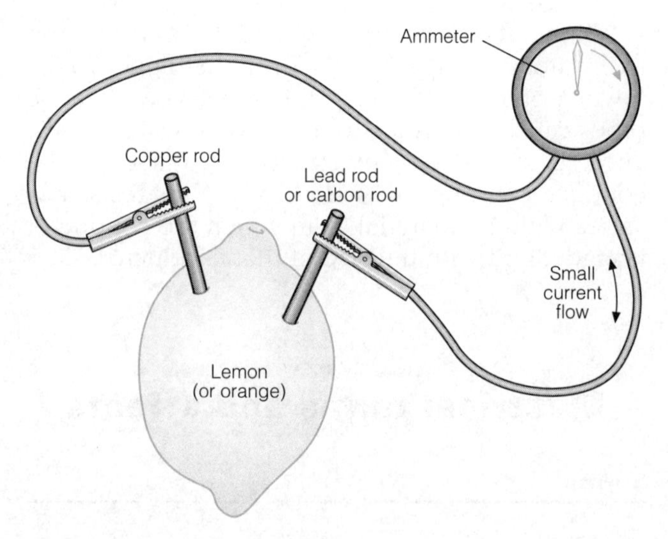

Figure 25.3 Producing an electric current from a lemon!

Heating effect

> When an electric current passes through conductors, heat may be generated.

Conductors can be designed to create large amounts of heat. The amount of heat is dependent upon the amount of the current and the nature of the resistance through which it flows. Electric cookers and filament lamps are two examples of such use.

Fuses make use of this effect to protect electrical circuits. If too much current flows through a circuit, heat will be created to melt the fuse and break the circuit.

The effect does have disadvantages, as with components such as ignition coils, which must be cooled.

Motor vehicles use all three effects:

1. Magnetic effect: ignition coil, generator, starter motor, solenoids and the horn.
2. Chemical effect: the battery.
3. Heating effect: the lighting system.

Fundamental laws of electricity

Ohm's law

The three fundamental characteristics of the electrical system are pressure (volts), current (amperes), and resistance (ohms), and there is a definite relationship between them. This relationship is known as **Ohm's law**.

> Ohm's law states that the current (amperes) flowing in a circuit is directly proportional to the pressure (volts) and inversely proportional to the resistance (ohms).

This simply means that an increase in voltage will result in an increase in current flow, but an increase in resistance will result in a decrease in current flow.

The law can be expressed as a useful equation:

$$I = \frac{E}{R}$$

where I is the current in **amperes** (A), E is the pressure or electromotive force (e.m.f.) in **volts** (V), and R is the resistance in **ohms** (Ω). Note: It is acceptable to replace the E with V in the above equation.

If the values of any two factors are known, we can quickly find the third by doing a simple calculation. If the voltage of a consumer is known, and the resistance of the circuit is measured with an ohmmeter, the current flow can be calculated. The correct size of fuse needed to protect the circuit can then be selected.

Another electrical unit is the **watt** (W).

> The watt is the unit of power. It is defined as the power used when a current of 1 A flows through a circuit having 1 V applied to it.

Expressed as a formula:

power = voltage × current

or

$$W = E \times I$$

Note: Again, it is acceptable to replace the E with V.

Here is a practical example of how this formula could be used. If two extra lamps each of 60 W are fitted to a 12 V system, the extra load that this will add to that already being supplied by the generator can be calculated.

The two lamps are added together:

$$60 + 60 = 120 \text{ W}$$
$$W = E \times I$$
$$120 = 12 \times I$$
$$\text{So } I = \frac{120}{12}$$
$$= 10 \text{ A}$$

This extra current must now be added to the electrical load already being supplied.

In order to understand the operation of many electrical components the mechanic needs to know two further fundamental laws of electricity.

> When a current flows in a circuit, it creates a magnetic field around the conductor.

Magnetic lines of force surround a permanent magnet and a conductor, but only when current flows in the conductor (Figure 25.4). If this wire is made into a coil and then fitted around a soft iron core made up of laminated strips, it greatly increases the magnetic field (Figure 25.5). This is the basis of ignition coils and of the electromagnets used in solenoids.

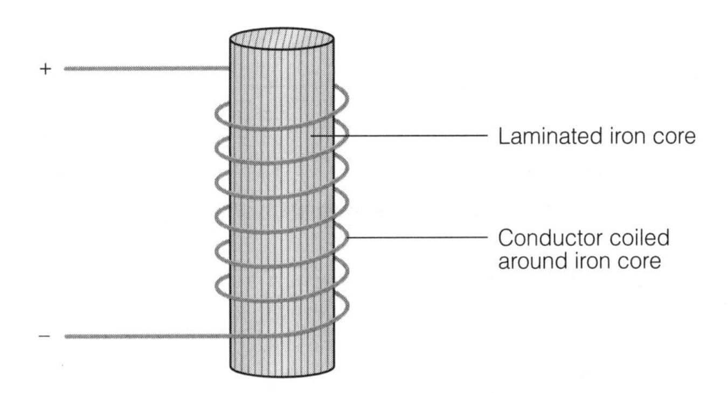

Figure 25.5 **If the conductor is coiled round a soft iron core, the magnetic field is greatly increased.**

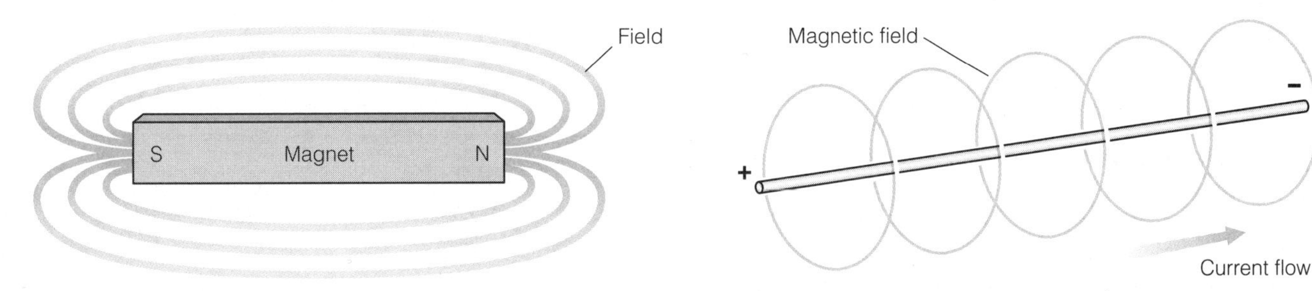

Figure 25.4 When a current flows in a circuit, it creates a magnetic field around the conductor.

When a magnetic field moves across a conductor, or a conductor is moved through a magnetic field, a current is induced in the circuit.

This principle is used in the generator, and also in ignition coils.

The vehicle electrical installation

A vehicle engine burns fuel and oxygen, and some of this is converted into mechanical energy. A small part of this energy is used to drive the generator, which provides power for electrical systems, and charges the vehicle battery.

Circuits and cables

If a lamp is connected to just one terminal of a battery it will not light (Figure 25.6a). The current must be able to travel through the lamp (or any other electrical component) and return to the battery (Figure 25.6b).

There must always be a complete circuit if current is to flow.

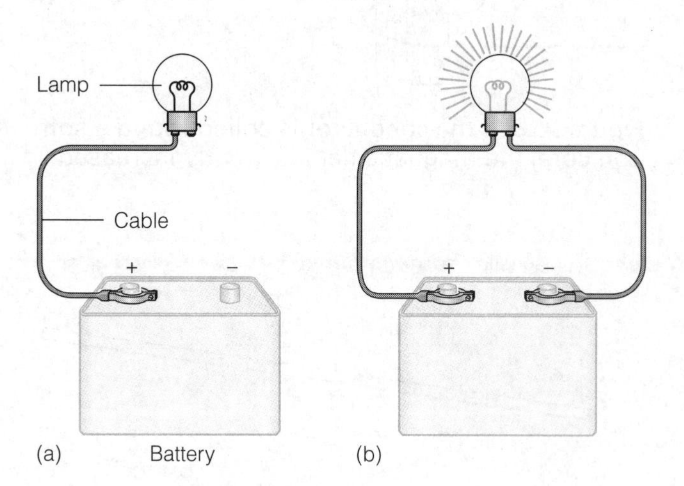

Figure 25.6 There must always be a complete circuit if current is to flow.

Types of circuit

There are two basic layouts of circuit: the **series circuit** and the **parallel circuit**.

The series circuit

Bulbs (or other **consumers**) connected one after the other in sequence are said to be connected in **series**, and the same current flows through all of them (Figure 25.7).

Note that a consumer is anything in an electrical circuit that uses (consumes) electricity to make it work: for example, bulbs, electric motors, and solenoids.

In Figure 25.7 there are two lamps; failure of only one means that the circuit is broken, and current will cease to flow.

The parallel circuit

Bulbs (or other consumers) connected independently of any others in the same circuit are said to be **in parallel**, and they will share the available current (Figure 25.8).

This is the general method of wiring the lighting circuit on a vehicle. The advantage for a lighting system is that if one lamp fails the others continue to work.

The wiring diagrams for vehicles show all the electrical components connected by lines to represent the wiring. This may seem confusing, but if each circuit is traced and considered separately it becomes quite easy to understand.

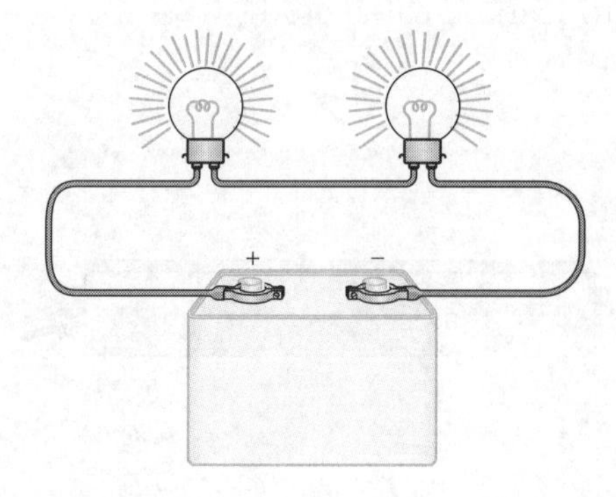

Figure 25.7 Series circuit.

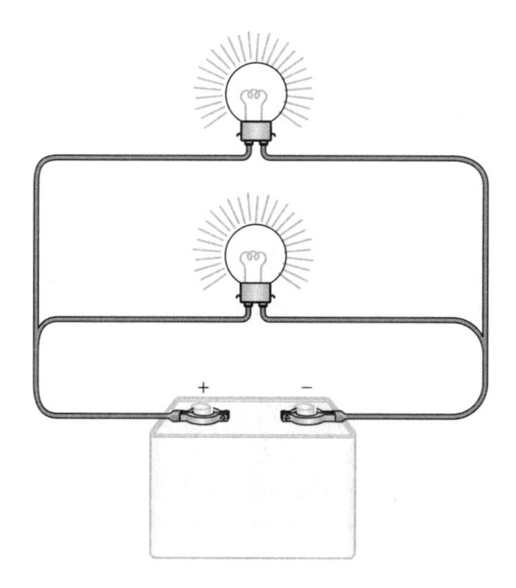

Figure 25.8 Parallel circuit.

Vehicle electrical equipment

A vehicle will normally have the following electrical equipment:

1. **Battery** – to provide electrical power when the engine is not running.
2. **Starter motor** – to turn the engine over for starting.
3. **Generator** – to supply consumers when the engine is running, and to charge the battery.
4. **Ignition system** – to ignite the fuel mixture in the combustion chambers of petrol-engined vehicles.
5. **Glow plugs** – to help starting on vehicles with diesel engines.
6. **Lighting** – for vision and visibility.
7. **General consumers** such as the ventilation/heater fan, air conditioning equipment, windscreen wipers and radio.

Electrical cables and wiring

The cables linking all the electrical equipment together are an essential part of any motor vehicle. It is important when replacing cables, or when installing additional equipment, to make sure that the cable is of the correct specification. A cable's resistance to current flow depends upon its cross-sectional area and its length. If too small a cable is used the resistance will be excessive, causing overheating and a reduction in voltage at the component end of the cable. Severe resistance may cause the cable to overheat sufficiently to cause a fire. Remember that the difference between the supply voltage (e.m.f.) and the voltage at the consumer (p.d.) is known as **voltage drop**, and is caused by resistance in the cable.

To fit around the inside of a vehicle's bodyshell or follow the contours of a chassis, and to resist fracture from vibration and movement, cables must be flexible. To achieve flexibility the cables are made up of a number of thin strands of copper wire rather than one thick wire.

Cable size varies with the type of circuit: the greater the current demanded by the consumer, the larger the cross-sectional area must be. For example, a cable feeding the starter motor will be much thicker than the cable feeding a sidelamp. As we have already seen, Ohm's law describes the relationship between voltage drop, resistance and current flow. Table 25.1 shows typical cable sizes and their resistance.

Earth return

Instead of passing through a cable the current returns to the battery through the chassis or body (Figure 25.9).

By earthing one terminal of the battery and one terminal of each component to the metal chassis or body, the number and the length of the cables needed on a vehicle can be halved. This saves considerably on manufacturing costs, weight and complication.

Table 25.1 Typical cable sizes and their resistance

Number and thickness of strands (mm)	Resistance per metre (Ω at 20 °C)	Continuous rating (A)	Typical application
9/0.30	0.0294	5.75	Low-tension ignition;
14/0.30	0.0189	8.75	side and tail lamps
28/0.30	0.095	17.50	Headlamps
44/0.30	0.0060	25.50	Battery supply
37/0.71 to 61/1.13	0.0001	105 to 415	Starter motors

Insulated return

Some specialist vehicles such as petrol and chemical tankers have what is known as an **insulated earth return**. This system use insulated cables to return current to the battery instead of using the chassis or body.

This type of return is used to minimise the build-up of static electricity on the vehicle body; this might otherwise cause a spark, which could ignite hazardous substances being carried by the vehicle. Also, some vehicles' bodies are made out of fibreglass; this is a very poor electrical conductor, and so an insulated earth cable is provided, which runs along the entire length of the vehicle's body to complete the electrical circuit.

Fusing of circuits

> When the load in a circuit (the consumer) is bypassed because a fault develops, excessive current will try to pass through the cables to return to the battery. This is known as a **short-circuit**.

Although the cables are surrounded by insulation, and are additionally protected at points where damage may occur, faults often develop where the insulation chafes through. In this situation the battery tries to force all its potential through the cable to the point where it is earthing on the chassis or body. Such a current can create sufficient heat to melt the cable and its insulation, probably causing a fire. This risk can be reduced by inserting a fuse in the circuit.

> A fuse is designed to melt when a specified current flow is exceeded, and it is carefully matched to the circuit.

It is very important that only fuses of the correct rating are used (Figure 25.10).

For convenience, all the main fuses are usually located in one place on the vehicle. They are mounted in a fuse block, where all the circuits converge to pass through appropriate fuses before continuing to the consumers around the vehicle. This is sometimes also used for the mounting of relays, when it may be called the **relay plate**.

Current generation, storage and consumer systems

Current supply

> Electric current may flow continuously in one direction, when it is called **direct current (d.c.)**, or it may continuously reverse its direction, when it is called **alternating current (a.c.)**.

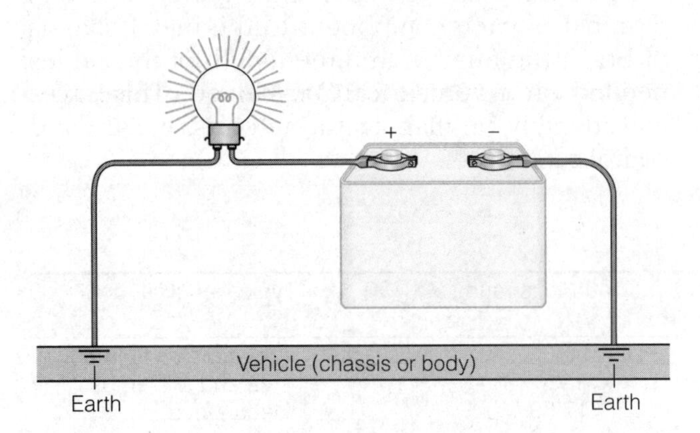

Figure 25.9 Using the vehicle body as earth return.

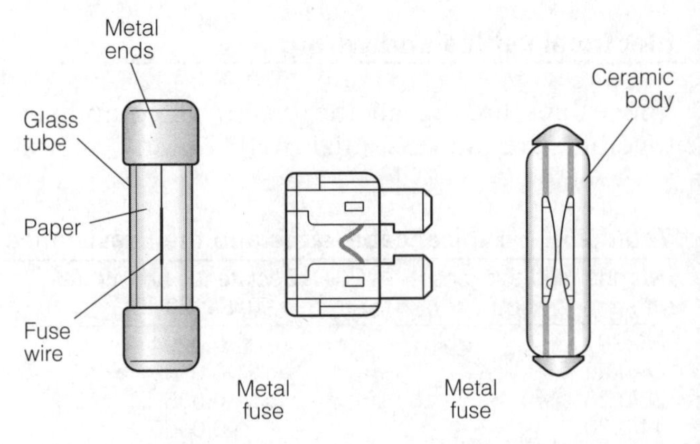

Figure 25.10 Fuses.

All cars and commercial vehicles require a battery to store electrical energy, and 6 V, 12 V or 24 V systems have been used. Typically now 12 V batteries are used in 12 V or 24 V systems. The electrical capacity of the battery is relative to its physical size, and varies from vehicle to vehicle. All batteries supply, and must be charged with, direct current.

To provide the energy to drive electrical components and charge the battery when the engine is running a generator is fitted. Early vehicles had a d.c. generator known as a **dynamo**. These units could cope quite happily with the electrical energy demands of the time. To provide the larger quantities of electrical energy needed by present-day vehicles a generator called an **alternator** is fitted. As its name implies it provides a.c., and this must be changed to d.c. to charge the battery. This process, called **rectification**, is carried out inside the unit.

The alternator provides important advantages compared with the earlier dynamo: size for size it can produce double the current, and it can do so at low engine speeds.

Ignition systems

Petrol engines need a spark to ignite the air/fuel mixture in the cylinder, and this is a vital electrical system. However, because it is a specialised topic it has already been dealt with separately in Chapter 4.

Lighting circuits

All road vehicles are fitted with white lights to the front so that the driver can see in the dark, and red lights at the rear to act as a warning to other road users. In addition, other warning lamps such as braking and direction indicators, together with number plate illumination lights, are fitted. Most countries have strict regulations regarding the fitting and use of vehicle lights.

Starting circuit

All motor vehicles are fitted with an electric starter motor to turn the engine for starting. This requires a heavy current from the battery, sometimes over 100 A, and demands large cables to prevent excessive resistance and consequent overheating.

Electronic systems on vehicles

The heart of an electronic control system is the **electronic control unit**, the ECU. All electronic systems use different forms of sensor to provide the ECU with information. The sensor data is read by the ECU, which then compares it with pre-programmed information contained within its memory. A response is calculated, and the various actuators connected to the ECU are adjusted as directed. The results are checked, and the process is repeated many times over, every second.

An ECU can be used to control the engine fuel system, ignition system, and exhaust emission controls, when it is collectively called an **engine management system**. Anti-lock brake systems (ABS) are controlled by an ECU, and sometimes automatic transmissions too.

Auxiliary circuits

Many modern vehicles have additional circuits for such things as in-car entertainment, heated and powered windows, heated and powered mirrors, heated and motorised seats, sunroofs, and motorised cabriolet tops. These are known as **auxiliary circuits**.

Wiring diagrams

The electrical systems of present-day vehicles are often very complex. To aid circuit identification, many manufacturers use colour-coded cables (Figure 25.11).

> With the aid of the circuit or wiring diagrams produced by the manufacturer, the colour coding can be used to identify particular circuits during fault finding.

Although at first glance a circuit diagram looks complicated, it can usually be broken down into sections. Indeed, some manufacturers present them in this way for ease of use.

In order to use any diagram, it is first necessary to know the symbols and the method of use. Most workshop manuals give this information, which is not, unfortunately, the same from one make to another. But cables are usually identified by printed colour code or a number, and components by name or a code (Figure 25.12).

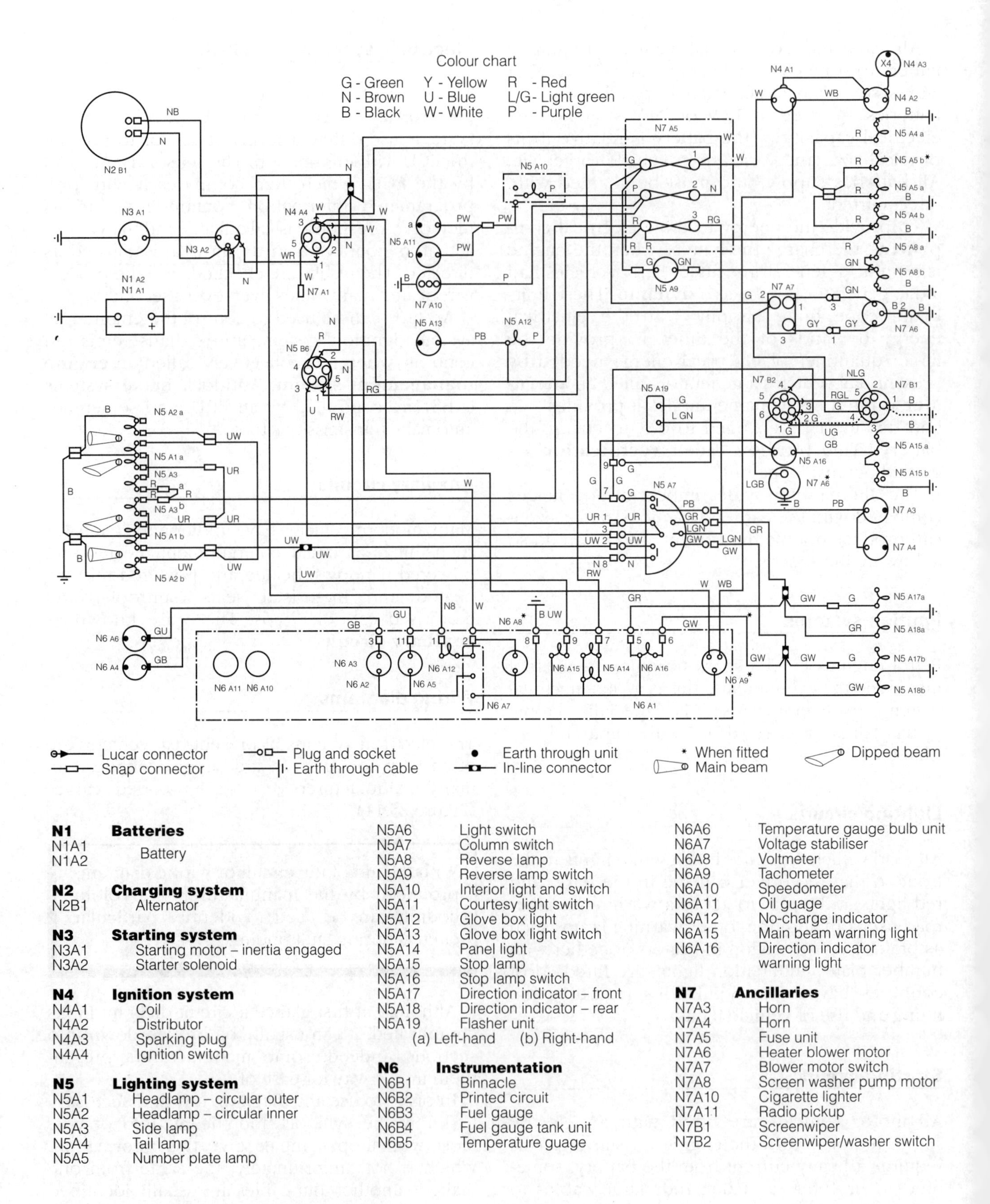

Figure 25.11 Typical wiring diagram.

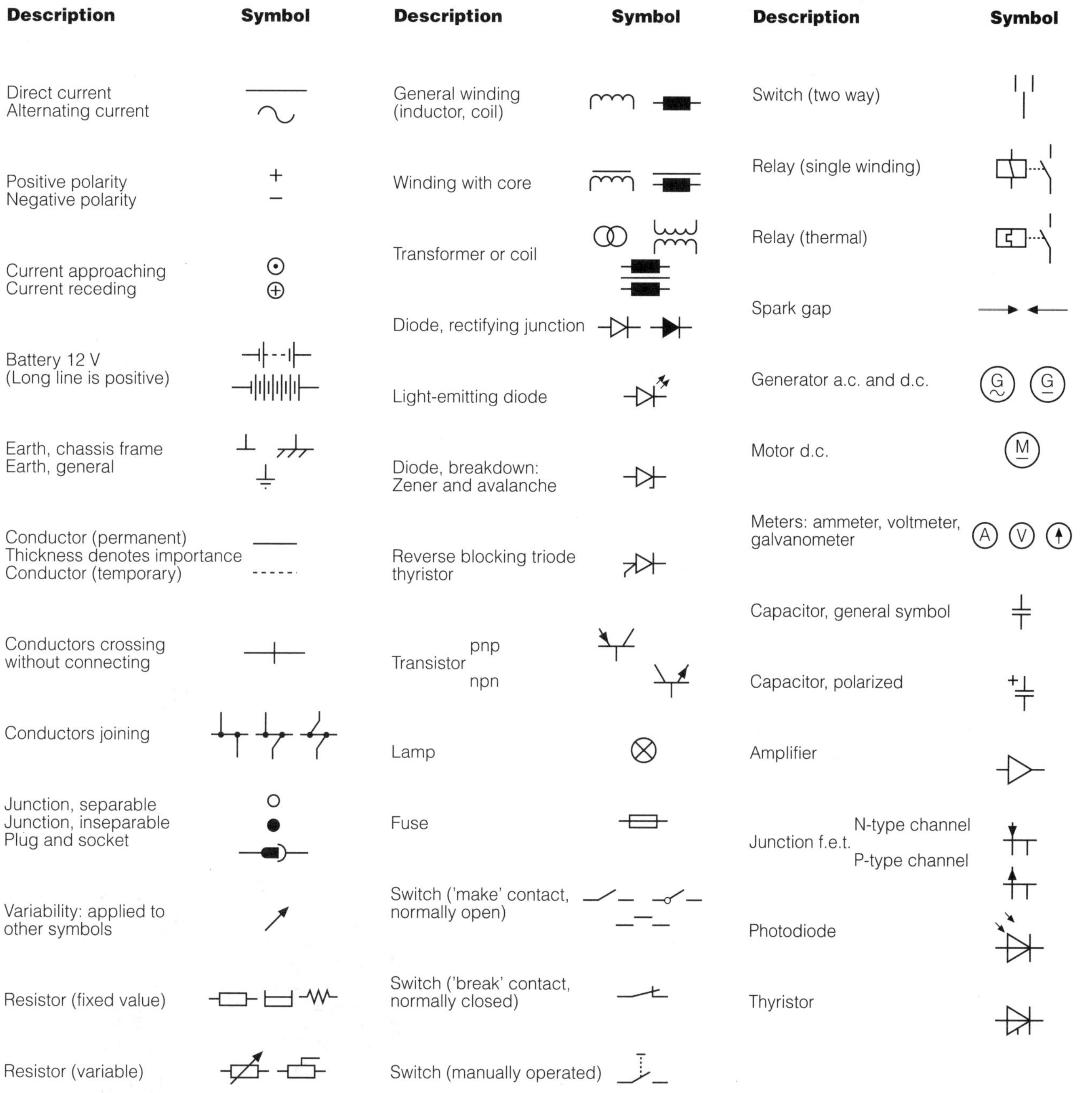

Description	Symbol	Description	Symbol	Description	Symbol
Direct current Alternating current		General winding (inductor, coil)		Switch (two way)	
Positive polarity Negative polarity	+ –	Winding with core		Relay (single winding)	
Current approaching Current receding		Transformer or coil		Relay (thermal)	
Battery 12 V (Long line is positive)		Diode, rectifying junction		Spark gap	
Earth, chassis frame Earth, general		Light-emitting diode		Generator a.c. and d.c.	G G
Conductor (permanent) Thickness denotes importance Conductor (temporary)		Diode, breakdown: Zener and avalanche		Motor d.c.	M
Conductors crossing without connecting		Reverse blocking triode thyristor		Meters: ammeter, voltmeter, galvanometer	A V
Conductors joining		Transistor pnp Transistor npn		Capacitor, general symbol	
Junction, separable Junction, inseparable Plug and socket		Lamp		Capacitor, polarized	+
Variability: applied to other symbols		Fuse		Amplifier	
Resistor (fixed value)		Switch ('make' contact, normally open)		Junction f.e.t. N-type channel Junction f.e.t. P-type channel	
Resistor (variable)		Switch ('break' contact, normally closed)		Photodiode	
		Switch (manually operated)		Thyristor	

Figure 25.12 Electrical symbols (BS 3939 : 1985).

Component location

The main operating components connected into the wiring harness tend to be hidden away behind panels or mounted under other parts. To aid the mechanic to find these components – every manufacturer positions them in different places – locations are often given in the workshop manuals (Figure 25.13).

Wiring harness connections

To help in finding all the parts connected to the wiring harness, every manufacturer produces location diagrams showing cable connectors and components (Figure 25.14).

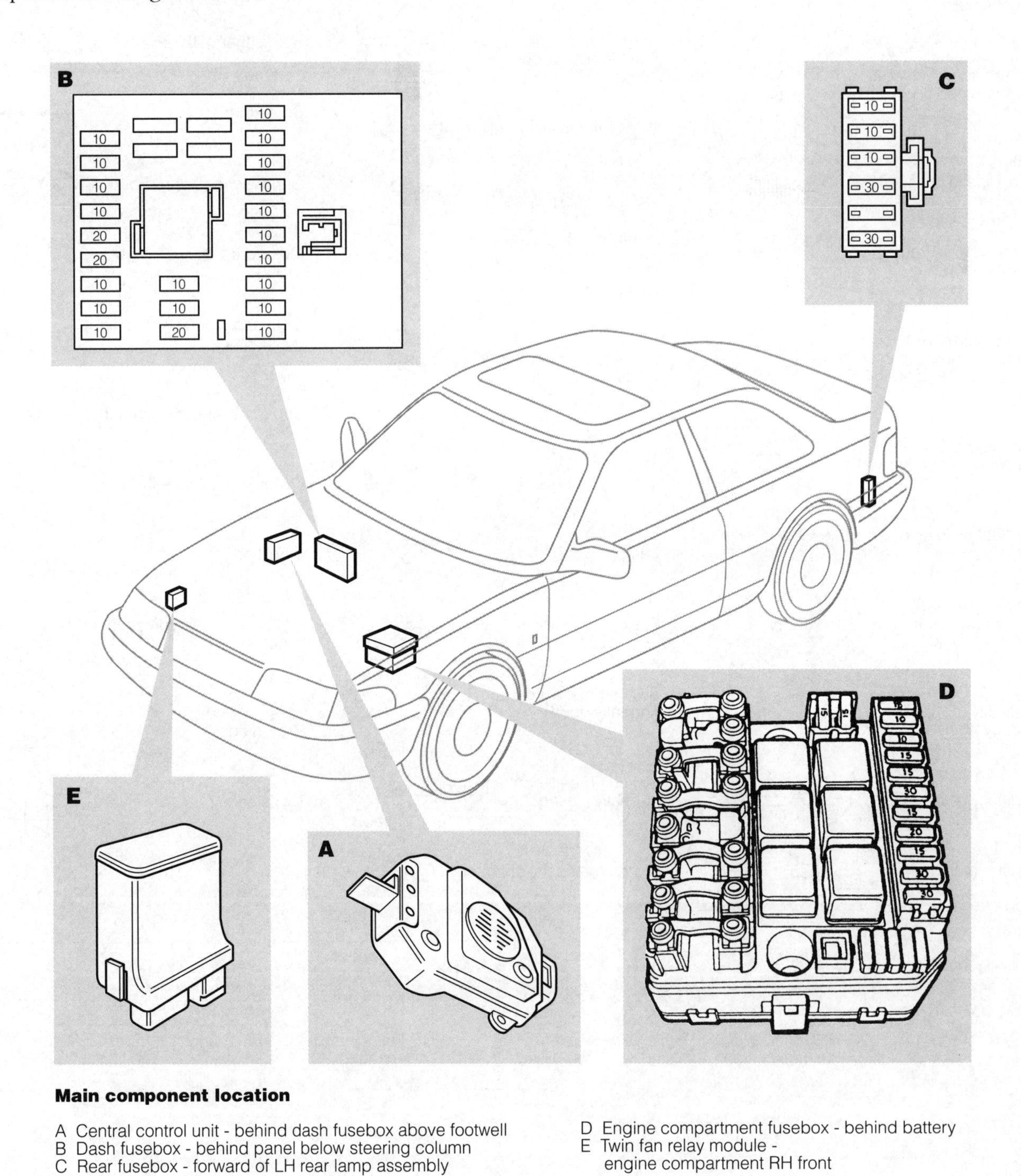

Figure 25.13 Component locations, as shown in workshop manual.

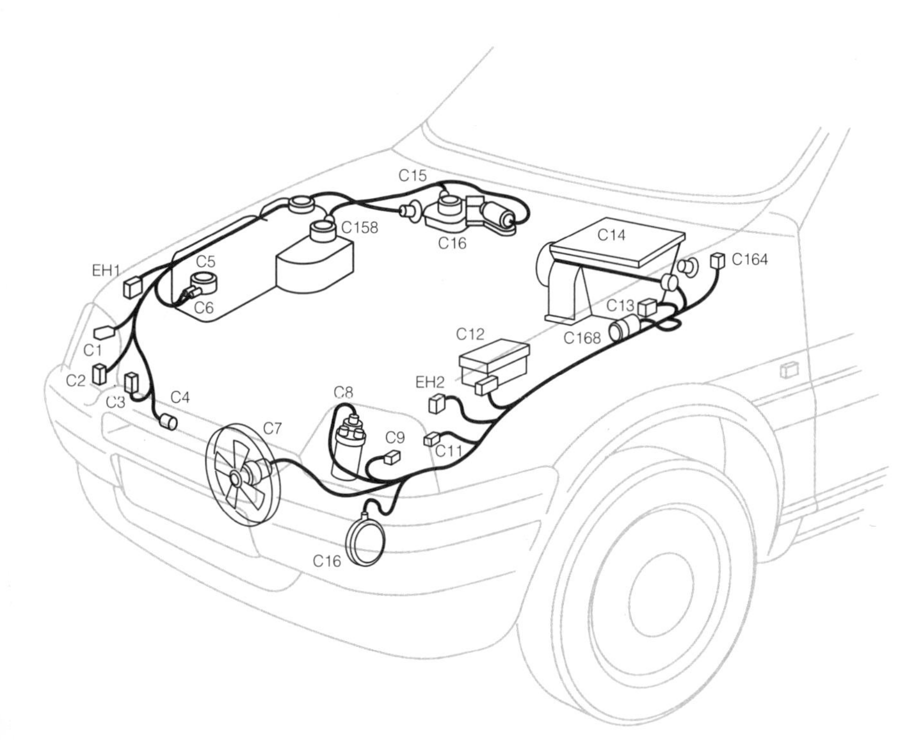

Main harness - under bonnet

EH1 Earth point 1
EH2 Earth point 2
C1 RH front direction indicator lamp
C2 Headlamp dim dip resistor
C3 RH headlamp
C4 Coolant temperature switch
C5 Rear washer motor
C6 Front washer motor
C7 Cooling fan motor
C8 Ignition coil
C9 LH headlamp
C10 Horn
C11 LH front direction indicator lamp
C12 Fusible link box
C13 Engine harness connector
C14 Heater motor
C15 Brake fluid level switch
C16 Wiper motor
C164 Bonnet switch
C158 Low coolant level switch - diesel models
C168 Diagnostic connector

Figure 25.14 Typical location diagram of wiring harness connections.

The lead–acid battery

The batteries used on motor vehicles are usually of the secondary cell, lead–acid type. A fully charged lead–acid cell is capable of creating a pressure of 2.2 V. A six-cell 12 V battery can actually provide 13.2 V when fully charged.

A secondary cell can be charged, discharged and recharged repeatedly. The action is said to be **reversible**. This contrasts with disposable dry cell batteries, which are primary cells (non-reversible) and cannot be recharged.

Passing an appropriate current through a secondary cell causes chemical changes to occur within the cell. Taking current out causes these changes to be reversed.

Construction

A lead–acid cell consists of lead plates, separated from each other, and immersed in a solution of dilute sulphuric acid, called the **electrolyte**. When the cell is connected to a d.c. supply to be charged, a chemical action takes place. The sulphuric acid, H_2SO_4, splits into two parts: the positive part, $2H^+$, is attracted to the negative plate (called the **cathode**), and the negative part, SO_4^-, combines with the hydrogen from the water (H_2O) to reform H_2SO_4. The oxygen (O^-) released from the water carries a negative charge, and combines with the positive plate (called the **anode**) to form lead peroxide (PbO_2). The electrical energy fed into the cell has now been stored as chemical energy, which can be reconverted when required (Figure 25.15).

During charging, some of the hydrogen and oxygen gases escape and form an explosive mixture. Keep sparks and naked lights away.

During discharge, the H_2SO_4 splits up, with the hydrogen ($2H^+$) passing to the positive plate and giving up its charge as it combines with the

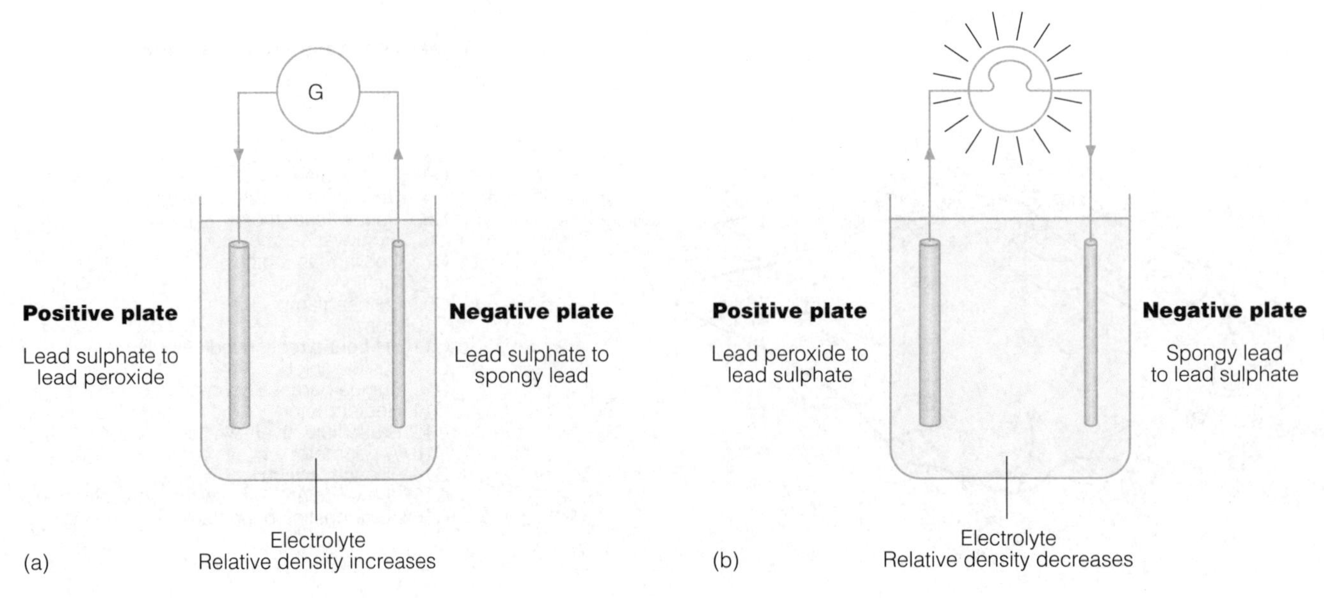

Figure 25.15 **The lead–acid cell: (a) charging; (b) discharging.**

oxygen of the lead peroxide to form water (H_2O). The SO_4^- part combines with the lead to form lead sulphate ($PbSO_4$). During recharging, the hydrogen will again combine with the sulphate to form H_2SO_4, and the oxygen combines with the lead to form lead peroxide, PbO_2.

Electrolyte

When topping up a battery, always use distilled water, as this is pure. Water from a tap or well may contain dirt and impurities that could damage the battery or reduce the effect of the chemical changes and therefore the battery's performance and life.

As you can see from the chemical reaction outlined above, the electrolyte changes as the cell is charged and discharged. During discharge, the electrolyte becomes more diluted.

The **relative density** or **specific gravity** of a liquid is its density or 'thickness' when compared with water. Above 1.0 the liquid is denser than water; below 1.0 it is less dense than water. In the preparation of electrolyte, the ratio should be 3 parts of water to 1 part of sulphuric acid.

In the event of a spillage the electrolyte should be washed away with large amounts of plain water.

Spilt acid will burn skin and clothing, and corrode other materials.
When mixing electrolyte, add the acid gently and slowly to the water; a violent reaction will occur if water is added to acid.

Battery maintenance

The main items of battery maintenance are as follows:

1. Top up the electrolyte level periodically with distilled water. The frequency of topping up depends on how much the vehicle is used, on the charging rate, and on the ambient temperature. The electrolyte should just cover the top of the plates; avoid overfilling.
2. Keep the terminals clean and dry. A coating of petroleum jelly retards corrosion.
3. Mount the battery securely, to avoid damage.

Battery testing

The quickest method of assessing the condition of a battery is to use an electronic tester (Figure 25.16). If the battery stoppers are removable the state of charge may be determined by means of a hydrometer. A charged cell should give a reading of between 1.25 and 1.28. If the cell readings are

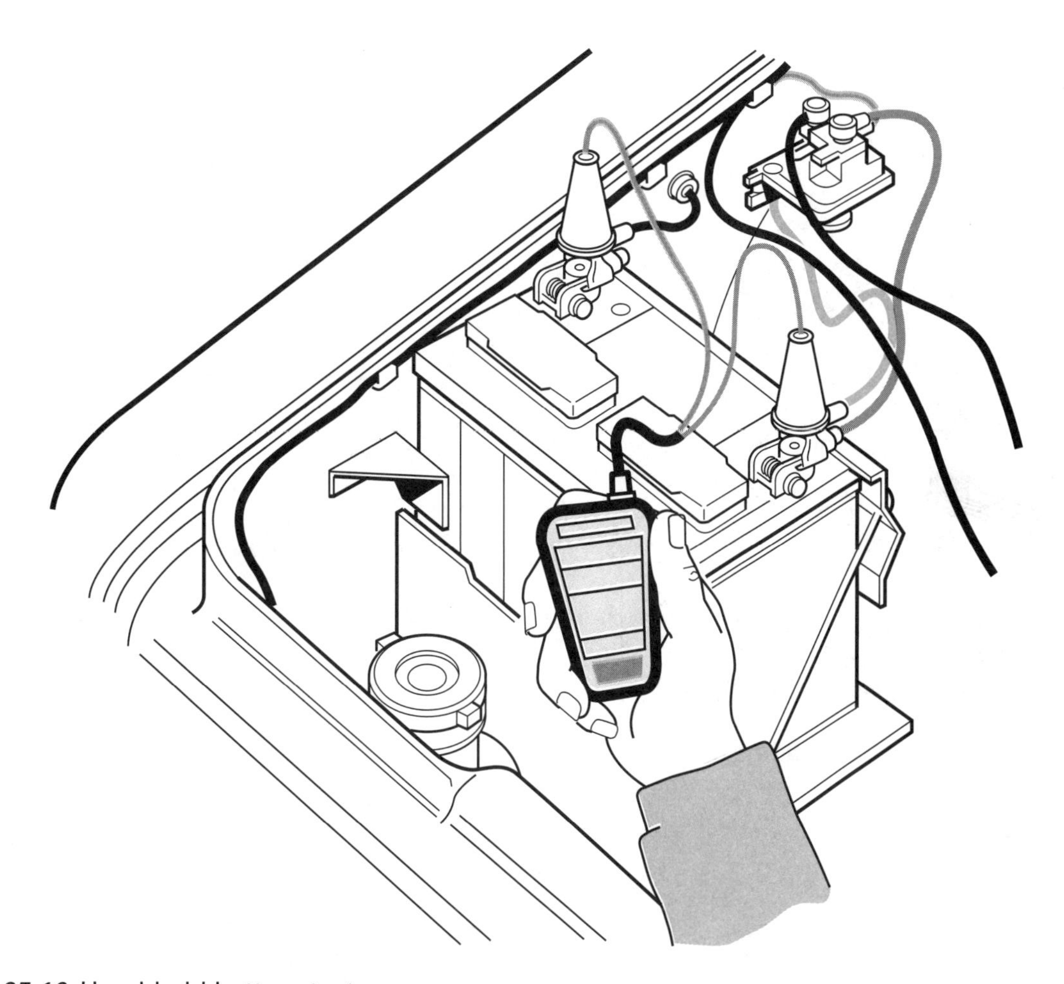

Figure 25.16 Hand-held battery tester.

low, the battery should be charged and checked again (Figure 25.17). For example, a discharged cell would give readings of 1.15 or less.

To determine the overall condition of the battery a high-rate discharge test must be used. This principally consists of a low-resistance shunt (which is a conductor that joins two parts of a circuit, and through which part of the current can pass), and a voltmeter. The two prongs of the tester are placed across the battery terminals for a few seconds to allow a current of 150–200 A to pass. If the battery is in good condition the voltage should not drop significantly. Where the reading drops below 10 V, this is a sign of cell failure (Figure 25.18). If cells can be seen to bubble during this test, that too is an indication of failure.

> This tester should *not* be used on batteries that are not fully charged.

The charging system

The dynamo

A dynamo is driven from the engine, usually by means of a belt, and it produces electric current to supply the various circuits and for charging the vehicle battery.

Creating e.m.f.

> When an electrical conductor is moved in a magnetic field, an **electromotive force** or **e.m.f.** is induced in it. In simple terms this means that if a copper wire is moved through a magnetic field an electric current will flow in that wire if it is part of a circuit.

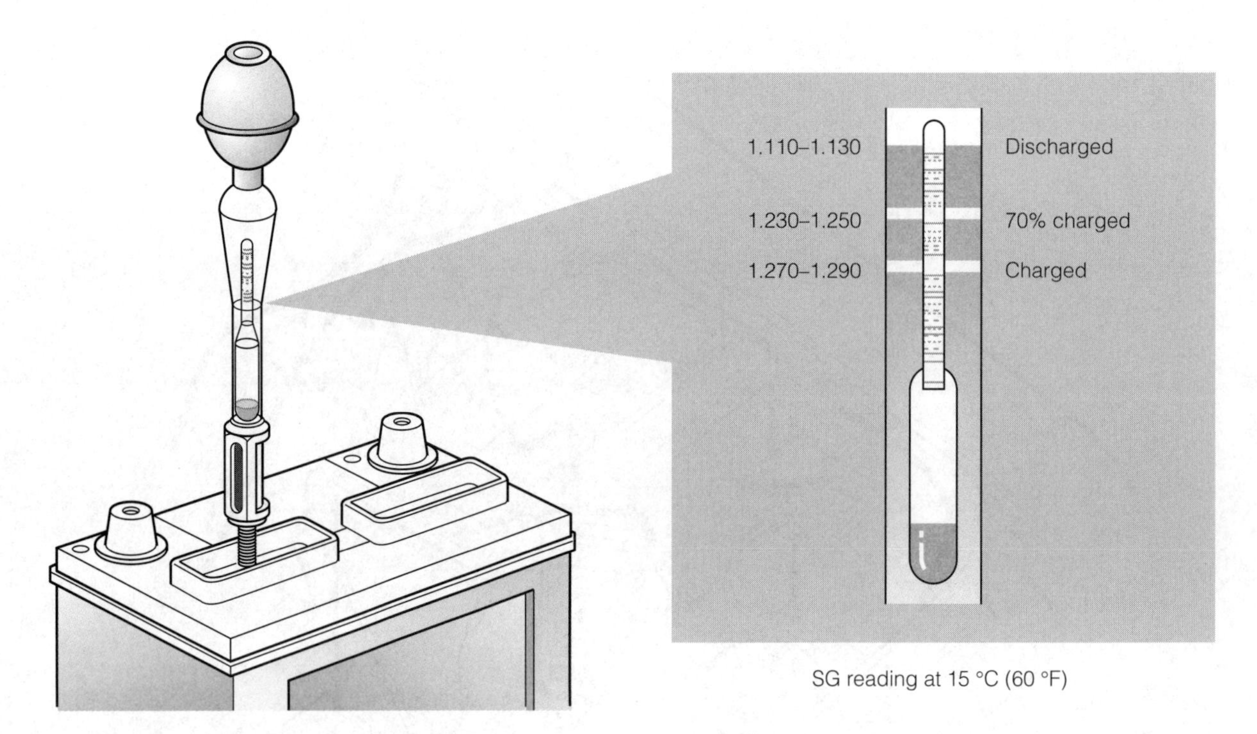

Figure 25.17 Specific gravity readings.

Figure 25.18 Heavy-duty battery discharge tester.

The direction of this current flow varies, and depends on the direction in which the wire is moved through the magnetic field (Figure 25.19).

It would be very difficult to make a generator that had a conductor moving back and forth through a magnetic field, and so generators have their conductors moving around in a circular path. The basic principle is carried a stage further by having a loop of wire in the magnetic field that has both ends attached to sections of a metal ring called a **commutator** (Figure 25.20). Carbon **brushes** make contact with the commutator. One brush is connected to the negative side of the circuit and the other to the positive side.

As the loop of wire revolves in the magnetic field, an alternating current (a.c.) is induced in it. The loop ends are connected to the positive and negative brushes alternately as the loop revolves.

This action causes the a.c. current to be rectified to direct current (d.c.).

As can be seen from the graph (Figure 25.21) the current output of a single loop fluctuates considerably. It rises to a maximum and then falls to zero, at which point the wire loop is moving parallel to the magnetic field, before rising to maximum again and returning to zero during the second half of the revolution.

In practice, a single loop would not be very effective. A practical dynamo has a number of loops connected to individual commutator

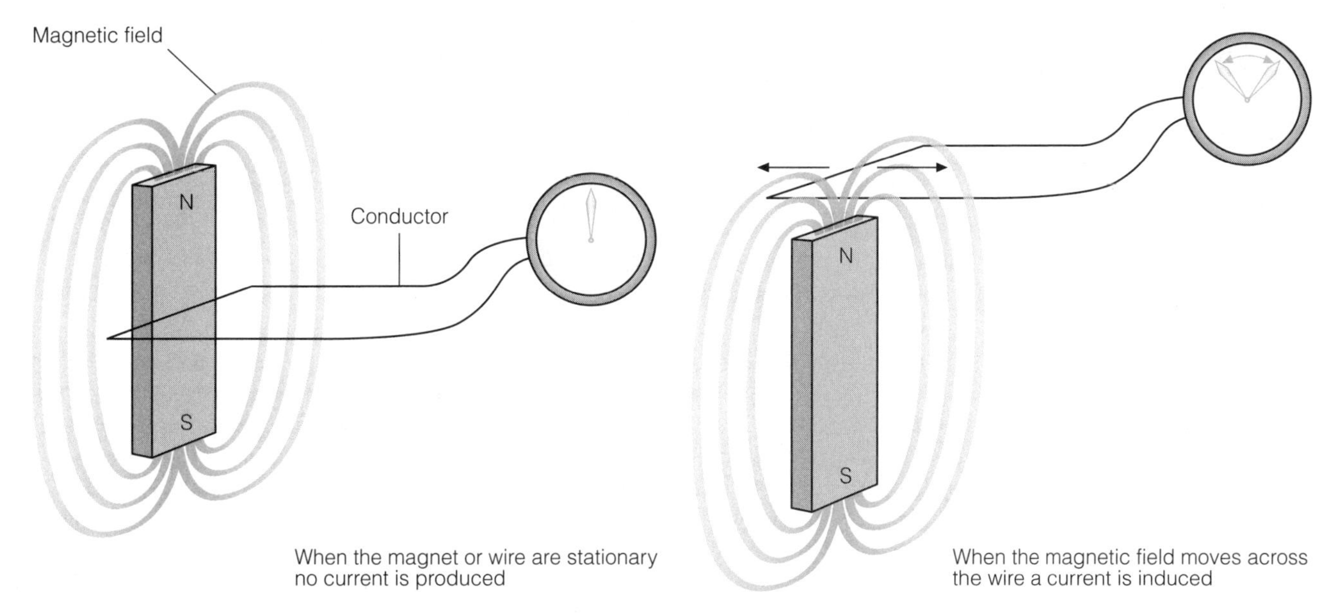

Figure 25.19 If a copper wire is moved through a magnetic field an electric current will flow in that wire if it is part of a circuit.

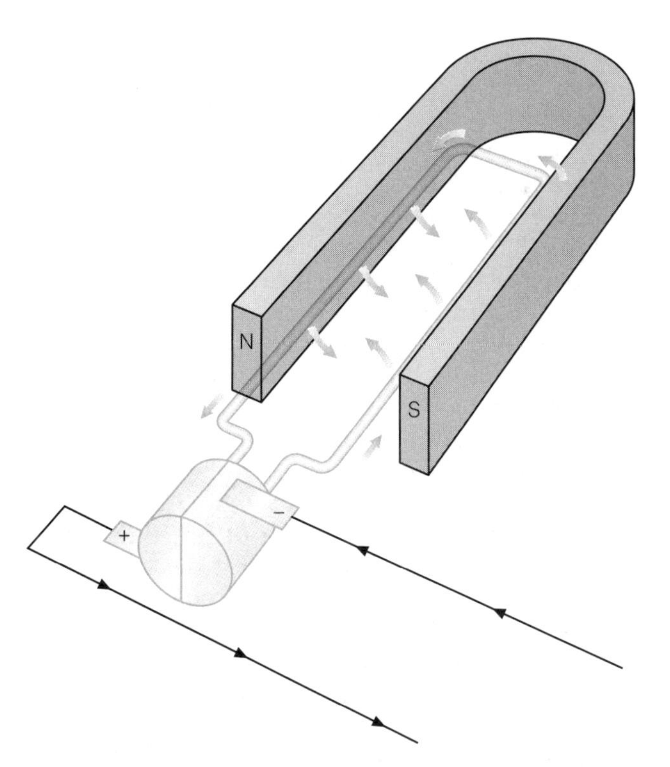

Figure 25.20 Alternating current converted to direct current by commutator.

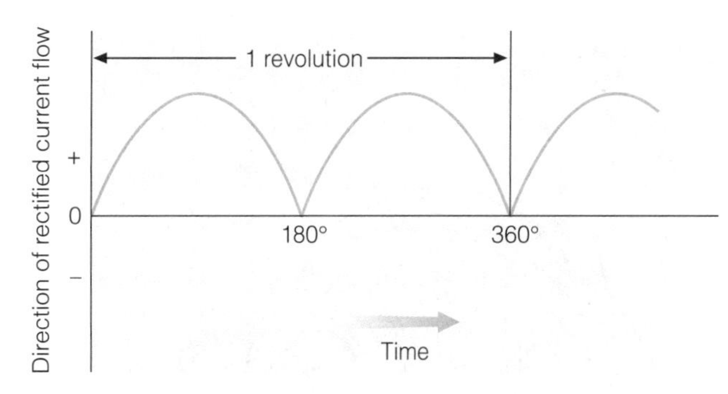

Figure 25.21 D.C. output from a single-coil (or single-loop) armature.

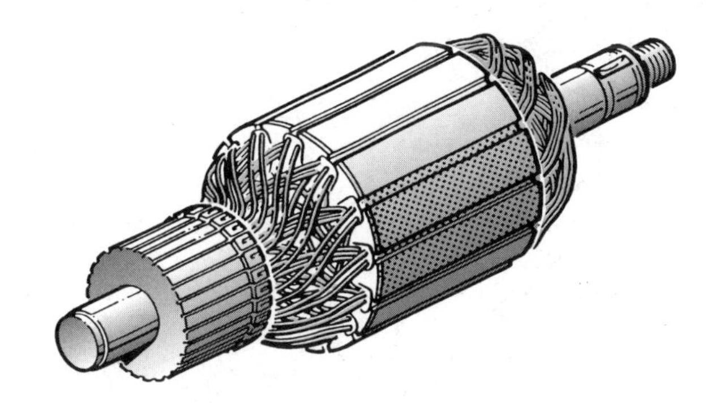

Figure 25.22 Dynamo armature.

segments (Figure 25.22). The output from this arrangement is much better and steadier because one loop is always moving through the area of maximum induction: that is, moving at right angles to the magnetic field.

Dynamo construction

The **armature** is the revolving part of the dynamo. It consists of a number of copper conductors wound onto a soft iron core, which is in turn mounted on a steel shaft running in bearings.

The commutator segments are made from copper, and are arranged in the form of a cylinder, accurately machined to provide a smooth running surface for the brushes. Each segment is insulated from the next. The commutator is fixed to the armature shaft, and the ends of the coils are soldered into slots in the commutator segments.

The generated current is collected from the commutator by means of two carbon brushes, which are held in contact with the surface by springs (Figure 25.23).

The magnetic field

The armature must be revolving in a magnetic field before any current can be generated. The magnetic field could be provided by permanent magnets, but in practice electromagnets known as **field coils** are used (Figure 25.24).

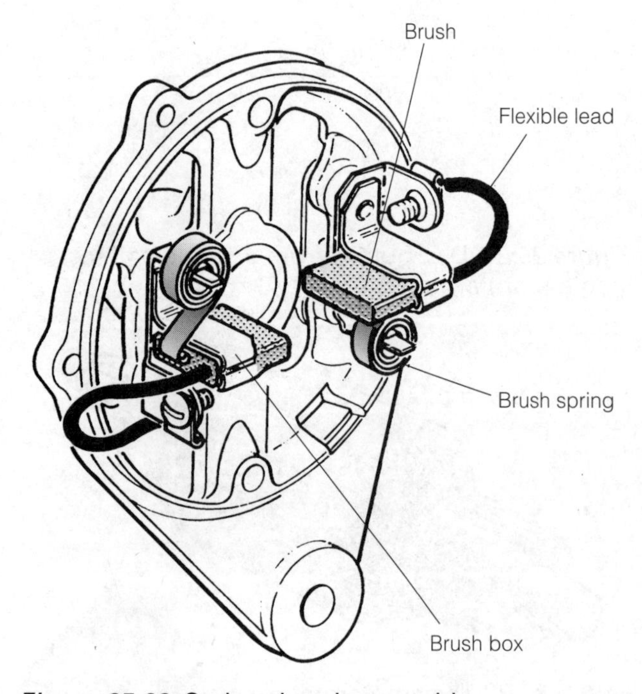

Figure 25.23 Carbon brush assembly.

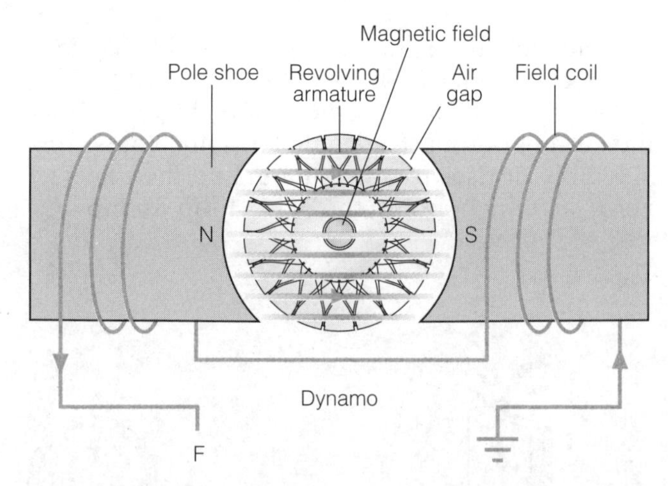

Figure 25.24 Field coils.

Two field coils are wound around two blocks of soft iron, called **pole shoes**. The pole shoes contain a small amount of residual magnetism, which allows them to act as permanent magnets. This residual magnetism is sufficient to induce a current in the armature when it starts to revolve, and some of this current is fed to the field coils. This increases the intensity of the magnetic field, and the output from the armature rises. The dynamo output is dependent on the strength of the magnetic field and the speed at which the armature is revolving. Clearly, the output must be controlled, as too much would overcharge the battery, and too little would not keep it fully charged.

Output controls

There are many different types of control but they tend to fall into two categories.

Compensated voltage control incorporates two magnetic relays: a voltage-sensitive regulator and a voltage sensitive cut-out. The **regulator** functions as a high-frequency switch in the field (magnetic) circuit of the dynamo. Its purpose is to limit the output voltage to a predetermined figure, usually around 16 V. Output voltage must be higher than battery voltage to enable the current to charge the battery. The **cut-out** functions as an automatic switch, connecting and disconnecting the charging circuit between the dynamo and the battery (Figure 25.25).

Current voltage control is achieved through three magnetic relays: a cut-out, a current regulator, and a voltage regulator. The **current regulator** allows the dynamo to deliver its maximum continuous output until the voltage reaches a predetermined figure. The **voltage reg-**

ulator takes over control of generator output during the final stage of charging, when the charging current tapers off to a trickle of 1–2 A.

Although the dynamo is adequate for many operations, it has generally been replaced by the alternator.

The alternator

Modern vehicles have more electrical components than their earlier counterparts. This requires a larger output from the generator, particularly at low speeds or when stopped in traffic jams, for example. Alternators provide the following benefits:

1. The rotating part, the **rotor**, forms the electromagnet. It is more robust than the dynamo armature and can therefore revolve at higher speeds. By fitting a smaller drive pulley the rotor revolves faster at low engine speeds and can even provide a battery charge when the engine is running at little more than idling speed. Because the revolving part has become an electromagnet, it needs an electrical input, which is achieved by having slip rings and brushes.
2. Less maintenance is required. The generating coils are stationary and surround the rotor; these are collectively called the **stator**. There is no complex commutator and brush gear through which the charging current has to be rectified and transferred as on the dynamo.
3. The alternator is more efficient for its size and weight. Although the position of the various parts of an alternator are different from a dynamo, the principle of operation – a magnetic field passing a conductor – has the same effect. The output in the stationary windings is still alternating current, but it is rectified by **diodes**. These are mounted on the rectifier pack (Figure 25.26).

Rectification

The current from the alternator has to be converted to d.c. in order to feed the battery. Rectification is achieved by fitting diodes into the output circuit. The diode is a device that allows current to flow in one direction, but prevents it from flowing the reverse way.

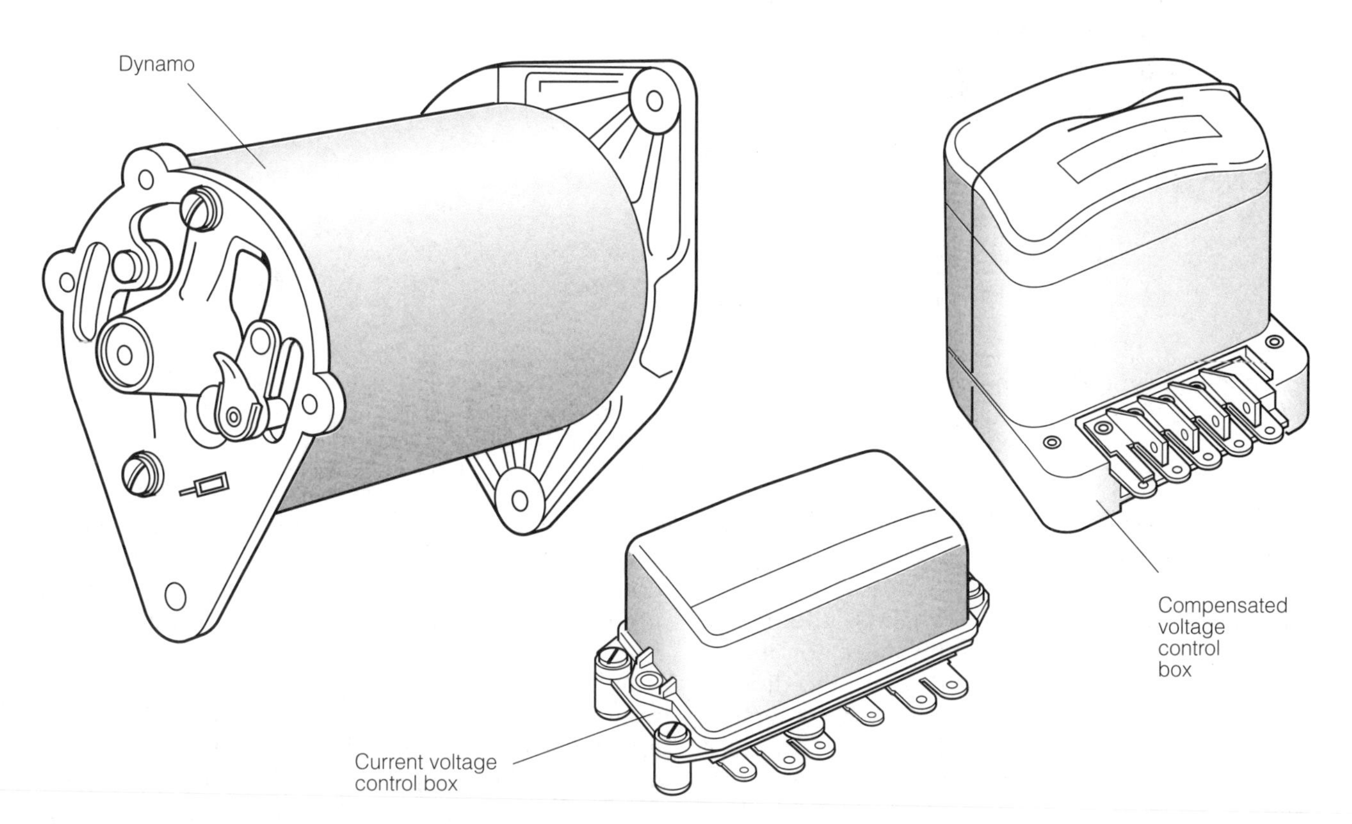

Figure 25.25 Dynamo and control boxes.

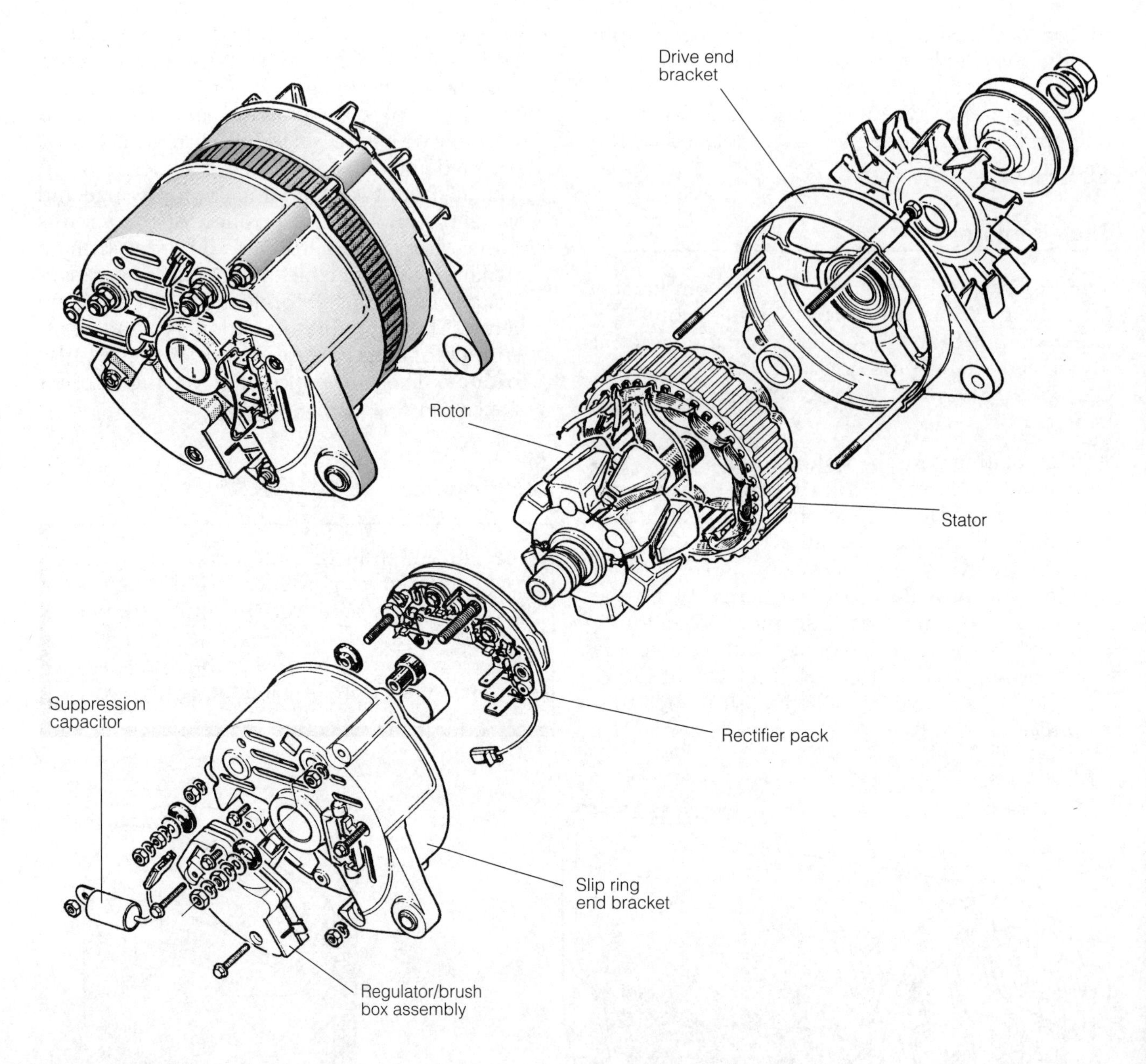

Figure 25.26 Typical alternator.

The basic principle of rectification involves the use of four diodes (Figure 25.27). As can be seen, current will flow through the diodes in the direction of the arrows, but not against them. By tracing the positive wire from the alternator, it can be seen that current can flow through the diodes and the battery. When the polarity reverses, current flows through the other pair of diodes, but always in the same direction through the battery.

A vehicle's alternator is a three-phase alternator. It has three coils of stator windings that produce the current, and requires a bridge of six diodes to complete the rectification. This gives it a much greater output than a simple, single-phase machine (Figure 25.28).

When the rotor is passing the vertical stator winding A, the current flow indicated by the arrows flows out through diode 1 to the battery, and returns to complete the circuit though diodes 5 and 6. You can trace the current flow through the other diodes in a similar way.

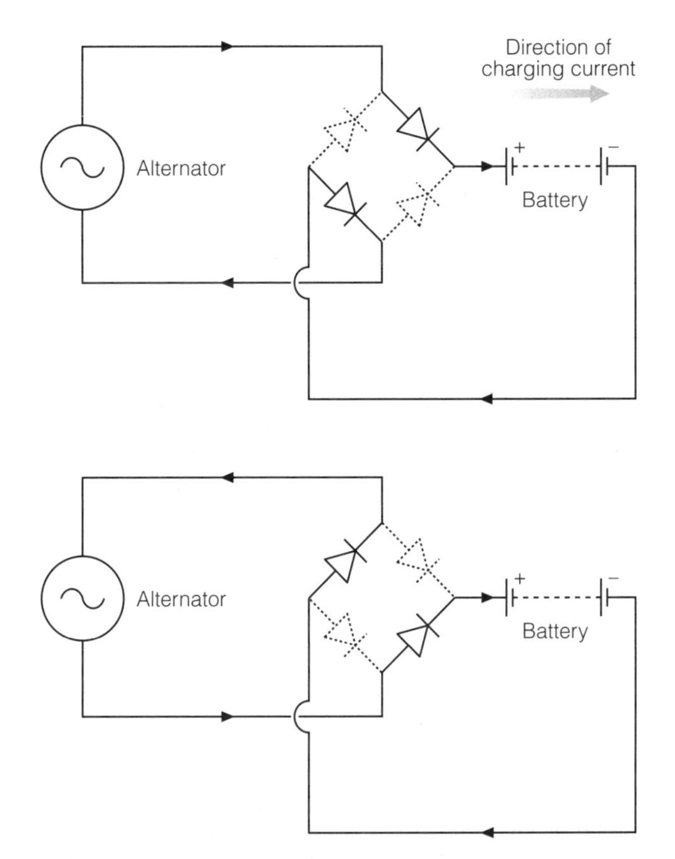

Figure 25.27 Action of the full-wave rectifier.

The starter motor

> The action of an electric motor is the opposite to that of the generator.

In a motor, current is passed to the rotating armature and field coils. Normally, when two opposing magnets are brought together they force each other apart. In the motor one magnet – the field coil – is fixed, and the other – the armature – can rotate. When an electric current passes through the field and armature coils, magnetic fields are created that oppose each other. The only way in which they can move apart is for the armature to rotate (Figure 25.29).

In operation, current is first passed in series around the field windings on the pole shoes and then through the brushes and commutator to the armature coils (Figure 25.30).

On a simple starter the armature spindle carries an inertia-engaged drive arrangement consisting of a pinion mounted on a screwed sleeve. When the motor is operated, the sudden movement screws the pinion along the sleeve into mesh with

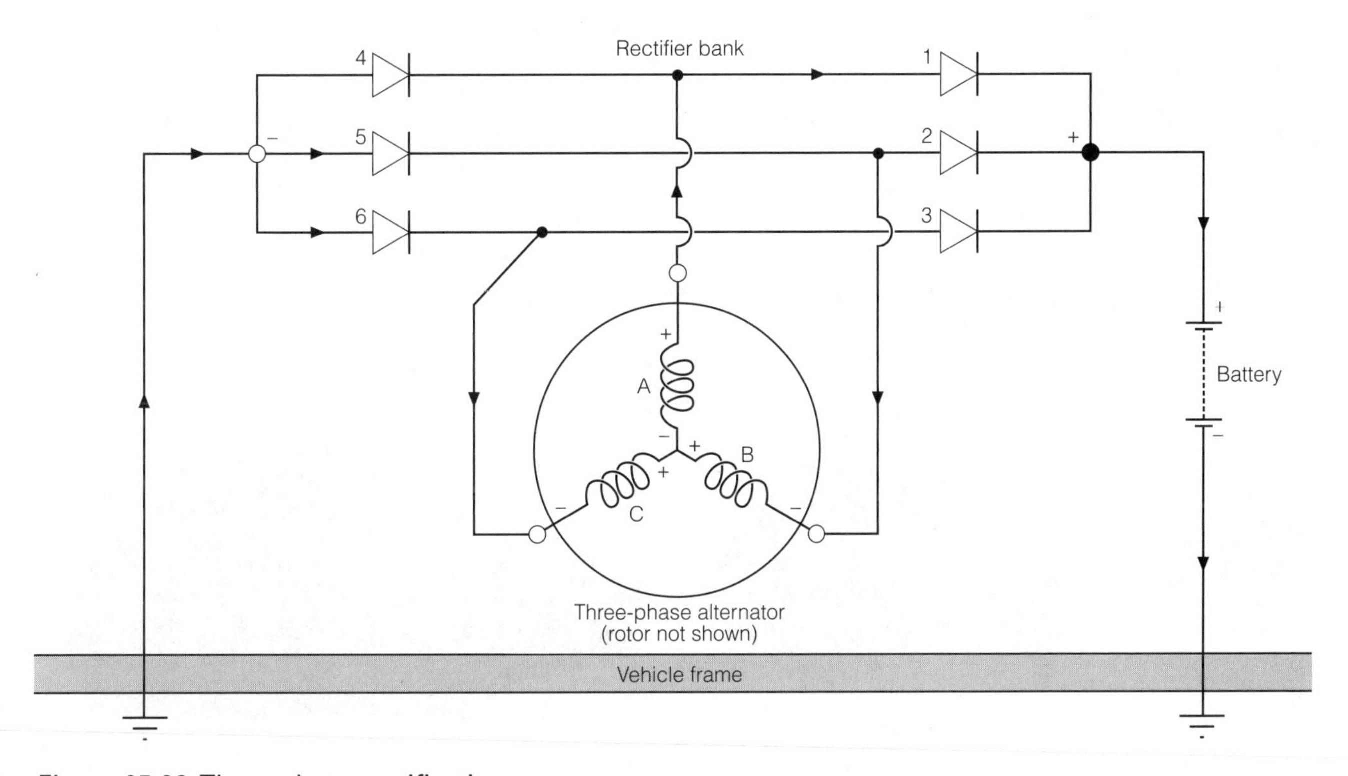

Figure 25.28 Three-phase rectification.

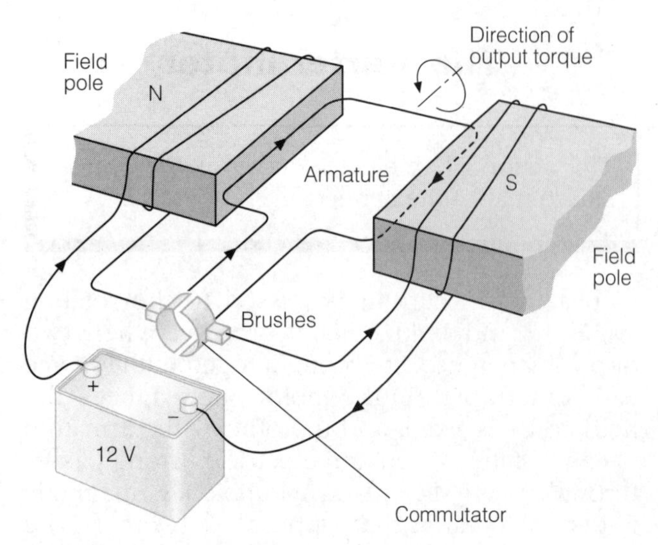

Figure 25.29 Simple circuit diagram of d.c. starter motor.

the flywheel ring gear, when its movement is arrested by a strong buffer spring. As the engine starts and the driver releases the starter switch, the flywheel spins faster than the starter pinion, forcing it out of mesh (Figure 25.31a).

As very large currents are required to turn an engine, a solenoid switch is needed to avoid fitting long lengths of heavy cable. The solenoid is a heavy-duty electromagnetic switch linking the battery to the starter motor. When the starter switch is activated, a small current flows through the solenoid coil. This creates a magnetic field, which draws in and closes the contacts, directly connecting the battery and starter motor together and allowing full starter current to flow.

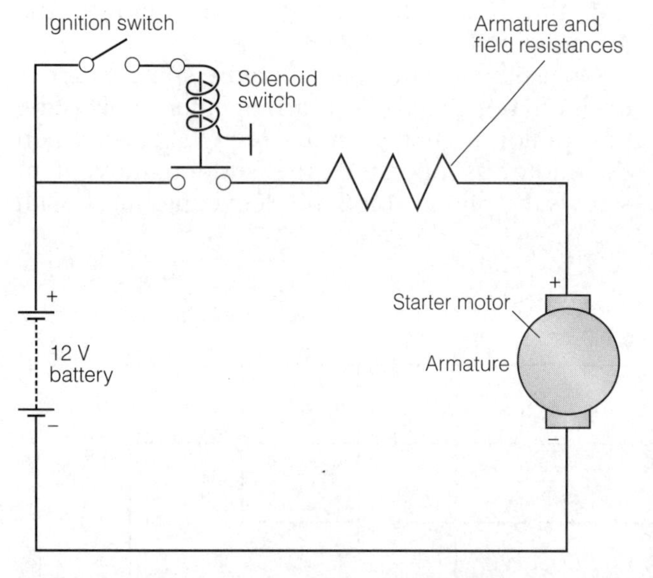

Figure 25.30 Simple starter circuit diagram.

Pre-engaged starters

Pre-engaged starters are almost always fitted to heavy diesel engines, and can be found on many modern cars. They differ from the inertia drive because the pinion is fully engaged with the flywheel before the starter motor starts to spin. This is achieved by mounting the solenoid on top of the motor and connecting it to a lever whose other end engages with the pinion. Activation of the switch draws in the solenoid, which pulls the lever and moves the pinion into mesh with the flywheel ring gear. In the last part of the lever movement the contacts are bridged that link the starter to the battery. Pre-engagement of the pinion greatly reduces the wear on the flywheel ring gear (Figure 25.31b).

Figure 25.31 Starter motors: (a) inertia type; (b) pre-engaged type.

Electrical consumers

The lighting system

Each country has laws governing vehicle lighting and its use, which often differ from one to another. But most countries broadly have these requirements:

1. sidelamps showing white to the front or, as in the USA, orange;
2. headlamps providing main and dipped beams (these should be correctly aimed to avoid dazzling oncoming drivers);
3. tail-lamps and reflectors showing red to the rear.

A basic lighting circuit has all the lights connected in parallel, to ensure that failure of one light does not affect the others in the circuit (Figure 25.32). Although they use the same master switch, the sidelamp circuit is separate from the headlamp circuit. When the headlamps are on, current flows to another switch in the circuit known as the **dip-switch**, which can divert the current to either the dipped or the main beams. Although some vehicles may employ two completely separate headlamps, many use a double-filament bulb in the same lamp. These fila-

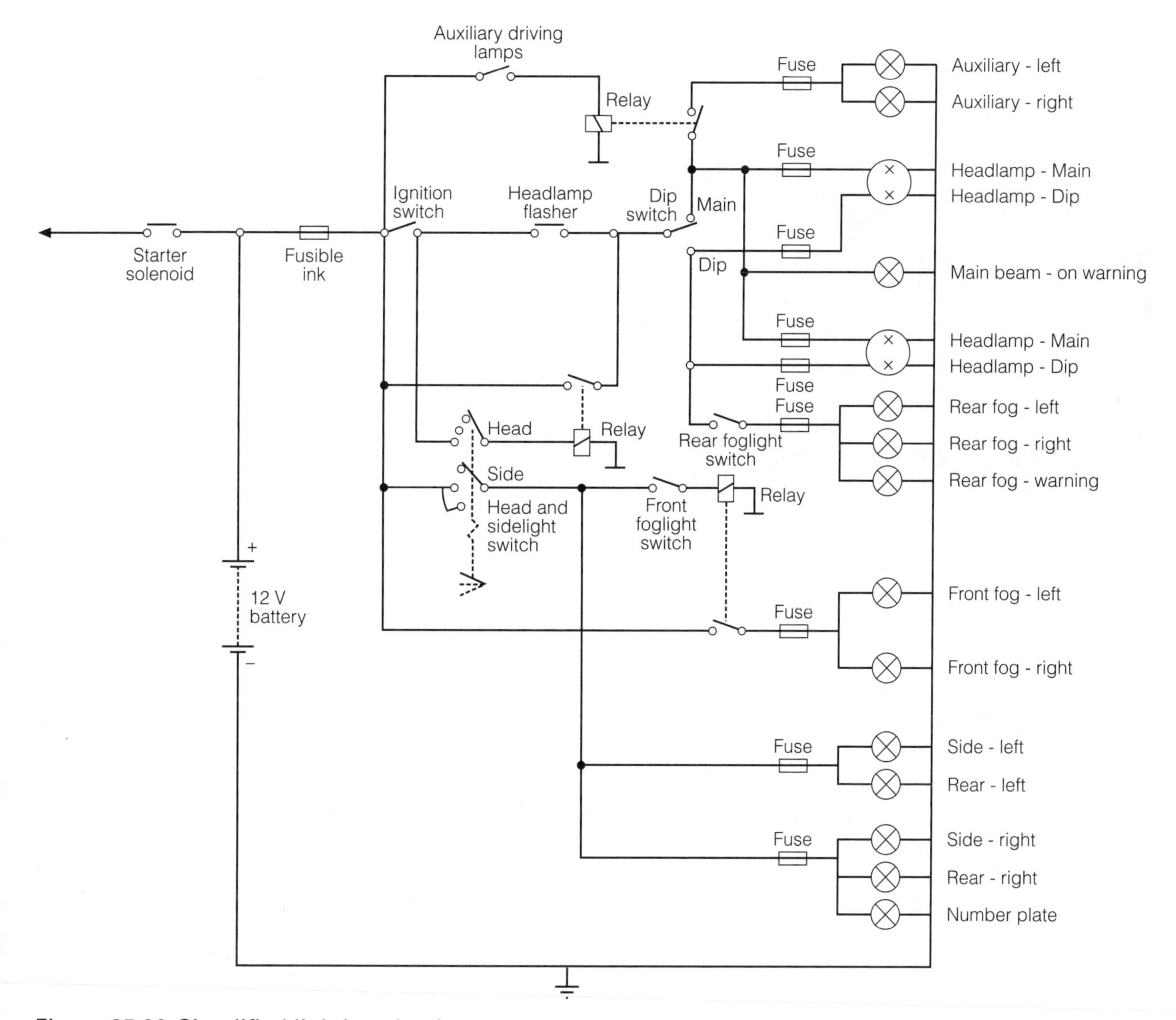

Figure 25.32 Simplified lighting circuit.

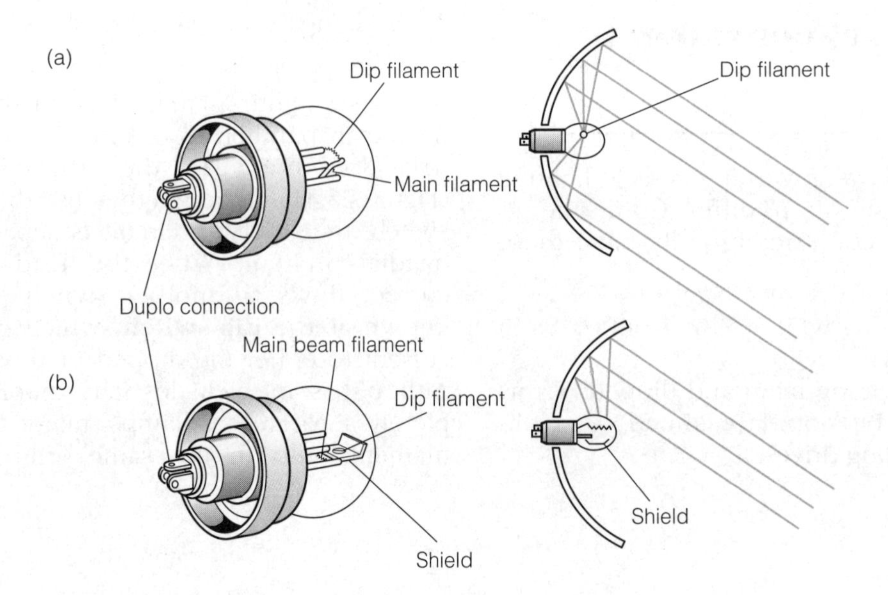

Figure 25.33 Headlamp bulbs. (a) Offset dip filament: whole beam is dipped. (b) Shield dip filament: only half of the reflector projects light downwards.

Figure 25.34 Typical headlamp.

ments are of different size and consume different amounts of power, the main beam being brighter than the dipped beam, typically 60 W and 40 W (Figure 25.33).

Headlamp lenses are designed to deflect the beam when dipped (Figure 25.34). All vehicles have some means of altering the aim of the headlamps, as correct headlamp alignment is essential to ensure that they do not cause dazzle (Figure 25.35).

Stop lamp circuit

This is a relatively simple circuit (Figure 25.36).

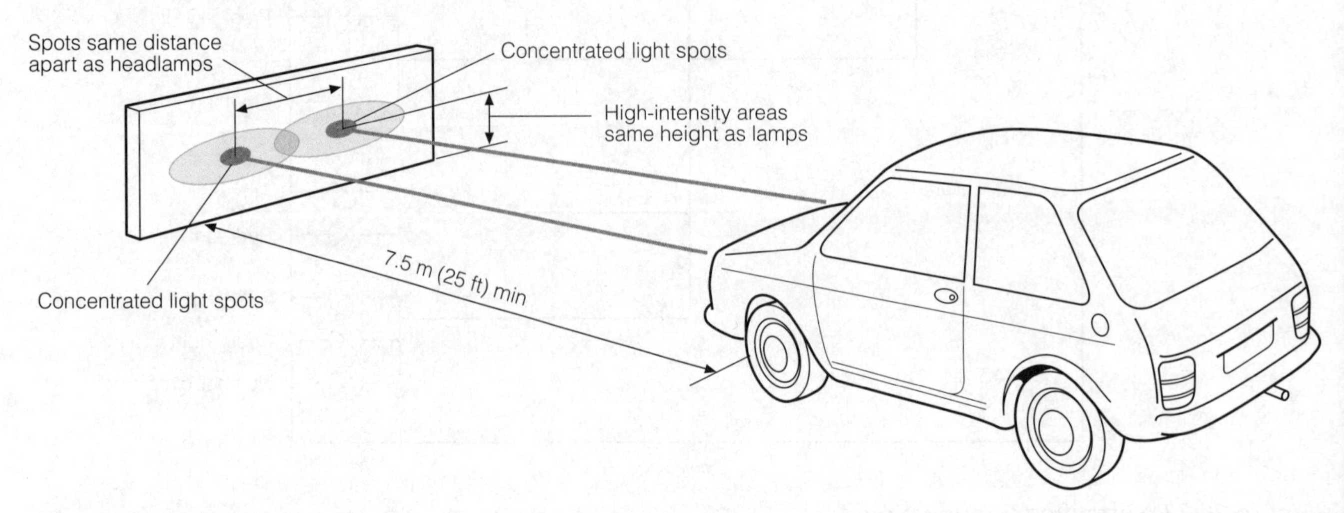

Figure 25.35 Headlamp aim.

When the ignition is turned on, the current flows through the appropriate fuse to the brake lamp switch. This switch may be mechanical, and attached to the brake pedal or operating mechanism, or a pressure-activated switch incorporated into the brake hydraulic system. Although the stop lamp may be separate from the tail-lamps, in many cases the same lens is used together with a double-filament bulb similar to those used in the headlamps. The stop lamp must be brighter than the tail-lamp so that it may be seen in daylight and when the lights are in use. To achieve this the stop lamp filament is of a higher wattage than the tail-lamp.

Directional signalling system

These are often called the **flasher circuits** (Figure 25.37). In this circuit a flasher relay makes and breaks the current flow between 60 and 120 times every minute, so producing the flashing lamps. Each lamp is usually between 20 and 30 W. Several different types of relay are in use, but all have the common principle that the lamp current itself actuates the interrupter. In many cases the heating effect of the current flow is used, the relay contacts being operated by either a spring steel vane or a bimetallic strip. Alternatively, an electronic **multivibrator oscillator** produces square wave pulses that provide the switching.

As with headlamps, there is a warning lamp or lamps to indicate to the driver that the flashers are operating.

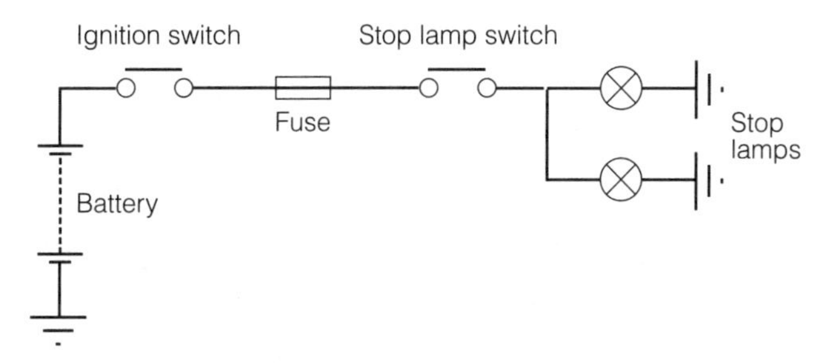

Figure 25.36 Stop lamp circuit.

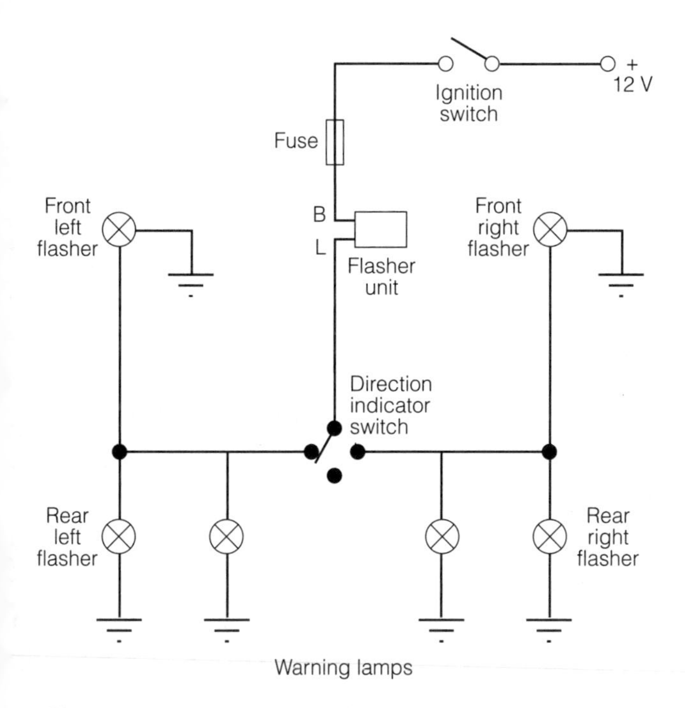

Figure 25.37 Flasher wiring diagram.

Vane-type flasher unit

The vane-type flasher is commonly used on basic flasher systems. A 'vane' made of spring steel is normally in a bent position and is held in place by a resistive conductor (Figure 25.38). When the flashers are switched on, the current flows through the resistive conductor, which heats up and expands, allowing the vane to snap to the upright position. This opens the contacts and current ceases to flow. The resistive conductor cools down and contracts, pulling the vane back to its original position and closing the contacts again. The movement of the vane produces the clicking sound that is heard when the flashers operate.

Other flasher units may provide clicks by artificial means as an audible warning of operation.

Hazard warning lights

The hazard warning lights use the flasher circuits to flash all the signalling lamps together as a warning. The same circuits and units are used with some additional circuitry, switching and a warning lamp.

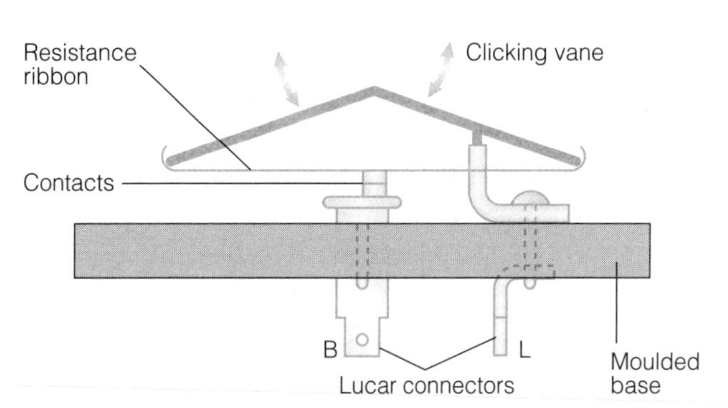

Figure 25.38 Vane flasher unit.

Electric horn

Most horns are of the vibrating diaphragm type. An iron armature is attracted by the magnetic field created by a current carrying coil; the movement of the armature then breaks a pair of contacts, which cuts off the current flow to the coil. The armature then returns under spring action and the cycle is repeated.

The armature is connected to a flexible diaphragm, which vibrates at high frequency, pushing the air back and forth. This creates a sound, which is increased by placing a tone disc, which vibrates at a different frequency, in front of the diaphragm (Figure 25.39).

The fuel gauge

The system usually consists of a fuel gauge mounted in the instrument cluster in front of the driver, and a sender unit mounted in the fuel tank. The fuel gauge indicates the level of fuel in the tank according to the position of the tank unit float. This rises and falls with the level of fuel, and in so doing moves a contact arm on the tank unit rheostat. This varies the amount of current flowing in the circuit and through the gauge.

The magnetic type of fuel gauge contains two small coils: a holding coil and a deflecting coil (Figure 25.40). These are fed with current through the ignition switch.

The holding coil is earthed while the deflecting coil is connected to the tank unit and then to earth. A needle attached to an iron armature is free to pivot between the two coils. As the fuel level changes, the magnetic field of the deflecting coil also varies, causing movement of the needle. By using two coils the accuracy of the gauge is unchanged by any alteration in battery voltage, as both are equally affected.

Bimetal gauges

Some instruments use a bimetallic strip in the form of a U to move the indicator (Figure 25.41). One leg has a heater coil wrapped around it, while the other leg is attached to the instrument

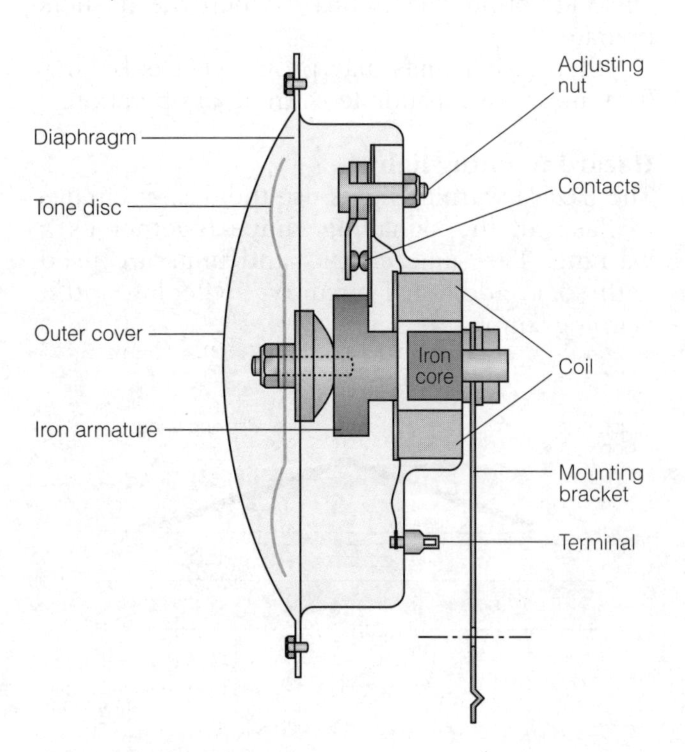

Figure 25.39 The horn.

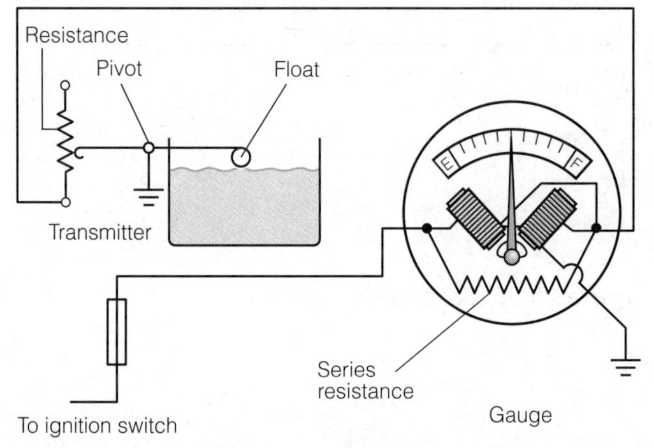

Figure 25.40 Magnetic fuel gauge.

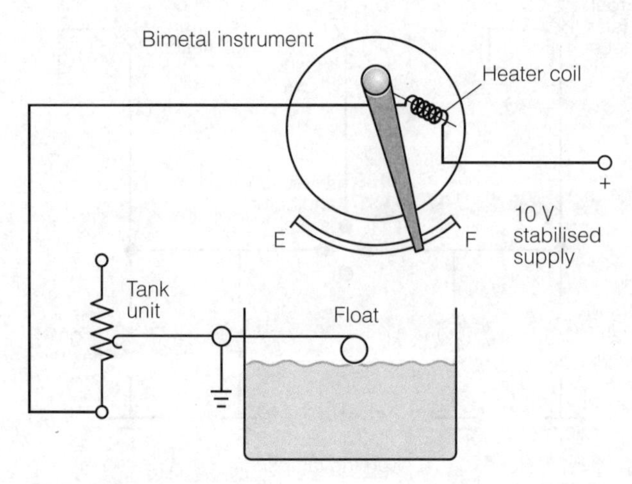

Figure 25.41 Bimetal fuel gauge.

pointer. When current flows the coil heats the strip. As the strip bends because of the unequal expansion of the two metals, a pointer moves across the scale to indicate the reading.

Other gauges

Many vehicles have additional gauges such as those for water, oil temperature and oil pressure. They will operate on similar principles to those already described, but the means of transmitting the current through the instrument may differ.

Temperature measurement may involve the use of a **thermistor**, a metal capsule containing a semiconductor resistor in close contact with a brass heat sink to dissipate the heat generated by the current flow. As the temperature of the unit increases, the resistance of the thermistor decreases (note that this is the opposite to normal metals). This increases the current flow through the instrument to alter the reading.

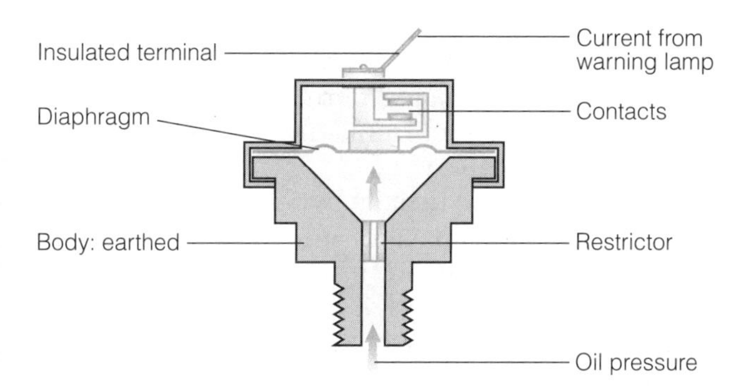

Figure 25.42 Pressure switch.

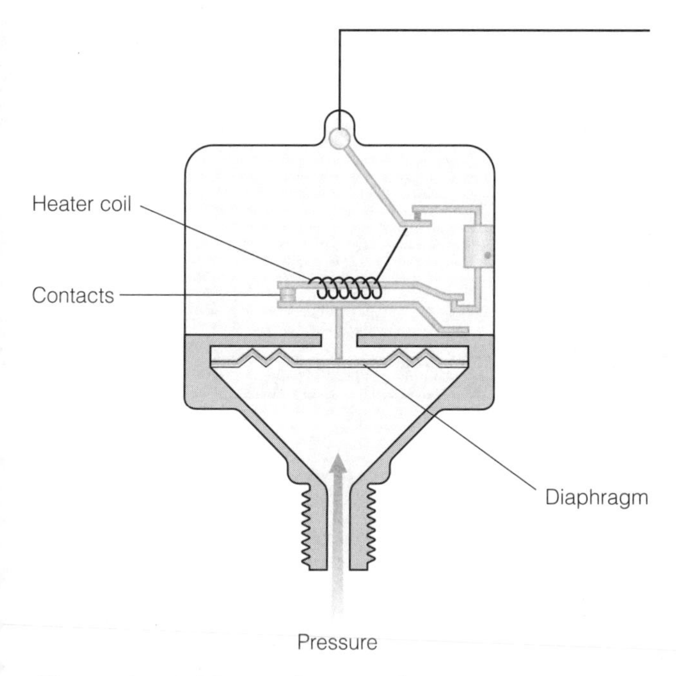

Figure 25.43 Thermal transmitter.

Oil pressure is often indicated by means of a warning lamp, which is operated by a pressure switch (Figure 25.42). In its simplest form, oil pressure acts on a diaphragm, which opens a contact. When the pressure drops sufficiently, the diaphragm returns towards its rest position and the contacts close, completing the circuit and lighting the warning lamp.

An electrically operated pressure gauge uses a more complicated transmitter as shown in Figure 25.43. When the diaphragm is subject to pressure it will flex. The movement is transmitted to the contacts, altering the tension. As the bimetallic strip heats up, it bends, opening the contacts. As the strip cools it returns and closes the contacts again.

The contacts vibrate as they constantly heat up and cool down, and the speed of the vibration depends on the pressure on the contacts. The vibration gives an average value current, which is used to control a gauge by the use of a voltage stabiliser.

Instrument voltage stabiliser

It is important that gauges such as those for fuel and temperature should read accurately, especially if they are of the bimetallic type, where the reading can be affected by small variations in voltage. Depending on the state of charge of the battery and electrical load conditions, voltage can vary from 11 V to 13 V. Such a variation could give incorrect instrument readings.

To overcome this problem a voltage stabiliser is placed in series in the instrument circuit. It consists of a set of contacts operated by a bimetallic strip, which is heated by a coil connected across the battery (Figure 25.44). As the current flows through the coil it heats the bimetallic strip, causing it to bend and open the contacts. This cuts off the supply to the instruments as well as the supply to the stabiliser heating coil. The strip then cools, closing the contacts. The cycle of opening and closing then continues at a relatively slow rate, varying a little with the voltage. This

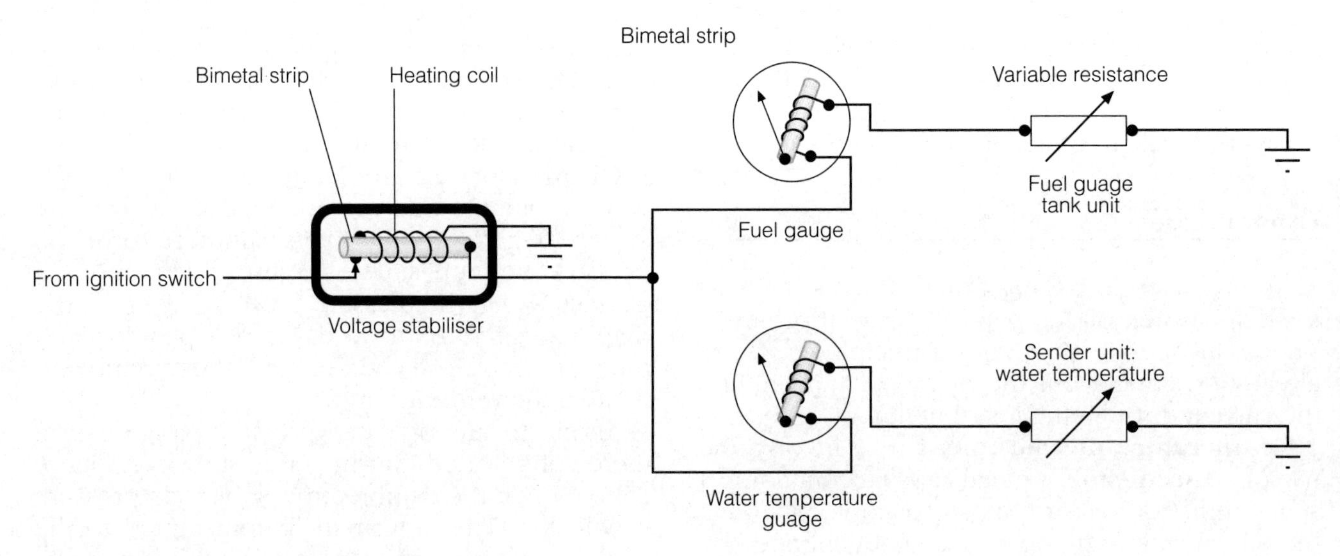

Figure 25.44 Voltage stabiliser circuit.

oscillation results in the instruments' being supplied with a mean value of 10 V.

Windscreen wiper motors

Electric windscreen wipers have an electric motor, which is geared down at the output shaft. The gearing is usually achieved by a worm drive attached to the armature, meshing with a wheel to which the wiper drive mechanism is attached.

The motor itself is generally of the permanent magnet type. These magnets are usually of the high-energy ceramic type, set in a cylindrical yoke of laminated steel, which surrounds the armature. The advantages of using permanent magnets are that they use less current, and are cheaper to make (Figure 25.45).

Wiper motors are usually two-speed with a self-parking mechanism and an intermittent-wipe facility. A single-speed motor would have its brushes set at 180° apart. Two-speed motors have an additional brush, which is used to vary the motor's speed.

Windscreen wiper drives

There are two types of drive in use today: the **link system**, driven by a crank from the armature

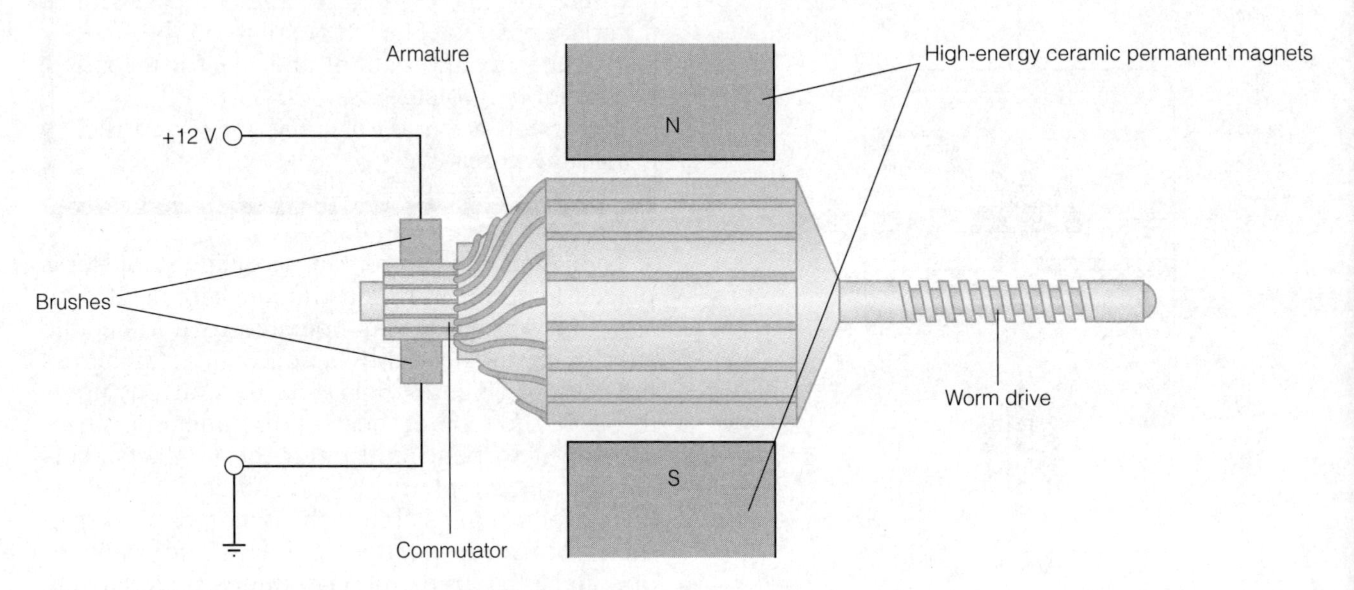

Figure 25.45 Permanent magnet wiper motor.

worm drive (Figure 25.46a); and the **rack system**, driven by a connecting rod from the worm gear (Figure 25.46b).

In-car entertainment

Most new cars are equipped with entertainment systems, often of some complexity. The construction, operation and fault rectification of individual components are outside the scope of this book, except for the basic supply circuits and speaker connections. These circuits follow the principles outlined in earlier sections.

Problems may arise in the refitting or replacement of a radio unit. When installing a radio receiver to a vehicle it is important to ensure that good earth connections are made, and that any wiring, including the aerial lead, is kept as short as possible.

The aerial should be fitted in a position where it can receive signals without being obstructed by the body, and in a position where it is least likely to pick up interference from the ignition and other components. Details of fitting are supplied with receivers, but the principles of good earthing, using the shortest supply cable and a properly mounted aerial, apply in all cases. On vehicles with heavy underbody layers of anti-corrosion protection, it is often easier to run a separate earth wire from the aerial mounting to a suitable under-bonnet earth point. This overcomes the need to cut away the protection and struggle to make a good earth.

Even when these requirements have been followed, interference may still occur. To overcome this problem, suppressors in the form of capacitors or chokes (a choke is an inductor device, and consists of a resistor surrounded by a coil, mounted in series) may be fitted to various components. Earthing straps may also be needed to provide an adequate earth path for current from body components such as the bonnet to the bodyshell.

Interference is often created by the ignition system. All spark ignition engines should have suppressed HT leads; in addition, a capacitor can be fitted between the switch side of the coil and

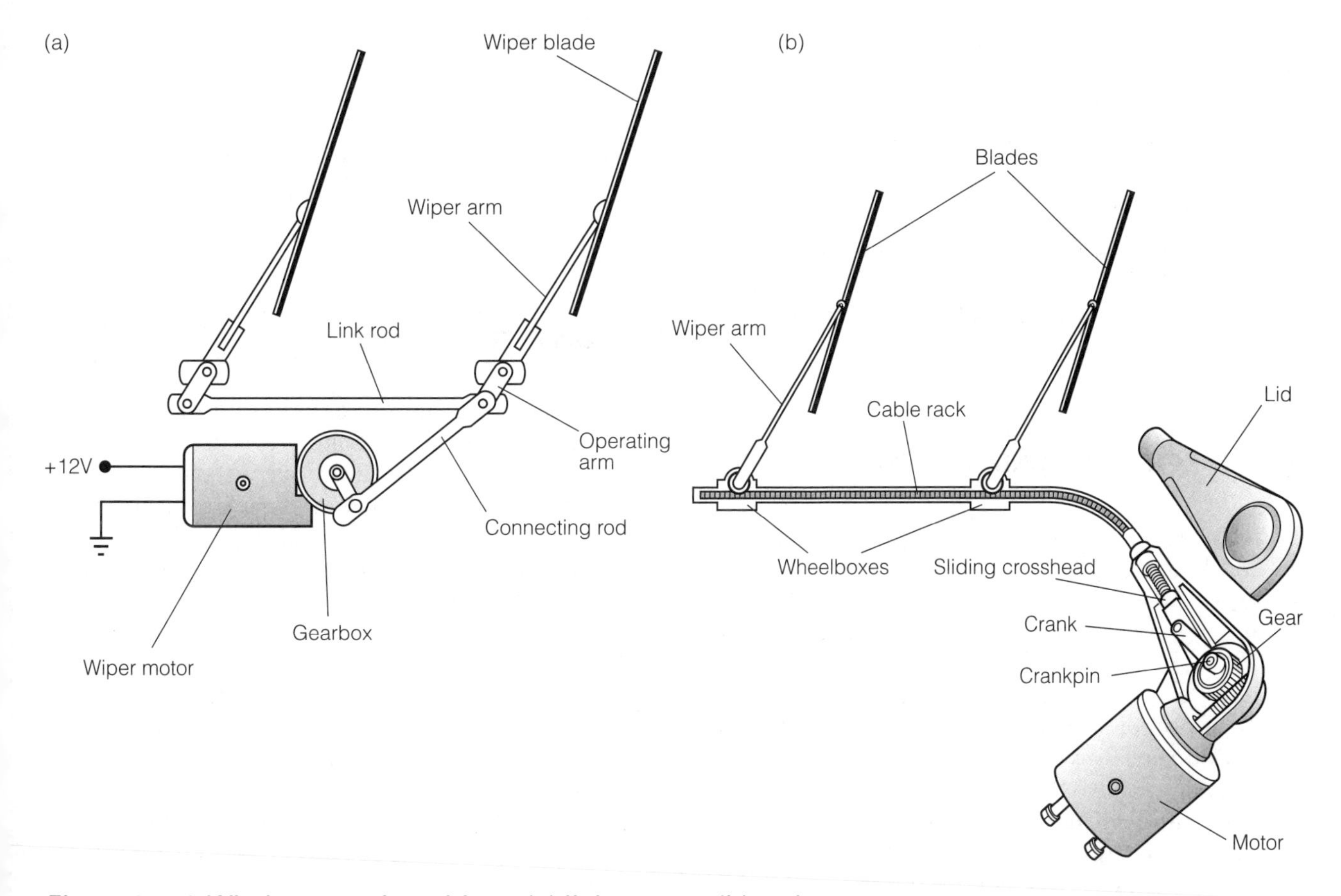

Figure 25.46 Windscreen wiper drives: (a) link system; (b) rack system.

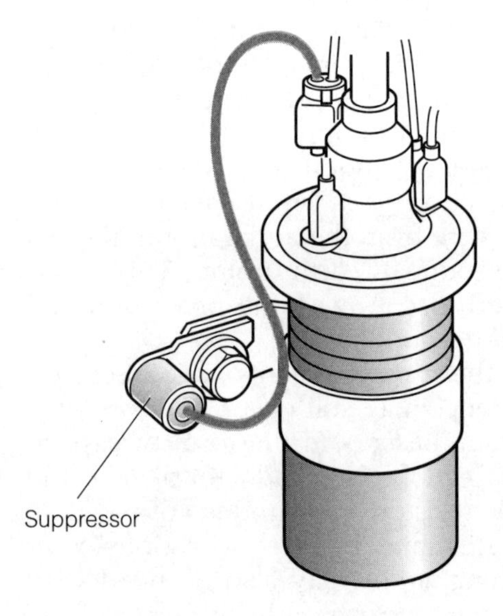

Figure 25.47 Suppressor on ignition coil.

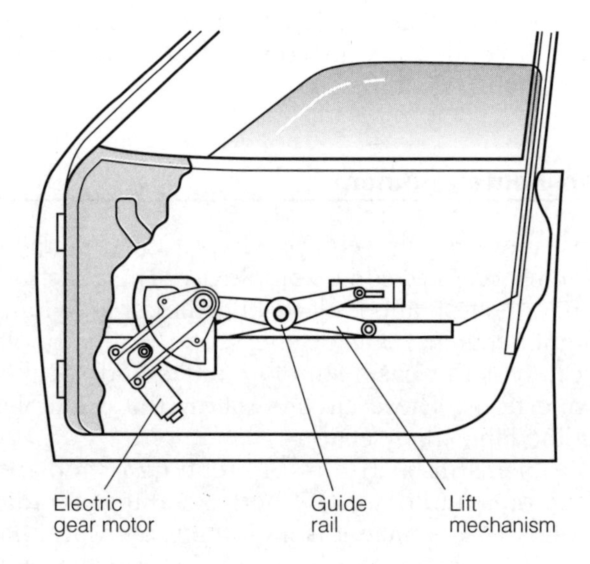

Figure 25.48 Window lift drive.

earth (Figure 25.47). If this does not cure the problem it may be necessary to fit suppressors or earth straps to individual components, such as the alternator, wiper motor and voltage stabilisers.

Electric windows

A conventional motor-driven, gear and segment window device is shown in Figure 25.48. The windows are operated by rocker switches in the front doors. Various overrides and protection from injury are incorporated into the latest systems. On vehicles with central locking, the windows may close automatically when locking is activated.

CHECK YOUR UNDERSTANDING

- Electricity has three effects: magnetic, chemical, and heating.
- Ohm's law defines the relationship between current, resistance and voltage with the formula $I = E/R$.
- There are two further fundamental laws on which most electrical applications are based: when a current flows in a circuit it creates a magnetic field around the conductor, and when a magnetic field is moved across a conductor (or vice versa) a current is induced in that conductor.
- Modern vehicles have many differing electrical circuits including starter, charging, ignition and lighting. Auxiliary circuits include the horn, windscreen wipers, direction indicators, power windows, in-car entertainment, power-adjusted mirrors and heated seats.
- Most circuits are protected against short-circuits by fuses.

This chapter has briefly covered a subject that has been changing rapidly for some years with the introduction of electronic systems. For further information, consult the manufacturer's service information.

PROJECTS

1 i) Check the state of charge of a battery using a hydrometer or voltmeter.
   ii) Check an alternator output using a voltmeter. Use the maker's service information and follow the instructions in the manual to make these checks. Record your results and the maker's data.
   Is the battery serviceable? YES/NO
   Is the alternator output correct? YES/NO

2 Connect three lamps of differing wattage in series with a battery. Measure and record current flow and voltage drop across each lamp, using a voltmeter and an ammeter.
   Connect the same three lamps in parallel and measure the voltage drop and current flow across each lamp.
   Record your results in the table.

Bulb no.	Series		Parallel		Resistance
	volts	amps	volts	amps	ohms
1					
2					
3					
Total					

Having built and tested each circuit, answer the following questions:

i) Lamps in series:
Do all the lamps have full brilliance? YES/NO
Disconnect one lamp; do the others stay lit? YES/NO

ii) Lamps in parallel:
Do all the lamps have full brilliance? YES/NO
Disconnect one lamp; do the others stay lit? YES/NO

REVISION EXERCISES AND QUESTIONS

1 Which component feeds the battery with current?

2 Why are nearly all automobile electrical components wired on the earth return system?

3 Why is it important that all the lights on a vehicle be wired in parallel?

4 Why is it important that the headlamps are aimed correctly?

5 Why is a solenoid used to operate the starter?

6 Explain why different sizes of cable are used in vehicle wiring systems.

7 State how the different circuits can be recognised.

8 Sketch a wiring diagram showing two spotlamps. Include switches and fuses.

9 What is a hydrometer used for?

10 What is a high rate discharge tester used for?

11 State the relative density of i) a fully charged battery and ii) a discharged battery.

12 State the purpose of a voltage stabiliser.

13 What effects may be produced by an electrical current?

14 State the purpose of a fuse, and explain how it works.

15 Explain why it is dangerous for a mechanic to wear rings, metal bracelets or metal watch straps when working on a vehicle.

Answers to questions and answering hints

Introduction

This section provides you with all the answers to the variety of questions and exercises given in the book. Always try a question or exercise yourself before you look at the answer. This will increase your understanding of the topic and give you practice in answering questions. If you are not sure of a particular answer, re-read the relevant section or chapter in the book to revise the work. You need to understand why a question has a particular answer, so that you can apply your understanding to similar types of question or exercise in your examinations and course assignments.

The book contains a variety of types of question and exercise. Find out the types of question that you will be expected to answer and their pattern. If possible, obtain past papers to support your work and revision. Some of the questions in the book require longer answers. We have provided hints on how to tackle these questions, and on the range of topics that you should include. Practise giving full answers to these questions and then check the answering hints to see that you have included all the relevant topics.

To revise a topic quickly you can also refer to the 'Check your understanding' sections given at the end of each chapter, and the list of key words with definitions given at the end of the book.

Hints to answering questions in examinations and course work

- Read all the questions carefully before you try anything. Make sure that you understand what each question is asking you to do.
- Plan the time that you will spend on each question. Use the marks as a guide: the more marks a question is worth, the more time it is worth spending on it.
- If you have a choice of questions, try to make your choice and stick to it. Don't change your mind halfway through the examination.
- Make sure that you earn all the 'easy' marks. Do not spend too long on a question you find difficult. Leave it; if you have time, you can try it again later when you have finished all the other questions.
- Keep an eye on the time. Make sure that you try all the questions you are required to answer.
- Always present your work as clearly as you can, whether you are writing or drawing. Make your work easy to follow for the examiner or assessor.
- Try and allow some time at the end to check your answers and improve them.
- In practical work, make sure that you understand what you are being asked to do by re-reading the question before you start. Follow all instructions carefully.

Chapter 1

1 Karl Benz.
2 The Ford Model T.
3 Look after yourself and those around you.
4 Good housekeeping.
5 Use the correct personal protective equipment (PPE).
6 Warn others.
7 At the fire point.
8 They must be kept clean and clear at all times.
9 Cut off the electricity supply or separate them from it.

Chapter 2

1 A chassis is a frame with the body mounted on it; in integral construction the body also acts as the chassis, perhaps with a subframe.

2 Unitary or monocoque
3 To carry the heavy units and prevent damage to the body.
4 A panel in an integral body that is part of the load-supporting structure.
5 To absorb the deceleration forces of a body impact and so protect the occupants.
6 Seat-belts and airbags.
7 When the airbag is to be removed:
   i) Disconnect the battery, and wait half an hour if it is an American vehicle.
   ii) Handle and store the module carefully to avoid damage.
   iii) Dispose of an untriggered module as instructed by the manufacturer.

Chapter 3

1 1, cylinder head; 2, crankcase and/or cylinder block; 3, flywheel; 4, crankshaft; 5, main bearing cap; 6, big-end journal; 7, main bearing journal; 8, conrod or connecting rod; 9, crankshaft pulley; 10, little end or small end; 11, piston; 12; toothed belt camshaft drive; 13, camshaft sprocket or toothed wheel; 14, camshaft; 15, rocker arm; 16, cam cover or rocker cover.
2 The fuel is burnt inside the engine's cylinder.
3 Induction, compression, power, exhaust.
4 The inlet valve or valves has a larger head.
5 Half speed.
6 Both valves open together.
7 It is the volume of a cylinder between t.d.c. and b.d.c., multiplied by the number of cylinders.
8 It is twice the crank radius.
9 To allow for expansion of the valve due to heat.
10 A toothed belt.
11 Uneven torque, a large flywheel and heavy weight make the single-cylinder engine unsuitable.
12 1, crown; 2, oil control grooves; 3, skirt; 4, gudgeon pin hole; 5, circlip groove; 6, compression ring grooves.
13 The operating cycle takes one revolution of the crankshaft on a two-stroke and two revolutions on a four-stroke.
14 It is one method of compressing the fresh charge of mixture on a two-stroke engine before transferring it to the cylinder.
15 Cylinder head gasket allowing leakage into the cooling system.

Chapter 4

1 Because they carry the high tension current (up to 20 000 V) and need thick insulation.
2 The coil.
3 To enable it to jump the electrode gap and make a spark when under pressure.
4 The distributor's automatic mechanical and vacuum advance mechanisms.
5 To act as an automatic switch, making and breaking the primary coil circuit.
6 The angle through which the distributor rotor turns while the contact breaker is closed.
7 The primary circuit is 'switched' by electronic means instead of by a contact breaker. This eliminates the problems associated with contact-breaker points.
8 It is much more accurate; electronic sensors provide signals (inputs) to a microcomputer that can make small adjustments immediately. The engine is always 'in tune'.
9 A hot plug has a long insulator tip at the firing end. The heat has to follow a long path before being transferred to the cylinder head: therefore more heat is retained by the plug. Hot plugs tend to be fitted to cold-running engines. The cold plug has a shorter insulator tip and retains less heat. Cold plugs are used in engines that tend to run with higher combustion temperatures.
10 i) 'Pinking' and excessive fuel consumption
   ii) Engine overheating, 'running on' after the ignition is switched off, and excessive fuel consumption.

Chapter 5

1 To allow for engine movement and vibration.
2 To enable atmospheric pressure to pressurise the fuel and force it into the pump.
3 The diaphragm return spring.
4 It can be fitted anywhere along the pipeline.
5 To prevent fuel and fumes from escaping.

Chapter 6

1 The float chamber.
2 By controlling the air flow through the choke and venturi.
3 The venturi acts as a restricter that speeds up the airflow to create a depression.
4 Some fuel condenses onto the manifold surfaces. The choke valve or a bypass cold-start device.
5 A fixed-choke carburettor has a venturi and fuel jets of fixed sizes; a constant-vacuum carburettor has a variable-size venturi and fuel jet.
6 To provide the correct fuel/air ratio for all engine operating conditions.
7 By the automatic movement of a tapered needle into and out of the jet.
8 Dirt entering the engine will cause rapid wear.
9 The engine will run rich, causing high fuel consumption and loss of power.

Chapter 7

1 i) The throttle butterfly.
   ii) A mechanical metering unit.
   The injectors.
2 i) A throttle butterfly.
   ii) A swinging flap, or hot wire or hot film sensor.
3 On the mechanical system they spray all the time; the ECU switches them on and off.

4 By altering the time for which the injector is open.
5 Single-point and multi-point.
6 It relies on the inlet manifold to distribute the air/fuel mixture to the cylinders.

Chapter 8

1 i) It needs less servicing.
ii) It produces more low-speed torque.
iii) The engine lasts longer.
iii) It is less polluting than petrol.
iv) The fuel is less of a fire risk than petrol.
v) It has better thermal efficiency.
vi) It is more economical.
2 By using a mechanical blower.
3 High compression raises the air temperature above that of the fuel ignition point.
4 A wet liner forms part of the water jacket; it has thick walls to withstand combustion pressure.
5 i) The CI engine has a higher compression ratio.
ii) On induction, only air only fills the cylinder.
iii) Fuel is injected after compression.
iv) The engine is slower reviving.
v) It is more robust.

Chapter 9

1 i) Minimum surface area to avoid heat loss.
ii) Design must promote air swirl.
2 i) Lower compression ratio.
ii) Less need for cold-start aids.
iii) Good thermal efficiency.
3 i) Good swirl characteristics.
ii) Smooth running.
iii) Higher rpm possible.
4 The large surface area of the combustion chamber absorbs heat and lowers air temperature, particularly when cold.
5 Answers between:
i) 12 : 1 and 17 : 1
ii) 22 : 1 and 24 : 1

Chapter 10

1 Fuel storage tank, lift pump, filters, fuel injection pump, and fuel injectors.
2 It is the lift pump inside a distributor-type injection pump.
3 To prevent undue wear of the precision-made components of the pump.
4 By sedimentation.
5 To enable the system to be primed by bleeding.

Chapter 11

1 i) To deliver the correct amount of fuel under all engine speed and load conditions.
ii) To deliver the fuel at the correct time.
iii) To raise the pressure of the fuel so that the fuel injectors can break up (or atomise) the fuel into a fine mist.
2 i) To ensure that an engine does not exceed its safe maximum rpm setting.
ii) To control the engine's speed within defined limits.
The three types of governor for an in-line fuel injection pump are:
i) pneumatic governor
ii) flyweight mechanical
iii) Leafspring mechanical.
3 Phasing is the interval, measured in degrees, between each successive injection of fuel from the pump. Calibration is the quantity of fuel that each injector element delivers to a particular injector.
4 To measure precisely the quantity of fuel entering the delivery part of the pump under all operating conditions.
5 i) It is generally smaller, lighter and more compact, and can be fitted in a variety of convenient locations on the engine block.
ii) It requires no separate lubrication supply, because the diesel fuel lubricates all the moving components inside the pump.
6 To assist in starting the engine from cold.
7 i) Measuring opening pressure.
ii) Back leakage.
iii) Seat leakage.
iv) Spray pattern.
8 To ensure that when starting a CI engine from cold it generates enough heat during the compression stroke to cause the fuel/air mixture to self-ignite.

Chapter 12

1 Sound waves created as the exhaust gases leave the engine.
2 Ensure adequate ventilation.
3 Mild steel.
4 Stainless steel.
5 Carbon monoxide.
6 To convert the exhaust gas pollutants into non-toxic gases.
7 Platinum, rhodium and palladium.
8 i) Use unleaded petrol.
ii) Service the car correctly to prevent oil burning and ignition misfires.

Chapter 13

1 It improves engine output, and reduces fuel consumption and harmful emissions.
2 It does not absorb engine power.
3 It responds immediately when engine power must be increased.
4 It controls the boost pressure.
5 To cool the intake air and so increase its density.

Chapter 14

1 The oil becomes dirty and contaminated with use, and deteriorates with the passing of time.

2 The bypass valve would open and allow unfiltered oil to lubricate the engine.
3 To ensure that the oil pressure remains within predetermined limits.
4 Gear pump and rotor pump.
5 Additives are substances added to the oil to improve its specific properties.
6 It is the measure of the oil's ability to flow.

Chapter 15

1 i) To control the temperature of the engine within precise limits.
ii) To increase the engine's efficiency.
iii) To provide heat for other devices, such as the interior and manifold heaters and the automatic choke.
2 Conduction – this is the way that heat travels through solids.
Convection – this is the way heat travels through both liquids and gases.
Radiation – this is the way that heat travels through transparent solids, gases and a vacuum.
3 Those with the greatest surface area are placed in close proximity to the hottest part, the combustion chamber: the larger the surface area, the greater the amount of heat conducted away.
4 i) The water jacket gives good sound deadening.
ii) Maintains a more even temperature for all the cylinders.
iii) Better engine thermal efficiency.
5 It helps to give a rapid warm-up when starting from cold, by preventing the circulation of coolant through the radiator before it is warm. It enables the engine to run at a constant temperature, which helps to improve fuel consumption and reduce wear.
6 The tube and fin type and the pack block type.
7 The fitting of an expansion tank to the radiator overflow pipe. This minimises any coolant loss by providing temporary storage space for the heated coolant as its volume increases. When the system cools, any displaced coolant is drawn back into the radiator.
8 A corrosion inhibitor is a chemical solution (normally sodium based), which prevents the formation of corrosive acids inside the cooling system.
9 The evaporator, which enables the refri-gerant to absorb heat from the air, and the condenser, which cools the refrigerant.
10 The refrigerant absorbs heat when it boils or vaporises under the influence of low pressure.
11 Refrigerant is heavier than air, and can collect in a pit and suffocate anyone working there. It is poisonous, and explosive when exposed to a naked flame.

Chapter 16

1 To help with gear changing.
2 When using the clutch, slip occurs between the faces, which causes a severe rubbing action and produces a great deal of heat. The driven plate must have good, long-lasting frictional properties, and must resist wear.
3 Clutch slip occurs when the clutch cannot transmit all the engine torque to the gearbox. It may be caused by:
i) insufficient free play;
ii) oil and grease on the friction linings;
iii) worn linings;
iv) weak clutch pressure plate spring or springs.
4 To allow for driven plate wear, which reduces the clearance in the mechanism and could result in a slipping clutch.
5 Flywheel, pressure plate, driven plate and release bearing.
6 Cracked or distorted pressure plate; loose or badly worn linings; misalignment of the gearbox due to a loose or distorted clutch housing and engine or gearbox mountings defective.

Chapter 17

1 It acts as an automatic clutch between the engine and the gearbox.
2 The impeller and the turbine.
3 Fluid flywheels are filled to the height of the level plug with engine oil. Torque converters are supplied with ATF from the automatic transmission.
4 Approximately 2.5 : 1.
5 The stator redirects the flow of fluid from the turbine to the impeller, and so gives it more thrust as the fluid circulates.

Chapter 18

1 i) It enables the engine's torque output to be multiplied so as to match the vehicle's operating conditions.
ii) It provides a means of reversing the vehicle.
iii) It provides a permanent neutral position.
2 The angled teeth mean that they are longer, stronger and quieter than straight-cut gears.
3

$$\text{Gear ratio} = \frac{\textit{driven}}{\textit{driver}} \times \frac{\textit{driven}}{\textit{driver}}$$

where *driven* is the number of teeth on the output gearwheel and *driver* is the number of teeth on the input gearwheel.
4 Sliding mesh; constant mesh.
5 Constant-load synchromesh; baulk ring synchromesh.
6 The interlock mechanism.
7 i) It allows connection of the front and rear axle final drives to the gearbox.
ii) It allows the driver to select two- or four-wheel drive.
8 Sun gear; planet gears; the annulus.
9 i) Check oil level or drain and refill as required.
ii) Check gear linkage for wear, security and ease of operation.

iii) Check gearbox casing for oil leaks and damage.
iv) Check gearbox mountings for security.

Chapter 19

1 i) A tubular shaft weighs less, and so helps to save fuel.
ii) The lower mass of a tubular shaft is less likely to go out of balance when rotating.
iii) It is stronger and less likely to bend or whip when spinning.
2 By welding on small balance weights.
3 Each joint is aligned to cancel out the speed variations of the other.
4 i) There would be a poor steering lock, as this joint is limited to 20° of movement.
ii) Speed variations would not give smooth steering operation.
5 The vehicle is driven forwards and the steering is alternately moved from right to left lock continuously; a defective joint will knock.
6 Check the gaiter for splits or tears.

Chapter 20

1 i) It enables the drive to be turned through 90°.
ii) It acts as a permanent reduction gear.
2 The centreline axes of the pinion and crown wheel of a spiral bevel drive intersect, while on the hypoid the pinion is offset below the axis of the crown wheel.
3 The differential enables the driving wheels to be driven at different speeds but with equal torque when cornering.
4 The differential lock ensures a positive drive to both wheels should one attempt to spin.
5 The third differential prevents transmission wind-up on vehicles with permanent four-wheel drive. It is located between the front and rear final drive units.
6 i) As a third differential.
ii) In a limited-slip differential.
7 Fully floating axle.

Chapter 21

1 i) A minimum of driver effort to steer the vehicle.
ii) The steering should be responsive at all times.
iii) The steering system should promote true rolling motion.
2 The roadwheels must rotate around a common centre of turn.
3 The steering linkage ensures that the inner roadwheel on the turn pivots more than the outer roadwheel, so that they all rotate round a common centre.
4 Front-wheel-drive vehicles.
5 Castor angle enables the roadwheels to self-centre. It is obtained by tilting the axis of the kingpin or swivel joints towards the rear to give caster trail.
6 The tyre centre point is inboard of the projected swivel axis at the road surface.
7 i) There should be some feedback of road conditions.
ii) Prevent road shocks being transmitted through the steering wheel.
iii) A minimum of backlash.
8 Integral; external ram or in-line cylinder; semi-integral.

Chapter 22

1 i) To ensure that the roadwheels remain in contact with the road surface.
ii) To ensure that the front and rear axles are correctly located.
iii) To support the sprung weight of the vehicle.
2 To allow the spring to increase in length as increasing weight stretches it.
3 To minimise tyre wear due to changes in vehicle track.
4 By an adjuster, or by repositioning the bar in its locating splines.
5 To control suspension spring oscillation.
6 Sprung weight is all that part of the vehicle supported by the springs, e.g. the body and engine; unsprung weight is all those components that move up and down with the roadwheel, and the roadwheel itself.
7 Hydrolastic; hydrogas; hydropneumatic.
They limit backwards and forwards pitching. Hydropneumatic suspension maintains a constant ride height.
8 Carbon fibre; glass fibre; kevlar.

Chapter 23

1 To bring the vehicle safely to rest.
2 Weight transference allows greater braking effort at the front.
3 Every brake receives the same force, even where there is uneven adjustment or wear.
4 It must not damage hoses or pipes. It must have a high boiling point. It must not freeze. Its viscosity must remain constant.
5 It must be kept in air-tight containers. It must not contact paintwork. As it is poisonous, it should not be bled into drinks containers.
6 Excessive brake pedal travel.
7 Self-adjusting, and less likely to suffer brake fade.
8 Air, and water when turned to steam, are both compressible, leading to possible loss of 'brake pedal'.
9 Friction between the tyre and the road; heat; the type of friction lining.
10 Double diaphragm; spring brake actuator.
11 Exhaust brake or retarder.

Chapter 24

1 A pneumatic tyre is fitted to a vehicle to:
i) absorb the shocks of rough roads;
ii) make frictional contact with the road.

2 A cross-ply tyre has the layers of ply material at an angle of approximately 45° to each other. Radial-ply tyres have the plies across the tyre from bead to bead.
3 i) The method of construction.
ii) Ply rating.
iii) Nominal (cross-section) width.
iv) Aspect ratio.
v) Tyre rim diameter.
vi) Speed rating.
vii) Load index rating.
4 Most manufacturers do not now recommend rotation.
5 When the wheel is freely rotated it will always stop with the heavy part at the lowest point.
6 Dynamic balancing means spinning a wheel at speed and correcting its imbalance.
7 The three methods of repairing a tyre are:
i) hot vulcanising patch;
ii) cold chemical cure patch;
iii) plug and patch.
8 The spring flange or lock ring must be checked for seating, or wheel clamping bolts checked for security. The tyre must then be placed inside a security cage for inflation.

Chapter 25

1 The generator.
2 By using the chassis or body to provide a return to the battery, less wire is needed, cutting the cost of the electrical system considerably.
3 To prevent failure of the complete system should one lamp fail.
4 To create an effective beam that does not dazzle oncoming drivers.
5 The solenoid is a remote electromagnetic switch that allows the use of short, heavy cables to carry the heavy current.
6 The resistance of a cable is relative to its cross-sectional area: a thin cable has a higher resistance than a thick cable made of the same material. The cable thickness or size depends upon the load the circuit is required to carry.
7 Wiring is coded by colour or numbers.
8 Similar to that in Figure 25.36.
9 To check the state of charge of the battery.
10 To check the state of charge and condition of the battery under load.
11 i) between 1.25 and 1.28; ii) 1.15 or less.
12 To provide the gauge with a steady voltage supply, e.g. 10 V, and to ensure that the gauge gives an accurate reading under all vehicle operating conditions.
13 Magnetic, heating and chemical.
14 A fuse is a circuit protection device that makes use of the heating effect of electricity. If excessive current flows it heats up the fuse, which then melts, breaking the circuit.
15 A metal object may cause a short-circuit if it bridges a live supply and earth. This is particularly dangerous if battery current can short-circuit through something such as a ring, as it may heat up or even melt, causing severe burns.

Key words and definitions

ABS Anti-lock brake system, which prevents roadwheels from locking up during hard braking.
airbag Inflatable bag, temporarily inflated with nitrogen on vehicle impact, which absorbs the movement of the human body caused by inertia, and prevents contact with hard surroundings.
air cleaner A device fitted to the air intake of an engine, commonly paper based, which removes any airborne particles of dirt.
air conditioning A system that cools the air for interior ventilation, and thereby automatically lowers the humidity.
alternating current (a.c.) An electrical current that flows alternately in one direction and then the other.
alternator An engine-driven unit that converts mechanical energy into alternating current (a.c.).
anti-roll bar A torsional steel bar, located between the body or chassis and the suspension arm, whose purpose is to limit the amount of body roll on corners.
aquaplaning A term used to describe a tyre's riding on a cushion of water that prevents contact with the road surface.
atomisation The process of breaking a substance into very fine particles as, for example, an injector spraying fuel.
automatic gearbox A unit that automatically adjusts its gear ratios to suit the prevailing conditions.
automatic transmission *See* **automatic gearbox**.

ball joint A spherical socket and ball-ended pin that allow an attached component to pivot in any direction.
battery A chemical form of electrical energy storage.
b.d.c. *See* **bottom dead-centre**
beam axle A one-piece axle that carries a roadwheel on each end.
bore The internal diameter of a cylinder or pipe.
bottom dead-centre The lowest position to which the piston travels when the crankpin is central, at which it reverses its direction of movement.
brake band A braking device used to control and limit the rotation of components, as in an epicyclic gear train, for example.
brake calliper A hydraulically operated device (on motor vehicles) that forces a pair of brake pads into contact with the brake disc.
brake disc A disc attached to the wheel hub that rotates between the brake pads.
brake drum A drum-shaped container, mounted on the wheel hub, surrounding some brake shoes, which provide braking effect when pressed against it.
brake fade The gradual loss of friction between the brake pads and discs or the brake shoes and brake drums that occurs when brakes become very hot.
brake fluid A specially formulated fluid, which is used in hydraulic systems of brakes and clutches.
brake lining A material with a high coefficient of friction that is bonded or riveted onto brake pads and brake shoes.
brake pressure regulator A device to restrict the braking effort applied to the rear wheels as the weight on them reduces.
brake shoe The arch-shaped component to which the brake lining is attached.
braking force A measure of a vehicle's retardation or stopping force.
butterfly valve A circular or near-circular disc mounted on a shaft inside an air intake to control the flow of air.
bypass oil filter An oil filter that cleans only some of the oil before it is recirculated.
bypass valve A valve located inside full-flow oil filters to allow oil to flow if the element becomes blocked.

cam An eccentric shape on a shaft or a protrusion from a base circle. (Cams are often egg-shaped.)
camber angle The angle at which a vehicle roadwheel is tilted from the vertical.
camshaft A shaft that has a number of cam lobes machined at precise intervals along its length.
capacitor An electrical device that can store electricity. Known as the **condenser** when used to reduce the arcing of ignition contact breaker points.
carburettor A device for mixing together precise quantities of petrol and air for combustion.
caster angle The amount by which the extended steering axis leads or trails the centre of contact of the roadwheel.
catalyst A substance that increases the rate of a chemical reaction without undergoing any permanent chemical change itself.
catalytic converter A silencer-like device that passes the exhaust gases through a honeycomb coated with catalysts to change the nature of the gases.
CB points *See* **contact breaker**.

choke A device used to increase the air/fuel ratio to aid cold starting. Also, the name usually given to the driver's control itself.
clutch A friction device that allows temporary disconnection and smooth reconnection of the drive from the engine to the roadwheels.
coil A transformer that is used to raise the 12 V of the vehicle's electrical system to 20 000 V or more for the purpose of igniting the mixture in the engine's cylinders.
coil spring A spiral-wound steel wire or rod, as on suspension systems or engine valves; sometimes called a **helical spring**.
combustion chamber The space above the piston when at t.d.c., where the air/fuel mixture is ignited.
compression ignition (CI) engine An engine in which the air/fuel mixture is ignited by the heat generated by compressing the air.
compression ratio Ratio comparing the volume of a cylinder swept by the piston plus the combustion chamber volume, with that of the combustion chamber.
compression ring The uppermost metal rings at the top of a piston, which seal the combustion and expansion of gases above the piston from the crankcase below.
compression stroke The second stroke of the four-stroke or Otto cycle, in which the full cylinder of fresh mixture is compressed.
condenser *See* **capacitor**.
connecting rod The forged steel link between the piston and the crankshaft, fundamental to converting the up-and-down or reciprocating piston movement into crankshaft rotation.
conrod *See* **connecting rod**.
constant velocity (CV) joint A universal coupling that transmits rotation without speed variation.
contact breaker A mechanically operated switch that triggers the induction of high tension (HT) current from the coil by interrupting the primary circuit.
cooling system An air- or fluid-based system that carries away the excess heat of combustion from the engine cylinders.
core plug An expandable metal disc that seals off the casting holes in the engine block or cylinder head.
corrosion The slow wearing away of solids, especially metals, by chemical attack. In vehicles, usually taken to mean rusting of steel surfaces that have not been protected.
crankcase The lower part of the engine that houses the crankshaft.
crankcase ventilation valve A valve fitted to the crankcase, which prevents the build-up of excessive gas pressure.
crankshaft The main shaft in the engine, which is rotated by the pistons and connecting rods, and also carries the flywheel.
cross-ply tyre A tyre constructed so that the plies cross over each other at an angle of 45°, providing a strong but stiff tyre.
CV joint *See* **constant velocity joint**.
cylinder block The housing for the cylinders. It is usually extended to house the crankshaft.
cylinder head The uppermost part of the engine, which forms a top to the cylinders and generally carries the valves and valve gear.
cylinder head gasket A flexible steel or asbestos material clamped between the cylinder head and the block to serve as a gas or water seal.
cylinder liner A finely machined, sleeved insert in which the piston operates.

detonation The uncontrolled and sudden burning of the air/fuel mixture inside the combustion chamber.
differential A mechanical device that permits an input shaft to turn two output shafts at varying speeds but provide the same torque through both of them.
diode An electrical component that permits current to flow through it in one direction but not the other; an electrical 'one-way valve'.
direct current (d.c.) An electrical current that constantly flows in one direction.
distributor The component that distributes the HT current to each of the spark plugs in turn. It often houses the contact breaker or electronic switch for the primary circuit.
dog clutch A mechanical coupling in which two sets of teeth lock together to transmit drive.
drain plug A removable screwed bung that is removed from the lowest point of engines, gearboxes, rear axles and cooling systems to release the lubricant or coolant.
driveshaft A shaft used to transmit drive from one component to another.
drum brakes *See* **brake drum**
dry-sump lubrication A lubrication system in which the oil reservoir is a separate tank, to which scavenged oil from the engine is returned after lubrication.
dynamo A generator that produces direct current (d.c.), which is required for charging lead–acid batteries.

electrolyte The chemical solution in batteries, typically dilute sulphuric acid for the lead–acid batteries normally used in vehicles.
emulsion block Part of a fixed-jet carburettor, which has a number of air holes drilled along its length to progressively weaken the mixture.
epicyclic gear train A gear set that consists of a sun wheel around which revolve the planet wheels, the whole being surrounded by the outer ring gear called the **annulus**.
exhaust manifold The component fitted to the side of the engine that carries away the exhaust gases and feeds them into the exhaust downpipe.
exhaust silencer A component in the exhaust system that reduces the noise of expanding exhaust gas.
exhaust stroke The final stroke of the four-stroke or Otto cycle, when the piston rises to push the exhaust gas out of the cylinder.

filter element Part of a filter, usually disposable, that traps the unwanted particles of dirt.

final drive The last reduction gear in a transmission system. For an in-line engine and transmission it is normally a crown wheel and pinion to turn the drive through 90°.

firing order The order in which an engine's power stroke occurs, starting at cylinder number one: e.g. 1, 3, 4 and 2.

first motion shaft The primary or input shaft of a gearbox, which is driven by the splined attachment of the clutch centre plate.

flasher unit An electrical device that operates the vehicle's turn signals.

float The floating 'box' that operates the needle valve in the float chamber of a carburettor.

float chamber The petrol reservoir of a carburettor.

fluid reservoir A container that provides a permanent store of fluid.

flywheel A heavy metal disc fitted to the rear of the crankshaft to smooth the firing impulses of the engine. It also provides a mounting for the starter motor ring gear, and carries the clutch.

four-stroke cycle The Otto cycle of induction, compression, power, and exhaust.

front-wheel drive Propulsion of a vehicle by means of the front wheels.

fuel pump A mechanically or electrically driven component that lifts fuel from the tank and supplies it to the engine.

full-flow oil filter An oil filter in which all the oil is pumped through the element to cleanse it from impurities.

fuse A device to protect wiring from excessive load by passing the current flow through a fusible link, which melts and breaks the circuit when the safe working limit is exceeded.

gear ratio A measure of the difference in revolutions turned by two meshed gears.

gearbox An assembly of gears of different ratios, mounted on shafts inside a casing, which permits a driver to select the most appropriate ratio for the purpose.

governor unit A device to limit maximum speed or set the best operating speed of an engine.

gudgeon pin The strong metal pin that connects the small end of a connecting rod to the piston.

halfshaft The steel shaft inside a rear axle that transmits the drive from the crown wheel to the roadwheel.

handbrake A mechanically operated brake system that provides a permanent brake when the vehicle is left unattended.

high-tension (HT) circuit The high-voltage secondary circuit of a vehicle's spark ignition system.

hydrogas suspension A suspension system that employs both hydrolastic fluid and nitrogen gas in separate compartments.

hydrolastic suspension A suspension system employing rubber cone springs and hydrolastic fluid in chambers.

hydrometer An instrument used to check the specific gravity of a fluid (usually electrolyte).

idler gear A gearwheel interposed between the driver and the driven gears to reverse the direction of rotation; several idler gears may be used to link two widely spaced shafts.

independent suspension A suspension system in which the roadwheels are able to respond to road irregularities independently of each other.

inlet manifold A casting fitted to the engine that carries the intake air or air/fuel mixture to each of the inlet ports.

input shaft *See* **first motion shaft**.

insulator A material with very few free-moving electrons, which prevents the flow of electricity e.g. rubber, mica.

integral body construction. Bodywork that is self-supporting, and which carries all the vehicle's components without any need for a separate chassis, although a subframe may be used for the heaviest items.

interlock A device to prevent more than one gear of a manual gearbox being selected at any one time, by locking the other selectors in position.

jacking point A specially strengthened lifting point underneath the vehicle.

jet A small, drilled opening inside a carburettor that meters a precise amount of fuel or air.

kingpin A machined, hardened pin that provides the steering pivot on each end of a beam axle.

kingpin inclination The inclination from the vertical of the kingpin on a beam axle or the axis of the pivots on independent suspension.

layshaft The auxiliary shaft in a gearbox providing a mounting for one gear of each pair.

leafspring A suspension spring that is (usually) made up of multiple layers of steel strips in a semi-elliptical shape.

load-sensing valve A valve that reduces the effort applied to the rear brakes as the weight on the rear wheels is reduced by weight transfer during braking.

low-tension (LT) circuit The low-voltage side of a coil ignition circuit: i.e. the primary circuit.

Macpherson strut A telescopic suspension strut combining spring and damper in one unit, and able to pivot on a top mounting attached to the bodywork and on a lower swivel on the suspension arm.

mainshaft The principal or output shaft in a gearbox, which carries all the output gears.

manual gearbox A gearbox in which the ratios are selected by the driver, using the clutch and gear lever.

master cylinder The cylinder operated by the driver's foot that forces brake fluid out to the slave or wheel cylinders and callipers.

monocoque body *See* **integral body construction**.

multigrade oil An engine oil containing additives that allow it to be the equivalent of a low-viscosity oil when cold, and a high-viscosity oil when hot.

needle valve A plunger with a tapered seat, which drops to permit petrol flow and rises to shut it off when the carburettor float chamber is full.
negative camber A roadwheel that is tilted inwards at the top from the vertical plane.
negative earth System in which the earth return to the battery negative terminal is provided through the bodywork.
neutral The position on a vehicle's transmission system in which no drive is transmitted.

ohm The unit of electrical resistance.
oil bath air cleaner An air cleaner that utilises a bath of engine oil to trap dirt particles in the intake air.
oil control piston ring A metal ring mounted beneath the compression rings, whose task is to remove excessive lubricant from the cylinder walls and return it to the sump.
oil filter The component that removes dirt from the engine oil in the lubrication system.
oil gallery The oilway (or oil rail) through a cylinder block that distributes oil around the engine.
oil pump The engine-driven device that pressurises oil to circulate it around the engine.
overhead camshaft (OHC) A camshaft mounted directly above the engine inlet and exhaust valves.
overhead valve (OHV) A layout in which the engine inlet and exhaust valves are in the cylinder head, but the camshaft may be in the cylinder block and operate them through pushrods and rocker arms.

petrol pump *See* **fuel pump**.
piston An inverted cup-shaped component that accurately fits and slides inside a cylinder to transmit the force of the expanding gas to the connecting rod.
piston rings *See* **compression ring** and **oil control piston ring**.
positive camber A roadwheel that is tilted outwards at the top from the vertical plane.
power steering A type of steering gear in which the driver's effort is assisted by pressurised oil.
power stroke The third stroke of the four-stroke or Otto cycle, in which the burning and expanding gases force the piston down the cylinder bore.
pre-ignition The premature ignition (before the spark occurs) of the air/fuel mixture in the combustion chamber.
pressure cap The cap on a coolant radiator or expansion tank that contains a pressure-limiting valve.
primary shaft *See* **first motion shaft**.
primary windings The outermost set of windings inside an ignition coil, which create the magnetic field.
propeller shaft A tubular steel shaft that transmits the drive from the gearbox to the final drive.

rack and pinion steering Steering mechanism that has a pinion moving a toothed rack from side to side.
radial-ply tyre A tyre with the plies laid radially around the tyre at 90° to the wheel rim, producing a soft sidewall.
radiator The multi-surfaced matrix that permits coolant to lose heat to atmosphere or to heat the vehicle interior.
radius arm An arm anchored at one end that controls a pivoted component within an arc of movement, as on suspension systems.
rear-wheel drive Propulsion of a vehicle by means of the rear wheels.
relay An electromagnetic or electronic switch, whereby a small current can be used to control a heavy current.
roller bearings A bearing that employs cylindrical or ball rollers, which can support high loading.

seat-belt Vehicle occupant restraint that prevents the wearer from being thrown forward by inertia.
selector mechanism A mechanical device to allow a driver moving a gear lever to select a gear ratio.
self-centring The action of the steering in trying to return to the straight-ahead position.
semi-floating axle A driving axle design in which the halfshafts support the weight of the vehicle and provide the drive.
semi-trailing arm A suspension arm that trails somewhat towards the rear of the vehicle.
shackle and pin A mechanical linkage that locates one end of a leafspring to the chassis.
shell bearing On vehicles this is generally a split, cylindrical, steel-walled bearing, coated with tin-based bearing metal: e.g. crankshaft and camshaft bearings.
shock absorber *See* **suspension damper**.
short-circuit Created when an electrical conductor touches earth, permitting full current flow without any limiting resistance.
single-plate clutch A clutch mechanism with only one centre friction plate, as commonly used on vehicles.
slave cylinder A hydraulic cylinder that actuates in response to the movement of fluid from a master cylinder; a name usually reserved for the clutch-operating components on vehicles.
sliding joint A sliding, splined connection, usually at the forward end of a propeller shaft to allow for rear axle movement.
solenoid An electromagnetic switch that is a heavy-duty version of a relay.
spark ignition engine An internal combustion engine that relies upon a spark to ignite the air/fuel mixture.
spark plug The insert that, when fed with HT current, produces the spark to ignite the air/fuel mixture.
splash-type lubrication Lubrication achieved solely by the splashing of oil inside an enclosure by the operating components, as with car transmissions.
sprung weight The weight of all the vehicle components supported by the suspension springs; the total weight of a vehicle less the unsprung weight.
starter motor An electric motor specifically designed to turn over an engine for starting.
stator Specifically, a static component, as with an alternator stator winding, but also used to describe the inner member of a torque converter.
steering damper *See* **suspension damper**.
steering gearbox A gear- or thread-based mechanism that reduces the driver's effort in turning the steering wheel.

steering geometry The term that describes all the measurable wheel pivot angles that are built into a vehicle's suspension. *See also* **caster**, **camber** and **kingpin inclination**.
stroke The distance travelled by the piston from the top of the cylinder (t.d.c.) to the bottom (b.d.c.).
subframe A strong frame that carries heavy components, and enables them to be fitted to a body of integral construction.
suspension damper A hydraulic mechanism that controls the movement of a suspension spring; a similar device is used to dampen sudden steering mechanism movement.
synchromesh unit A device that synchronises or matches the speed of rotation of gearbox components to allow smooth gear engagement.

tandem master cylinder A unit of two master cylinders working from one pushrod, supplying independent brake circuits.
taper roller bearing A bearing that employs tapered rollers running on inward-sloping tracks to provide an end-thrust capability.
t.d.c. *See* **top dead-centre**
temperature gauge An instrument to indicate the temperature of a vehicle's coolant or oil.
thermostat An automatic, heat-sensitive valve fitted into a vehicle cooling system to promote fast warm-up and control the running temperature.
thermosyphon system A pumpless cooling system that relies upon convection currents to circulate the coolant around the system.
three-quarter floating wheel hub A type of wheel hub in which the major part of the vehicle's weight is carried by the axle casing.
throttle valve A disc inside the air intake, carburettor or injection unit that controls the air or air/fuel mixture intake into the engine.
thrust bearing A bearing, often of 'plain' construction, that carries end thrust (i.e. thrust along the shaft), as on the crankshaft or gearbox layshaft.
timing marks Reference markings on moving and static components that permit the correct alignment of shafts that must function at the correct rotational time.
toe in and toe out The terms used to describe the setting of the steered roadwheels so that they have true rolling motion in a forward direction.
top dead-centre The highest position reached by the piston in the cylinder, when the crankpin is precisely central, and where the piston reverses direction.
torque The turning effort applied by an engine; alternatively, turning effort via a spanner when tightening a nut or bolt.
torque converter A fluid drive that multiplies the torque available from the engine.
torsion bar suspension A type of suspension in which the springing medium is provided by the twisting of a bar or multiple strips of spring steel.
track The width between the roadwheels.
track rod end A pivoting ball joint attached to a track rod or tie bar, which links elements of the steered roadwheels together.
traction control A system that holds a driven roadwheel to the limit of traction without slipping.
transverse engine A power unit mounted across the engine compartment at 90° to the vehicle centreline.
two-stroke cycle An engine in which all four actions of the operating cycle are carried out in one revolution of the crankshaft.

U bolt A fastener designed to fit around a component of circular section that needs clamping to another, such as an axle to a leafspring, or two pipes together.
unitary bodywork *See* **integral body construction**.
universal joint A coupling that permits two shafts at different angles to be linked together to transmit drive.
unsprung weight The weight of all those components that are not supported by the springs.

valve A component that controls the flow of a liquid or vapour through an orifice.
valve guide The sleeves in the cylinder head that provide a bearing surface for the valves as they slide open and closed.
valve overlap The period when both the inlet and exhaust valves are open together.
vee engine An engine in which there are two banks of cylinders at an angle to each other but sharing a common crankshaft.
venturi A constriction in a passage that restricts the air flow to increase its speed.
viscosity The flow rate of a liquid at any given temperature.
volatility The ability of a liquid to become a vapour.

water pump An engine-driven device with an impeller that circulates the coolant.
wet-sump lubrication A lubrication system in which all the oil is carried in the base of the unit, as with the engine oil in most vehicle engines.
wheel alignment *See* **toe in and toe out**.
wheelbase The distance between the centres of the front and rear roadwheels.

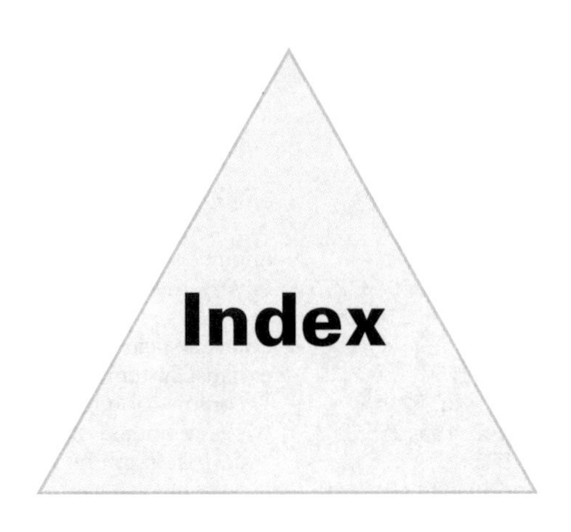

Index

Note: page numbers in *italics* refer to illustrations separated from the textual reference

STRATTON
UPPER SCHOOL
LIBRARY